Student Quick Tips

Use this Student Quick Tips guide for a quick and easy start with McGraw-Hill Connect. You'll get valuable tips on registering, doing assignments, and accessing resources, as well as information about the support center hours.

Getting Started

TIP: To get started in Connect, you will need the following:

- Your instructor's Connect Web Address

> Sample of Connect Web Address:
>
> http://www.mcgrawhillconnect.com/class/instructorname_section_name

- Connect Access Code

TIP: If you do not have an access code or have not yet secured your tuition funds, you can click "Free Trial" during registration. This trial will provide temporary Connect access (typically three weeks) and will remind you to purchase online access before the end of your trial.

Registration and Sign In

1. Go to the Connect Web Address provided by your instructor
2. Click on **Register Now**
3. Enter your email address

TIP: If you already have a McGraw-Hill account, you will be asked for your password and will not be required to create a new account.

4. Enter a registration code or choose **Buy Online** to purchase access online

5. Follow the on-screen directions

TIP: Please choose your Security Question and Answer carefully. We will ask you for this information if you forget your password.

6. When registration is complete, click on **Go to Connect Now**

7. You are now ready to use **Connect**

Trouble Logging In?

- Ensure you are using the same email address you used during registration

- If you have forgotten your password, click on the "Forgot Password?" link at your Instructor's Connect Course Web Address

- When logged into Connect, you can update your account information (e.g. email address, password, and security question/answer) by clicking on the *"My Account"* link located at the top-right corner

Home (Assignments)

TIP: If you are unable to begin an assignment, verify the following:

- The assignment is available (start and due dates)

- That you have not exceeded the maximum number of attempts

- That you have not achieved a score of 100%

- If your assignment contains questions that require manual grading, you will not be able to begin your next attempt until your instructor has graded those questions

(Continued: **Home Assignments**)

TIP: Based on the assignment policy settings established by your Instructor, you may encounter the following limitations when working on your assignment(s):

- Ability to Print Assignment

- Timed assignments – once you begin a "*timed assignment*," the timer will not stop by design

TIP: "*Save & Exit*" vs. "*Submit*" button

- If you are unable to complete your assignment in one sitting, utilize the "*Save & Exit*" button to save your work and complete it at a later time

- Once you have completed your assignment, utilize the "*Submit*" button in order for your assignment to be graded

Library

TIP: The *Library* section of your Connect account provides shortcuts to various resources.

- If you purchased ConnectPlus, you will see an *eBook* link, which can also be accessed from the section information widget of the *Home* tab

- *Recorded Lectures* can be accessed if your instructor is using *Tegrity Campus* to capture lectures. You may also access recorded lectures when taking an assignment by clicking on the projector icon in the navigation bar

- Many McGraw-Hill textbooks offer additional resources such as narrated slides and additional problems, which are accessible through the *Student Resources* link

Reports

TIP: Once you submit your assignment, you can view your available results in the *Reports* tab.

- If you see a dash (-) as your score, your instructor has either delayed or restricted your ability to see the assignment feedback

- Your instructor has the ability to limit the amount of information (e.g. questions, answers, scores) you can view for each submitted assignment

Need More Help?

CONTACT US ONLINE

Visit us at:

www.mcgrawhillconnect.com/support

Browse our support materials including tutorial videos and our searchable Connect knowledge base. If you cannot find an answer to your question, click on "Contact Us" button to send us an email.

GIVE US A CALL

Call us at:

1-800-331-5094

Our live support is available:

Mon-Thurs:	8 am – 11 pm CT
Friday:	8 am – 6 pm CT
Sunday:	6 pm – 11 pm CT

Principles of
BIOLOGY

Robert J. Brooker
University of Minnesota - Minneapolis

Eric P. Widmaier
Boston University

Linda E. Graham
University of Wisconsin - Madison

Peter D. Stiling
University of South Florida

BSC 2011
Bio II - Biological Diversity
University of South Florida Tampa

Mc
Graw
Hill
Education

2 3 4 5 6 7 8 9 0 BKM BKM 17 16 15 14

ISBN-13: 978-1-259-35026-9
ISBN-10: 1-259-35026-6

Learning Solutions Consultant: Salim Bradley
Project Manager: Kathy Phelan
Cover Photo Credits:
124581127 – Konstantin Tavrov
86490031 – Jupiter Images

Robert J. Brooker

Rob Brooker received his Ph.D. in genetics from Yale University in 1983. At Harvard, he studied lactose permease, the product of the *lacY* gene of the *lac* operon. He continues working on transporters at the University of Minnesota, where he is a Professor in the Department of Genetics, Cell Biology, and Development and has an active research laboratory. At the University of Minnesota, Dr. Brooker teaches undergraduate courses in biology, genetics, and cell biology. In addition to many other publications, he has written two undergraduate genetics texts: *Genetics: Analysis & Principles*, 5th edition, copyright 2015, and *Concepts of Genetics*, copyright 2012; and he is the lead author of *Biology*, 3rd edition, copyright 2014, all published by McGraw-Hill Education.

Eric P. Widmaier

Eric Widmaier received his Ph.D. in 1984 in endocrinology from the University of California at San Francisco. His research focuses on the control of body mass and metabolism in mammals, the hormonal correlates of obesity, and the effects of high-fat diets on intestinal cell function. Dr. Widmaier is currently Professor of Biology at Boston University, where he teaches undergraduate human physiology and recently received the university's highest honor for excellence in teaching. Among other publications, he is a coauthor of *Vander's Human Physiology: The Mechanisms of Body Function*, 13th edition, copyright 2014; and *Biology*, 3rd edition, copyright 2014, both published by McGraw-Hill Education.

Linda E. Graham

Linda Graham received her Ph.D. in botany from the University of Michigan, Ann Arbor. Her research explores the evolutionary origin of land-adapted plants, focusing on their cell and molecular biology as well as ecological interactions. Dr. Graham is now Professor of Botany at the University of Wisconsin–Madison. She teaches undergraduate courses in biology and plant biology. She is the coauthor of, among other publications, *Algae*, 2nd edition, copyright 2008, a major's textbook on algal biology; and *Plant Biology*, 2nd edition, copyright 2006, both published by Prentice

Left to right: Eric Widmaier, Linda Graham, Peter Stiling, and Rob Brooker

Hall/Pearson. She is also a coauthor of *Biology*, 3rd edition, copyright 2014, published by McGraw-Hill Education.

Peter D. Stiling

Peter Stiling obtained his Ph.D. from University College, Cardiff, Wales, in 1979. Subsequently, he became a postdoctoral fellow at Florida State University and later spent two years as a lecturer at the University of the West Indies, Trinidad. During this time, he began photographing and writing about butterflies and other insects, which led to publication of several books on local insects. Dr. Stiling is currently a Professor of Biology at the University of South Florida at Tampa. His research interests include plant-insect relationships, parasite-host relationships, biological control, restoration ecology, and the effects of elevated carbon dioxide levels on plant–herbivore interactions. He teaches graduate and undergraduate courses in ecology and environmental science as well as introductory biology. He has published many scientific papers and is the author of *Ecology: Global Insights and Investigations*, 2nd edition, copyright 2015, and is coauthor of *Biology*, 3rd edition, copyright 2014, both published by McGraw-Hill Education.

Ian Quitadamo

Ian Quitadamo served as lead digital author for *Principles of Biology*, overseeing the development of the digital content by a team of subject matter experts. He is an Associate Professor with a dual appointment in Biological Sciences and Science Education at Central Washington University in Ellensburg, WA. He teaches introductory and majors biology courses and cell biology, genetics, and biotechnology as well as science teaching methods courses for future science teachers and interdisciplinary content courses in alternative energy and sustainability. Dr. Quitadamo was educated at Washington State University and holds a Bachelor's degree in biology, Master's degree in genetics and cell biology, and an interdisciplinary Ph.D. in science, education, and technology. Previously a researcher of tumor angiogenesis, he now investigates critical thinking and has published numerous studies of factors that affect student critical thinking performance. He has received the Crystal Apple award for teaching excellence, led various initiatives in critical thinking and assessment, and is active in training future and currently practicing science teachers. He served as a co-author on *Biology*, 11th edition, by Mader and Windelspecht, copyright 2013, and is the lead digital author for *Biology*, 3rd edition by Brooker and *Biology*, 10th edition by Raven, both copyright 2014, and *Understanding Biology* by Mason, all published by McGraw-Hill Education.

A Note about *Principles of Biology* . . .

A recent trend in science education is the phenomenon that is sometimes called *"flipping the classroom."* This phrase refers to the idea that some of the activities that used to be done in class are now done out of class, and vice versa. For example, instead of spending the entire class time lecturing about textbook and other materials, some of the class time is spent engaging students in various activities, such as problem solving, working through case studies, and designing experiments. This approach is called *active learning*. For many instructors, the classroom has become more learner-centered rather than teacher-centered. A learner-centered classroom provides a rich environment in which students can interact with each other and with their instructors. Instructors and fellow students often provide formative assessment—immediate feedback that helps each student understand if his or her learning is on the right track.

What are some advantages of active learning? Educational studies reveal that active learning usually promotes greater learning gains. In addition, active learning often focuses on skill development rather than the memorization of facts that are easily forgotten. Students become trained to "think like scientists" and to develop a skill set that enables them to apply scientific reasoning.

A common concern among instructors who are beginning to try out active learning is that they think they will have to teach their students less material. However, this may not be the case. Although students may be provided with online lectures, "flipping the classroom" typically gives students more responsibility for understanding the textbook material on their own. Along these lines, *Principles of Biology* is intended to provide students with a resource that can be effectively used out of the classroom. Several key pedagogical features include the following:

- **Focus on Core Concepts:** Although it is intended for majors in the biological sciences, *Principles of Biology* is a shorter textbook that emphasizes core concepts. Twelve principles of biology are enunciated in Chapter 1 and those principles are emphasized throughout the textbook with specially labeled figures. An effort has also been made to emphasize some material in bulleted lists and numbered lists, so students can more easily see the main points.
- **Learning Outcomes:** Each section of every chapter begins with a set of learning outcomes. These outcomes help students understand what they should be able to do if they have mastered the material in that section.
- **Formative Assessment:** When students are expected to learn textbook material on their own, it is imperative that they be given regular formative assessments so they can gauge whether or not they are mastering the material. Formative assessment is a major feature of this textbook and is bolstered by McGraw-Hill Connect®—a state-of-the-art digital assignment and assessment platform. In *Principles of Biology*, formative assessment is provided in multiple ways.

  1. Each section of every chapter ends with multiple-choice questions.
  2. Most figures have concept check questions so students can determine if they understand the key points in the figure.
  3. End-of-chapter questions continue to provide students with feedback regarding their mastery of the material.
  4. Further assessment tools are available in Connect. Question banks, Test banks, and Quantitative Question banks can be assigned by the professor. McGraw-Hill LearnSmart® allows for individual study as well as assignments from the professor.

- **Quantitative Analysis:** Many chapters have a subsection that emphasizes quantitative reasoning, an important skill for careers in science and medicine. In these subsections, the quantitative nature of a given topic is described, and then students are asked to solve a problem related to that topic.
- **BioConnections and Evolutionary Connections:** To help students broaden their understanding of biology, two recurring features are BioConnections and Evolutionary Connections. BioConnections are placed in key figure legends in each chapter and help students relate a topic they are currently learning to another topic elsewhere in the textbook, often in a different unit. Evolutionary Connections provide a framework for understanding how a topic in a given chapter relates to evolution, the core unifying theme in Biology.

Overall, the pedagogy of *Principles of Biology* has been designed to foster student learning. Instead of being a collection of "facts and figures," *Principles of Biology* is intended to be an engaging and motivating textbook in which formative assessment allows students to move ahead and learn the material in a productive way. We welcome your feedback so we can make future editions even better!

Rob Brooker
Eric Widmaier
Linda Graham
Peter Stiling

GUIDING YOU THROUGH *PRINCIPLES OF BIOLOGY*

Principles of Biology and its online assets have been carefully crafted to help you, the student, work efficiently and effectively through the material in the course, making the most of your study time. This *Guiding You Through Principles of Biology* section explains how you can use the text and online resources to help you succeed in Majors Biology.

Prepare for the Course

Many biology students struggle the first few weeks of class. Many institutions expect students to start majors biology having a working knowledge of basic chemistry and cellular biology. If you need a primer to help you get up to speed, consider McGraw-Hill's new program, *LearnSmart Prep*.

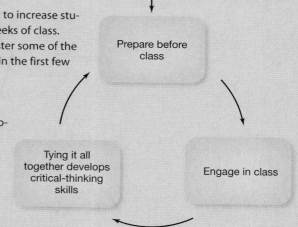

LEARNSMART PREP™

LearnSmart Prep is an adaptive learning tool designed to increase student success and aid retention through the first few weeks of class. Using this digital tool, Majors Biology students can master some of the most fundamental and challenging principles of biology before they begin to struggle in the first few weeks of class.

1 A diagnostic establishes your baseline comprehension and knowledge; then the program generates a learning plan tailored to your academic needs and schedule.

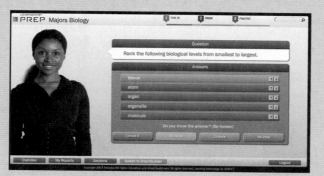

2 As you work through the learning plan, the program asks you questions and tracks your mastery of concepts. If you answer questions about a particular concept incorrectly, the program will provide a learning resource (ex. animation or tutorial) on that concept, then ensure that you understand the concept by asking you more questions. Didn't get it the first time? Don't worry—*LearnSmart Prep* will keep working with you!

3 Using *LearnSmart Prep*, you can identify the content you don't understand, focus your time on content you need to know but don't, and therefore improve your chances of success in your majors biology course.

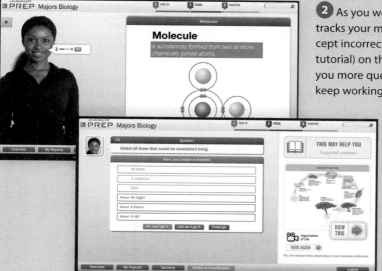

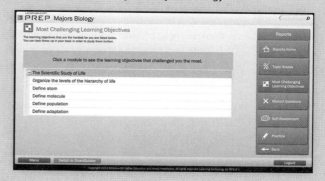

Prepare Before Class

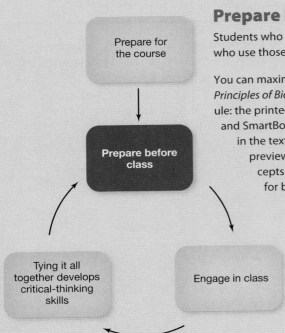

Prepare for the course

Prepare before class

Tying it all together develops critical-thinking skills

Engage in class

Students who are most successful in college are those who have developed effective study skills and who use those skills, before, during, and after class.

You can maximize your time in class by previewing the material before stepping into the lecture hall. *Principles of Biology* is available in several formats that allow you to fit studying into your busy schedule: the printed text as well as online offerings that include the interactive eBook in ConnectPlus+ and SmartBook. All three formats deliver the chapter material and valuable learning aids presented in the text, but the online options offer additional resources. Use any or all of these options to preview the material before lecture. Familiarizing yourself with terminology and basic concepts will allow you to follow along in class and engage in the content in a way that allows for better retention.

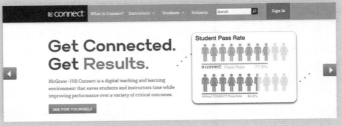

The gateway to your online Resources

❶ The traditional printed text offers many embedded study aids.

Guiding You Through *Principles of Biology*

Every chapter opens with a ▶ Chapter Outline that walks through the main concepts and organizes the material in the chapter and provides a story that puts the topic of the chapter into context.

7.2 Reactions That Harness Light Energy

Learning Outcomes:

1. Describe the general properties of light.
2. Explain how pigments absorb light energy and describe the types of pigments found in plants and green algae.
3. Outline the steps in which photosystems II and I capture light energy and produce O_2, ATP, and NADPH.

▲

Chapters are broken down into sections that cover skills or ideas you should master. Learning Outcomes at the beginning of each section tell you exactly what you should be able to do by the end of the section.

Reviewing the ▶ Concepts provides a summary of the key concepts presented in the section.

Testing Your Knowledge allows you to check your understanding of key concepts in the section before moving on. Additional questions are available at the end of the chapter.

Many figures throughout ▶ the text are supported with *Concept Check* questions that test your understanding of the concept illustrated in the figure.

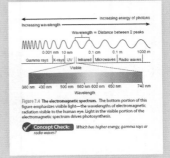

2 Online interactive eBook in ConnectPlus+ offers additional animations and study aids.

Enhancements found in the interactive eBook

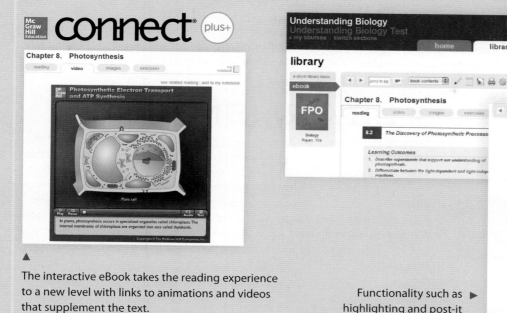

The interactive eBook takes the reading experience to a new level with links to animations and videos that supplement the text.

Functionality such as ▶ highlighting and post-it notes allow you to compile a personalized study guide.

Figure 6.2 Entropy, a measure of the disorder of a system. An increase in entropy means an increase in disorder.

3 SmartBook provides a personalized, adaptive reading experience.

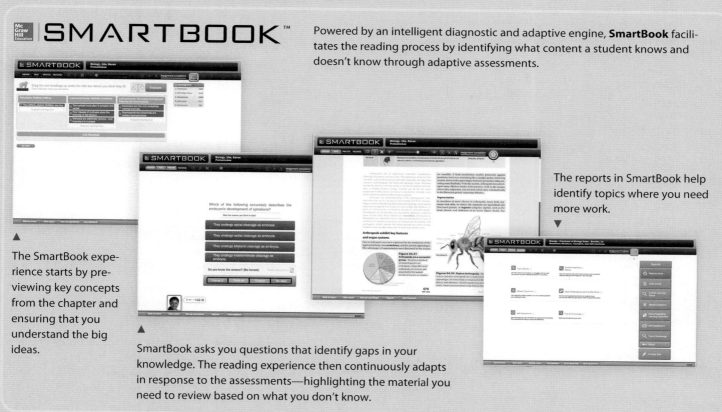

Powered by an intelligent diagnostic and adaptive engine, **SmartBook** facilitates the reading process by identifying what content a student knows and doesn't know through adaptive assessments.

The SmartBook experience starts by previewing key concepts from the chapter and ensuring that you understand the big ideas.

The reports in SmartBook help identify topics where you need more work.
▼

SmartBook asks you questions that identify gaps in your knowledge. The reading experience then continuously adapts in response to the assessments—highlighting the material you need to review based on what you don't know.

Engage in Class

Assignments in Connect and LearnSmart will help you understand concepts so that you and your professor can make the most of in-class time.

If you come to class having a working knowledge of concepts and terminology, the professor will be able to use the class period to help you develop critical thinking and analytical skills—skills that you will need to be successful in upper level courses and in your career.

Prepare for the course

Prepare before class

Engage in class

Tying it all together develops critical-thinking skills

 **LEARNSMART®**

McGraw-Hill LearnSmart™ is available as an integrated feature of McGraw-Hill Connect Biology. It is an adaptive learning system designed to help students learn faster, study more efficiently, and retain more knowledge for greater success. LearnSmart assesses a student's knowledge of course content through a series of adaptive questions. It pinpoints concepts the student does not understand and maps out a personalized study plan for success. This innovative study tool also has features that allow students access to rich reporting and provides instructors with a built-in assessment tool for grading assignments. Visit www.mhlearnsmart.com for a demonstration.

1 Your professor may make pre-class assignments to help you engage in the content during class.

connect® plus+ |BIOLOGY

Assignments are accessed through Connect and could include homework assignments, quizzes, reading assignments, LearnSmart assignments, and other resources. ►

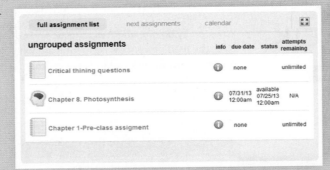

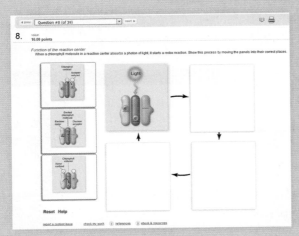

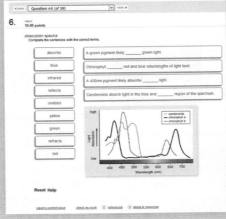

◄ Interactive and traditional questions help assess your knowledge of the material.

2 Your professor can assign modules in LearnSmart, which are also available in Connect or on your mobile device for self-study.

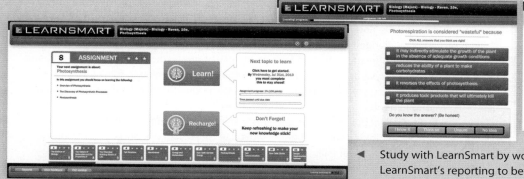

◀ Study with LearnSmart by working through modules and using LearnSmart's reporting to better understand your strengths and weaknesses.

◀ Download the LearnSmart app from iTunes or Google Play and work on LearnSmart from anywhere!

The Tree of Knowledge tracks your progress, reporting on short term successes and long term retention.

3 Your professor may record his or her lectures. If your professor is using Tegrity, you can review the lecture after class along with the corresponding PowerPoint® presentations. A Search function allows quick access to the content you want to review.

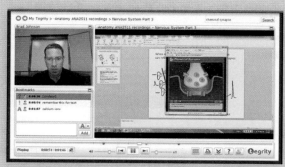

To save time, search through the Tegrity lecture using key terms—all PowerPoint slides that contain the term are identified for a quick review.

▼

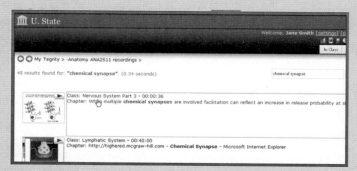

▲

More than just a recorded lecture, Tegrity lets you search and bookmark content, take notes, and work with fellow classmates in order to make learning incredibly efficient.

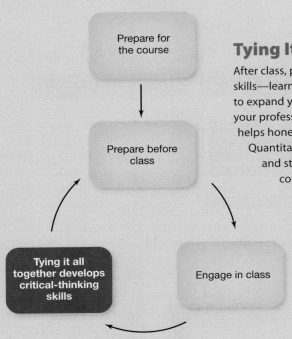

Prepare for
the course

Prepare before
class

Tying it all
together develops
critical-thinking
skills

Engage in class

Tying It All Together Develops Critical-Thinking Skills

After class, put your new-found knowledge to work by developing your critical thinking skills—learning to apply, analyze, and synthesize information. There are many opportunities to expand your skills. End-of-chapter questions in the book and online assignments from your professor challenge your understanding, revisiting LearnSmart/SmartBook modules helps hone your understanding, and Feature Investigations, Evolutionary Connections, and Quantitative Analysis are features in the book that encourage you to think past the facts and start putting your understanding to work. The Quantitative Analysis features are complemented by an online component to help you develop data analysis skills. BioConnection questions and *Principles of Biology* figures help you see how topics in biology are interconnected. All of these help develop critical-thinking and analytical skills.

1 Working through problems and questions that develop critical-thinking skills is key to understanding the concepts at a higher level.

Questions that challenge your comprehension

Following lecture, you should be able to answer Conceptual and Collaborative questions at the end of the chapter. A "Principles" question tests your understanding of how chapter concepts relate to the principles of biology that provide a framework for organizing concepts in biology.

Quantitative questions assigned in Connect allow you to practice answering mathematically-based biological problems—with hints and guided solutions to help you along the way. Numerical values in these questions change so that you can keep practicing until you understand the concept.

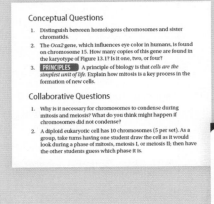

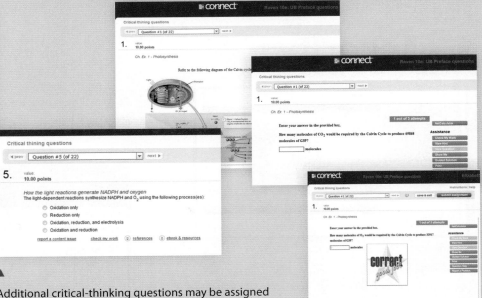

▲

Additional critical-thinking questions may be assigned by your professor in Connect.

2 The development of critical thinking and analytical tools is also achieved by analyzing scientific research.

Think like a scientist

Feature Investigations walk you through a scientific investigation looking at the experimental and conceptual aspects. The Investigation lays out the hypothesis, test procedures, data, and conclusion. Experimental questions test your understanding of the experiment, data, and conclusions.

▼

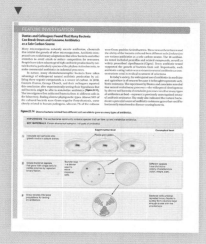

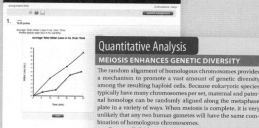

EVOLUTIONARY CONNECTIONS

Cell Division in Bacteria Involves FtsZ, a Protein Related to Eukaryotic Tubulin

As discussed in Chapter 15 (see Figure 15.11), bacteria divide by a process called binary fission. Because bacteria usually have only one type of chromosome, the process of sorting different types of chromosomes is not necessary. Even so, events during bacterial cell division may provide insights as to the manner in which mitosis evolved in eukaryotes.

Prior to cell division, bacterial cells copy, or replicate, their chromosomal DNA. This produces two identical copies of the genetic material, as shown at the top of Figure 13.6. During binary fission, the two daughter cells become separated from each other by the formation of a septum. Recent evidence has shown that bacterial species produce a protein called FtsZ, which is important in cell division. This protein assembles into a ring at the future site of the septum. FtsZ is thought to be the first protein to move to this division site, and it recruits other proteins that produce a new cell wall between the daughter cells.

FtsZ is evolutionarily related to the eukaryotic protein called tubulin, which is the main component of microtubules, which compose the mitotic spindle. In all eukaryotes, the midpoint of the mitotic spindle, which is called the metaphase plate, identifies the site for cytokinesis (look ahead to Figure 13.7d and f). This observation indicates that tubulin is also critical for cytokinesis in eukaryotic cells.

◄ The Evolutionary Connections feature examines the evolutionary implications of scientific research.

The Quantitative Analysis feature explores the quantitative aspect of the study of biology. The features walk you through biological concepts that have a quantitative component. The Crunching the Numbers provides a sample problem that tests your understanding. Associated online activities can help you practice your data analysis skills. ▶

Quantitative Analysis
MEIOSIS ENHANCES GENETIC DIVERSITY

The random alignment of homologous chromosomes provides a mechanism to promote a vast amount of genetic diversity among the resulting haploid cells. Because eukaryotic species typically have many chromosomes per set, maternal and paternal homologs can be randomly aligned along the metaphase plate in a variety of ways. When meiosis is complete, it is very unlikely that any two human gametes will have the same combination of homologous chromosomes.

For any diploid species the possible number of different, random alignments during metaphase I of meiosis equals 2^n, where n equals the number of chromosomes per set. The random alignments equal 2^n because each chromosome is found in a homologous pair and each member of the pair can align on either side of the metaphase plate. It is a matter of chance which daughter cell of meiosis I will get the maternal chromosome of a homologous pair, and which will get the paternal chromosome. Because the homologs are genetically similar but not identical, the random alignment of homologous chromosomes provides a mechanism to promote a vast amount of genetic diversity among the resulting haploid cells.

Crunching the Numbers: Humans have 23 chromosomes per set. How many possible random alignments could occur during metaphase I? How does crossing over further contribute to the genetic diversity of the resulting haploid cells?

3 A key component to learning is understanding the underlying principles of biology and making connections between different topics.

Biology principles and making connections

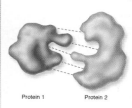

Biology Principle

New Properties Emerge from Complex Interactions

This principle of biology is apparent at the protein level. The primary sequence of proteins determines their final three-dimensional structures. Compare this with the chapter-opening depiction of two real proteins, and the several intermediate levels of protein structure shown in Figure 3.13. It is the three-dimensional shape of different proteins that determines their ability to interact with other molecules, including other proteins.

Figure 3.14 Protein-protein interaction. Two different proteins may interact with each other due to hydrogen bonding, ionic bonding, the hydrophobic effect, and van der Waals forces. Interaction is also facilitated by their respective three-dimensional shapes.

Protein 1   Protein 2

▲ Figures that are highlighted as Biology Principles discuss not only how the figure relates to the topic under consideration, but also how that figure illustrates a biological principle. Biology Principles provide a framework for organizing concepts in biology.

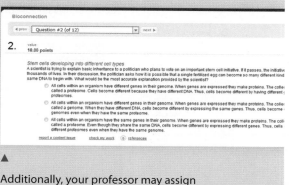

▲ Additionally, your professor may assign questions in Connect that require you to pull together and synthesize information from various chapters to address a more complex issue.

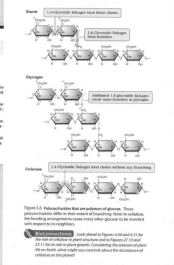

Figure 3.6 Polysaccharides that are polymers of glucose. These polysaccharides differ in their extent of branching. Note: In cellulose, the bonding arrangements cause every other glucose to be inverted with respect to its neighbors.

BioConnections Look ahead to Figures 4.30 and 4.31 for the role of cellulose in plant structure and to Figures 27.10 and 27.11 for its role in plant growth. Considering the amount of plant life on Earth, what might you conclude about the abundance of cellulose on the planet?

▲

BioConnections in figure legends direct you to figures in other chapters that are related to the topic or concept being illustrated. Although material is presented in separate chapters, many concepts in biology are related. BioConnections help you examine connections between seemingly unrelated concepts.

GUIDE YOUR STUDENTS THROUGH PRINCIPLES OF BIOLOGY

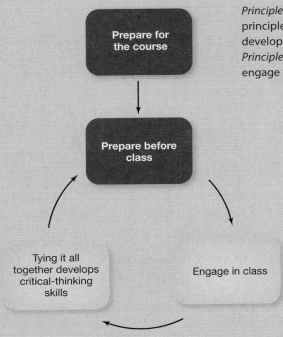

Prepare for the course

↓

Prepare before class

Tying it all together develops critical-thinking skills

Engage in class

Assessment with timely learning resources helps students with foundational material that you want them to know coming into the course.

Principles of Biology offers professors a text focused on developing an understanding of the core principles that provide a foundation for students intending to pursue a degree in biology and developing critical thinking skills that will serve them well into the future. This *Guide Through Principles of Biology* explains how professors can use the text and online resources to help engage their students and maximize their instructional time.

Prepare for the Course and for the Class

The Majors Biology class is changing in new and exciting ways, with more emphasis on active learning. Digital resources can help you achieve your instructional goals—making your students more responsible for learning outside of class by meeting your students where they live: on the go and online. Use the text and digital tools to empower students to come to class more prepared and ready to engage!

To help your students get up to speed, assign *LearnSmart Prep* at the beginning of the course. **LearnSmart™** *Prep* is an adaptive learning tool designed to increase student success and aid retention through the first few weeks of class. Using this digital tool, Majors Biology students can master some of the most fundamental and challenging principles of biology before they begin to struggle in the first few weeks of class.

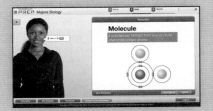

1 Create assignments and use adaptive resources to introduce terminology and basic concepts to students before class.

Help your students prepare for class by making assignments— reading, homework, and LearnSmart

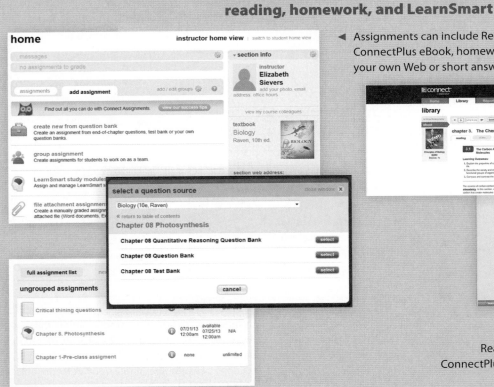

◀ Assignments can include Reading assignments from the ConnectPlus eBook, homework or quizzes, LearnSmart, your own Web or short answer activities, and more.

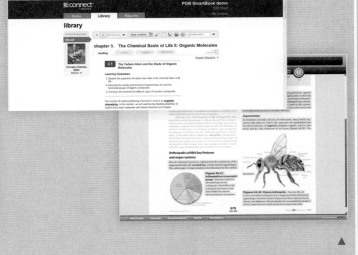

Reading assignments can be made using the ConnectPlus eBook, but students also have access to SmartBook or the standard printed text.

McGraw-Hill Connect Biology provides online presentation, assignment, and assessment solutions. It connects your students with the tools and resources they'll need to achieve success. With Connect Biology you can deliver assignments, quizzes, and tests online. A robust set of questions and activities are presented in the Question Bank and a separate set of questions to use for exams are presented in the Test Bank. As an instructor, you can edit existing questions and author entirely new problems. Track individual student performance—by question, assignment, or in relation to the class overall—with detailed grade reports. Integrate grade reports easily with Learning Management Systems such as Blackboard and Canvas—and much more. ConnectPlus Biology provides students with all the advantages of Connect Biology plus 24/7 online access to an eBook. This media-rich version of the book is available through the McGraw-Hill Connect platform and allows seamless integration of text, media, and assessments.

To learn more, visit www.mcgrawhillconnect.com

2 Customize Connect and LearnSmart assignments to address knowledge gaps so students can get the most out of class.

Customize your assignments using Connect filters

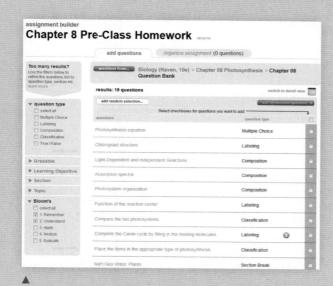

You can customize your LearnSmart assignments by topic (selecting the sections in the chapter you will cover in class) and by the amount of time investment you expect from your students. Reducing the length of time focuses the LearnSmart questions on core concepts in the chapter.

Use the filters in Connect to select questions that match your desired level of assessment—filter questions for lower-level Blooms to assess basic concepts and understanding prior to lecture. Filter using upper-level Blooms after class to develop critical-thinking and analytical skills.

Reports in Connect and LearnSmart help you monitor student assignments and performance, allowing for "just-in-time" teaching to clarify concepts that are more difficult for your students to understand.

Engage Your Students in Class

Prepare for the course

Prepare before class

Engage in class

Tying it all together develops critical-thinking skills

Flip your classroom and make time for active learning in class by creating preclass assignments using Connect and LearnSmart. Your students will come to class better prepared and you can make the most of your valuable class time to work on developing their critical thinking and analytical skills.

McGraw-Hill Tegrity® records and distributes your class activities or lectures with just a click of a button. Students can view the recorded videos anytime/anywhere via computer, iPod, or mobile device. Tegrity indexes your PowerPoint® presentations and anything shown on your computer so that students can use keywords to find exactly what they want to study. Tegrity is available as an integrated feature of McGraw-Hill Connect Biology and as a standalone resource.

1 Within Connect, you will find presentation materials to enhance your class.

Presentation Tools in Connect

The Presentation Tools in Connect provide everything you need for outstanding presentations all in one place.

◀ Animation PowerPoints contain full-color animations illustrating important processes, which are fully embedded in PowerPoint slides for easy use in your presentations.

FlexArt PowerPoints contain editable art from the text. For all figures, labels and leader lines are editable allowing you to customize your PowerPoint presentations.

▼

3-D Animations bring biology to life with dynamic imagery and interesting presentation tools, such as the highlighting pen.

▼

◀ Enhance your presentations with lecture PowerPoints with animations fully embedded.

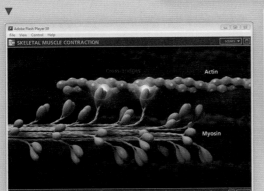

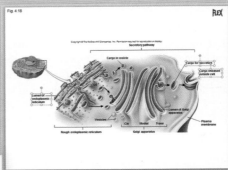

◀ Labeled and unlabeled JPEG files of all art and photos in the text can be readily incorporated into presentations, exams, or custom-made classroom materials.

2 Engage your students during class with Active Learning resources. Use Tegrity, the lecture-capture program in Connect, to reach your students outside of class.

Active Learning in Connect

Chapter	Guided Collaborative Activities	Minute Papers	Clicker Questions	Concept Mapping
All Chapters	Guided Collaborative Learning Activities (11986.0K)	Available soon	Available soon	Available soon
Ch01 An Introduction to Biology	Experimental Design - Metabo-Herb (91.0K) / Hypothesis Testing (172.0K)	Ch01 Minute Papers PPT (324.0K)	Ch01 Clicker Questions PPT (350.0K)	Ch1 Concept Map Scientific Theory (296.0K)
Ch02 The Chemical Basis of Life I: Atoms, Molecules, and Water		Ch02 Minute Papers PPT (177.0K)	Ch02 Clicker Questions PPT (215.0K)	Ch2 Concept Map Chemistry (226.0K)
Ch03 The Chemical Basis of Life II: Organic Molecules	Fatty Acids, Nutrition, Health (432.0K) / How Expensive Are You? (125.0K)	Ch03 Minute Papers PPT (175.0K)	Ch03 Clicker Questions PPT (221.0K)	Ch3 Concept Map Biomolecules (150.0K)
Ch04 General Features of Cells	Organelles and Illness (91.0K)	Ch04 Minute Papers PPT (168.0K)	Ch04 Clicker Questions PPT (227.0K)	Ch4 Concept Map Eukaryotic Cell Components (145.0K)

Use Tegrity to record your class activities. Your students can revisit your presentations and discussions after class with access to all the materials you covered.

▼

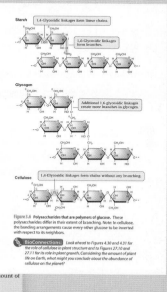

▲

Active-learning resources in Connect are sorted by chapter and designed to help you offer activities with varying degrees of participation: from Collaborative In-class Activities that are supported with instructor resources and prebuilt student assignments to Clicker Questions, Minute Papers, and Concept Maps.

3 If your students are better prepared when they walk into class, you can expand your coverage beyond the scope of basic concepts, incorporating discussion sessions and working on critical thinking skills.

Challenge your students

The authors of *Principles of Biology* understand that today's biology majors need to move beyond memorization and content acquisition. Features in the text such as Feature Investigations, Quantitative Analysis, Biology Principles figures, Evolutionary Connections, and Bio-Connections questions challenge students to apply their knowledge. Assignable online assessments and activities support the development of critical-thinking skills.

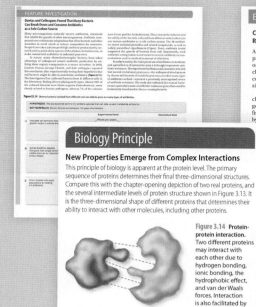

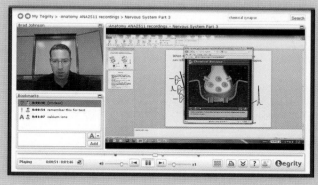

Tying It All Together for Your Students

Follow up your class with assessment that helps students develop critical-thinking skills. Set up assignments from the various assessment banks in Connect.

Prepare for the course

↓

Prepare before class

Tying it all together develops critical-thinking skills

Engage in class

The Question and Test Banks contain higher order critical thinking questions that require students to demonstrate a more in-depth understanding of the concepts—as described on page xiii, you can quickly and easily filter the banks for these questions using higher level Blooms. BioConnections question banks provide questions that require students make connections among topics across chapters, developing critical-thinking skills.

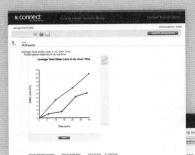

◀ **Quantitative Analysis** features in the text have assignable online activities that encourage students to practice and strengthen their quantitative reasoning skills.

Many chapters also contain a **Quantitative Question Bank.** These are more challenging algorithmic questions, intended to help your students practice their quantitative reasoning skills. Hints and guided solution options step students through a problem.

▶

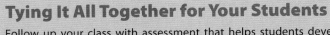

Based on the same world-class superadaptive technology as LearnSmart, McGraw-Hill LearnSmart-Labs is a must-see, outcomes-based lab simulation. It assesses a student's knowledge and adaptively corrects deficiencies, allowing the student to learn faster and retain more knowledge with greater success. Whether your need is to overcome the logistical challenges of a traditional lab, provide better lab prep, improve student performance, or create an online experience that rivals the real world, LabSmart accomplishes it all.

Learn more at www.mhlabsmart.com

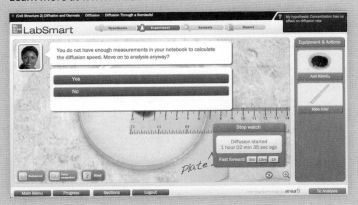

LearnSmart Labs can be used to help students apply the scientific process, thinking and doing like scientists via rich simulations.

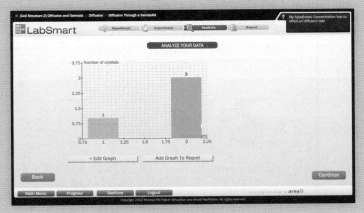

ACKNOWLEDGMENTS

The lives of most science-textbook authors do not revolve around an analysis of writing techniques. Instead, we are people who understand science and are inspired by it, and we want to communicate that information to our students. Simply put, we need a lot of help to get it right.

Editors are a key component that help the authors modify the content of their book so it is logical, easy to read, and inspiring. The editorial team for *Principles of Biology* has been a catalyst that kept this project rolling. The members played various roles in the editorial process. Rebecca Olson, Brand Manager for Majors Biology, did an outstanding job of overseeing the development of this new text. Her insights with regard to pedagogy, content, and organization have been invaluable. Elizabeth Sievers, Director of Development—Biology, has been the master organizer. Liz's success at keeping us on schedule is greatly appreciated.

Our Freelance Developmental Editor, Joni Fraser, worked directly with the authors to greatly improve the presentation of the textbook's content. She did a great job of editing chapters and advising the authors on improvements. We would also like to acknowledge our copy editor, Linda Davoli, for keeping our grammar on track.

Another important aspect of the editorial process is the actual design, presentation, and layout of materials. It's confusing if the text and art aren't near each other or if a figure is too large or too small. We are indebted to the tireless efforts of Sandy Wille, Content Project Manager, and David Hash, Senior Designer at McGraw-Hill Education. Likewise, our production company, Lachina Publishing Services, did an excellent job with the paging, extensive revisions of the art, and the creation of new art. Their artistic talents, ability to size and arrange figures, and attention to the consistency of the figures has been remarkable.

We would like to acknowledge the ongoing efforts of the superb marketing staff at McGraw-Hill Education. Special thanks to Patrick Reidy, Executive Marketing Manager—Life Sciences, for his ideas and enthusiasm for this book.

Other staff members at McGraw-Hill Education have ensured that the authors and editors were provided with adequate resources to achieve the goal of producing a superior textbook. These include Kurt Strand, Senior Vice President, Products & Markets; Marty Lange, Vice President, General Manager, Products & Markets; Michael Hackett, Managing Director for Life Science; and Lynn Breithaupt, Director for Biology.

We would like to thank the subject matter experts who helped in the development of the digital assets in Connect that support *Principles of Biology*. Finally, we need to thank our reviewers. Instructors from across the country are continually invited to share their knowledge and experience with us through reviews and focus groups. The feedback we received shaped this new text. All of these people took time out of their already busy lives to help us build a text to reach out to introductory biology students, and they have our heartfelt thanks.

The authors are grateful for the help, support, and patience of their families, friends, and students: Deb, Dan, Nate, and Sarah Brooker; Maria, Rick, and Carrie Widmaier; Jim, Michael, and Melissa Graham; and Jacqui, Zoe, Leah, and Jenna Stiling.

Thomas D. Abbott
University of Connecticut
Karen Aguirre
Coastal Carolina University
Phillip Allman
Florida Gulf Coast University
Patti L Allen
Dixie State College of Utah
Ricardo Azpiroz
Richland College
Ellen Baker
Santa Monica College
Keith Bancroft
Southeastern Louisiana University
Michael C. Bell
Richland College
Laura Hill Bermingham
University of Vermont
James Bottesch
Eastern Florida State College
Randy Brooks
Florida Atlantic University
Jill Buettner
Richland College
Steve Bush
Coastal Carolina University
Karen Champ
College of Central Florida
Thomas Chen
Santa Monica College

James Crowder
Brookdale Community College
Jennifer Cymbola
Grand Valley State University
Deborah Dardis
Southeastern Louisiana University
Hartmut Doebel
George Washington University
David Fitch
New York University
Deborah Garrity
Colorado State University
Amy Helms
Collin College
Brian Helmuth
University of South Carolina
Lisa Dondero Hermann
Edison State College
Thomas E. Hetherington
Ohio State University
Christopher L. Higgins
Tarleton State University
Lisa Hines
University of Colorado—Colorado Springs
Robert Hines
North Hennepin Community College
Nicole Huber
University of Colorado—Colorado Springs
Regina M. Huse
Tarrant County College

Dianne Jennings
Virginia Commonwealth University
Gregory Jones
Santa Fe College
Bridgette Kirkpatrick
Collin College
Stephen Kucera
The University of Tampa
Jennifer Leavey
Georgia Institute of Technology
Stephanie Lee
Pearl River Community College
Craig Longtine
North Hennepin Community College
Stefanie Maruhnich
Florida State College at Jacksonville
Mark McRae
The University of Tampa
Michael Meighan
University of California—Berkeley
Alexey Nikitin
Grand Valley State University
Katherine Phillips
North Hennepin Community College
Nirmala V. Prabhu
Edison State College
Amy Reber
Georgia State University
Brenden Rickards
Gloucester County College

Luis A. Rodriguez
San Antonio College
Tinna M. Ross
North Hennepin Community College
Heidi Sleister
Drake University
Jagan V. Valluri
Marshall University
William Velhagen
New York University
Beth Vlad
College of Dupage
Kimberlyn Williams
California State University—San Bernardino
Tom Wolkow
University of Colorado—Colorado Springs

Digital Subject Matter Experts
LearnSmart Team:

Laurie Russell (Lead), *St. Louis University;*
Tonya Bates, *University of North Carolina, Charlotte;* Megan Berdelman, *freelance subject matter* expert; Johnny ElRady, *University of South Florida;* Elizabeth Harris, *Appalachian State University;* Murad Odeh, *South Texas College,* Danielle Ruffatto, *University of Illinois at Urbana-Champaign*

CONTENTS

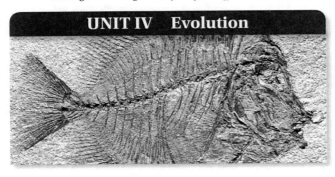
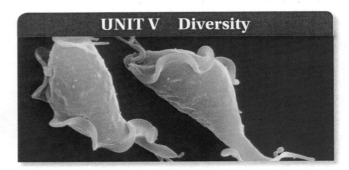

UNIT VIII   Ecology

CHAPTER 46

Ecosystem Ecology   937

CHAPTER 47

Biodiversity and Conservation Biology   953

BRIEF CONTENTS

UNIT IV
EVOLUTION

Evolution is a change in one or more heritable characteristics of a population from one generation to the next. This process not only alters the characteristics of populations, it also leads to the formation of new species.

We will begin Chapter 18 with a discussion of the hypotheses that have been proposed to explain the origin of life on Earth, and then examine a timeline for the evolution of species from 4 billion years ago to the present. In Chapter 19, you will be introduced to the fundamental concepts of evolution and examine observations of evolutionary change, which include (1) the fossil record, (2) a comparison of the characteristics of modern species, and (3) an analysis of molecular data. We will consider how evolution occurs at the molecular level and focus on how changes in allele and genotype frequencies from one generation to the next are driven by a variety of different factors. By comparison, Chapter 20 shifts the emphasis of evolution to the level of species. We will examine how species are identified and discuss the mechanisms by which new species arise via evolution. Finally, in Chapter 21, we will examine how biologists determine the evolutionary relationships among different species and produce branching diagrams, or "trees," that describe those relationships.

The following biology principles will be emphasized in this unit:

- **Populations of organisms evolve from one generation to the next.** *This concept will be emphasized throughout the entire unit.*

- **Living organisms interact with their environment.** *As discussed in Chapters 18, 19, and 20, natural selection is a process in which certain individuals have greater reproductive success. This success is often due to their ability to survive in a given environment.*

- **Structure determines function.** *Chapters 19 and 20 will also consider how structural features change during the evolution of new species. Such changes are related to changes in function.*

- **All species (past and present) are related by an evolutionary history.** *Chapter 21 is devoted to examining how biologists determine evolutionary relationships among different species.*

- **Biology is an experimental science.** *Most chapters have a Feature Investigation that describes a pivotal experiment that provided insights into our understanding of evolution.*

The Origin and History of Life on Earth

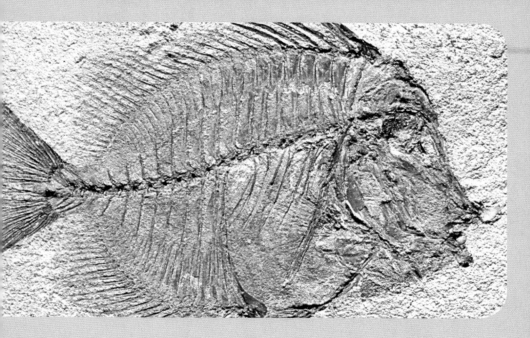

A fossil fish. This 50-million-year-old fossil of a unicorn fish (*Naso rectifrons*) is an example of the many different kinds of organisms that have existed during the history of life on Earth.

Chapter Outline

The amazing origin of the universe is difficult to comprehend. Astronomers think the universe began with a cosmic explosion called the Big Bang about 13.8 billion years ago (bya), when the first clouds of the elements hydrogen and helium were formed. Over a long time period, gravitational forces collapsed these clouds to create stars that converted hydrogen and helium into heavier elements, including carbon, nitrogen, and oxygen, which are the atomic building blocks of life on Earth. These elements were returned to interstellar space by exploding stars called supernovas, which created clouds in which simple molecules such as water, carbon monoxide, and hydrocarbons formed. The clouds then collapsed to make a new generation of stars and solar systems.

Our solar system began about 4.6 bya after one or more local supernova explosions. According to one widely accepted scenario, hundreds of planetesimals consisting of rocky or icy bodies such as asteroids and comets occupied the region where Venus, Earth, and Mars are now found. The Earth, which is estimated to be 4.55 billion years old, grew from the aggregation of such planetesimals over a period of 100 to 200 million years. For the first half billion years or so after its formation, the Earth was too hot to allow liquid water to accumulate on its surface. By 4 bya, the Earth had cooled enough for the outer layers of the planet to solidify and for oceans to begin to form.

The period between 4.0 and 3.5 bya marked the emergence of life on our planet. The first forms of life that we know about produced microscopic fossils, the preserved remains of organisms that existed in the past. These fossils, estimated to be about 3.5 billion years old, resemble modern cyanobacteria, which are photosynthetic bacteria (**Figure 18.1**). Researchers cannot travel back through time and observe how the first life-forms came into being. However, plausible hypotheses regarding how life first arose have emerged from our understanding of modern life.

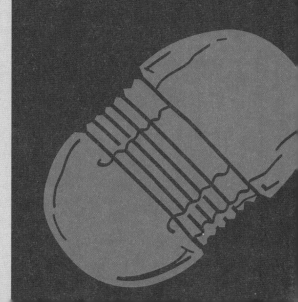

This chapter, the first in the Evolution unit, emphasizes when particular forms of life arose. The first section surveys a variety of hypotheses regarding (1) the origin of organic molecules on Earth, (2) the formation of complex molecules such as DNA, RNA, and proteins, (3) the formation of primitive cell-like structures, and (4) the process that gave rise to the first living cells. We will then consider how fossils, such as the one shown in the chapter-opening photo, have provided biologists with evidence of the history of life on Earth from its earliest beginnings to the present day. The last section provides a broad overview of the geologic time scale and the major events in the history of life on Earth.

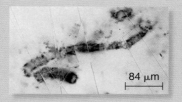
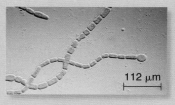

(a) Fossil prokaryote   **(b) Modern cyanobacteria**

Figure 18.1 Earliest fossils and living cyanobacteria. (a) A fossilized prokaryote about 3.5 billion years old that is thought to be an early cyanobacterium. **(b)** A modern cyanobacterium, which has a similar morphology. Cyanobacterial cells connect to each other to form chains, as shown here.

18.1 Origin of Life on Earth

Learning Outcomes:

1. Outline the four overlapping stages that are hypothesized to have led to the origin of life.
2. List various hypotheses about how complex organic molecules formed.
3. Explain the concept of an RNA world and how it could have evolved into a DNA/RNA/protein world.

As we have seen, living cells are complex collections of molecules and macromolecules. DNA stores genetic information, RNA acts as an intermediary in the process of protein synthesis and plays other important roles, and proteins form the foundation for the structure and activities of living cells. Life as we know it requires this interplay between DNA, RNA, and proteins for its existence and perpetuation. On modern Earth, every living cell is made from a pre-existing cell.

But how did life get started? As described in Chapter 1, living organisms have several characteristics that distinguish them from nonliving materials. Because DNA, RNA, and proteins are the central players in the enterprise of life, scientists who are interested in the origin of life have focused much of their attention on the formation of these macromolecules and their building blocks, namely, nucleotides and amino acids. To understand the origin of life, we can view the process as occurring in four overlapping stages:

- **Stage 1:** Nucleotides and amino acids were produced prior to the existence of cells.
- **Stage 2:** Nucleotides became polymerized to form RNA and/or DNA, and amino acids became polymerized to form proteins.
- **Stage 3:** Polymers became enclosed in membranes.
- **Stage 4:** Polymers enclosed in membranes acquired cellular properties.

Researchers have followed a variety of experimental approaches to determine how life may have begun, including the synthesis of organic molecules in the laboratory without the presence of living cells or cellular material. This work has led researchers to propose a variety of hypotheses regarding the origin of life. In this section, we will examine the origin of life at each of these stages and consider a few scientific viewpoints that wrestle with the question, "How did life on Earth begin?"

Stage 1: Organic Molecules Formed Prior to the Existence of Cells

Let's begin our inquiry into the first stage of the origin of life by considering how nucleotides and amino acids may have been made prior to the existence of living cells. In the 1920s, the Russian biochemist Alexander Oparin and the Scottish biologist J.B.S. Haldane independently proposed that organic molecules, such as nucleotides and amino acids, arose spontaneously under the conditions that occurred on early Earth. According to this hypothesis, the spontaneous appearance of organic molecules produced what they called a "primordial soup," which eventually gave rise to living cells.

The conditions on early Earth, which were much different from today, may have been more conducive to the spontaneous formation of organic molecules. Current hypotheses suggest that organic molecules, and eventually macromolecules, formed spontaneously. This is termed prebiotic (before life) or abiotic (without life) synthesis. These slowly forming organic molecules accumulated because there was little free oxygen gas, so they were not spontaneously oxidized, and there were as yet no living organisms, so they were also not metabolized. The slow accumulation of these molecules in the early oceans over a long period of time formed what is now called the **prebiotic soup.** The formation of this medium was a key event that preceded the origin of life.

Though most scientists agree that life originated from the assemblage of nonliving matter on early Earth, the mechanism of how and where these molecules originated is widely debated. Many intriguing hypotheses have been proposed, which are not mutually exclusive. A few of the more widely debated ideas are the reducing atmosphere hypothesis, the extraterrestrial hypothesis, and the deep-sea vent hypothesis.

Reducing Atmosphere Hypothesis Based largely on geological data, many scientists in the 1950s proposed that the atmosphere on early Earth was rich in water vapor (H_2O), hydrogen gas (H_2), methane (CH_4), and ammonia (NH_3). These components, along with a lack of atmospheric oxygen (O_2), produce a reducing atmosphere because methane and ammonia readily give up electrons to other molecules, thereby reducing them. Such oxidation-reduction reactions, or redox reactions, are required for the formation of complex organic molecules from simple inorganic molecules.

In 1953, American chemist Stanley Miller, a student in the laboratory of the physical chemist Harold Urey, was the first scientist to use experimentation to test whether the prebiotic synthesis of organic molecules is possible. His experimental apparatus was intended to simulate the conditions on early Earth that were postulated in the 1950s (Figure 18.2). Water vapor from a flask of boiling water rose into another chamber containing hydrogen gas (H_2), methane (CH_4), and ammonia (NH_3). Miller inserted two electrodes that sent electrical discharges into the chamber to simulate lightning bolts. A condenser jacket cooled some of the gases from the chamber, causing droplets to form that fell into a trap. He then took samples from this trap for chemical analysis. In his first experiments, he observed the formation of hydrogen cyanide (HCN) and formaldehyde (CH_2O). Such molecules are precursors of more complex organic molecules. These precursors also combined to make larger molecules such as the amino acid glycine. At the end of one week of operation, 10–15% of the carbon had been incorporated into organic compounds. Later experiments by Miller and others demonstrated the formation of sugars, a few types of amino acids, lipids, and nitrogenous bases found in nucleic acids (for example, adenine).

In a study published in 2011, researchers analyzed samples that Miller had preserved from a 1958 experiment in which he used a mixture of CH_4, NH_3, hydrogen sulfide (H_2S), and carbon dioxide (CO_2). For unknown reasons, Miller had not analyzed what products were made in this experiment. When these preserved samples were analyzed using modern technology, they were found to contain 23 different amino acids and 4 amines (another type of organic molecule), more organic compounds than seen in Miller's classic experiments.

Why were these studies important? The work of Miller and Urey was the first attempt to apply scientific experimentation to our quest to understand the origin of life. Their pioneering strategy showed that the prebiotic synthesis of organic molecules is possible, although it could not prove that it really happened that way. In spite of the importance of these studies, critics of the so-called reducing atmosphere hypothesis have argued that Miller and Urey were wrong about the composition of early Earth's environment. More recently, many scientists have suggested that the atmosphere on early Earth was not reducing, but instead was a neutral environment composed mostly of carbon monoxide (CO), carbon dioxide (CO_2), nitrogen gas (N_2), and H_2O. These newer ideas are derived from studies of volcanic gas, which has much more CO_2

Biology Principle

Biology Is an Experimental Science

By conducting experiments, researchers were able to demonstrate the feasibility of the synthesis of organic molecules prior to the emergence of living cells.

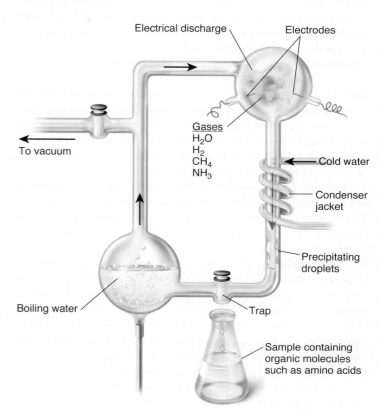

Figure 18.2 **Testing the reducing atmosphere hypothesis for the origin of life—the Miller and Urey experiment.**

Concept Check: *With regard to the origin of life, why are biologists interested in the abiotic synthesis of organic molecules?*

and N_2 than CH_4 and NH_3, and from the observation that ultraviolet (UV) radiation destroys CH_4 and NH_3, so these molecules would have been short-lived on early Earth, which had high levels of UV radiation. Nevertheless, since the experiments of Miller and Urey, many newer investigations have shown that organic molecules can be made under a variety of conditions. For example, organic molecules can be made prebiotically from a neutral environment composed primarily of CO, CO_2, N_2, and H_2O.

Extraterrestrial Hypothesis Many scientists have argued that sufficient organic molecules may have been present in meteorites, material from asteroids and comets that reached the surface of early Earth. A significant proportion of meteorites belong to a class known as carbonaceous chondrites. Such meteorites may contain a substantial amount of organic carbon, including amino acids and nucleic acid bases. Based on this observation, some scientists have postulated that such meteorites could have transported a significant amount of organic molecules from outer space to early Earth.

Opponents of this hypothesis argue that most of this material would have been destroyed by the intense heating that accompanies the passage of large bodies through the atmosphere and their subsequent collision with the surface of the Earth. Though some organic molecules are known to reach the Earth via such meteorites, the degree to which heat would have destroyed many of the organic molecules remains a matter of controversy.

Deep-Sea Vent Hypothesis   In 1988, German lawyer and organic chemist Günter Wächtershäuser proposed that key organic molecules may have originated in deep-sea vents, which are cracks in the Earth's surface where superheated water rich in metal ions and hydrogen sulfide (H_2S) mixes abruptly with cold seawater. These vents release hot gaseous substances from the interior of the Earth at temperatures in excess of 300°C (572°F). Supporters of this hypothesis propose that biologically important molecules may have been formed in the temperature gradient between the extremely hot vent water and the cold water that surrounds the vent (Figure 18.3a).

Experimentally, the temperatures within this gradient are known to be suitable for the synthesis of molecules that form components of biological molecules. For example, the reaction between iron and H_2S yields pyrites and H_2 and has been shown to provide the energy necessary for the reduction of N_2 to NH_3. Nitrogen is an essential component of both nucleic acids and amino acids—the molecular building blocks of life. But N_2, which is found abundantly on Earth, is chemically inert, so it is unlikely to have given rise to life. The conversion of N_2 to NH_3 at deep-sea vents may have led to the production of amino acids and nucleic acids.

Interestingly, complex biological communities are found in the vicinity of modern deep-sea vents. Various types of fish, worms, clams, crabs, shrimp, and bacteria are found in significant abundance in those areas (Figure 18.3b). Unlike most other forms of life on our planet, these organisms receive their energy from chemicals in the vent and not from the Sun. In 2007, American scientist Timothy Kusky and colleagues discovered 1.43 billion-year-old fossils of deep-sea microbes near ancient deep-sea vents. This study provided more evidence that life may have originated on the bottom of the ocean. However, debate continues as to the primary way that organic molecules were made prior to the existence of life on Earth.

Stage 2: Organic Polymers May Have Formed on the Surface of Clay or in Water

The preceding three hypotheses provide reasonable mechanisms by which small organic molecules could have accumulated on early Earth. Scientists hypothesize that the second stage in the origin of life was a period in which simple organic molecules polymerized to form more complex organic polymers such as

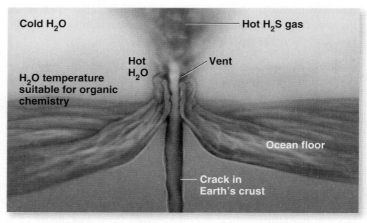

(a) Deep-sea vent hypothesis

(b) A deep-sea vent community

Figure 18.3 **The deep-sea vent hypothesis for the origin of life.** **(a)** Deep-sea vents are cracks in the Earth's surface that release hot gases such as hydrogen sulfide (H_2S). This heats the water near the vent and results in a gradient between the very hot water adjacent to the vent and the cold water farther from the vent. The synthesis of organic molecules occurs in this gradient. **(b)** Photograph of a biological community near a deep-sea vent, which includes giant (orange) tube worms, crabs, and eels.

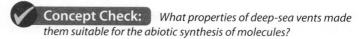

Concept Check: *What properties of deep-sea vents made them suitable for the abiotic synthesis of molecules?*

DNA, RNA, or proteins. Most ideas regarding the origin of life assume that polymers with lengths of at least 30–60 monomers are needed to store enough information to make a viable genetic system. Because hydrolysis competes with polymerization, many scientists have speculated that the synthesis of polymers did not occur in a watery prebiotic soup, but instead took place on a solid surface or in evaporating tidal pools.

In 1951, Irish X-ray crystallographer John Bernal first suggested that the prebiotic synthesis of polymers took place on clay. In his book *The Physical Basis of Life*, he wrote that "clays, muds and inorganic crystals are powerful means to concentrate and polymerize organic molecules." Many clay minerals are known to bind organic molecules such as nucleotides and amino acids. Experimentally, many research groups have demonstrated the formation of nucleic acid polymers and polypeptides on the surface of clay, given the presence of monomer building blocks. During the prebiotic synthesis of RNA, the purine bases of the nucleotides interact with the silicate surfaces of the clay. Cations, such as Mg^{2+}, bind the nucleotides to the negative surfaces of the clay, thereby positioning the nucleotides in a way that promotes bond formation between the phosphate of one nucleotide and the ribose sugar of an adjacent nucleotide. In this way, polymers such as RNA may have formed.

Though the formation of polymers on clay remains a reasonable hypothesis, studies by American chemist Luke Leman and his colleagues English chemist Leslie Orgel and Iranian-American chemist M. Reza Ghadiri indicate that polymers can also form in aqueous solutions, which is contrary to popular belief. Their work in 2004 showed that carbonyl sulfide, a simple gas present in volcanic gases and deep-sea vent emissions, can bring about the formation of peptides from amino acids under mild conditions in water. These results indicate that the synthesis of polymers could have taken place in the prebiotic soup.

Stage 3: Cell-Like Structures May Have Originated When Polymers Were Enclosed by a Boundary

The third stage in the origin of living cells is hypothesized to be the formation of a boundary that separated the internal polymers such as RNA from the environment. The term **protobiont** is used to describe an aggregate of prebiotically produced molecules and macromolecules that acquired a boundary, such as a lipid bilayer, that allowed it to maintain an internal chemical environment distinct from that of its surroundings. What characteristics make protobionts possible precursors of living cells? Scientists envision the existence of four key features:

1. A boundary, such as a membrane, separated the internal contents of the protobiont from the external environment.
2. Polymers inside the protobiont contained information.
3. Polymers inside the protobiont had catalytic functions.
4. The protobionts eventually developed the capability of self-replication.

Protobionts were not capable of precise self-reproduction like living cells, but could divide to increase in number. Such protobionts are thought to have exhibited simple metabolic pathways in which the structures of organic molecules were changed. In particular, the polymers inside protobionts must have gained the catalytic ability to link organic building blocks to produce new polymers. This would have been a critical step in the process that eventually provided protobionts with the ability to self-replicate. According to this scenario, metabolic pathways became more complex, and the ability of protobionts to self-replicate became more refined over time. Eventually, these structures exhibited the characteristics that we attribute to living cells. As described next, researchers have hypothesized that

protobionts may have exhibited different types of structures, such as coacervates and liposomes.

In 1924 Alexander Oparin hypothesized that living cells evolved from **coacervates,** droplets that form spontaneously from the association of charged polymers such as proteins, carbohydrates, or nucleic acids surrounded by water. Their name derives from the Latin *coacervare*, meaning to assemble together or cluster. Coacervates measure 1–100 µm (micrometers) across, are surrounded by a tight skin of water molecules, and possess osmotic properties (**Figure 18.4a**). This boundary allows the selective absorption of simple molecules from the surrounding medium.

Enzymes trapped within coacervates can perform primitive metabolic functions. For example, researchers have made coacervates containing the enzyme glycogen phosphorylase. When glucose-1-phosphate was made available to the coacervates, it

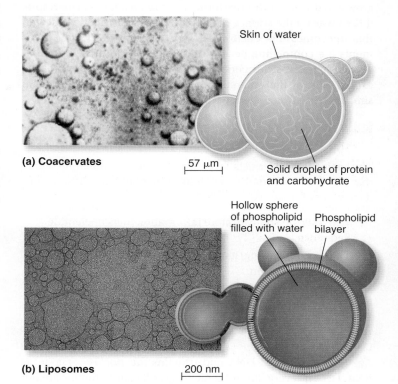

(a) **Coacervates**   57 µm

Skin of water

Solid droplet of protein and carbohydrate

(b) **Liposomes**   200 nm

Hollow sphere of phospholipid filled with water

Phospholipid bilayer

Figure 18.4 **Protobionts and their lifelike functions.** Primitive cell-like structures such as coacervates and liposomes could have given rise to living cells. **(a)** A micrograph and illustration of coacervates, which are droplets of protein and carbohydrate surrounded by a skin of water molecules. **(b)** An electron micrograph and illustration of liposomes. Each liposome is made of a phospholipid bilayer surrounding an aqueous compartment.

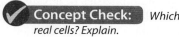

Concept Check: *Which protobiont seems most similar to real cells? Explain.*

BioConnections: *Look back at Figure 3.9. What is the physical/chemical reason why phospholipids tend to form a bilayer?*

was taken up into them, and starch was produced. The starch merged with the wall of the coacervates, which increased in size and eventually divided into two. When the enzyme amylase was included, the starch was broken down to maltose, which was released from the coacervates.

As a second possibility, protobionts may have resembled **liposomes**—vesicles surrounded by a lipid bilayer (Figure 18.4b). When certain types of lipids are dissolved in water, they spontaneously form liposomes. As discussed in Chapter 5, lipid bilayers are selectively permeable (refer back to Figure 5.8), and some liposomes can even store energy in the form of an electrical gradient. Such liposomes can discharge this energy in a neuron-like fashion, showing rudimentary signs of excitability, which is characteristic of living cells.

In 2003, Danish chemist Martin Hanczyc, American chemist Shelly Fujikawa, and Canadian American biologist Jack Szostak showed that clay can catalyze the formation of liposomes that grow and divide, a primitive form of self-replication. Furthermore, if RNA was on the surface of the clay, the researchers discovered that liposomes that enclosed RNA were formed. These experiments are compelling because they showed that the formation of membrane vesicles containing RNA molecules is a plausible explanation of the emergence of cell-like structures based on simple physical and chemical properties.

Stage 4: Cellular Characteristics May Have Evolved via Chemical Selection, Beginning with an RNA World

The majority of scientists favor RNA as the first macromolecule that was found in protobionts. Unlike other polymers, RNA exhibits three key functions:

1. RNA has the ability to store information in its nucleotide sequence.
2. Due to base pairing, its nucleotide sequence has the capacity for self-replication.
3. RNA can perform a variety of catalytic functions. The results of many experiments have shown that some RNA molecules function as **ribozymes**—RNA molecules that catalyze chemical reactions.

By comparison, DNA and proteins are not as versatile as RNA. DNA has very limited catalytic activity, and proteins are not known to undergo self-replication. RNA can perform functions that are characteristic of proteins and, at the same time, can serve as genetic material with replicative and informational functions.

How did the RNA molecules that were first made prebiotically evolve into more complex molecules that produced cell-like characteristics? Researchers propose that a process called chemical selection was responsible. **Chemical selection** occurs when a chemical within a mixture has special properties or advantages that cause it to increase in number relative to other chemicals in the mixture. (As we will discuss in Chapter 19, natural selection is a similar process except that it describes changes in a population of living organisms over time due to survival and reproductive advantages.) Chemical selection results in **chemical evolution,** in which a population of molecules changes over time to become a new population with a different chemical composition.

Scientists speculate that initially the special properties enabling certain RNA molecules to undergo chemical selection were their ability (1) to self-replicate and (2) to perform other catalytic functions. As a way to understand the concept of chemical selection, let's consider a hypothetical scenario showing two steps of chemical selection. The first step of Figure 18.5 shows a group of protobionts that contain RNA molecules that were made prebiotically. RNA molecules inside these protobionts can be used as templates for the prebiotic synthesis of complementary RNA molecules. Such a process of self-replication, however, would be very slow because it would not be catalyzed by enzymes in the protobiont. In a first step of chemical selection, the sequence of one of the RNA molecules has undergone a mutation that gives it the catalytic ability to attach nucleotides together, using RNA molecules as a template. This protobiont would have an advantage over the others because it would be capable of faster self-replication of its RNA molecules. Over time, due to its enhanced rate of replication, protobionts carrying such RNA molecules would increase in number compared with the others. Eventually, the group of protobionts shown in the figure contains only this type of catalytic RNA.

In the second step of chemical selection (Figure 18.5, right side), a second mutation in an RNA molecule produces a catalytic function that promotes the synthesis of ribonucleotides, the building blocks of RNA. For example, a hypothetical ribozyme may catalyze the attachment of a base to a ribose, thereby catalyzing one of the steps necessary for making a ribonucleotide. This protobiont would not solely rely on the prebiotic synthesis of ribonucleotides, which also is a very slow process. Therefore, the protobiont having the ability to both self-replicate and catalyze a step in the synthesis of ribonucleotides would have an advantage over a protobiont that could only self-replicate. Over time, the faster rate of self-replication and ribonucleotide synthesis would cause an increase in the numbers of the protobionts with both functions.

The **RNA world** is a hypothetical period on early Earth when both the information needed for life and the catalytic activity of living cells were contained solely in RNA molecules. In this scenario, lipid membranes enclosing RNA exhibited the properties of life due to RNA genomes that were copied and maintained through the catalytic function of RNA molecules. Scientists envision that, over time, mutations occurred in these RNA molecules, occasionally introducing new functional possibilities. Chemical selection would have eventually produced an increase in complexity in these cells, with RNA molecules accruing activities such as the ability to link amino acids together into proteins and other catalytic functions.

But is an RNA world a plausible scenario? Remarkably, scientists have been able to perform experiments in the laboratory that can select for RNA molecules with a particular function. American biologists David Bartel and Jack Szostak conducted the first study of this type in 1993 in which they selected for RNA molecules with the catalytic ability to link nucleotides together.

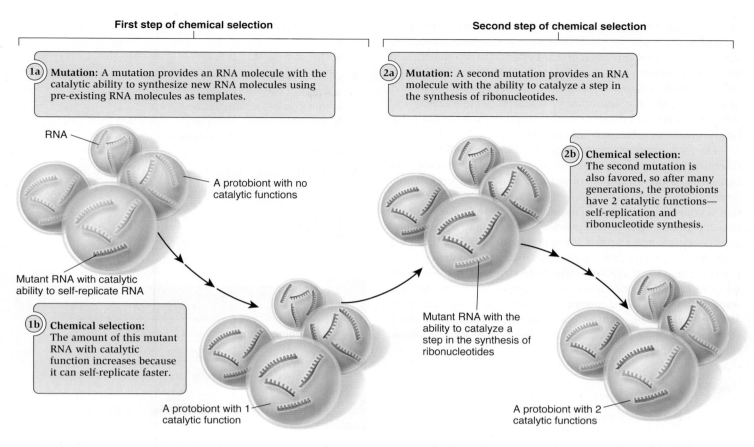

First step of chemical selection

1a **Mutation:** A mutation provides an RNA molecule with the catalytic ability to synthesize new RNA molecules using pre-existing RNA molecules as templates.

RNA

A protobiont with no catalytic functions

Mutant RNA with catalytic ability to self-replicate RNA

1b **Chemical selection:** The amount of this mutant RNA with catalytic function increases because it can self-replicate faster.

A protobiont with 1 catalytic function

Second step of chemical selection

2a **Mutation:** A second mutation provides an RNA molecule with the ability to catalyze a step in the synthesis of ribonucleotides.

2b **Chemical selection:** The second mutation is also favored, so after many generations, the protobionts have 2 catalytic functions—self-replication and ribonucleotide synthesis.

Mutant RNA with the ability to catalyze a step in the synthesis of ribonucleotides

A protobiont with 2 catalytic functions

Figure 18.5 **A hypothetical scenario illustrating the process of chemical selection.** This figure shows a two-step scenario. In the first step, RNAs that can self-replicate are selected, and in the second step, RNAs with the ability to catalyze a step in ribonucleotide synthesis are selected.

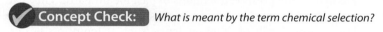 **Concept Check:** *What is meant by the term chemical selection?*

After 10 rounds of chemical selection, they obtained a collection of RNA molecules that had catalytic activity that was 3 million times higher than their original random collection of molecules! Like the work of Miller and Urey, Bartel and Szostak showed the feasibility of another phase of the prebiotic process that led to life. In this case, chemical selection resulted in chemical evolution. The results showed that chemical selection can change the functional characteristics of a group of RNA molecules over time by increasing the proportion of those molecules with enhanced function.

The RNA World Was Superseded by the Modern DNA/RNA/Protein World

Assuming that an RNA world was the origin of life, researchers have asked the question, "Why and how did the RNA world evolve into the DNA/RNA/protein world we see today?" The RNA world may have been superseded by a DNA/RNA world or an RNA/protein world before the emergence of the modern DNA/RNA/protein world. Let's now consider the advantages of a DNA/RNA/protein world as opposed to the simpler RNA world and explore how this modern biological world might have come into being.

Information Storage RNA can store information in its base sequence. If so, why did DNA take over that function, as is the case in modern cells? During the RNA world, RNA had to perform two roles: information storage and the catalysis of chemical reactions. Scientists have speculated that the incorporation of DNA into cells would have relieved RNA of its role of storing information, thereby allowing RNA to perform a greater variety of other functions. For example, if DNA stored the information for the synthesis of RNA molecules, such RNA molecules could bind cofactors, have modified bases, or bind peptides that might enhance their catalytic function. Cells with both DNA and RNA would have had an advantage over those with just RNA, and so they would have been selected. Another advantage of DNA is its stability. Compared with RNA, DNA strands are less likely to spontaneously break.

A second issue is how DNA came into being. Scientists have proposed that an ancestral RNA molecule had the ability to make DNA using RNA as a template. This function, known as reverse transcription, is described in Chapter 15 in the discussion of retroviruses.

Metabolism and Other Cellular Functions The emergence of proteins as catalysts may have been a great benefit to early cells. Due to the different chemical properties of the 20 amino acids, proteins have vastly greater catalytic ability than do RNA molecules, again providing a major advantage to cells that had both RNA and proteins. In modern cells, proteins have taken over most, but not all, catalytic functions. In addition, proteins can perform other important tasks. For example, cytoskeletal proteins carry out structural roles, and certain membrane proteins are responsible for the uptake of substances into living cells.

How would proteins have come into being in an RNA world? Chemical selection experiments have shown that RNA molecules can catalyze the formation of peptide bonds and even attach amino acids to primitive tRNA molecules. Similarly, modern protein synthesis still involves a central role for RNA in the synthesis of polypeptides. First, mRNA provides the information for a polypeptide sequence. Second, tRNA molecules act as adaptors for the formation of a polypeptide chain. And finally, ribosomes containing rRNA provide a site for polypeptide synthesis. Furthermore, rRNA within the ribosome acts as a ribozyme to catalyze peptide bond formation. Taken together, the analysis of translation in modern cells is consistent with an evolutionary history in which RNA molecules were instrumental in the emergence and formation of proteins.

18.1 Reviewing the Concepts

- Life on Earth is hypothesized to have occurred in four overlapping stages. The first stage involved the synthesis of organic molecules to form a prebiotic soup. Possible scenarios of how this occurred are the reducing atmosphere, extraterrestrial, and deep-sea vent hypotheses (Figures 18.2, 18.3).
- The second stage was the formation of polymers from simple organic molecules. This may have occurred on the surface of clay or in water. The third stage occurred when polymers became enclosed in structures called protobionts that separated them from the external environment (Figure 18.4).
- In the fourth stage, polymers enclosed in membranes acquired properties of cells, such as self-replication and other catalytic functions, via chemical selection (Figure 18.5).
- In the hypothesized period called the RNA world, the first living cells used RNA for both information storage and catalytic functions.
- The RNA world was eventually superseded by the modern DNA/RNA/protein world.

18.1 Testing Your Knowledge

1. Place the following four stages for the origin of life in their correct order:
   1. Nucleotides became polymerized to form RNA and/or DNA, and amino acids became polymerized to form proteins.
   2. Nucleotides and amino acids were produced prior to the existence of cells.
   3. Polymers enclosed in membranes acquired cellular properties.

   4. Polymers became enclosed in membranes.
   a. 1, 2, 3, 4   **c.** 2, 1, 4, 3
   b. 1, 3, 2, 4   **d.** 2, 3, 4, 1

2. Which of the following is *not* a hypothesis to explain the origin of the first organic molecules on Earth?
   a. the reducing atmosphere hypothesis
   b. the extraterrestrial (meteorite) hypothesis
   c. the chemical selection hypothesis
   d. the deep sea vent hypothesis

3. Many evolutionary biologists hypothesize that the macromolecule that had informational and catalytic function and arose first in primordial cells was
   a. DNA.   **d.** carbohydrates.
   b. RNA.   **e.** both a and c.
   c. proteins.

18.2 The Fossil Record

Learning Outcomes:

1. Describe how fossils are formed.
2. Explain how radiometric dating is used to estimate the age of a fossil.
3. List several factors that affect the completeness of the fossil record.

We will now turn our attention to a process that has given us a window into the history of life over the past 3.5 billion years. **Fossils** are the preserved remains of past life on Earth. They can take many forms, including bones, shells, and leaves, and the impression of cells or other evidence, such as footprints or burrows. Scientists who study fossils are called **paleontologists** (from the Greek *palaios*, meaning ancient). Because our understanding of the history of life is derived primarily from the fossil record, it is important to appreciate how fossils are formed and dated and to understand why the fossil record cannot be viewed as complete.

Fossils Are Formed Within Sedimentary Rock

How are fossils usually formed? Most fossils are found in sedimentary rocks that were formed from particles of older rocks broken apart by water or wind. These particles, such as gravel, sand, and mud, settle and bury living and dead organisms at the bottoms of rivers, lakes, and oceans. Over time, more particles pile up, and sediments at the bottom of the pile eventually become compressed into rock. Most fossils are formed when organisms are buried quickly, and then during the process of sedimentary rock formation, their hard parts are gradually replaced over millions of years by minerals, producing a recognizable representation of the original organism (see, for example, the chapter-opening photo).

The relative ages of fossils can sometimes be revealed by their locations in sedimentary rock formations. Because sedimentary rocks are formed particle by particle and bed by bed, the layers are piled one on top of the other. In a sequence of layered rocks, the lower rock layers are usually older than the upper

Figure 18.6 An example of layers of sedimentary rock that contain fossils.

Concept Check: *Which rock layer in this photo is most likely to be the oldest?*

layers. Paleontologists often study changes in life-forms over time by studying the fossils in layers from bottom to top (Figure 18.6). The more ancient life-forms are found in the lower layers, and newer species are found in the upper ones. However, such an assumption can occasionally be misleading when geological processes such as folding have flipped the layers.

Quantitative Analysis

RADIOISOTOPES PROVIDE A WAY TO DATE FOSSILS

A common way to estimate the age of a fossil is by analyzing the decay of radioisotopes within the accompanying rock, a process called **radiometric dating.** Elements can exist in multiple forms, called isotopes, that differ in the number of neutrons they contain. A radioisotope is an unstable isotope of an element that decays spontaneously, releasing radiation at a constant rate. The **half-life** is the length of time required for a radioisotope to decay to exactly one-half of its initial quantity. Each radioisotope has its own unique half-life (Figure 18.7a). Within a sample of rock, scientists can measure the amount of a given radioisotope as well as the amount of the decay product—the isotope that is produced when the original isotope

decays. For dating geological materials, several types of isotope decay patterns are particularly useful, including carbon-14 to nitrogen-14 and uranium-235 to lead-207 (Figure 18.7b).

To determine the age of a rock using radiometric dating, paleontologists need to have a way to set the clock—extrapolate back to a starting point in which a rock did not have any amount of the decay product. Except for fossils less than 50,000 years old, in which carbon-14 (^{14}C) dating can be employed, fossil dating is not usually conducted on the fossil itself or on the sedimentary rock in which the fossil is found. Most commonly, igneous rock—rock formed through the cooling and solidification of lava—in the vicinity of the sedimentary rock is dated. Why is igneous rock chosen? One reason is that igneous rock derived from an ancient lava flow initially contains uranium-235 (^{235}U) but no lead-207 (^{207}Pb). The ultimate decay product of ^{235}U is ^{207}Pb. By comparing the relative proportions of ^{235}U and ^{207}Pb in a sample, the age of igneous rock can be accurately determined.

The relationship between a radioisotope and the process of decay is represented by the following equation:

$$N = N_0 e^{-(0.693t/T_{1/2})}$$

where

N is the number of atoms of a radioisotope after a certain time period.

N_0 is the number of atoms of that radioisotope that were originally present prior to any decay.

e is the natural logarithm.

t is the time period during which decay has occurred.

$T_{1/2}$ is the half-life of the radioisotope.

Crunching the Numbers: A paleontologist discovered a fossil of a previously unidentified reptile. A sample of nearby igneous rock that was 1 kg in weight contained 0.11 mg of uranium-235 and 0.035 mg of lead-207. Estimate the age of this new fossil. (Note: Uranium and lead have different molecular masses, so you first need to calculate the number of uranium and lead atoms in this sample.)

Several Factors Affect the Completeness of the Fossil Record

The fossil record should not be viewed as a complete and balanced representation of the species that existed in the past. Several factors affect the likelihood that extinct organisms have been preserved as fossils and will be identified by paleontologists (Table 18.1).

- Certain organisms are more likely than others to become fossilized. Organisms with hard shells or bones tend to be over-represented.
- Factors such as anatomy, size, and numbers of the species, and the environment and time in which they lived play

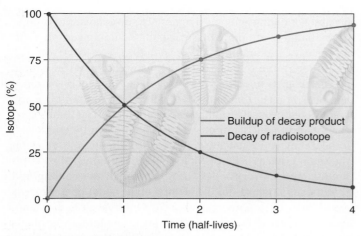

(a) Decay of a radioisotope

Radioisotope	Decay product	Half-life (years)	Useful dating range (years)
Carbon-14	Nitrogen-14	5,730	100–50,000
Potassium-40	Argon-40	1.3 billion	100,000–4.5 billion
Rubidium-87	Strontium-87	47 billion	10 million–4.5 billion
Uranium-235	Lead-207	710 million	10 million–4.5 billion
Uranium-238	Lead-206	4.5 billion	10 million–4.5 billion

(b) Radioisotopes that are useful for geological dating

Figure 18.7 **Radiometric dating of fossils.** **(a)** A rock can be dated by measuring the relative amounts of a radioisotope and its decay product within the rock. **(b)** These five isotopes, each of which has a characteristic useful dating range, are particularly useful for the dating of fossils.

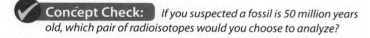 **Concept Check:** *If you suspected a fossil is 50 million years old, which pair of radioisotopes would you choose to analyze?*

important roles in determining the likelihood that organisms will be preserved in the fossil record.

- Geological processes may favor the fossilization of certain types of organisms.

- Unintentional biases arise that are related to the efforts of paleontologists. For example, scientific interests may favor searching for and analyzing certain species over others. For example, researchers have been greatly interested in finding the remains of dinosaurs.

Although the fossil record is incomplete, it has provided a wealth of information regarding the history of the types of life that existed on Earth. The rest of this chapter will survey the emergence of life-forms from 3.5 bya to the present.

Table 18.1	Factors That Affect the Fossil Record
Factor	**Description**
Anatomy	Organisms with hard body parts, such as animals with a skeleton or thick shell, are more likely to be preserved than are organisms composed of only soft tissues.
Size	The fossil remains of larger organisms are more likely to be found than those of smaller organisms.
Number	Species that existed in greater numbers or over a larger area are more likely to be preserved within the fossil record than those that existed in smaller numbers or in a smaller area.
Environment	Inland species are less likely to become fossilized than are those that lived in a marine environment or near the edge of water because sedimentary rock is more likely to be formed in or near water.
Time	Organisms that lived relatively recently or existed for a long time are more likely to be found as fossils than organisms that lived very long ago or for a relatively short time.
Geological processes	Due to the chemistry of fossilization, certain organisms are more likely to be preserved than are other organisms.
Paleontology	Certain types of fossils may be more interesting to paleontologists. In addition, a significant bias exists with regard to the locations where paleontologists search for fossils. For example, they tend to search in regions where other fossils have already been found.

18.2 Reviewing the Concepts

- Fossils, which are preserved remnants of past life-forms, are formed in sedimentary rock. Our understanding of the history of life on Earth is derived primarily from the fossil record (Figure 18.6).

- Radiometric dating is one way of estimating the age of a fossil (Figure 18.7).

- Several factors affect the likelihood that organisms have been preserved in the fossil record (Table 18.1).

18.2 Testing Your Knowledge

1. Fossils are typically formed
   a. within igneous rock.
   b. within sedimentary rock.
   c. when dead organisms are exposed to intense sunlight.
   d. when dead organisms are left undisturbed for long periods of time.
   e. when dead organisms are quickly frozen.

2. Which of the following may account for biases in the fossil record?
   a. Certain organisms are more likely than others to become fossilized.

b. Various factors, such as anatomy and number, affect the likelihood that organisms will be preserved in the fossil record.

c. Geological processes may favor the fossilization of certain types of organisms.

d. Unintentional biases arise that are related to the efforts of paleontologists.

e. All of the above may cause biases.

18.3 History of Life on Earth

Learning Outcomes:

1. List the types of environmental changes that have affected the history of life on Earth.

2. Describe the cell structure and energy utilization of the first living organisms that arose during the Archaean eon.

3. Explain how the origin of eukaryotic cells involved a union between bacterial and archaeal cells.

4. Describe the key features of multicellular organisms, which arose during the Proterozoic eon.

5. Outline the major events and changes in species diversity during the Paleozoic, Mesozoic, and Cenozoic eras.

Thus far, we have considered how the first cells may have come into existence and the characteristics of fossils. The first fossils that we know of were from single-celled organisms, which were preserved approximately 3.5 bya. In this section, we will begin with a brief description of the geological changes on Earth that have affected the emergence of new forms of life and then examine some of the major changes in life that have occurred since it began.

Many Environmental Changes Have Occurred Since the Origin of the Earth

The **geological time scale** is a time line of the Earth's history and major events from its origin approximately 4.55 bya to the present (**Figure 18.8**). This time line is subdivided into four eons—the Hadean, Archaean, Proterozoic, and Phanerozoic—and then further subdivided into eras. The first three eons are collectively known as the Precambrian because they preceded the Cambrian era, a geological era that saw a rapid increase in the diversity of life. We will examine these time periods later in this section.

The changes that occurred in species over the past 4 billion years are the result of two interactive processes. First, as discussed in the next several chapters, genetic changes in organisms can affect their characteristics. Such changes can influence the ability of organisms to survive and reproduce in their native environment. Second, the environment on Earth has undergone dramatic changes that have profoundly influenced the types of organisms that have existed during different periods of time. In some cases, an environmental change might allow new types of organisms to flourish. Alternatively, environmental changes can result in

extinction—the complete loss of a species or group of species. The major types of environmental changes are described next.

Changes in Temperature   During the first 2.5 billion years of its existence, the surface of the Earth gradually cooled. However, during the last 2 billion years, the Earth has undergone major fluctuations in temperature, producing periods of widespread glaciation called Ice Ages that alternate with warmer periods. Furthermore, the temperature on Earth is not uniform, which produces a range of environments, such as tropical rain forests and arctic tundra, where the temperatures are quite different.

Changes in Atmosphere Composition   The chemical composition of the gases surrounding the Earth has changed substantially over the past 4 billion years. One notable change has been the amount of oxygen. Prior to 2.4 bya, relatively little oxygen gas was in the atmosphere, but at that time, levels of oxygen in the form of O_2 began to rise significantly. The emergence of organisms capable of photosynthesis added oxygen to the atmosphere. Our current atmosphere contains about 21% O_2. Increased levels of oxygen are thought to have a played a key role in various aspects of the history of life, including the following:

- The origin of many animal body plans coincided with a rise in atmospheric O_2.
- The conquest of land by arthropods (about 410 million years ago [mya]) and a second conquest by arthropods and vertebrates (about 350 mya) occurred during periods in which O_2 levels were high or increasing.
- Increases in animal body sizes are associated with higher O_2 levels.

Higher levels of O_2 could have contributed to these events because higher O_2 levels may enhance the ability of animals to carry out aerobic respiration. These events are also discussed later in this chapter and in more detail in Unit V.

Shifting of Landmasses   As the Earth cooled, landmasses formed that were surrounded by bodies of water. This produced two different environments: terrestrial and aquatic. Furthermore, over the course of billions of years, Earth's major landmasses, known as the continents, have shifted their positions, changed their shapes, and separated from each other. This phenomenon, called **continental drift,** is shown in **Figure 18.9**.

Floods and Glaciations   Catastrophic floods have had major effects on the organisms in the flooded regions. Glaciers have periodically moved across continents and altered the composition of species on those landmasses.

Volcanic Eruptions   The eruptions of volcanoes harm organisms in the vicinity of the eruption, sometimes causing extinctions. In addition, volcanic eruptions in the oceans lead to the formation of new islands. Massive eruptions may also spew so much debris into the atmosphere that they affect global temperatures and limit solar radiation, which restricts photosynthetic production.

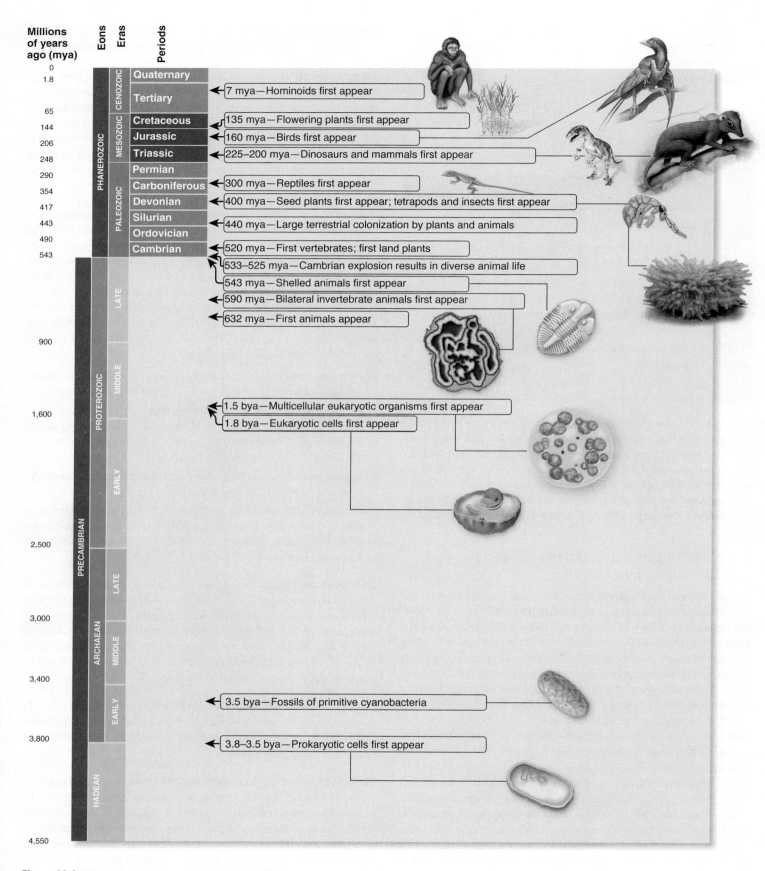

Figure 18.8 The geological time scale and an overview of the history of life on Earth.

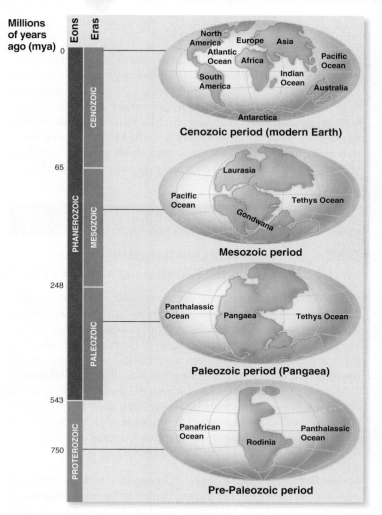

Millions of years ago (mya)

Eons | Eras

CENOZOIC

North America
Europe
Asia
Atlantic Ocean
Africa
Pacific Ocean
South America
Indian Ocean
Australia
Antarctica

Cenozoic period (modern Earth)

65

MESOZOIC

Laurasia
Pacific Ocean
Tethys Ocean
Gondwana

Mesozoic period

248

PALEOZOIC

Panthalassic Ocean
Pangaea
Tethys Ocean

Paleozoic period (Pangaea)

543

PROTEROZOIC

Panafrican Ocean
Rodinia
Panthalassic Ocean

Pre-Paleozoic period

750

PHANEROZOIC

Figure 18.9 Continental drift. The relative locations of the continents on Earth have changed dramatically over time.

Meteorite Impacts   During its long history, the Earth has been struck by many meteorites. Large meteorites have significantly affected the Earth's environment.

The effects of one or more of the changes described earlier have sometimes caused large numbers of species to go extinct at the same time. Such events are called **mass extinctions.** Five large mass extinctions occurred near the end of the Ordovician, Devonian, Permian, Triassic, and Cretaceous periods, respectively. The boundaries between geological time periods are often based on the occurrence of mass extinctions. A recurring pattern seen in the history of life is the extinction of some species and the emergence of new ones. The rapid extinction of many modern species due to human activities is sometimes referred to as the sixth mass extinction.

Prokaryotic Cells Arose During the Archaean Eon

The Archaean (from the Greek, meaning ancient) was an eon when diverse microbial life flourished in the primordial oceans. As mentioned previously, the first known fossils of living cells were preserved in rocks that are about 3.5 billion years old (see Figure 18.1), though scientists postulate that cells arose many

millions of years prior to this time. Based on the morphology of fossilized remains, these first cells were prokaryotic. During the more than 1 billion years of the Archaean eon, all life-forms were prokaryotic. Because Earth's atmosphere had very little free oxygen (O_2), the single-celled microorganisms of this eon almost certainly used only anaerobic respiration, which occurs in the absence of oxygen.

Organisms with prokaryotic cells are divided into two groups: bacteria and archaea. Bacteria are more prevalent on modern Earth, though many species of archaea have also been identified. Archaea are found in many different environments, with some found in extreme environments such as hot springs. Both bacteria and archaea share fundamental similarities, indicating that they are derived from a common ancestor. Even so, certain differences suggest that these two types of prokaryotes diverged from each other quite early in the history of life. In particular, bacteria and archaea show some interesting differences in cellular and molecular features (look ahead to Chapter 21, Table 21.1).

Biologists Are Undecided About Whether Heterotrophs or Autotrophs Came First

An important factor that greatly influenced the emergence of new species is the availability of energy. As we learned in Unit II, all organisms require energy to survive and reproduce. Organisms may follow two different strategies to obtain energy.

- **Heterotrophs** derive their energy from the chemical bonds within organic molecules they consume. Because the most common sources of organic molecules today are other organisms, heterotrophs typically consume other organisms or materials from other organisms.

- **Autotrophs** directly harness energy from either light or inorganic molecules. Among modern species, plants are an important example of autotrophs. Plants can directly absorb light energy and use it (via photosynthesis) to synthesize organic molecules such as glucose. On modern Earth, heterotrophs ultimately rely on autotrophs for the production of food.

Were the first forms of life heterotrophs or autotrophs? The answer is not resolved. Some biologists have speculated that autotrophs, such as those living near deep-sea vents, may have arisen first. These organisms would have used chemicals that were made near the vents as an energy source to make organic molecules. Alternatively, many scientists have hypothesized that the first living cells were heterotrophs. They reason that it would have been simpler for the first primitive cells to use the organic molecules in the prebiotic soup as a source of energy.

If heterotrophs came first, why were cyanobacteria, which are autotrophs, preserved in the earliest fossils rather than heterotrophs? One possible reason is related to their manner of growth. Certain cyanobacteria promote the formation of a layered structure called a **stromatolite** (Figure 18.10a). The aquatic environment where these cyanobacteria survive is rich in minerals such as calcium. The cyanobacteria grow in large mats that form layers. As they grow, they deplete the carbon dioxide (CO_2) in the

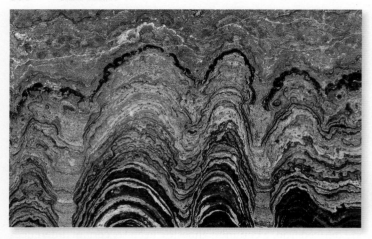

(a) Fossil stromatolite

(b) Modern stromatolites

Figure 18.10 Fossil and modern stromatolites: Evidence of early autotrophs. Each stromatolite is a rocklike structure, typically 1 meter in diameter. **(a)** Section of a fossilized stromatolite. These layers are mats of mineralized cyanobacteria, one layer on top of the other. The existence of fossil stromatolites provides evidence of early autotrophic organisms. **(b)** Modern stromatolites that have formed in western Australia.

surrounding water. This causes calcium carbonate in the water to gradually precipitate over the bacterial cells, calcifying the older cells in the lower layers into rock and also trapping grains of sediment. Newer cells produce a layer on top. Over time, many layers of calcified cells and sediment are formed, thereby producing a stromatolite. This process still occurs today in places such as Shark Bay in western Australia, which is renowned for the stromatolites along its beaches (Figure 18.10b).

The emergence and proliferation of ancient cyanobacteria had two critical consequences. First, the autotrophic nature of these bacteria enabled them to produce organic molecules from CO_2. This prevented the depletion of organic foodstuffs that would have been exhausted if only heterotrophs existed. Second, cyanobacteria produce oxygen (O_2) as a waste product of photosynthesis. During the Archaean and Proterozoic eons, the activity of cyanobacteria led to the gradual rise in O_2 discussed earlier. The

increase in O_2 spelled doom for many anaerobic species, which became restricted to a few anoxic (without oxygen) environments, such as deep within the ground. However, O_2 enabled the formation of new bacterial and archaeal species that used aerobic (with oxygen) respiration (see Chapter 6). In addition, aerobic respiration is likely to have played a key role in the emergence and eventual explosion of eukaryotic life-forms, which typically have high energy demands. These eukaryotic life-forms are described next.

EVOLUTIONARY CONNECTIONS

The Origin of Eukaryotic Cells Is Hypothesized to Involve a Union Between Bacterial and Archaeal Cells

Eukaryotic cells arose during the Proterozoic eon, which began 2.5 bya and ended 543 mya (see Figure 18.8). The manner in which the first eukaryotic cells originated is not entirely understood. In modern eukaryotic cells, genetic material is found in three distinct organelles. All eukaryotic cells contain DNA in the nucleus and mitochondria, and plant and algal cells also have DNA in their chloroplasts. To address the issue of the origin of eukaryotic species, scientists have examined the DNA sequences found in these three organelles. From such studies, the nuclear, mitochondrial, and chloroplast genomes appear to be derived from once-separate cells that came together.

Nuclear Genome   From a genome perspective, both bacteria and archaea have contributed substantially to the nuclear genome of eukaryotic cells. Eukaryotic nuclear genes encoding proteins involved in metabolic pathways and lipid biosynthesis appear to be derived from ancient bacteria, whereas genes involved with transcription and translation appear to be derived from an archaeal ancestor.

To explain the origin of the nuclear genome, several hypotheses have been proposed. The most widely accepted hypothesis involves a symbiotic relationship between ancient bacteria and archaea. **Endosymbiosis** describes a relationship in which a smaller organism (the endosymbiont) lives inside a larger organism (the host).

Researchers have suggested that an archaeal species evolved the ability to invaginate its plasma membrane, which could have two results (Figure 18.11). First, it could eventually lead to the formation of an extensive internal membrane system and enclose the genetic material in a nuclear envelope. Second, the ability to invaginate the plasma membrane provides a mechanism to take up materials from the environment via endocytosis, which is described in Chapter 5. In the scenario described in Figure 18.11, an ancient archeon (an archaeal cell) engulfed a bacterium via endocytosis, maintaining the bacterium in its cytoplasm as an endosymbiont. Over time, many genes from the bacterium were transferred to the archaeal host cell, and the resulting genetic material eventually became the nuclear genome.

Mitochondrial and Chloroplast Genomes   Mitochondria found in eukaryotic cells are likely derived from a bacterial species that

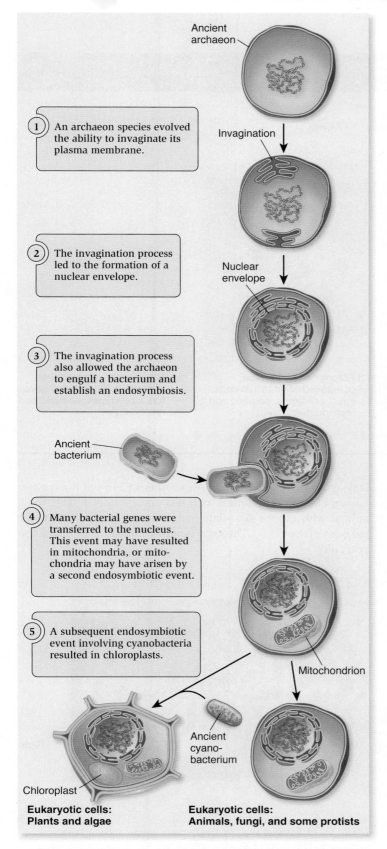

Figure 18.11 buttons:

1 An archaeon species evolved the ability to invaginate its plasma membrane.

Invagination

2 The invagination process led to the formation of a nuclear envelope.

Nuclear envelope

3 The invagination process also allowed the archaeon to engulf a bacterium and establish an endosymbiosis.

Ancient bacterium

4 Many bacterial genes were transferred to the nucleus. This event may have resulted in mitochondria, or mitochondria may have arisen by a second endosymbiotic event.

5 A subsequent endosymbiotic event involving cyanobacteria resulted in chloroplasts.

Ancient cyanobacterium

Mitochondrion

Chloroplast

Eukaryotic cells: Plants and algae

Eukaryotic cells: Animals, fungi, and some protists

Ancient archaeon

Figure 18.11 Possible endosymbiotic relationships that gave rise to the first eukaryotic cells.

BioConnections: *Look back at Figure 5.22. Explain how endocytosis played a role in endosymbiosis.*

resembles modern α-proteobacteria, a diverse group of bacteria that carry out oxidative phosphorylation to make ATP. One possibility is that an endosymbiotic event involving an ancestor of this bacterial species produced the first eukaryotic cell and that the mitochondrion is a remnant of that event. Alternatively, endosymbiosis may have produced the first eukaryotic cell, and then a subsequent endosymbiosis resulted in mitochondria (see Figure 18.11). DNA-sequencing data indicate that chloroplasts were derived from a separate endosymbiotic relationship between a primitive eukaryotic cell and a cyanobacterium. As discussed in Chapter 22, plastids, such as chloroplasts, have arisen on several independent occasions via primary, secondary, and tertiary endosymbiosis (see Figure 22.23).

Multicellular Eukaryotes and the Earliest Animals Arose During the Proterozoic Eon

The first multicellular eukaryotes are thought to have emerged about 1.5 bya, in the middle of the Proterozoic eon. The oldest fossil evidence for multicellular eukaryotes was an organism that resembled modern red algae; this fossil was dated at approximately 1.2 billion years old.

Simple multicellular organisms are believed to have originated in one of two different ways. One mechanism is that many individual cells can find each other and aggregate to form a colony. Cellular slime molds are examples of modern organisms in which groups of single-celled organisms can come together to form a small multicellular organism. According to the fossil record, such organisms have remained very simple for hundreds of millions of years.

Alternatively, another way that multicellularity can occur is when a single cell divides and the resulting cells stick together. This pattern occurs in many simple multicellular organisms, such as algae and fungi, as well as in species with more complex body plans, such as plants and animals. Biologists cannot be certain whether the first multicellular organisms arose by an aggregation process or by cell division and adhesion. However, the development of complex, multicellular organisms now occurs by cell division and adhesion.

An interesting example showing changes in the level of complexity from unicellular organisms to more complex multicellular organisms is found among evolutionarily related species of volvocine green algae. These algae exist as unicellular species, as small clumps of cells of the same cell type, or as larger groups of cells with two distinct cell types. **Figure 18.12** compares four species of volvocine algae. *Chlamydomonas reinhardtii* is a unicellular alga (Figure 18.12a). It is called a biflagellate because each cell has two flagella. *Gonium pectorale* is a multicellular organism composed of eight cells (Figure 18.12b). This simple multicellular organism is formed from a single cell by cell division and adhesion. All of the cells in this species are biflagellate. Other volvocine algae have evolved into larger and more complex organisms. *Pleodorina californica* has 64–128 cells (Figure 18.12c), and *Volvox aureus* has about 1,000–2,000 cells (Figure 18.12d). A feature of these

Biology Principle

New Properties Emerge from Complex Interactions

The formation of different cell types is an emergent property of multicellularity.

Flagella

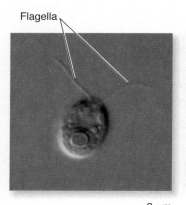

$3 \ \mu m$

(a) *Chlamydomonas reinhardtii,* a unicellular alga

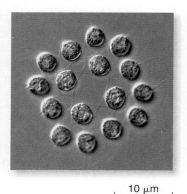

$10 \ \mu m$

(b) *Gonium pectorale,* composed of 16 identical cells

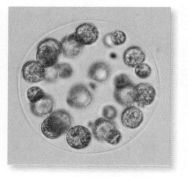

$30 \ \mu m$

(c) *Pleodorina californica,* composed of 64 to 128 cells, has 2 cell types, somatic and reproductive

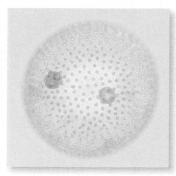

$100 \ \mu m$

(d) *Volvox aureus,* composed of about 1,000 to 2,000 cells, has 2 cell types, somatic and reproductive

Figure 18.12 Variation in the level of multicellularity among volvocine algae.

more complex organisms is they have two cell types: somatic and reproductive cells. The somatic cells are biflagellate cells, but the reproductive cells are not. *V. aureus,* which is larger, has a higher percentage of somatic cells than *P. californica.*

Overall, an analysis of these four species of algae illustrates three important principles found among complex multicellular species:

1. Multicellular organisms arise from a single cell that divides to produce daughter cells that adhere to one another.
2. The daughter cells can follow different fates, thereby producing multicellular organisms with different cell types.
3. As organisms get larger, a greater percentage of the cells tend to be somatic cells. The somatic cells carry out the activities required for the survival of the multicellular organism, whereas the reproductive cells are specialized for the sole purpose of producing offspring.

Toward the end of the Proterozoic eon, the first multicellular animals emerged. The first animals were invertebrates—animals without a backbone. Most animals, except for organisms such as sponges and jellyfish, exhibit bilateral symmetry—a two-sided body plan with a right and left side that are mirror images. Because each side of the body has appendages such as legs, one advantage of bilateral symmetry is that it facilitates locomotion. Bilateral animals also have anterior and posterior ends, with the mouth at the anterior end. In 2004, Chinese paleontologist Jun-Yuan Chen, American paleobiologist David Bottjer, and their

colleagues discovered a fossil in southern China of the earliest known ancestor of animals with bilateral symmetry. This small animal, with a shape like a flattened helmet, is barely visible to the naked eye (**Figure 18.13**). The fossil is approximately 580–600 million years old.

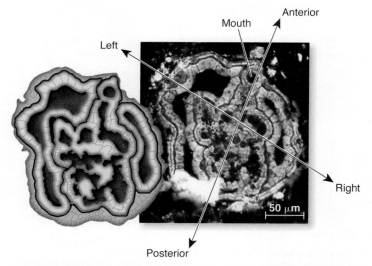

Anterior

Mouth

Left

Right

Posterior

$50 \ \mu m$

Figure 18.13 Fossil of an early invertebrate animal showing bilateral symmetry. This fossil of an early animal, *Vernanimalcula guizhouena,* dates from 580 to 600 mya.

Concept Check: *Name three other species that exhibit bilateral symmetry.*

Phanerozoic Eon: The Paleozoic Era Saw the Diversification of Invertebrates and the Colonization of Land by Plants and Animals

The proliferation of multicellular eukaryotic life has been extensive during the Phanerozoic eon, which started 543 mya and extends to the present day. Phanerozoic means "well-displayed life," referring to the abundance of fossils of plants and animals that have been identified from this eon. As described in Figure 18.8, the Phanerozoic eon is subdivided into three eras: the Paleozoic, Mesozoic, and Cenozoic. Because they are relatively recent and we have many fossils from these eras, each of them is further subdivided into periods. We will consider each era with its associated conditions and prevalent forms of life separately.

The term Paleozoic means ancient animal life. The Paleozoic era covers approximately 300 million years, from 543 to 248 mya, and is subdivided into six periods: the Cambrian, Ordovician, Silurian, Devonian, Carboniferous, and Permian. Periods are usually named after regions where rocks and fossils of that age were first discovered.

Cambrian Period (543–490 mya)   The climate in the Cambrian period was generally warm and wet, with no evidence of ice at the poles. During this time, the diversity of animal species increased rapidly, an event called the **Cambrian explosion.** However, recent evidence suggests that many types of animal groups present during the Cambrian period actually arose prior to this time.

- By the middle of the Cambrian period, all of the existing major types of marine invertebrates were present, plus many others that no longer exist.
- Examples of animals that first appeared in the Cambrian period that still exist include echinoderms (sea urchins and starfish), arthropods (insects, spiders, and crustaceans), mollusks (clams and snails), chordates (organisms with a dorsal nerve chord), and vertebrates (animals with backbones).

The cause of the Cambrian explosion is not understood. Because it occurred shortly after marine animals evolved shells, some scientists have speculated that the changes observed in animal species may have allowed them to exploit new environments. Alternatively, others have suggested that the increase in diversity may be related to atmospheric oxygen levels. During this period, oxygen levels were increasing, and perhaps more complex body plans became possible only after the atmospheric oxygen surpassed a certain threshold. In addition, as atmospheric oxygen reached its present levels, an ozone (O_3) layer was produced that screens out harmful ultraviolet radiation, thereby allowing complex life to live in shallow water and eventually on land. Another possible contributor to the Cambrian explosion was an "evolutionary arms race" between interacting species. The ability of predators to capture prey and the ability of prey to avoid predators may have been a major factor that resulted in a diversification of animals into many different species.

Ordovician Period (490–443 mya)   As in the Cambrian period, the climate of the early and middle parts of the Ordovician period was warm, and the atmosphere was moist.

- A diverse group of hard-shelled marine invertebrates, including trilobites and brachiopods, appeared in the fossil record (Figure 18.14). Marine communities consisted of invertebrates, algae, early jawless fishes (a type of early vertebrate), mollusks, and corals.
- Early land plants and arthropods may have first invaded the land during this period.

Toward the end of the Ordovician period, the climate changed rather dramatically. Large glaciers formed, which drained the relatively shallow oceans, causing the water levels to drop. This resulted in a mass extinction in which as much as 60% of the existing marine invertebrates became extinct.

Silurian Period (443–417 mya)   In contrast to the dramatic climate changes observed during the Ordovician period, the climate

(a) Trilobite

(b) Brachiopod

Figure 18.14 **Shelled, invertebrate fossils of the Ordovician period.** Trilobites existed for millions of years before becoming extinct about 250 mya. Many species of brachiopods exist today.

during the Silurian was relatively stable. The glaciers largely melted, which caused the ocean levels to rise.

- No new major types of invertebrate animals appeared during this period, but significant changes were observed among existing vertebrate and plant species.
- Many new types of fishes appeared in the fossil record.
- Coral reefs made their first appearance during this period.
- The Silurian marked a major colonization of land by terrestrial plants and animals. For this to occur, certain species evolved adaptations that prevented them from drying out, such as a hard cuticle.
- Ancestral relatives of spiders and centipedes became widespread.
- The earliest vascular plants, which have tissues that are specialized for the transport of water, sugar, and salts throughout the plant body, arose during this period.

Devonian Period (417–354 mya)   In the Devonian period, generally dry conditions occurred across much of the northern landmasses. However, the southern landmasses were mostly covered by cool, temperate oceans.

- The Devonian saw a major increase in the number of terrestrial plant species. At first, the vegetation consisted primarily of small plants, only a meter tall or less. Later, ferns, horsetails, and seed plants, such as gymnosperms, also emerged. By the end of the Devonian, the first trees and forests were formed.
- A major expansion of terrestrial animals also occurred. Insects first appeared in the fossil record, and other invertebrates became plentiful. In addition, the first tetrapods—vertebrates with four legs—are believed to have arisen in the Devonian. Early tetrapods included amphibians, which lived on land but required water in which to lay their eggs.
- In the oceans, many types of invertebrates flourished, including brachiopods, echinoderms, and corals. This period is sometimes called the Age of Fishes, as many new types of fishes emerged.

During a period of approximately 20 million years near the end of the Devonian period, a prolonged series of extinctions eliminated many marine species. The cause of this mass extinction is not well understood.

Carboniferous Period (354–290 mya)   The term Carboniferous refers to the rich deposits of coal, a sedimentary rock primarily composed of carbon, that were formed during this period. The Carboniferous had the ideal conditions for the subsequent formation of coal. It was a cooler period, and much of the land was covered by forest swamps. Coal was formed over many millions of years from compressed layers of rotting vegetation.

- Very large plants and trees became prevalent. For example, tree ferns such as *Psaronius* grew to a height of 15 meters or more (**Figure 18.15**).

Psaronius

Figure 18.15 **A giant tree fern, *Psaronius*, from the Carboniferous period.** This genus became extinct during the Permian. The illustration is a re-creation based on fossil evidence. The inset shows a fossilized section of the trunk.

- The first flying insects emerged. Giant dragonflies with a wingspan of over 2 feet inhabited the forest swamps.
- Terrestrial vertebrates also became more diverse.
- Amphibians were very widespread.
- The amniotic egg was one of the most important evolutionary innovations of the Carboniferous. This innovation was critical for the emergence of reptiles, tetrapods that had the ability to lay eggs on land. In reptiles, the amniotic egg was covered with a leathery or hard shell, which prevented the desiccation of the embryo inside.

Permian Period (290–248 mya)   At the beginning of the Permian, continental drift had brought much of the total land together into a supercontinent known as Pangaea (see Figure 18.9). The interior regions of Pangaea were dry, with large seasonal fluctuations.

- The forests of fernlike plants were replaced with gymnosperms, seed-bearing land plants. Species resembling modern conifers first appeared in the fossil record.
- Amphibians were prevalent, but reptiles became the dominant vertebrate species.

At the end of the Permian period, the largest known mass extinction in the history of life on Earth occurred; 90–95% of marine species and a large proportion of terrestrial species were eliminated. The cause of the Permian extinction is the subject of much research and controversy. One possibility is that glaciation destroyed the habitats of terrestrial species and lowered ocean levels, which would have caused greater competition among marine species. Another hypothesis is that enormous volcanic eruptions in Siberia produced large ash clouds that abruptly changed the climate on Earth.

Phanerozoic Eon: The Mesozoic Era Saw the Rise and Fall of the Dinosaurs

The Permian extinction marks the division between the Paleozoic and Mesozoic eras. Mesozoic means "middle animals." It was a time period that saw great changes in animal and plant species. This era is sometimes called the Age of Dinosaurs, which flourished during this time. The climate during the Mesozoic era was consistently hot, and terrestrial environments were relatively dry. Little if any ice was found at either pole. The Mesozoic is divided into three periods: the Triassic, Jurassic, and Cretaceous.

Triassic Period (248–206 mya)

- Reptiles were plentiful in this period, including new groups such as crocodiles and turtles.
- The first dinosaurs emerged during the middle of the Triassic, as did the first mammals, such as the small *Megazostrodon* (Figure 18.16).
- Gymnosperms were the dominant land plant.

Volcanic eruptions near the end of the Triassic are thought to have caused global warming, resulting in mass extinctions that eliminated many marine and terrestrial species.

Jurassic Period (206–144 mya)

- Gymnosperms, such as conifers, continued to be the dominant vegetation.
- Mammals were not prevalent.
- Reptiles continued to be the dominant land vertebrate. These included dinosaurs, which were predominantly

Figure 18.16 *Megazostrodon*, **the first known mammal of the Triassic period.** The illustration is a re-creation based on fossilized skeletons. The *Megazostrodon* was 10 to 12 cm long.

BioConnections: *Look ahead to Table 26.1. What are the common characteristics of mammals?*

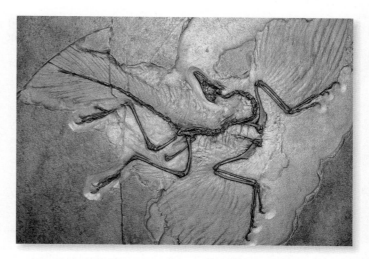

Figure 18.17 A fossil of an early birdlike animal, *Archaeopteryx lithographica*, which emerged in the Jurassic period.

terrestrial reptiles that shared certain anatomical features, such as an erect posture. Modern birds are descendants of a dinosaur lineage called theropod (meaning "beast-footed") dinosaurs. *Tyrannosaurus rex* is one of the best known theropod dinosaurs. An early birdlike animal, *Archaeopteryx lithographica* (Figure 18.17), emerged in the Jurassic period. However, paleontologists are debating whether or not *Archaeopteryx* is a true ancestor of modern birds.

Cretaceous Period (144–65 mya)

- On land, dinosaurs continued to be the dominant animals.
- The earliest flowering plants, called angiosperms, which form seeds within a protective chamber, emerged and began to diversify.

The end of the Cretaceous witnessed another mass extinction, which brought an end to many previously successful groups of organisms. Except for the lineage that gave rise to birds, dinosaurs abruptly died out, as did many other species. As with the Permian extinction, the cause or causes of this mass extinction are still debated. One plausible hypothesis suggests that a large meteorite hit the region that is now the Yucatan Peninsula of Mexico, lifting massive amounts of debris into the air and thereby blocking the sunlight from reaching the Earth's surface. Such a dense haze could have cooled the Earth's surface by 11–15°C (20–30°F). Evidence also points to huge volcanic eruptions as a contributing factor to this mass extinction.

Phanerozoic Eon: Mammals and Flowering Plants Diversified During the Cenozoic Era

The Cenozoic era spans the most recent 65 million years. It is divided into two periods: the Tertiary and Quaternary. In many parts of the world, tropical conditions were replaced by a colder, drier climate. During this time, mammals became the largest terrestrial animals, which is why the Cenozoic is sometimes called the Age of Mammals. However, the Cenozoic era also saw an amazing diversification of many types of organisms, including birds, fishes, insects, and flowering plants.

Tertiary Period (65–1.8 mya)

- On land, the mammals that survived from the Cretaceous began to diversify rapidly during the early part of the Tertiary period.

- Angiosperms became the dominant land plant, and insects became important for their pollination.

- Fishes also diversified, and sharks became abundant.

- Toward the end of the Tertiary period, about 7 mya, hominoids came into existence. **Hominoids** include humans, chimpanzees, gorillas, orangutans, and gibbons, plus all of their recent ancestors. The subset of hominoids called **hominins** includes modern humans, extinct human species (for example, of the *Homo* genus), and our immediate ancestors. In 2002, a fossil of the earliest known hominin, *Sahelanthropus tchadensis,* was discovered in Central Africa. This fossil was dated at between 6 and 7 million years old. Another early hominin genus, called *Australopithecus,* first emerged in Africa about 4 mya. Australopithecines walked upright and had a protruding jaw, prominent eyebrow ridges, and a small braincase.

Quaternary Period (1.8 mya–present)

Periodic Ice Ages have been prevalent during the last 1.8 million years, covering much of Europe and North America.

- This period has witnessed the widespread extinction of many species of mammals, particularly larger ones.

- Certain species of hominins became increasingly more like modern humans. Near the beginning of the Quaternary period, fossils were discovered of *Homo habilis,* or handy man, so called because stone tools were found with the fossil remains. *Homo sapiens*—modern humans—first appeared about 170,000 years ago. The evolution of hominins is discussed in more detail in Chapter 26.

18.3   Reviewing the Concepts

- The geological time scale, which is divided into four eons and many eras and periods, charts the major events that occurred during the history of life on Earth (Figure 18.8).

- The formation of new species, as well as mass extinctions, are correlated with changes in temperature, amount of O_2 in the atmosphere, landmass locations, floods and glaciation, volcanic eruptions, and meteorite impacts (Figure 18.9).

- During the Archaean eon, bacteria and archaea arose. The proliferation of cyanobacteria led to a gradual rise in O_2 levels (Figure 18.10).

- Eukaryotic cells arose during the Proterozoic eon. This origin involved a union between bacterial and archaeal cells that is hypothesized to have been endosymbiotic. The origin of mitochondria and chloroplasts was an endosymbiotic relationship (Figure 18.11).

- Multicellular eukaryotes arose about 1.5 bya during the Proterozoic eon. Multicellularity now occurs via cell division and the adherence of the resulting cells to each other. A multicellular organism can produce multiple cell types. The first bilateral animal emerged toward the end of the Proterozoic eon (Figures 18.12, 18.13).

- The Phanerozoic eon is subdivided into the Paleozoic, Mesozoic, and Cenozoic eras. During the Paleozoic era, invertebrates greatly diversified, particularly during the Cambrian explosion, and the land became colonized by plants and animals. Terrestrial vertebrates, including tetrapods, became more diverse (Figures 18.14, 18.15).

- Mammals, dinosaurs, and birds emerged during the Mesozoic era. Dinosaurs were particularly prevalent during the Jurassic period (Figures 18.16, 18.17).

- During the Cenozoic era, mammals diversified, and flowering plants became the dominant plant species. The first hominoids emerged approximately 7 mya. Fossils classified as *Homo sapiens*, our species, appeared about 170,000 years ago.

18.3   Testing Your Knowledge

1. A heterotroph is an organism that
   a. only consumes autotrophs.
   b. only consumes other heterotrophs.
   c. derives its energy from the chemical bonds within organic molecules.
   d. directly harnesses energy from inorganic sources.

2. Eukaryotic cells were originally derived from
   a. an endosymbiotic relationship between archaeal and bacterial cells.
   b. an endosymbiotic relationship between different archaeal cells.
   c. an endosymbiotic relationship between different bacterial cells.
   d. a single archaeal species.
   e. a single bacterial species.

3. Multicellularity in most modern species occurs because
   a. individual cells find each other and aggregate.
   b. a single cell undergoes multiple divisions and the cells adhere to one another.
   c. both a and b.
   d. neither a or b.

4. Humans arose during
   a. the Archaean eon.
   b. the Proterozoic eon.
   c. the Paleozoic era of the Phanerozoic eon.
   d. the Mesozoic era of the Phanerozoic eon.
   e. the Cenozoic era of the Phanerozoic eon.

Assess and Discuss

Test Yourself

1. The prebiotic soup was
   a. the assemblage of unicellular prokaryotes that existed in the oceans of early Earth.
   b. the accumulation of organic molecules in the oceans of early Earth.
   c. the mixture of organic molecules found in the cytoplasm of the earliest cells on Earth.
   d. a pool of nucleic acids that contained the genetic information for the earliest organisms.
   e. none of the above.

2. Which of the following is *not* a characteristic of protobionts necessary for the evolution of living cells?
   a. a membrane-like boundary separating the external environment from an internal environment
   b. polymers capable of functioning in information storage
   c. polymers capable of catalytic activity
   d. self-replication
   e. compartmentalization of metabolic activity

3. RNA is believed to be the first functional macromolecule in protobionts because it
   a. is easier to synthesize than other macromolecules.
   b. has the ability to store information, self-replicate, and perform catalytic activity.
   c. is the simplest of the macromolecules commonly found in living cells.
   d. All of the above are correct.
   e. Only a and c are correct.

4. The movement of landmasses that have changed their positions, shapes, and association with other landmasses is called
   a. glaciation.   d. biogeography.
   b. Pangaea.   e. geological scale.
   c. continental drift.

5. Paleontologists estimate the dates of fossils by
   a. the layer of rock in which the fossils are found.
   b. analysis of radioisotopes found in nearby igneous rock.
   c. the complexity of the body plan of the organism.
   d. all of the above.
   e. a and b only.

6. The fossil record does not give us a complete picture of the history of life because
   a. not all past organisms have become fossilized.
   b. only organisms with hard skeletons can become fossilized.
   c. fossils of very small organisms have not been found.
   d. fossils of early organisms are located too deep in the crust of the Earth to be found.
   e. all of the above.

7. According to endosymbiosis theory, eukaryotic cells came into existence by
   a. endocytosis of an archaeal cell by a bacterial cell.
   b. endocytosis of a bacterial cell by an archaeal cell.
   c. fusion of an archaeal cell and a bacterial cell.
   d. fusion of a bacterial cell and an archaeal cell.
   e. a and c only.

8. Which of the following explanations of multicellularity in eukaryotes is seen in the development of complex, multicellular organisms today?
   a. endosymbiosis
   b. aggregation of cells to form a colony
   c. division of cells with the resulting cells adhering together
   d. multiple cell types aggregating to form a complex organism
   e. none of the above

9. The earliest fossils of vascular plants were formed during the _____ period.
   a. Ordovician   c. Devonian   e. Jurassic
   b. Silurian   d. Triassic

10. The appearance of the first hominoids dates to the _____ period.
    a. Triassic   c. Cretaceous   e. Quaternary
    b. Jurassic   d. Tertiary

Conceptual Questions

1. What four stages led to the origin of living cells?

2. How are the ages of fossils determined? In your answer, you should discuss which types of rocks are analyzed and explain the concepts of radiometric dating and half-life.

3. **PRINCIPLES** Two principles of biology are (1) *living organisms interact with their environment* and (2) *populations of organisms evolve from one generation to the next*. Describe two examples in which changes in the global climate affected the evolution of species.

Collaborative Questions

1. Discuss possible hypotheses of how organic molecules were first formed.

2. Discuss the key features of a protobiont. What distinguishes a protobiont from a living cell?

Online Resource

www.brookerprinciples.com

Stay a step ahead in your studies with animations that bring concepts to life and practice tests to assess your understanding. Your instructor may also recommend the interactive eBook, individualized learning tools, and more.

19

An Introduction to Evolution and Population Genetics

Selective breeding. The horses in this race have been bred for a particular trait, in this case, speed. Such a practice, called selective breeding, can dramatically change the traits of organisms over several generations.

Chapter Outline

Organic life beneath the shoreless waves
Was born and nurs'd in Ocean's pearly caves
First forms minute, unseen by spheric glass,
Move on the mud, or pierce the watery mass;
These, as successive generations bloom,
New powers acquire, and larger limbs assume;
Whence countless groups of vegetation spring,
And breathing realms of fin, and feet, and wing.

From *The Temple of Nature* by Erasmus Darwin, grandfather of Charles Darwin. Published posthumously in 1803.

The term **evolution** is used to describe a change in one or more heritable characteristics of a population from one generation to the next. It is a process of change over time. In the first part of this chapter, we will examine the development of evolutionary thought and some of the basic tenets of evolution, particularly those proposed by the British naturalist Charles Darwin in the mid-1800s. Our understanding of evolution has been refined over the past 150 years or so, but the fundamental principle of evolution remains unchanged and has provided a cornerstone for our understanding of biology.

We will then survey the extensive data that illustrate the processes by which evolution occurs. These data not only support the idea that populations change over time, or evolve, but also allow us to understand the interrelatedness of different species, whose similarities are often due to descent from a common ancestor. Much of the early evidence supporting evolution came from direct observations and comparisons of living and extinct species. More recently, advances in molecular genetics, particularly those related to DNA sequencing and genomics, have revolutionized the study of evolution. Scientists now have information that allows us to understand how evolution involves changes in the DNA sequences of a given species that affect a species' genes and the proteins they encode.

The remainder of the chapter is concerned with **population genetics,** the study of genes and genotypes in a population. The central issue in population genetics is genetic variation—its extent within populations, why it exists, how it is maintained, and how it changes over the course of many generations. We will examine the various evolutionary mechanisms that promote genetic change in a population, including mutation, natural selection, genetic drift, migration, and nonrandom mating.

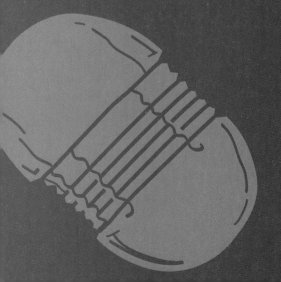

Overview of Evolution

Learning Outcomes:

1. Describe the process of evolution.
2. List the factors that led Darwin to propose the theory of descent with modification through variation and natural selection.
3. Explain how natural selection works.

Undoubtedly, the question, "Where did we come from?" has been asked and debated by people for thousands of years. Many of the early ideas regarding the existence of living organisms were strongly influenced by religion and philosophy. Some of these ideas suggested that all forms of life have remained the same since their creation. In the 17th century, however, scholars in Europe began a revolution that created the basis of empirical thought. **Empirical thought** relies on observation to form an idea or hypothesis rather than trying to understand life from a non-physical or spiritual point of view. As described in this section, the shift toward empirical thought encouraged scholars to look for the basic rationale behind a given process or phenomenon.

The Work of Several Scientists Set the Stage for Darwin's Ideas

Late in the 1700s, a small number of European scientists began to quietly challenge the belief that life-forms are fixed and unchanging. A French zoologist, George Buffon, actually proposed that living things change through time. However, Buffon was careful to hide his views in a 44-volume series of books on natural history. Around the same time, a French naturalist named Jean-Baptiste Lamarck suggested an intimate relationship between variation and evolution. By examining fossils, he realized that some species had remained the same over the millennia and others had changed. Lamarck hypothesized that species change over the course of many generations by adapting to new environments. According to Lamarck, organisms altered their behavior in response to environmental change. He thought that behavioral changes modified traits and hypothesized that these traits were inherited by offspring. He called this idea the **inheritance of acquired characteristics.** For example, according to Lamarck's hypothesis, giraffes developed their elongated necks and front legs by feeding on the leaves at the top of trees. The exercise of stretching up to the leaves altered the neck and legs, and Lamarck presumed that these acquired characteristics were transmitted to offspring. However, further research has rejected Lamarck's idea that acquired traits can be inherited. Even so, Lamarck's work was important in promoting the idea of evolutionary change.

Interestingly, Erasmus Darwin, the grandfather of Charles Darwin, was a contemporary of Buffon and Lamarck and an early advocate of evolutionary change. He was a physician, a plant biologist, and also a poet (see poem at the beginning of the chapter). He was aware that modern species were different from related types of fossilized organisms and also saw how plant and animal breeders used breeding practices to change the traits of domesticated species such as horses (see chapter-opening photo). He knew that offspring inherited features from their parents and went so far as to say that life on Earth could have descended from a common ancestor.

Darwin Suggested That Existing Species Are Derived from Pre-Existing Species

Charles Darwin played a central role in developing the theory that existing species have evolved from pre-existing ones. Darwin's unique perspective and ability to formulate evolutionary principles were shaped by several different fields of study, including ideas of his time about geological and biological processes.

Two main hypotheses about geological processes predominated in the early 19th century.

1. Catastrophism was first proposed by French zoologist and paleontologist Georges Cuvier to explain the age of the Earth. Cuvier suggested that the Earth was just 6,000 years old and that only catastrophic events had changed its geological structure. This idea fit well with certain religious teachings.
2. Uniformitarianism, proposed by Scottish geologist James Hutton and popularized by fellow Scotsman geologist Charles Lyell, suggested that changes in the Earth are directly caused by recurring events. For example, they suggested that geological processes such as erosion existed in the past and happened at the same gradual and uniform rate as they do in the present. For such slow geological processes to eventually lead to substantial changes in the Earth's characteristics, a great deal of time was required. Hutton and Lyell were the first to propose that the age of the Earth is well beyond 6,000 years. The ideas of Hutton and Lyell helped to shape Darwin's view of the world.

Darwin's thinking was also influenced by a paper published in 1798 called *Essay on the Principle of Population* by Thomas Malthus, an English economist. Malthus asserted that the population size of humans can, at best, increase linearly due to increased land usage and improvements in agriculture, whereas our reproductive potential is exponential (for example, doubling with each generation). He argued that famine, war, and disease, especially among the poor, keep population growth within existing resources. The relevant message from Malthus's work was that not all members of any population will survive and reproduce.

Darwin's ideas, however, were most influenced by his own experiences and observations. His work as a young man aboard the HMS *Beagle*, a survey ship, lasted from 1831 to 1836 and involved a careful examination of many different species (**Figure 19.1**). The main mission of the *Beagle* was to map the coastline of southern South America and take oceanographic measurements. As the ship's naturalist, Darwin's job was to record information about the weather, geological features, plants, animals, fossils, rocks, minerals, and indigenous people.

Though Darwin made many interesting observations on his journey, he was particularly struck by the distinctive traits of island species. For example, Darwin observed several species of finches found on the Galápagos Islands, a group of volcanic islands

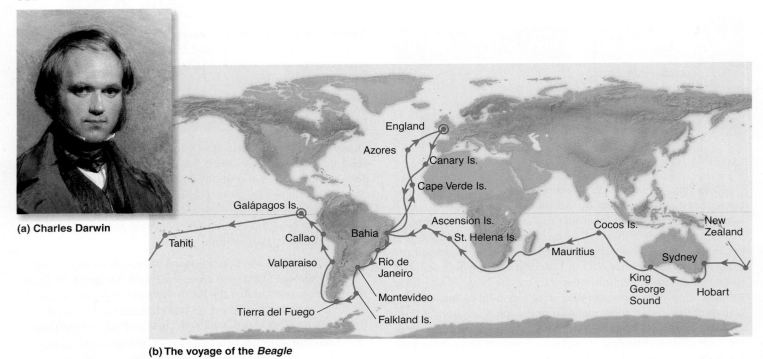

(a) Charles Darwin

(b) The voyage of the *Beagle*

Figure 19.1 **Charles Darwin and the voyage of the *Beagle*, 1831–1836. (a)** A portrait of Charles Darwin (1809–1882) at age 31. **(b)** Darwin's voyage on the *Beagle*, which took almost 5 years to circumnavigate the world.

600 miles off the coast of Ecuador. Though it is often assumed that Darwin's personal observations of these finches directly inspired his ideas regarding evolution, this is not the case. Initially, Darwin thought the birds were various species of blackbirds, grosbeaks, and finches. Later, however, the bird specimens from the islands were given to the British ornithologist John Gould, who identified them as several new finch species. Gould's observations helped Darwin in the later formulation of his theory.

As seen in **Table 19.1**, the finches differed widely in the size and shape of their beaks and in their feeding habits. Darwin clearly saw the similarities among these species, yet he noted the differences that provided them with specialized feeding strategies. It is now known these finches all evolved from a single species similar to the dull-colored grassquit finch (*Tiaris obscura*), commonly found along the Pacific Coast of South America. Once they arrived on the Galápagos Islands, the finches' ability to survive and reproduce in their new habitat depended, in part, on changes in the size and shape of their beaks over many generations. These specializations enabled succeeding generations to better obtain particular types of food.

In 1856, Darwin began to write a long book to explain his ideas regarding evolution. In 1858, however, Alfred Wallace, a British naturalist working in the East Indies, sent Darwin an unpublished manuscript to read prior to its publication. In it, Wallace proposed the same ideas concerning evolution. In response to this, Darwin decided to publish some of his own writings on this subject, and two papers, one by Darwin and one by Wallace, appeared in the *Proceedings of the Linnean Society of London*. These papers were not widely recognized. A year later, however, Darwin finished his book *On the Origin of Species* (1859), which described his ideas in greater detail and included observational support. This book,

which received high praise from many scientists and scorn from others, started a great debate concerning evolution. Although some of his ideas were incomplete because the genetic basis of traits was not understood at that time, Darwin's work remains a foundation of our understanding of biology.

Natural Selection Changes Populations from Generation to Generation

Darwin proposed that existing life-forms on our planet result from the modification of pre-existing life-forms. He expressed this concept of evolution as "the theory of descent with modification through variation and natural selection." The term evolution refers to the process of change. What factors bring about evolutionary change? According to Darwin's ideas, evolution occurs from generation to generation due to two interacting factors: genetic variation and natural selection.

1. Variation in traits may occur among individuals of a given species. Those traits that are heritable are then passed from parents to offspring. The genetic basis for variation within a species was not understood during Darwin's time. We now know that such variation is due to different types of genetic changes such as random mutations in genes. Even though Darwin did not fully appreciate the genetic basis of variation, he and many other people before him observed that offspring resemble their parents more than they do unrelated individuals. Therefore, he assumed that some traits are passed from parent to offspring.

2. In each generation, many more offspring are usually produced than will survive and reproduce. Often times, resources in the environment are limiting so that some

Table 19.1	A Comparison of Beak Type and Diet Among the Galápagos Finches Darwin Studied			
Type of finch	**Species**		**Type of beak**	**Diet**
Ground finches	Large ground finch (*Geospiza magnirostris*)		Crushing	Seeds—Ground finches have crushing beaks to crush various sizes of seeds; large beaks can crush large seeds, whereas smaller beaks are better for crushing small seeds.
	Medium ground finch (*G. fortis*)			
	Small ground finch (*G. fuliginosa*)			
	Sharp-billed ground finch (*G. difficilis*)			
Vegetarian finch	Vegetarian finch (*Platyspiza crassirostris*)		Crushing	Buds—Vegetarian finches have crushing beaks to pull buds from branches.
Tree finches	Large tree finch (*Camarhynchus psittacula*)		Grasping	Insects—Tree finches have grasping beaks to pick insects from trees. Those with heavier beaks can also break apart wood in search of insects.
	Medium tree finch (*Camarhynchus pauper*)			
	Small tree finch (*Camarhynchus parvulus*)			
Tree and warbler finches	Mangrove finch (*Cactospiza heliobates*)		Probing	Insects—These finches have probing beaks to search for insects in crevices and then to pick them up. The woodpecker finch can also use a cactus spine for probing.
	Woodpecker finch (*Camarhynchus pallidus*)			
	Warbler finch (*Certhidea olivacea*)			
Cactus finches	Large cactus finch (*G. conirostris*)		Probing	Seeds—Cactus finches have probing beaks to open cactus fruits and take out seeds.
	Cactus finch (*G. scandens*)			

members of a population do not survive. During the process of **natural selection,** individuals with heritable traits that make them better suited to their native environment tend to flourish and reproduce, whereas other individuals are less likely to survive and reproduce. As a result of natural selection, certain traits that favor reproductive success become more prevalent in a population over time.

As an example, let's consider a population of finches that migrates from the South American mainland to a distant island (Figure 19.2). Variation exists in the beak sizes among the migrating birds. If the seeds produced on the distant island were larger than those produced on the mainland, those birds with larger beaks would be better able to feed on these larger seeds and therefore would be more likely to survive and pass that trait to their

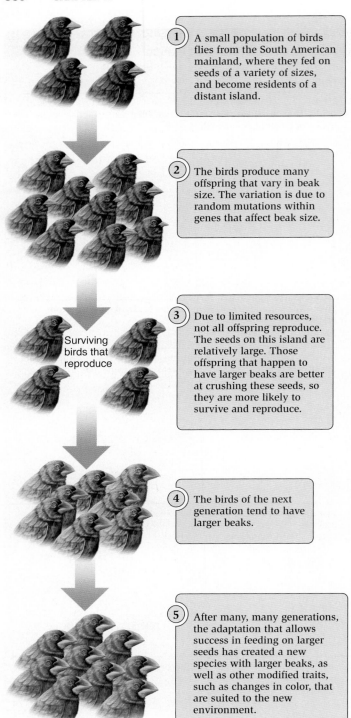

1. A small population of birds flies from the South American mainland, where they fed on seeds of a variety of sizes, and become residents of a distant island.

2. The birds produce many offspring that vary in beak size. The variation is due to random mutations within genes that affect beak size.

Surviving birds that reproduce

3. Due to limited resources, not all offspring reproduce. The seeds on this island are relatively large. Those offspring that happen to have larger beaks are better at crushing these seeds, so they are more likely to survive and reproduce.

4. The birds of the next generation tend to have larger beaks.

5. After many, many generations, the adaptation that allows success in feeding on larger seeds has created a new species with larger beaks, as well as other modified traits, such as changes in color, that are suited to the new environment.

Figure 19.2 Evolutionary adaptation to a new environment via natural selection. The example shown here involves a species of finch adapting to a new environment on a distant island. According to Darwin, the process of adaptation can lead to the formation of a new species with traits that are better suited to the new environment.

Concept Check: *The phrase "an organism evolves" is incorrect. Explain why.*

BioConnections: *Look back at Figure 18.5. How is natural selection similar to chemical selection? How are they different?*

offspring. What are the consequences of this selection process? In succeeding generations, the population tends to have a greater proportion of finches with larger beaks.

Alternatively, if a trait happens to be detrimental to an individual's ability to survive and reproduce, natural selection is likely to eliminate this type of variation. For example, if a finch in the same environment had a small beak, this bird would be less likely to acquire food, which would decrease its ability to survive and pass this trait to its offspring. Natural selection may ultimately result in a new species with a combination of multiple traits that are quite different from those of the original species, such as finches with larger beaks and changes in coloration. In other words, the newer species has evolved from a pre-existing one.

19.1 Reviewing the Concepts

- Evolution is the process of change in one or more heritable characteristics of a population from one generation to the next.
- Charles Darwin proposed the theory of descent with modification through variation and natural selection based on his understanding of geology and population growth and his observations of species in their natural settings. His voyage on the *Beagle*, during which he studied many species, including finches on the Galápagos Islands, was particularly influential in the development of his ideas (Figure 19.1, Table 19.1).
- Darwin proposed that evolution occurred from generation to generation through two interacting factors: genetic variation and natural selection. As a result of natural selection, certain traits that favor reproductive success become more prevalent in a population over time (Figure 19.2).

19.1 Testing Your Knowledge

1. What core concept(s) underlie the process of evolution?
   a. inheritance of acquired characteristics
   b. genetic variation
   c. natural selection
   d. all of the above
   e. both b and c

2. What may change as a result of natural selection?
   a. an individual's characteristics
   b. the genetic composition of populations from one generation to the next
   c. the characteristics found in populations from one generation to the next
   d. all of the above
   e. both b and c

19.2 Evidence of Evolutionary Change

Learning Outcomes:

1. Summarize different types of evidence for evolutionary change, including the fossil record, biogeography, convergent traits, selective breeding, and homologies.
2. Provide examples of three types of homologies.

Table 19.2	Evidence of Biological Evolution
Type of observation	**Description**
Studies of natural selection	By following the characteristics of populations over time, researchers have observed how natural selection alters such populations in response to environmental changes.
Fossil record	When fossils are compared according to their age, from oldest to youngest, successive evolutionary change becomes apparent.
Biogeography	Unique species found on islands and other remote areas have arisen because the species in these locations have evolved in isolation from the rest of the world.
Convergent evolution	Two different species from different lineages sometimes become anatomically similar because they occupy similar environments. This indicates that natural selection results in adaptation to a given environment.
Selective breeding	The traits in domesticated species have been profoundly modified by selective breeding (also called artificial selection) in which breeders choose the parents that have desirable traits.
Homologies	
Anatomical	Homologous structures are structures that are anatomically similar to each other because they evolved from a structure in a common ancestor. In some cases, such structures have lost their original function and become vestigial.
Developmental	An analysis of embryonic development often reveals similar features that point to past evolutionary relationships.
Molecular	At the molecular level, certain characteristics are found in all living cells, suggesting that all modern species are derived from an interrelated group of common ancestors. In addition, the genes of species that are closely related evolutionarily have DNA sequences that are more similar to each other than they are to distantly related organisms.

Evidence that reflects the process of evolution has been obtained from many sources (**Table 19.2**). Historically, the first evidence of biological evolution came from studies of the characteristics of populations over time, studies of the fossil record, the distribution of species on Earth, the comparison of similar anatomical features in different species, and selective breeding experiments. More recently, additional evidence that illustrates the process of evolution has been found at the molecular level. By comparing DNA sequences from many different species, biologists have gained great insight into the relationship between the evolution of species and the associated changes in the genetic material. In this section, we will survey a variety of evidence that shows the process of evolutionary change.

Fossils Show Successive Evolutionary Change

As discussed in Chapter 18, the fossil record has provided biologists with evidence of the history of life on Earth. Let's consider a couple of examples in which paleontologists have studied fossils that illustrate evolutionary change. In 2005, fossils of *Tiktaalik*

roseae, nicknamed fishapod, were discovered by paleontologists Ted Daeschler, Neil Shubin, and Farish Jenkins. The discovery of fishapod illuminates one of several steps that led to the evolution of tetrapods, which are animals with four legs. *T. roseae* is called a **transitional form** because it displays an intermediate state between an ancestral form and the form of its descendants (**Figure 19.3**). In this case, the fishapod is a transitional form between fishes, which have fins for locomotion, and tetrapods, which are four-limbed animals. Unlike a true fish, *T. roseae* had a broad skull, a flexible neck, and eyes mounted on the top of its head like a crocodile. Its interlocking rib cage suggests it had primitive lungs. Perhaps the most surprising discovery was that its pectoral fins (those on the side of the body) revealed the beginnings of a primitive wrist and five finger-like bones. These appendages would have allowed *T. roseae* to support its body on shallow river bottoms and lift its head above the water to search for prey and perhaps even move out of the water for short periods. During the Devonian period (417–354 mya), this could have been an important advantage in the marshy floodplains of large rivers.

One of the best-studied observations of evolutionary change through the fossil record is that of the horse family, modern members of which include horses, zebras, and donkeys. These species, which are large, long-legged animals adapted to living in open

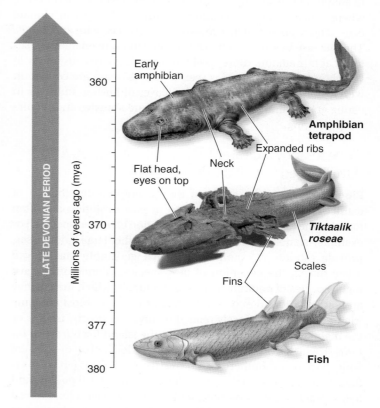

Figure 19.3 A transitional form in the tetrapod lineage. This figure shows two early tetrapod ancestors, a Devonian fish and the transitional form *Tiktaalik roseae*, as well as a descendant, an early amphibian. An analysis of the fossils shows that *T. roseae*, also known as a fishapod, had both fish and amphibian characteristics, so it was likely able to survive brief periods out of the water.

grasslands, are the remaining descendants of a long lineage that produced many species that have subsequently become extinct since its origin approximately 55 mya. Examination of the horse lineage through fossils provides a particularly interesting case of how evolution involves adaptation to changing environments.

The earliest known fossils of the horse family revealed that the animals were small with short legs and broad feet (Figure 19.4). Early horses, such as *Hyracotherium*, lived in wooded habitats and are thought to have browsed on leaves. The fossil record has revealed changes in size, foot anatomy, and tooth morphology among this group of related species over time. Early horses were the size of dogs, whereas modern horses typically weigh more than a half ton. *Hyracotherium*, an early horse, had four toes on its front feet and three on its hind feet. The toes were encased in fleshy pads. By comparison, the feet of modern horses have a single toe, enclosed in a tough, bony hoof. The fossil record shows an increase in the length of the central toe, the development of a bony hoof, and the loss of the other toes. Finally, the teeth of *Hyracotherium* were relatively small compared with those of modern horses. Over the course of millions of years, horse molars have increased in size and developed a complex pattern of ridges.

How do evolutionary biologists explain these changes in horse characteristics? The changes can be attributed to natural selection, which acted on existing genetic variation and resulted in adaptations to changes in global climates. Over North America, where much of horse evolution occurred, changes in climate caused large areas of dense forests to be replaced with grasslands. The increase in size and changes in foot structure enabled horses to escape predators more easily and travel greater distances in search of food. The changes seen in horses' teeth are consistent with a shift from eating the tender leaves of bushes and trees to eating grasses and other vegetation that are abrasive and require more chewing.

Biogeography Indicates That Species in a Given Area Have Evolved from Pre-Existing Species

Biogeography is the study of the geographic distribution of extinct and living species. Patterns of past evolution are often found in the natural geographic distribution of related species. For example, islands, which are isolated from other large landmasses, provide numerous examples in which geography has played a key role in the evolution of new species. Islands often have many species of **endemic** plants and animals, which means they are naturally found only in a particular location. Most endemic island species have closely related relatives on nearby islands or the mainland. For example, consider the island fox (*Urocyon littoralis*), which lives on the Channel Islands located off the coast of Santa Barbara in southern California (Figure 19.5). This type of fox is found nowhere else in the world. It weighs about 3–6 pounds and feeds largely on insects, mice, and fruits. The island fox evolved from the mainland gray fox (*Urocyon cinereoargenteus*), which is much larger, usually 7–11 pounds. During the last Ice Age, about 16,000–18,000 years ago, the Santa Barbara channel was frozen and narrow enough for ancestors of the mainland gray fox to cross over to the Channel Islands. When the Ice Age ended, the

Biology Principle

All Species (Past and Present) Are Related by an Evolutionary History

This diagram shows the morphological changes that occurred in the evolution of the horse.

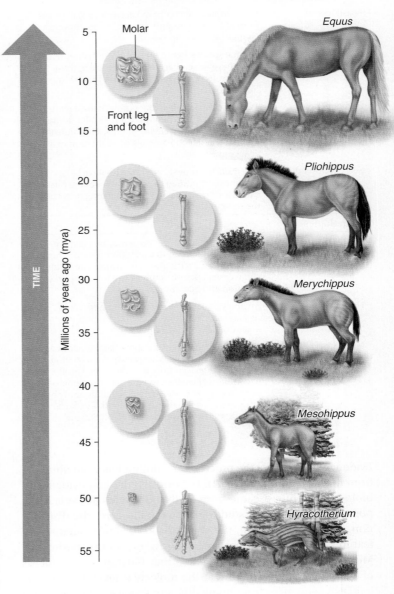

Figure 19.4 Evolutionary changes in horse morphology. Some major changes observed in the fossil record relate to body size, foot anatomy, and tooth morphology. These anatomical changes are hypothesized to be due to adaptations to a changing environment over the last 55 million years. Note: This figure is meant to emphasize general anatomical changes in horse morphology. The evolutionary pathway that produced modern horses involves several branches and is shown in Figure 21.5.

(a) Island fox
(*Urocyon littoralis*)

California

Santa Barbara

Channel Islands

Santa Barbara channel

San Miguel

Santa Rosa

Santa Cruz

Anacapa

(b) Gray fox (*Urocyon cinereoargenteus*)

Figure 19.5 **The evolution of an endemic island species from a mainland species.** **(a)** The smaller island fox (*Urocyon littoralis*) found on the Channel Islands is hypothesized to have evolved from **(b)** the gray fox (*Urocyon cinereoargenteus*) found on the California mainland.

Concept Check: *Explain how geography played a key role in the evolution of the island fox.*

ice melted and sea levels rose, causing the foxes to be cut off from the mainland. Over the last 16,000–18,000 years, the population of foxes on the Channel Islands evolved into the smaller island fox, which is now considered a different species from the larger gray fox, which is still found on the mainland. The smaller size of the island fox is an example of island dwarfing, a phenomenon in which the size of large animals on an isolated island shrinks dramatically over many generations. It is the result of natural selection in which a smaller size provides a survival and reproductive advantage, probably because of limited food and other resources.

Convergent Evolution Suggests Adaptation to the Environment

The process of natural selection is also evident in the study of plants and animals that have similar characteristics, even though they are not closely related evolutionarily. This similarity is the result of **convergent evolution,** in which two species from different lineages have independently evolved similar characteristics because they occupy similar environments. For example, both the giant anteater (*Myrmecophaga tridactyla*), found in South America, and the echidna (*Tachyglossus aculeatus*), found in Australia, have a long snout and tongue. Both species independently evolved these adaptations that enable them to feed on ants (Figure 19.6a). The giant anteater is a placental mammal, whereas the echidna is an egg-laying mammal known as a monotreme, so they are not closely related evolutionarily.

Another example of convergent evolution involves aerial rootlets found in vines such as English ivy (*Hedera helix*) and wintercreeper (*Euonymus fortunei*) (Figure 19.6b). Based on differences in their structures, these aerial rootlets appear to have developed independently as an effective means of clinging to the support on which a vine attaches itself.

The similar characteristics shown in Figure 19.6—for example, the snouts of the anteater and the echidna—are called **analogous structures** or convergent traits. They represent cases in which characteristics have arisen independently, two or more times, because different species have occupied similar types of environments on the Earth.

Selective Breeding Is a Human-Driven Form of Selection

The term **selective breeding** refers to programs and procedures designed to modify traits in domesticated species. This practice, also called artificial selection, is related to natural selection. The primary difference between natural and artificial selection is how the parents are chosen. Natural selection occurs because individuals that are able to survive and reproduce are more likely to pass their genes to future generations. Environmental factors often determine which individuals will be successful parents. In artificial selection, the breeder chooses as parents those individuals with traits that are desirable from a human perspective.

The underlying phenomenon that makes selective breeding possible is genetic variation. Within a population, variation may exist in a trait of interest. The underlying cause of the phenotypic variation is usually related to differences in **alleles,** variant forms of a particular gene, that determine the trait. The breeder chooses parents with desirable phenotypic characteristics. For centuries, humans have employed selective breeding to obtain domesticated species with interesting or agriculturally useful characteristics. For example, many common breeds of dog are the result of selective breeding strategies (Figure 19.7). All dogs are members of the same species, *Canis lupus*, subspecies *familiaris*, so they can interbreed to produce offspring. Selective breeding can dramatically modify the traits in a species. When you compare certain breeds of dogs (for example, a greyhound and a dachshund), they hardly look like members of the same species! Recent work in 2007 by American geneticist Nathan Sutter and colleagues indicates that the size of dogs may be determined by alleles in the *Igf1* gene that encodes a growth hormone called insulin-like growth factor 1. A particular allele of this gene was found to be common to all small breeds of dogs and nearly absent from very large breeds, suggesting that this allele is a major contributor to body size in small breeds of dogs.

Figure 19.6 **Examples of convergent evolution.** Both pairs of species shown in this figure are not closely related evolutionarily but occupy similar environments, suggesting that natural selection results in similar adaptations to a particular environment.

✓ Concept Check: *Can you think of another example in which two species that are not closely related have a similar adaptation?*

(a) The long snouts and tongues of the giant anteater (left) and the echidna (right) allow them to feed on ants.

(b) The aerial rootlets of English ivy (left) and wintercreeper (right) enable them to climb up supports.

(a) Bulldog   **(b) Greyhound**   **(c) Dachshund**

Figure 19.7 **Common breeds of dogs that have been obtained by selective breeding.** By selecting individuals carrying the alleles that influence traits desirable to humans, dog breeders have produced breeds with distinctive features. The dogs in this figure carry the same kinds of genes (for example, genes that affect their size, shape, and fur color). However, the alleles for many of these genes are different among these dogs, thereby allowing breeders to select for or against them and produce breeds with strikingly different phenotypes.

A Comparison of Homologies Shows Evolution of Related Species from a Common Ancestor

Let's now consider other widespread observations of the process of evolution among living organisms. In biology, the term **homology** refers to a similarity that occurs due to descent from a common ancestor. Two species may have a similar trait because the trait was originally found in a common ancestor. As described next, such homologies may involve anatomical, developmental, or molecular features.

Anatomical Homologies An examination of the limbs of modern vertebrate species reveals similarities that indicate the same set of bones has undergone evolutionary changes, becoming modified to perform different functions in different species. As seen in **Figure 19.8**, the forelimbs of vertebrates have a strikingly similar

Biology Principle

Structure Determines Function

These homologous sets of bones have evolved into somewhat different structures, which result in differences in their functions in humans, turtles, bats, and whales.

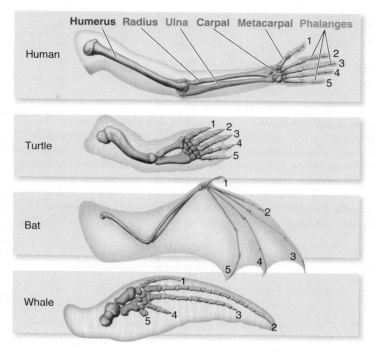

Figure 19.8 **An example of anatomical homology: Homologous structures found in vertebrates.** The same set of bones is found in the human arm, turtle arm, bat wing, and whale flipper, although their relative sizes and shapes differ significantly. This homology suggests that all of these animals evolved from a common ancestor.

Table 19.3	Examples of Vestigial Structures in Animals
Organism	**Vestigial structure(s)**
Humans	Tail bone and muscles to wiggle ears in adult
Boa constrictors	Skeletal remnants of hip and hind leg bones
Whales	Skeletal remnants of a pelvis
Manatees	Fingernails on the flippers

Within the context of evolutionary theory, vestigial structures are evolutionary relics. Natural selection maintains functional structures in a population of individuals. However, if a species changes its lifestyle so the structure loses its purpose, the selection that would normally keep the structure in a functional condition is no longer present. When this occurs, the structure may degenerate over the course of many generations due to the accumulation of mutations that limit its size and shape. Natural selection may eventually eliminate such traits due to the inefficiency and cost of producing unused structures.

Developmental Homologies   Species that differ substantially at the adult stage often bear striking similarities during early stages of embryonic development. These temporary similarities are called developmental homologies. In addition, evolutionary history is revealed during development in certain organisms, such as vertebrates. For example, if we consider human development, several features are seen in the embryo that are not present at birth. Human embryos have rudimentary gill ridges like a fish embryo, even though human embryos receive oxygen via the umbilical cord. The presence of gill ridges indicates that humans evolved from an aquatic species that had gill slits. A second observation is that human embryos have a bony tail. It is difficult to see the advantage of such a structure in utero, but easier to understand its presence assuming that an ancestor of the human lineage possessed a tail. These observations, and many others, illustrate that closely related species share similar developmental pathways.

Molecular Homologies   A similarity between organisms at the molecular level due to descent from a common ancestor is called a **molecular homology.** A compelling observation at the molecular level indicating that modern life-forms are derived from an interrelated group of common ancestors is revealed by analyzing genetic sequences. The same type of gene is often found in diverse organisms. Furthermore, the degree of similarity between genetic sequences from different species reflects the evolutionary relatedness of those species. As an example, let's consider the *p53* gene, which encodes the p53 protein—a checkpoint protein of the cell cycle (see Chapter 13, Figure 13.3). **Figure 19.9** shows a short amino acid sequence that makes up part of the p53 protein from a variety of species, including five mammals, one bird, and three fish. The top sequence is the human p53 sequence, and the right column describes the percentages of amino acids within the entire sequence that are identical to those in the entire human sequence. Amino acids in the other species that are identical to

pattern of bone arrangements. These are termed **homologous structures**—structures that are similar to each other because they evolved from a common ancestor. The forearm has developed different functions among various vertebrates, including grasping, walking, flying, swimming, and climbing. The process of evolution explains how these animals have descended from a common ancestor and how natural selection has resulted in modifications to the structure of the original set of bones in ways that ultimately allowed them to be used for several different functions.

Another result of evolution is the phenomenon of **vestigial structures,** anatomical features that have no current function but resemble structures of their presumed ancestors (**Table 19.3**). An interesting case is found in humans. People have a complete set of muscles for moving their ears, even though most people are unable to do so. By comparison, many modern mammals can move their ears to determine the direction of sounds, and presumably this was an important trait in a distant human ancestor. Why would organisms have structures that are no longer useful?

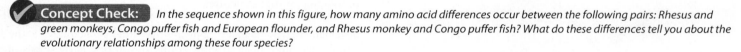

	Short amino acid sequence within the p53 protein	Percentages of amino acids in the whole p53 protein that are identical to human p53
Human (*Homo sapiens*)	Val Pro Ser Gln Lys Thr Tyr Gln Gly Ser Tyr Gly Phe Arg Leu Gly Phe Leu His Ser Gly Thr	100
Rhesus monkey (*Macaca mulatta*)	Val Pro Ser Gln Lys Thr Tyr His Gly Ser Tyr Gly Phe Arg Leu Gly Phe Leu His Ser Gly Thr	95
Green monkey (*Cercopithecus aethiops*)	Val Pro Ser Gln Lys Thr Tyr His Gly Ser Tyr Gly Phe Arg Leu Gly Phe Leu His Ser Gly Thr	95
Rabbit (*Oryctolagus cuniculus*)	Val Pro Ser Gln Lys Thr Tyr His Gly Asn Tyr Gly Phe Arg Leu Gly Phe Leu His Ser Gly Thr	86
Dog (*Canis lupus familiaris*)	Val Pro Ser Pro Lys Thr Tyr Pro Gly Thr Tyr Gly Phe Arg Leu Gly Phe Leu His Ser Gly Thr	80
Chicken (*Gallus gallus*)	Val Pro Ser Thr Glu Asp Tyr Gly Gly Asp Phe Asp Phe Arg Val Gly Phe Val Glu Ala Gly Thr	53
Channel catfish (*Ictalurus punctatus*)	Val Pro Val Thr Ser Asp Tyr Pro Gly Leu Leu Asn Phe Thr Leu His Phe Gln Glu Ser Ser Gly	48
European flounder (*Platichthys flesus*)	Val Pro Val Val Thr Asp Tyr Pro Gly Glu Tyr Gly Phe Gln Leu Arg Phe Gln Lys Ser Gly Thr	46
Congo puffer fish (*Tetraodon miurus*)	Val Pro Val Thr Thr Asp Tyr Pro Gly Glu Tyr Gly Phe Lys Leu Arg Phe Gln Lys Ser Gly Thr	41

Figure 19.9 **An example of genetic homology: A comparison of a short amino acid sequence within the p53 protein from nine different animals.** This figure compares a short region of the p53 protein, a tumor suppressor that plays a role in preventing cancer. Amino acids are represented by three-letter abbreviations. The orange-colored amino acids in the sequences are identical to those in the human sequence. The numbers in the right column indicate the percentage of amino acids within the whole p53 protein that is identical with the human p53 protein, which is 393 amino acids in length. For example, 95% of the amino acids, or 373 of 393, are identical between the p53 sequence found in humans and the one in Rhesus monkeys.

Concept Check: *In the sequence shown in this figure, how many amino acid differences occur between the following pairs: Rhesus and green monkeys, Congo puffer fish and European flounder, and Rhesus monkey and Congo puffer fish? What do these differences tell you about the evolutionary relationships among these four species?*

BioConnections: *Look back at Table 17.4. How are genetic sequences that are retrieved from a database using the BLAST program correlated with the evolutionary relatedness of the species?*

those in humans are highlighted in orange. The sequences from the two monkeys are the most similar to those in humans, followed by the other two mammalian species (rabbit and dog). The three fish sequences are the least similar to the human sequence, but the fish sequences tend to be similar to each other.

Taken together, the data shown in Figure 19.9 illustrate two critical points about evolution at the gene level. First, specific genes are found in a diverse array of species such as mammals, birds, and fishes. Second, the sequences of closely related species tend to be more similar to each other than they are to distantly related species.

- Selective breeding, the selecting and breeding of individual organisms having desired traits, is a human-driven form of selection (Figure 19.7).
- Homologies are similarities that occur due to descent from a common ancestor. Homologous structures, such as the set of bones in the forearms of vertebrates, and vestigial structures, structures that were functional in an ancestor but no longer have a useful function in modern species, are evidence of evolutionary change. Homologies can also be seen during embryonic development and at the molecular level (Figures 19.8, 19.9, Table 19.3).

19.2 Reviewing the Concepts

- Evidence of evolutionary change is found in studies of the fossil record, biogeography, convergent evolution, selective breeding, and homologies (Table 19.2).
- Fossils provide evidence of evolutionary change in a series of related organisms. The fossil record often reveals transitional forms that link past ancestors to modern species (Figures 19.3, 19.4).
- Biogeography provides information on the geographic distribution of related species. When populations become isolated on islands or continents, they often evolve into new species (Figure 19.5).
- In convergent evolution, independent adaptations result in similar characteristics, or analogous structures, because different species occupy similar environments (Figure 19.6).

19.2 Testing Your Knowledge

1. Which of the following provides evidence of evolutionary change?
   a. an analysis of fossils of the horse lineage
   b. the identification of transitional species in the fossil record
   c. the identification of island species that are closely related to mainland species
   d. the similarity of homologous genes
   e. all of the above

2. Homologous traits show similarities because the species exhibiting those traits
   a. occupy similar environments.
   b. evolved from a common ancestor.
   c. evolved in a similar environment.
   d. are geographically close to each other.

19.3 Genes in Populations

Learning Outcomes:

1. Define gene pool.
2. Distinguish between allele and genotype frequency.
3. Use the Hardy-Weinberg equation to calculate allele and genotype frequencies of a given population.
4. List the conditions that must be met for a population to be in Hardy-Weinberg equilibrium.
5. Describe the factors that cause microevolution to happen.

Population genetics is an extension of our understanding of Darwin's theory of natural selection, Mendel's laws of inheritance, and newer studies in molecular genetics. All of the alleles for every gene in a given population make up the **gene pool.** Each member of the population receives its genes from its parents, which, in turn, are members of the gene pool. Individuals that reproduce contribute to the gene pool of the next generation. Population geneticists study the genetic variation within a gene pool and how such variation changes from one generation to the next. The emphasis is often on understanding the variation in alleles among members of a population. In this section, we will examine some of the general features of populations and gene pools.

Populations Are Dynamic Units

A population is a group of individuals of the same species that occupy the same environment at the same time and (for sexually reproducing organisms) can interbreed with one another. Certain species occupy a wide geographic range and are divided into discrete populations due to geographic isolation. For example, distinct populations of a given species may be located on different sides of a physical barrier, such as a mountain.

Populations may change in size and geographic location from one generation to the next. As the size and location of a population change, their genetic composition generally changes as well. Some of the genetic changes involve adaptation, in which a population becomes better suited to its environment, consisting of individuals that are more likely to survive and successfully reproduce. For example, a population of mammals may move from a warmer to a colder geographic location. Natural selection may favor those individuals in the population that have thicker fur, which over time will produce a population of individuals that are better insulated against the colder temperatures.

EVOLUTIONARY CONNECTIONS

Genes Are Usually Polymorphic

The term **polymorphism** (from the Greek, meaning many forms) refers to the presence of two or more variants or traits for a given character within a population. **Figure 19.10** illustrates a striking example of polymorphism in the elder-flowered orchid (*Dactylo-*

Figure 19.10 An example of polymorphism: The two color variations found in the orchid *Dactylorhiza sambucina*.

rhiza sambucina). Throughout the range of this species in Europe, both yellow- and red-flowered individuals are prevalent.

Polymorphism in a character is usually due to two or more alleles of a gene that influences the character. Geneticists also use the term polymorphism to describe the variation in the DNA sequence of genes. A gene that commonly exists as two or more alleles in a population is a **polymorphic gene.** To be considered polymorphic, a gene must exist in at least two different forms or alleles, and each allele must occur at a frequency that is greater than 1%. By comparison, a **monomorphic gene** exists predominantly as a single allele in a population. When 99% or more of the alleles of a given gene are identical in a population, the gene is considered to be monomorphic.

What types of molecular changes cause genes to be polymorphic? A polymorphism may involve various types of changes, such as a deletion of a significant region of the gene, a duplication of a region, or a change in a single nucleotide. This last type of variation is called a **single-nucleotide polymorphism (SNP).** SNPs ("snips") are the smallest type of genetic variation that can occur within a given gene and also the most common. For example, the allele that causes the recessive disorder called sickle cell disease involves a single-nucleotide change in the human β-globin gene, which encodes a subunit of the oxygen-carrying protein called hemoglobin. The non-disease-causing allele and sickle cell allele represent a SNP of the β-globin gene:

Region of the human β-globin gene

A C T C C T G A G G A A
T G A G G A C T C C T T

Region of the non-disease-causing allele

A single-nucleotide polymorphism

A C T C C T G T G G A A
T G A G G A C A C C T T

Region of the sickle cell allele

Relative to the non-disease-causing allele, this is a single-nucleotide substitution of an A (in the top strand) to a T (in the sickle cell allele).

SNPs represent 90% of all variation in human DNA sequences that occurs among different people. In human populations, a gene that is 2,000–3,000 bp in length, on average, contains 10 different SNPs. Likewise, SNPs with a frequency of 1% or more are found very frequently among genes of nearly all species. Polymorphism is the norm for relatively large, healthy populations of nearly all species, as evidenced by the occurrence of SNPs within most genes.

Population Genetics Is Concerned with Allele and Genotype Frequencies

One approach to analyzing genetic variation in populations is to consider the frequency of specific alleles and genotypes in a quantitative way. Two fundamental calculations are central to population genetics: **allele frequency** and **genotype frequency.** Allele and genotype frequency are defined as follows:

$$\text{Allele frequency} = \frac{\text{Number of copies of a specific allele in a population}}{\text{Total number of all alleles for that gene in a population}}$$

$$\text{Genotype frequency} = \frac{\text{Number of individuals with a particular genotype in a population}}{\text{Total number of individuals in a population}}$$

Although allele and genotype frequencies are related, make sure you clearly distinguish between them. As an example, let's consider a population of 100 four-o'clock plants (*Mirabilis jalapa*) with the following genotypes:

49 red-flowered plants with the genotype $C^R C^R$

42 pink-flowered plants with the genotype $C^R C^W$

9 white-flowered plants with the genotype $C^W C^W$

When calculating an allele frequency for a diploid species, remember that homozygous individuals have two copies of a given allele, whereas heterozygotes have only one. For example, in tallying the C^W allele, each of the 42 heterozygotes has one copy of the C^W allele, and each white-flowered plant has two copies. Therefore, the allele frequency for C^W (the white color allele) equals

$$\text{Frequency of } C^W = \frac{(C^R C^W) + 2(C^W C^W)}{2(C^R C^R) + 2(C^R C^W) + 2(C^W C^W)}$$

$$\text{Frequency of } C^W = \frac{42 + (2)(9)}{(2)(49) + (2)(42) + (2)(9)}$$

$$= \frac{60}{200} = 0.3, \text{ or } 30\%$$

This result tells us that the allele frequency of C^W is 0.3. In other words, 30% of the alleles for this gene in the population are the white color (C^W) allele.

Let's now calculate the genotype frequency of $C^W C^W$ homozygotes (white-flowered plants).

$$\text{Frequency of } C^W C^W = \frac{9}{49 + 42 + 9}$$

$$= \frac{9}{100} = 0.09, \text{ or } 9\%$$

We see that 9% of the individuals in this population have the homozygous white-flower genotype.

Quantitative Analysis

THE HARDY-WEINBERG EQUATION RELATES ALLELE AND GENOTYPE FREQUENCIES IN A POPULATION

In 1908, Godfrey Harold Hardy, an English mathematician, and Wilhelm Weinberg, a German physician, independently derived a simple mathematical expression, now called the Hardy-Weinberg equation, that describes the relationship between allele and genotype frequencies when a population is not evolving. Let's examine the Hardy-Weinberg equation using the population of four-o'clock plants that we just considered. If the allele frequency of C^R is denoted by the symbol p and the allele frequency of C^W by q, then

$$p + q = 1$$

For example, if $p = 0.7$, then q must be 0.3. In other words, if the allele frequency of C^R equals 70%, the remaining 30% of alleles must be C^W, because together they equal 100%.

For a gene that exists in two alleles, the **Hardy-Weinberg equation** states that

$$p^2 + 2pq + q^2 = 1$$

If we apply this equation to our flower color gene, then

p^2 = the genotype frequency of $C^R C^R$ homozygotes

$2pq$ = the genotype frequency of $C^R C^W$ heterozygotes

q^2 = the genotype frequency of $C^W C^W$ homozygotes

If $p = 0.7$ and $q = 0.3$, then

Frequency of $C^R C^R = p^2 = (0.7)^2 = 0.49$

Frequency of $C^R C^W = 2pq = 2(0.7)(0.3) = 0.42$

Frequency of $C^W C^W = q^2 = (0.3)^2 = 0.09$

In other words, if the allele frequency of C^R is 70% and the allele frequency of C^W is 30%, the expected genotype frequency of $C^R C^R$ is 49%, $C^R C^W$ is 42%, and $C^W C^W$ is 9%.

Figure 19.11 uses a Punnett square to illustrate the relationship between allele frequencies and the way that gametes combine to produce genotypes. To be valid, the Hardy-Weinberg equation carries the assumption that two gametes combine randomly with each other to produce offspring. In a population, the frequency of a gamete carrying a particular allele is equal to the allele frequency in that population. For example, if the allele frequency of C^R equals 0.7, the frequency of a gamete carrying the C^R allele also equals 0.7. The probability of producing a $C^R C^R$ homozygote with red flowers is $0.7 \times 0.7 = 0.49$, or 49%. The probability of inheriting both C^W alleles, which produces white flowers, is $0.3 \times 0.3 = 0.09$, or 9%. Two different gamete combinations produce heterozygotes with pink flowers. An offspring could inherit the C^R allele from the pollen and C^W from the egg, or C^R from the egg and C^W from the pollen. Therefore, the frequency of heterozygotes is $pq + pq$, which equals $2pq$. In our example, this is $2(0.7)(0.3) = 0.42$, or 42%. Note that the frequencies for all three genotypes total 100%.

The Hardy-Weinberg equation predicts that allele and genotype frequencies will remain the same, generation after generation, provided that a population is in equilibrium. To be in equilibrium, evolutionary mechanisms that can change allele and genotype frequencies are not acting on a population. For this to occur, the following conditions must be met:

- No new mutations occur to alter allele frequencies.
- No natural selection occurs; that is, no survival or reproductive advantage exists for any of the genotypes.
- The population is so large that allele frequencies do not change due to chance.
- No migration occurs between different populations, altering the allele frequencies.
- Random mating occurs; that is, the members of the population mate with each other without regard to their genotypes.

Why is the Hardy-Weinberg equilibrium a useful concept? An equilibrium is a null hypothesis, which suggests that evolutionary change is not occurring. In reality, however, populations rarely achieve equilibrium, though in large natural populations with little migration and negligible natural selection, the Hardy-Weinberg equilibrium may be nearly approximated for certain genes. Sometimes, when researchers experimentally examine allele and genotype frequencies for one or more genes in a given species, they discover that the frequencies are not in Hardy-Weinberg equilibrium. In such cases, they assume that one or more of the conditions are being violated—in other words, mechanisms of evolutionary change are affecting the population. Conservation biologists and wildlife managers may wish to determine why such disequilibrium has occurred because it may affect the future survival of the species.

Crunching the Numbers: A disease-causing allele is present at a frequency of 0.01 (that is, 1%) in a population. Assuming a Hardy-Weinberg equilibrium, what percentage of individuals would be heterozygous carriers?

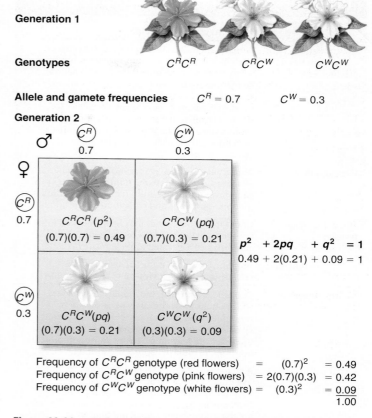

Generation 1

Genotypes $\quad C^R C^R \quad C^R C^W \quad C^W C^W$

Allele and gamete frequencies $\quad C^R = 0.7 \quad C^W = 0.3$

Generation 2

♂ $\quad \widehat{C^R} \quad \widehat{C^W}$
$\quad 0.7 \quad 0.3$

♀

$\widehat{C^R}$
0.7 | $C^R C^R (p^2)$
 $(0.7)(0.7) = 0.49$ | $C^R C^W (pq)$
 $(0.7)(0.3) = 0.21$

$p^2 + 2pq + q^2 = 1$
$0.49 + 2(0.21) + 0.09 = 1$

$\widehat{C^W}$
0.3 | $C^R C^W (pq)$
 $(0.7)(0.3) = 0.21$ | $C^W C^W (q^2)$
 $(0.3)(0.3) = 0.09$

Frequency of $C^R C^R$ genotype (red flowers) $= (0.7)^2 = 0.49$
Frequency of $C^R C^W$ genotype (pink flowers) $= 2(0.7)(0.3) = 0.42$
Frequency of $C^W C^W$ genotype (white flowers) $= (0.3)^2 = \underline{0.09}$
1.00

Figure 19.11 **Calculating allele and genotype frequencies with the Hardy-Weinberg equation.** A population of four-o'clock plants has allele and gamete frequencies of 0.7 for the C^R allele and 0.3 for the C^W allele. Knowing the allele frequencies allows us to calculate the genotype frequencies in the population.

✓ **Concept Check:** *What would be the frequency of pink flowers in a population in which the allele frequency of C^R is 0.4 and the population is in Hardy-Weinberg equilibrium? Assume that C^R and C^W are the only two alleles.*

Microevolution Involves Changes in Allele Frequencies from One Generation to the Next

The term **microevolution** is used to describe changes in a population's gene pool, such as changes in allele frequencies, from generation to generation. What causes microevolution to happen? Such change is rooted in two related phenomena (**Table 19.4**). First, the introduction of new genetic variation into a population is one essential aspect of microevolution. New alleles of preexisting genes arise by random mutation and, as discussed in Chapters 17 and 21, new genes can be introduced into a population by gene duplication and horizontal gene transfer. Such changes, albeit rare, provide a continuous source of new variation to populations. In 1926, the Russian geneticist Sergei Chetverikov was the first to suggest that random mutations are the raw material for evolution. However, due to their low rate of occurrence, mutations by

Table 19.4	**Factors That Govern Microevolution**
Sources of new genetic variation*	
New mutations within genes that produce new alleles	Random mutations within pre-existing genes introduce new alleles into populations, but at a very low rate. New mutations may be neutral, deleterious, or beneficial. Because mutations are rare, the change from one generation to the next is generally very small. For alleles to rise to a significant percentage in a population, evolutionary mechanisms, such as natural selection, genetic drift, and migration, must operate on them.
Gene duplication	Abnormal crossover events and transposable elements may increase the number of copies of a gene. Over time, the additional copies accumulate random mutations and constitute a gene family.
Horizontal gene transfer	Genes from one species may be introduced into another species. The transferred gene may be acted on by evolutionary mechanisms.
Evolutionary mechanisms that alter the frequencies of existing genetic variation	
Natural selection	The process in which individuals that possess certain traits are more likely to survive and reproduce than individuals without those traits. Over the course of many generations, beneficial traits that are heritable become more common and detrimental traits become less common.
Genetic drift	A change in genetic variation from generation to generation due to random chance. Allele frequencies may change as a matter of chance from one generation to the next. Genetic drift has a greater influence in a small population.
Migration	Migration can occur between two populations that have different allele frequencies. The introduction of migrants into a recipient population may change the allele frequencies of that population.
Nonrandom mating	The phenomenon in which individuals select mates based on their phenotypes or genetic lineage. This alters the relative proportion of homozygotes and heterozygotes that is predicted by the Hardy-Weinberg equation, but it does not change allele frequencies.

*These are examples that affect single genes. Other events, such as crossing over, independent assortment, and changes in chromosome structure and number, may alter the genetic variation among many genes.

19.3 Reviewing the Concepts

- Population genetics is the study of genes and genotypes in a population. A population is a group of individuals of the same species that occupy the same environment and can interbreed. All of the alleles for every gene in a population constitute a gene pool.
- Polymorphism, which is very common in nearly all populations, refers to two or more variants of a character in a population. A monomorphic gene exists as a single allele (>99%) in a population (Figure 19.10).
- Allele frequency is the number of copies of a specific allele divided by the total number of all alleles in a population. Genotype frequency is the number of individuals with a given genotype divided by the total number of individuals in a population.
- The Hardy-Weinberg equation ($p^2 + 2pq + q^2 = 1$) predicts that allele and genotype frequencies will remain in equilibrium if no new mutations are formed, no natural selection occurs, the population size is very large, migration does not occur, and mating is random (Figure 19.11).
- Sources of new genetic variation include random gene mutations, gene duplications, and horizontal gene transfer. Natural selection, genetic drift, migration, and nonrandom mating may alter allele and genotype frequencies and cause a population to evolve (Table 19.4).

19.3 Testing Your Knowledge

1. The frequency of individuals in a population that exhibit a rare recessive disorder is 0.0025. The value of 0.0025 is an example of
   a. an allele frequency.
   b. a genotype frequency.
   c. a phenotype frequency.
   d. all of the above.
   e. both b and c.

2. A Hardy-Weinberg equilibrium assumes
   a. a very large population with no random fluctuations (no genetic drift).
   b. no natural selection.
   c. random mating.
   d. no new mutations.
   e. all of the above.

themselves do not have a major effect in changing allele frequencies in a population over time. They do not significantly disrupt a Hardy-Weinberg equilibrium.

The second phenomenon required for evolution to occur is one or more mechanisms that alter the prevalence of a given allele or genotype in a population. These mechanisms are natural selection, genetic drift, migration, and nonrandom mating (see Table 19.4). Over the course of many generations, these mechanisms may promote widespread genetic changes in a population. In the remainder of this chapter, we will examine how natural selection, genetic drift, migration, and nonrandom mating affect genetic variation from one generation to the next.

19.4 Natural Selection

Learning Outcomes:

1. Explain how natural selection results in a population that is better adapted to its environment and more successful at reproduction.
2. Calculate the fitness values of given genotypes.
3. Compare and contrast four different types of natural selection.
4. Define sexual selection and distinguish between intrasexual and intersexual selection.

As discussed earlier in this chapter, natural selection is the process in which individuals with certain heritable traits tend to survive and reproduce at higher rates than those without those traits. As a result, favorable heritable traits become more common, while detrimental heritable traits become less common in a population over many generations. Keep in mind that natural selection itself is not evolution. Rather it is a key mechanism that causes evolution to happen. Over time, natural selection results in **adaptations**—changes in populations of living organisms that increase their ability to survive and reproduce in a particular environment. In this section, we will examine various ways that natural selection produces such adaptations.

Natural Selection Favors Individuals with Greater Reproductive Success

Reproductive success is the likelihood of an individual contributing fertile offspring to the next generation. Natural selection occurs because some individuals in a population have greater reproductive success than other individuals. Those individuals having heritable traits that favor reproductive success are more likely to pass such traits to their offspring. Reproductive success is commonly attributed to two categories of traits:

1. Certain characteristics make organisms better adapted to their environment and therefore more likely to survive to reproductive age. Therefore, natural selection favors individuals with characteristics that provide a survival advantage.

2. Reproductive success may involve traits that are directly associated with reproduction, such as the abilities to find a mate and produce viable gametes and offspring. Traits that enhance the ability of individuals to reproduce, such as brightly colored plumage in male birds, are often subject to natural selection.

A modern description of the principles of natural selection can relate our knowledge of molecular genetics to the process of evolution:

1. Within a population, allelic variation arises from random mutations that cause differences in DNA sequences. A mutation that creates a new allele may alter the amino acid sequence of the encoded protein. This, in turn, may alter the function of the protein.

2. Some alleles encode proteins that enhance an individual's survival or reproductive capability over other members of the population. For example, an allele may produce a protein that is more efficient at a higher temperature, conferring on the individual a greater probability of survival in a hot climate.

3. Individuals with beneficial alleles are more likely to survive and reproduce and thereby contribute their alleles to the gene pool of the next generation.

4. Over the course of many generations, allele frequencies of many different genes may change through natural selection, thereby significantly altering the characteristics of a

population. The net result of natural selection is a population that is better adapted to its environment and more successful at reproduction.

Fitness Is a Quantitative Measure of Reproductive Success

To continue our discussion of natural selection, we need to consider the concept of **fitness,** which is the relative likelihood that one genotype will contribute to the gene pool of the next generation compared with other genotypes. Although this property often correlates with physical fitness, the two ideas should not be confused. Fitness is a measure of reproductive success. An extremely fertile individual may have a higher fitness than a less fertile individual that appears more physically fit.

To examine fitness, let's consider an example of a hypothetical gene existing in A and a alleles. We assign fitness values to each of the three possible genotypes according to their relative reproductive success. For example, let's suppose the average reproductive successes of the three genotypes are

AA produces 5 offspring

Aa produces 4 offspring

aa produces 1 offspring

By convention, the genotype with the highest reproductive success is given a fitness value of 1.0. Fitness values are denoted by the variable w. The fitness values of the other genotypes are assigned values relative to this 1.0 value.

Fitness of AA: $w_{AA} = 1.0$

Fitness of Aa: $w_{Aa} = 4/5 = 0.8$

Fitness of aa: $w_{aa} = 1/5 = 0.2$

Variation in fitness occurs because certain genotypes result in individuals that have greater reproductive success than other genotypes.

Natural Selection Follows Different Patterns

By studying species in their native environments, population geneticists have discovered that natural selection can occur in several ways. In most of the examples described next, natural selection leads to adaptations in which certain members of a species are more likely to survive to reproductive age.

Directional Selection   During **directional selection,** individuals at one extreme of a phenotypic range have greater reproductive success in a particular environment. Different phenomena may initiate the process of directional selection. A common reason for directional selection is that a population may be exposed to a prolonged change in its living environment. Under the new environmental conditions, the relative fitness values may change to favor one genotype, which will promote the elimination of other genotypes. As an example, let's suppose a population of finches on a mainland already has genetic variation that affects beak size (refer back to Figure 19.2). A small number of birds migrate to an island where the seeds are generally larger than on the mainland. In this new environment, birds with larger beaks have a higher fitness because they are better able to crack open the larger seeds and thereby survive to reproduce. Over the course of many generations, directional selection produces a population of birds carrying alleles that promote larger beak size.

Another way that directional selection may arise is that a new allele may be introduced into a population by mutation, and the new allele may confer a higher fitness in individuals that carry it (Figure 19.12). What are the long-term effects of directional selection? If the homozygote carrying the favored allele has the highest fitness value, directional selection may cause this favored allele to eventually predominate in the population, perhaps even leading to a monomorphic gene.

Stabilizing Selection   A type of natural selection called **stabilizing selection** favors the survival of individuals with intermediate phenotypes and selects against those with extreme phenotypes. Stabilizing selection tends to decrease genetic diversity, because it eliminates alleles that cause extreme phenotypes. An example

of stabilizing selection involves clutch size (number of eggs laid) in birds, which was first studied by British biologist David Lack in 1947. Under stabilizing selection, birds that lay too many or too few eggs per nest have lower fitness values than do those that lay an intermediate number. When a bird lays too many eggs, many offspring die due to inadequate parental care and food. In addition, the strain on the parents themselves may decrease their likelihood of survival and consequently their ability to produce more offspring. Having too few offspring, however, does not contribute many individuals to the next generation. Therefore, the most successful parents are those that produce an intermediate clutch size. In the 1980s, Swedish evolutionary biologist Lars Gustafsson and his colleagues examined the phenomenon of stabilizing selection in the collared flycatcher (*Ficedula albicollis*) on the Swedish island of Gotland. They discovered that Lack's hypothesis concerning an optimal clutch size appears to be true for this species (Figure 19.13).

Diversifying Selection   **Diversifying selection** (also known as disruptive selection) favors the survival of two or more different genotypes that produce different phenotypes. In diversifying

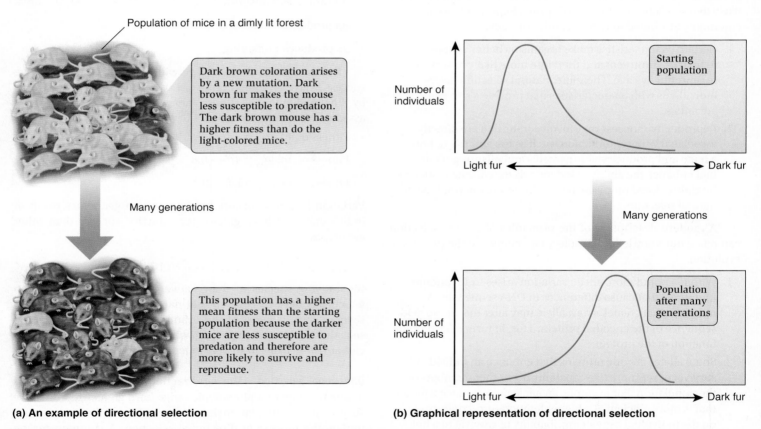

Population of mice in a dimly lit forest

Dark brown coloration arises by a new mutation. Dark brown fur makes the mouse less susceptible to predation. The dark brown mouse has a higher fitness than do the light-colored mice.

Many generations

This population has a higher mean fitness than the starting population because the darker mice are less susceptible to predation and therefore are more likely to survive and reproduce.

(a) An example of directional selection

Number of individuals

Light fur ⟷ Dark fur

Starting population

Many generations

Number of individuals

Light fur ⟷ Dark fur

Population after many generations

(b) Graphical representation of directional selection

Figure 19.12 **Directional selection.** This pattern of natural selection selects for one extreme of a phenotype that confers the highest fitness in the population's environment. **(a)** In this example, a mutation causing darker fur arises in a population of mice. This new genotype confers higher fitness, because mice with darker fur can evade predators and are more likely to survive and reproduce. Over many generations, directional selection favors the prevalence of individuals with darker fur. **(b)** These graphs show the change in fur color phenotypes before and after directional selection.

Concept Check: *Let's suppose the climate on an island abruptly changed such that the average temperature was 10°C higher. The climate change is permanent. How would directional selection affect the genetic diversity in a population of mice on the island (1) over the short run and (2) over the long run?*

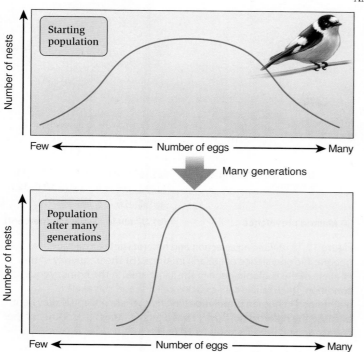

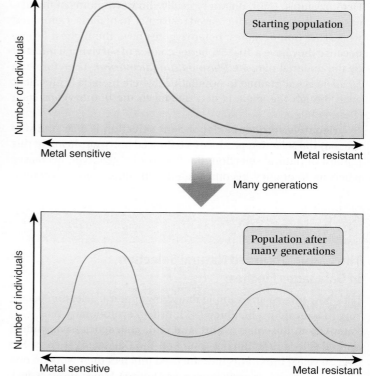

Figure 19.13 **Stabilizing selection.** In this pattern of natural selection, the extremes of a phenotypic distribution are selected against. Those individuals with intermediate traits have the highest fitness. These graphs show the results of stabilizing selection on clutch size in a population of collared flycatchers (*Ficedula albicollis*). This process results in a population with less diversity and more uniform traits.

Concept Check: *Why does stabilizing selection decrease genetic diversity?*

selection, the fitness values of a particular genotype are higher in one environment and lower in a different one, whereas the fitness values of the second genotype vary in an opposite manner. Diversifying selection is likely to occur in populations that occupy heterogeneous environments, so some members of the species are more likely to survive in each type of environmental condition.

An example of diversifying selection involves colonial bentgrass (*Agrostis capillaris*) (**Figure 19.14**). In certain locations where this grass is found, such as near abandoned mines in Wales, places occur where the soil is contaminated with high levels of heavy metals due to mining. The relatively recent metal

Biology Principle

Populations of Organisms Evolve from One Generation to the Next

In this example, the frequencies of metal-resistant alleles become more prevalent when populations of *Agrostis capillaris* are exposed to toxic metals in the soil.

(a) Growth of *Agrostis capillaris* on contaminated soil

Figure 19.14 **Diversifying selection.** This pattern of natural selection selects for two different phenotypes, each of which is most fit in a particular environment. **(a)** In this example, random mutations have resulted in metal-resistant alleles in colonial bentgrass (*Agrostis capillaris*) that allow it to grow on contaminated soil. In uncontaminated soils, the grass does not show metal tolerance. The existence of both metal-resistant and metal-sensitive alleles in the population is an example of diversifying selection due to heterogeneous environments. **(b)** Graphs showing the change in phenotypes in this bentgrass population before and after diversifying selection.

(b) Graphical representation of disruptive selection

contamination has selected for the proliferation of mutant strains of *A. capillaris* that are tolerant of the heavy metals (Figure 19.14a). Such genetic changes enable these mutant strains to grow on contaminated soil but tend to inhibit their growth on normal, noncontaminated soil. These metal-resistant plants often grow on contaminated sites that are close to plants that grow on uncontaminated land and do not show metal tolerance.

Balancing Selection   Contrary to a popular misconception, natural selection does not always cause the elimination of "weaker" or less-fit alleles. **Balancing selection** is a type of natural selection that maintains genetic diversity in a population. Over many generations, balancing selection results in a **balanced polymorphism,** in which two or more alleles are kept in balance and therefore are maintained in a population over many generations.

How does balancing selection maintain a polymorphism? Population geneticists have identified two common ways that balancing selection occurs. First, for genetic variation involving a single gene, balancing selection can favor the heterozygote over either corresponding homozygote. This situation is called **heterozygote advantage.** Heterozygote advantage sometimes explains the persistence of alleles that are deleterious in a homozygous condition.

A classic example of heterozygote advantage involves the H^S allele of the human β-globin gene. A homozygous $H^S H^S$ individual has sickle cell disease, which causes the red blood cells to have a deformed sickle shape. Sickle-shaped cells deliver less oxygen to the body's tissues and can block the flow of blood through the vessels. The $H^S H^S$ homozygote has a lower fitness than a homozygote with two copies of the more common β-globin allele, $H^A H^A$. Heterozygotes, $H^A H^S$, do not typically show symptoms of the disease, but they have an increased resistance to malaria. Compared with $H^A H^A$ homozygotes, heterozygotes have the highest fitness because they have a 10–15% better chance of surviving if infected by the malarial parasite *Plasmodium falciparum*. Therefore, the H^S allele is maintained in populations where malaria is prevalent even though the allele is detrimental in the homozygous state (Figure 19.15).

Negative frequency-dependent selection is a second way that natural selection produces a balanced polymorphism. In this pattern of natural selection, the fitness of a genotype decreases when its frequency becomes higher. In other words, common

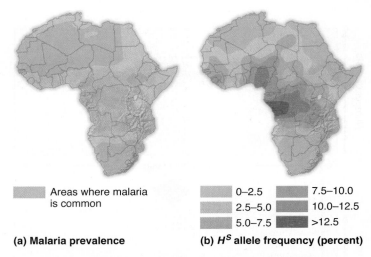

Areas where malaria is common		0–2.5	7.5–10.0
		2.5–5.0	10.0–12.5
		5.0–7.5	>12.5

(a) Malaria prevalence   **(b) H^S allele frequency (percent)**

Figure 19.15   Balancing selection and heterozygote advantage. (a) The geographic prevalence of malaria in Africa. **(b)** The frequency of the H^S allele of the β-globin gene in the same area. In the homozygous condition, the H^S allele causes sickle cell disease. This allele is maintained in human populations in areas where malaria is prevalent, because the heterozygote ($H^A H^S$) has a higher fitness than either of the corresponding homozygotes ($H^A H^A$ or $H^S H^S$).

Concept Check: *If malaria was eradicated, what would you expect to happen to the frequencies of the H^A and H^S alleles over the long run?*

individuals have a lower fitness, and rare individuals have a higher fitness. Therefore, common individuals are less likely to reproduce, whereas rare individuals are more likely to reproduce, thereby producing a balanced polymorphism in which no genotype becomes too rare or too common.

Negative frequency-dependent selection is thought to maintain polymorphisms among species that are preyed upon by predators. Research has shown that certain predators form a mental "search image" for their prey, which is usually based on the common type of prey in an area. A prey that exhibits a rare polymorphism that affects its appearance is less likely to be recognized by the predator. For example, a prey that is a different color from most other members of its species may not be readily recognized by the predator. Such relatively rare organisms are subject to a lower rate of predation. This type of selection maintains polymorphism among certain prey.

FEATURE INVESTIGATION

The Grants Observed Natural Selection in Galápagos Finches

Let's now turn to an example that shows natural selection occurring as a recent event. Since 1973, British evolutionary biologists Peter Grant, Rosemary Grant, and their colleagues have studied natural selection in finches found on the Galápagos Islands. For over 30 years, the Grants have focused much of their work on one of the Galápagos Islands known as Daphne Major (Figure 19.16a). This small island (0.34 km²) has a moderate degree of isolation

(it is 8 km from the nearest island), an undisturbed habitat, and a resident population of *Geospiza fortis*, the medium ground finch (Figure 19.16b).

To study natural selection, the Grants observed various traits in finches over the course of many years. One trait they observed is beak size. The medium ground finch has a relatively small crushing beak, allowing it to more easily feed on small, tender

Populations of Organisms Evolve from One Generation to the Next

On this island, the Grants analyzed how beak size may change from one generation to the next.

(a) Daphne Major   **(b) Medium ground finch**

Figure 19.16 Daphne Major and a resident finch. **(a)** Daphne Major, one of the Galápagos Islands. **(b)** One of the medium ground finches (*Geospiza fortis*) that populate this island.

seeds (see Table 19.1). The Grants quantified beak size among the medium ground finches of Daphne Major by carefully measuring beak depth—a measurement of the beak from top to bottom (**Figure 19.17**). The small size of the island made it possible for them to measure a large percentage of birds and their offspring. During the course of their studies, they compared the beak depths of parents and offspring by examining many broods over several years and found that the depth of the beak was transmitted from

parents to offspring, indicating that differences in beak depths are due to genetic differences in the population. In other words, they found that beak depth was a heritable trait.

By measuring many birds every year, the Grants were able to assemble a detailed portrait of natural selection in action. In the study shown in Figure 19.17, they measured beak depth from 1976 to 1978. In the wet year of 1976, the plants of Daphne Major produced an abundance of the small, tender seeds that these finches could easily eat. However, a severe drought occurred in 1977. During this year, the plants on Daphne Major tended to produce few of the smaller seeds, which the finches rapidly consumed. Therefore, the finches resorted to eating larger, drier seeds, which are harder to crush. As a result, birds with larger beaks were more likely to survive and reproduce because they were better at breaking open the large seeds. As shown in the data, the average beak depth of birds in the population increased substantially, from 8.8 mm in predrought offspring to 9.8 mm in postdrought offspring. How do we explain these results? Birds with larger beaks were more likely to survive and pass this trait to their offspring. Overall, these results illustrate the power of natural selection to alter the features of a trait—in this case, beak depth—in a given population over time. This is an example of directional selection.

Experimental Questions

1. What features of Daphne Major made it a suitable field site for studying the effects of natural selection?

2. Why is beak depth in finches a good trait for a study of natural selection? What environmental conditions were important in allowing the Grants to collect information concerning natural selection?

3. What were the results of the Grants' study following the drought in 1977? What effect did these results have on ideas regarding evolution?

Figure 19.17 The Grants' investigation of natural selection among the medium ground finch.

HYPOTHESIS Dry conditions produce larger seeds and may result in larger beaks in succeeding generations of *Geospiza fortis* due to natural selection.

KEY MATERIALS A population of *G. fortis* on the Galápagos Island called Daphne Major.

	Experimental level	Conceptual level
1 In 1976, measure beak depth in parents and offspring of the species *G. fortis*.	Capture birds and measure beak depth. 	This is a way to measure a trait that may be subject to natural selection.
2 Repeat the procedure on offspring that were born in 1978 and had reached mature size. A drought had occurred in 1977 that caused plants on the island to produce mostly large dry seeds and relatively few small seeds.	Capture birds and measure beak depth. 	This is a way to measure a trait that may be subject to natural selection.

3 THE DATA

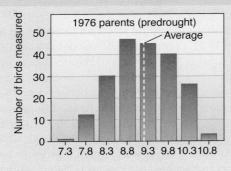

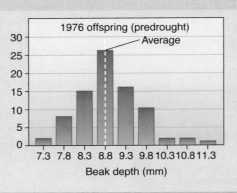

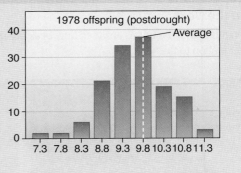

Beak depth (mm)

4 CONCLUSION Because a drought produced larger seeds, birds with larger beaks were more likely to survive and reproduce. The process of natural selection produced postdrought offspring that had larger beaks compared to predrought offspring.

5 SOURCE Grant, B. Rosemary, and Grant, Peter R. 2003. What Darwin's Finches Can Teach Us about the Evolutionary Origin and Regulation of Biodiversity. *Bioscience* 53:965–975.

Sexual Selection Is a Type of Natural Selection Pertaining to Traits That Are Directly Involved with Reproduction

Thus far, we have largely focused on examples of natural selection that produce adaptations for survival in particular environments. Now let's turn our attention to a form of natural selection, called **sexual selection,** in which individuals with certain traits are more likely to engage in successful reproduction than other individuals. Darwin originally described sexual selection as "the advantage that certain individuals have over others of the same sex and species solely with respect to reproduction."

In many species of animals, sexual selection affects the characteristics of males more intensely than those of females. Unlike females, which tend to be fairly uniform in their reproductive success, male success tends to be more variable, with some males mating with many females and others not mating at all. Sexual selection results in the evolution of traits, called secondary sex characteristics, that favor reproductive success. The process can result in **sexual dimorphism**—a significant difference between the appearances of the two sexes within a species.

Sexual selection operates in one of two ways.

- In **intrasexual selection,** members of one sex, usually males, directly compete with each other for the opportunity to mate with individuals of the opposite sex. Examples of traits that result from intrasexual selection in animals include horns in male sheep, antlers in male moose, and the enlarged claw of male fiddler crabs (Figure 19.18a). In fiddler crabs (*Uca paradussumieri*), males enter the burrows of females that are ready to mate. If another male attempts to enter the burrow, the male already inside stands in the burrow shaft and blocks the entrance with his enlarged claw. Males with the largest claws are more likely to be successful at driving off their rivals and being able to mate and therefore more likely to pass on their genes to future generations.

- In **intersexual selection,** also called mate choice, members of one sex, usually females, choose their mates from individuals of the other sex on the basis of certain desirable characteristics. This type of sexual selection often results in showy characteristics in males. Figure 19.18b shows a classic example that involves the Indian peafowl (*Pavo cristatus*). Male peacocks have long and brightly colored tail feathers, which they fan out as a mating behavior. Female peahens select among males based on feather color and pattern as well as the physical prowess of the display.

Many animals have secondary sexual characteristics, and evolutionary biologists generally agree that sexual selection is responsible for such traits. But why should males compete, and why should females be choosy? Researchers have proposed various hypotheses to explain the underlying mechanisms. One possible reason is related to the different roles that males and females play in the nurturing of offspring. In some animal species, the female is the primary caregiver, whereas the male plays a minor role. In such species, mating behavior may influence the fitness of both males and females. Males increase their fitness by mating with multiple females. This increases their likelihood of passing their genes on to the next generation. By comparison, females may produce relatively fewer offspring, and their reproductive success may not be limited by the number of available males. In these circumstances, females will have higher fitness if they choose males that are good defenders of their territory and have alleles that confer a survival advantage to their offspring.

(a) Intrasexual selection

(b) Intersexual selection

Figure 19.18 Examples of the results of sexual selection, a type of natural selection. (a) An example of intrasexual selection. The enlarged claw of the male fiddler crab is used in direct male-to-male competition. In this photograph, a male inside a burrow is extending its claw out of the burrow to prevent another male from entering and mating with the female. **(b)** An example of intersexual selection. Female peahens choose male peacocks based on the males' colorful and long tail feathers and the robustness of their display.

✓ **Concept Check:** *Male birds of many species have loud and elaborate courtship songs. Is this likely to be the result of intersexual or intrasexual selection? Explain.*

19.4 Reviewing the Concepts

- Natural selection is the process in which individuals with certain heritable traits that favor survival and reproduction tend to become more prevalent in a population. Fitness, the relative likelihood that a genotype will contribute to the gene pool of the next generation, is a measure of reproductive success.
- Directional selection is the process in which one extreme of a phenotypic distribution is favored (Figure 19.12).
- Stabilizing selection is the process in which an intermediate phenotype is favored (Figure 19.13).
- Diversifying selection is the process in which two or more phenotypes are favored. An example is a population that occupies a diverse environment (Figure 19.14).
- Balancing selection maintains genetic polymorphism in a population. Examples include heterozygote advantage and negative frequency-dependent selection (Figure 19.15).
- A study by the Grants showed natural selection occurring in a population of finches (Figures 19.16, 19.17).
- Sexual selection is a form of natural selection in which individuals with certain traits are more likely than others to engage in successful mating.
- In intrasexual selection, members of one sex compete with each other for the opportunity to mate with individuals of the opposite sex. In intersexual selection, members of one sex choose their mates on the basis of certain desirable characteristics (Figure 19.18).

19.4 Testing Your Knowledge

1. In a population of fish, body coloration varies from a light shade, almost white, to a very dark shade of green. Changes in the environment that result in decreased predation of individuals with the lightest coloration is an example of _____ selection.
   a. diversifying
   b. stabilizing
   c. directional
   d. balancing

2. Considering the same population of fish described in the previous question, if the stream environment included several areas of sandy, light-colored bottom areas and a lot of dark-colored vegetation, both the light- and dark-colored fish would have selective advantage and increased survival in certain places. This type of scenario could explain the occurrence of which type of natural selection?
   a. diversifying
   b. stabilizing
   c. directional
   d. balancing

3. The enlarged claw of male fiddler crabs is an example of
   a. intrasexual selection.
   b. intersexual selection.
   c. both intrasexual and intersexual selection.
   d. neither intrasexual or intersexual selection.

19.5 Genetic Drift

Learning Outcomes:

1. Define genetic drift and explain its effects on allele frequencies over time.
2. Compare and contrast the bottleneck and founder effects.
3. Explain how neutral mutations can spread through a population.

Thus far, we have focused on natural selection as a mechanism that promotes widespread genetic changes in a population. Let's now turn our attention to a second important way the gene pool of a population can change. In the 1930s, Sewall Wright played a large role in developing the concept of **genetic drift** (also called random genetic drift), which refers to changes in allele frequencies due to random chance. The term genetic drift is derived from the observation that allele frequencies may "drift" randomly from generation to generation as a matter of chance.

Changes in allele frequencies due to genetic drift happen regardless of the fitness of individuals that carry those alleles. For example, an individual with a high fitness value may, by chance, not encounter a member of the opposite sex. Likewise, random chance can influence which alleles happen to be found in the gametes that fuse with each other in a successful fertilization. In this section, we will examine how genetic drift alters allele frequencies in populations.

Genetic Drift Has a Greater Effect in Small Populations

What are the effects of genetic drift? Over the long run, genetic drift favors either the elimination or the fixation of an allele, that is, when its frequency reaches 0% or 100% in a population, respectively. However, the number of generations it takes for an allele to be lost or fixed greatly depends on the population size. Figure 19.19 illustrates the potential consequences of genetic drift in one large ($N = 1,000$) and two small ($N = 10$) populations. This simulation involves the frequency of hypothetical B and b alleles of a gene for fur color in a population of mice—B is the black allele, and b is the white allele.

At the beginning of this hypothetical simulation, which runs for 50 generations, all three populations had identical allele frequencies: $B = 0.5$ and $b = 0.5$. In the small populations, the allele frequencies fluctuated substantially from generation to generation. Eventually, in one population, the b allele was eliminated; in another, it was fixed at 100%. These small populations then consist of only black mice or white mice, respectively. At this point, the gene has become monomorphic and cannot change any further. By comparison, the frequencies of B and b in the large population fluctuated much less. As discussed in your statistics primer

at the textbook website, the relative effect of random chance, also termed random sampling error, is much smaller when the sample size is large. Nevertheless, genetic drift can eventually lead to allele elimination or fixation even in large populations, but this will take many more generations to occur than it does in small populations.

In nature, genetic drift may rapidly alter allele frequencies when the size of a population dramatically decreases. Two examples of this phenomenon are the bottleneck effect and the founder effect, which are described next.

Bottleneck Effect A population can be dramatically reduced in size by events such as earthquakes, floods, drought, and human destruction of habitat. These occurrences may eliminate most members of the population without regard to their genetic composition. The population is said to have passed through a bottleneck. The change in allele frequencies of the resulting population due to genetic drift is called the **bottleneck effect.** Some alleles may be overrepresented, whereas others may even be eliminated. Such changes may happen for two reasons. First, the surviving members may have allele frequencies that differ from those of the original population that was much larger. Second, as we saw in Figure 19.19, genetic drift acts more quickly to reduce genetic variation when the population size is small. Eventually, a population that has gone through a bottleneck may regain its original size. However, the new population is likely to have less genetic variation than the original one.

A hypothetical example of the bottleneck effect is shown with a population of frogs in Figure 19.20. In this example, a starting population of frogs is found in three phenotypes: yellow, dark green, and striped. Due to a bottleneck caused by a drought, the dark green variety is lost from the population.

As a real-life example, the Northern elephant seal (*Mirounga angustirostris*) has lost much of its genetic variation. This was caused by a bottleneck effect in which the population decreased

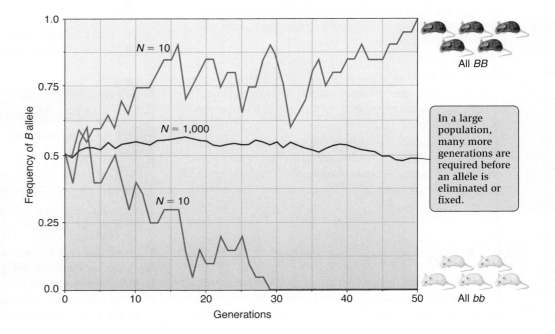

Figure 19.19 Genetic drift and population size. This graph shows three hypothetical simulations of genetic drift and their effects on small and large populations of black (B allele) and white (b allele) mice. In all cases, the starting allele frequencies are $B = 0.5$ and $b = 0.5$. The red lines illustrate two populations of mice in which $N = 10$; the blue line shows a population in which $N = 1,000$.

In a large population, many more generations are required before an allele is eliminated or fixed.

Biology Principle

Populations of Organisms Evolve from One Generation to the Next

Genetic drift randomly changes allele frequencies and (in the long run) leads to a loss or fixation of an allele.

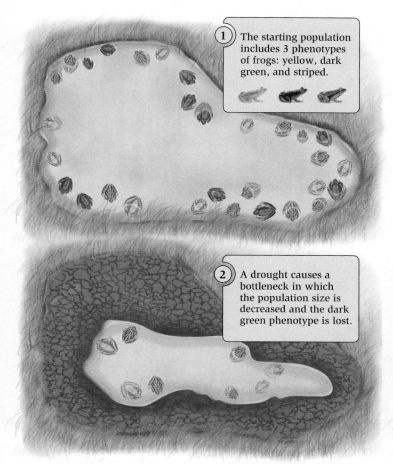

1. The starting population includes 3 phenotypes of frogs: yellow, dark green, and striped.

2. A drought causes a bottleneck in which the population size is decreased and the dark green phenotype is lost.

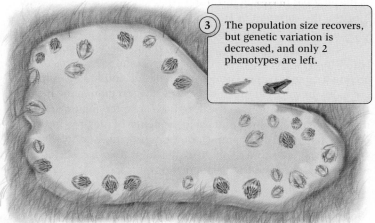

3. The population size recovers, but genetic variation is decreased, and only 2 phenotypes are left.

Figure 19.20 A hypothetical example of the bottleneck effect. This example involves a population of frogs in which a drought dramatically reduced population size, resulting in a bottleneck. The bottleneck reduced the genetic diversity in the population.

Concept Check: *How does the bottleneck effect undermine the efforts of conservation biologists who are trying to save species nearing extinction?*

---

to approximately 20 to 30 surviving members in the 1890s due to hunting. The species has rebounded in numbers to over 100,000, but the bottleneck reduced its genetic variation to very low levels.

Founder Effect   Another common phenomenon in which genetic drift may rapidly alter allele frequencies is the **founder effect.** This occurs when a small group of individuals separates from a larger population and establishes a colony in a new location. For example, a few individuals may migrate from a large population on a continent and become the founders of an island population. The founder effect differs from a bottleneck in that it occurs in a new location, although both effects are related to a reduction in population size. The founder effect has two important consequences. First, the founding population, which is relatively small, is expected to have less genetic variation than the larger original population from which it was derived. Second, as a matter of

chance, the allele frequencies in the founding population may differ markedly from those of the original population.

Population geneticists have studied many examples in which isolated populations were founded via colonization by members of another population. For example, in the 1960s, American geneticist Victor McKusick studied allele frequencies in the Amish of Lancaster County, Pennsylvania. At that time, this group included about 8,000 people, descended from just three couples that immigrated to the U.S. in 1770. Among this population of 8,000, a genetic disease known as the Ellis–van Creveld syndrome (a recessive form of dwarfism) was found at a frequency of 0.07, or 7%. By comparison, this disorder is extremely rare in other human populations, even the population from which the founding members had originated. Evidence suggests that the high frequency in the Lancaster County population can be traced to one couple, one of whom carried the mutated gene that causes the syndrome.

Genetic Drift Plays an Important Role in Promoting Genetic Change

In 1968, Japanese evolutionary biologist Motoo Kimura proposed that much of the DNA sequence variation seen in genes in natural populations is the result of genetic drift rather than natural selection. Genetic drift is a random process that does not preferentially select for any particular allele—it can alter the frequencies of both beneficial and deleterious alleles. Much of the time, genetic drift promotes **neutral variation**—changes in genes and proteins that do not have an effect on reproductive success.

According to Kimura, most variation in DNA sequences is due to the accumulation of neutral mutations that have attained high frequencies in a population via genetic drift. This is called the **neutral theory of evolution.** For example, a new mutation within a gene that changes a glycine codon from GGG to GGC would not affect the amino acid sequence of the encoded protein. Both genotypes are equal in fitness. However, such new mutations can spread throughout a population due to genetic drift (**Figure 19.21**). Kimura agreed with Darwin that natural selection is responsible for adaptive changes in a species during evolution. The long neck of the giraffe is the result of natural selection. His main idea is that much of the variation in DNA sequences is explained by neutral variation rather than adaptive variation.

The sequencing of genomes from many species is consistent with Kimura's theory. When researchers examine changes of the coding sequence within structural genes, nucleotide substitutions are more prevalent in the third base of a codon than in the first or second base. Mutations in the third base are often neutral; that is, they do not change the amino acid sequence of the protein (refer back to Table 10.1). In contrast, random mutations at the first or second base are more likely to be harmful than beneficial and tend to be eliminated from a population.

19.5   Reviewing the Concepts

- Genetic drift involves changes in allele frequencies over time due to chance events. It occurs more rapidly in small populations and leads to either the elimination or the fixation of alleles (Figure 19.19).
- In the bottleneck effect, an environmental event dramatically reduces a population size and the allele frequencies of the resulting population change due to genetic drift (Figure 19.20).
- The founder effect occurs when a small population moves to a new geographic location and genetic drift alters the genetic composition of that population.
- Kimura proposed the neutral theory of evolution in which genetic drift promotes the accumulation of neutral genetic changes that do not affect reproductive success. Much of the variation in DNA sequences in populations appears to be the result of genetic drift rather than natural selection (Figure 19.21).

19.5   Testing Your Knowledge

1. A hurricane kills 98% of a population of cranes. The population eventually rebounds to its original size, but the amount of

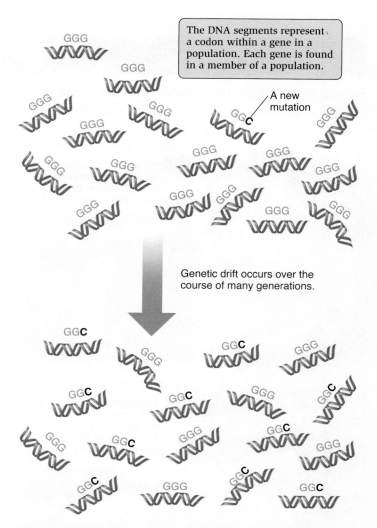

The DNA segments represent a codon within a gene in a population. Each gene is found in a member of a population.

A new mutation

Genetic drift occurs over the course of many generations.

Figure 19.21   Neutral evolution in a population. In this example, a mutation within a gene changes a glycine codon from GGG to GGC, which does not affect the amino acid sequence of the encoded protein. Each gene shown represents a copy of the gene in a member of a population. Over the course of many generations, genetic drift may cause this neutral allele to become prevalent in the population, perhaps even monomorphic.

BioConnections: *Look back at the genetic code described in Table 10.1. Describe three different genetic changes that you would expect to be neutral.*

genetic variation in the rebounded population is significantly less. This is an example of
   a. the founder effect.   **c.** diversifying selection.
   b. the bottleneck effect.   **d.** both a and b.

2. Kimura's proposal regarding neutral mutations differs from Darwinian evolution in that
   a. natural selection does not exist.
   b. most of the genetic variation in a population is due to neutral mutations, which do not affect reproductive success.
   c. neutral variation alters survival and reproductive success.
   d. neutral mutations are not affected by population size.
   e. both b and c.

19.6 Migration and Nonrandom Mating

Learning Outcomes:

1. Describe how gene flow affects genetic variation in neighboring populations.

2. Define inbreeding and explain how it may have detrimental consequences.

Thus far, we have considered how natural selection and genetic drift are key mechanisms that cause evolution to happen. In addition, migration between neighboring populations and nonrandom mating may influence genetic variation and the relative proportions of genotypes. In this section, we will explore how these mechanisms work.

Migration Between Two Populations Tends to Increase Genetic Variation

Earlier in this chapter, we considered the founder effect, in which migration to a new location by a relatively small group can result in a population with an altered genetic composition due to genetic drift. In addition, migration between two different established populations can alter allele frequencies. As an example, let's consider two populations of a particular species of deer that are separated by a mountain range running north and

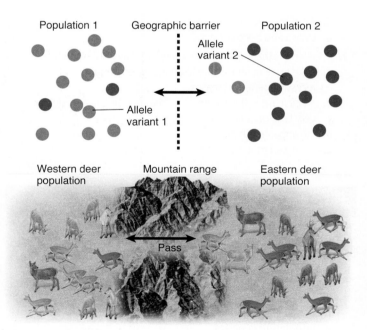

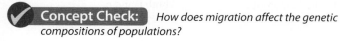

Figure 19.22 **Migration and gene flow.** In this example, two populations of a deer species are separated by a mountain range. On rare occasions, a few deer from one population travel through a narrow pass and become members of the other population. If the two populations differ in regard to genetic variation, this migration will alter the frequencies of alleles in the populations.

✓ **Concept Check:** *How does migration affect the genetic compositions of populations?*

south (**Figure 19.22**). On rare occasions, a few deer from the western population may travel through a narrow pass between the mountains and become members of the eastern population. If the two populations are different with regard to genetic variation, this migration will alter the frequencies of certain alleles in the eastern population. Of course, this migration could occur in the opposite direction as well and would then affect the western population. This transfer of alleles into or out of a population, called **gene flow,** occurs whenever individuals move between populations having different allele frequencies.

What are the consequences of migration? First, migration tends to reduce differences in allele frequencies between neighboring populations. Population geneticists can evaluate the extent of migration between two populations by analyzing the similarities and differences between their allele frequencies. Populations that frequently mix their gene pools via migration tend to have similar allele frequencies, whereas the allele frequencies of isolated populations tend to differ due to the effects of natural selection and genetic drift. Second, migration generally increases genetic diversity within populations. As discussed earlier in this chapter, new mutations are relatively rare events. Therefore, a new mutation may arise in only one population, and migration may then introduce this new allele into a neighboring population.

Nonrandom Mating Affects the Relative Proportion of Homozygotes and Heterozygotes in a Population

As mentioned earlier, one of the conditions required to establish Hardy-Weinberg equilibrium is random mating, which means that members of a population choose their mates irrespective of their genotypes or phenotypes. In many species, including human populations, this condition is violated. Such **nonrandom mating** takes different forms. Assortative mating occurs when individuals with similar phenotypes are more likely to mate. If the similar phenotypes are due to similar genotypes, assortative mating tends to increase the proportion of homozygotes and decrease the proportion of heterozygotes in the population. The opposite situation, where dissimilar phenotypes mate preferentially, causes heterozygosity to increase.

Another form of nonrandom mating involves the choice of mates based on their genetic history rather than their phenotypes. Individuals may choose a mate that is part of the same genetic lineage. The mating of two genetically related individuals, such as cousins, is called **inbreeding.** This sometimes occurs in human societies and is more likely to take place in nature when population size becomes very small.

In the absence of other evolutionary factors, nonrandom mating does not affect allele frequencies in a population. However, it will alter the balance of genotypes predicted by the Hardy-Weinberg equilibrium. As an example, let's consider a human pedigree involving a mating between cousins (**Figure 19.23**). Individuals III-2 and III-3 are cousins and have produced the daughter labeled IV-1. She is said to be inbred, because her parents are genetically related. The parents of an inbred individual have one or more common ancestors. In the pedigree of Figure 19.23, I-2 is the grandfather of both III-2 and III-3.

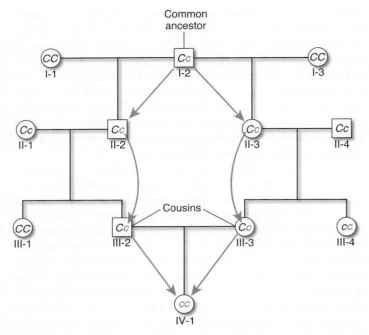

Figure 19.23 **A human pedigree containing inbreeding.** The parents of individual IV-1 are genetically related (cousins), and, therefore, individual IV-1 is inbred. Inbreeding increases the likelihood that an individual will be homozygous for any given gene. The red arrows show how IV-1 could become homozygous by inheriting the same allele (*c*) from the common ancestor (I-2) to both of her parents.

BioConnections: *Many inherited human diseases show a recessive pattern of inheritance (see Table 14.2). Explain whether inbreeding would increase or decrease the likelihood of such diseases.*

Inbreeding increases the relative proportions of homozygotes and decreases the likelihood of heterozygotes in a population. Why does this happen? An inbred individual has a higher chance of being homozygous for any given allele because the same allele for that gene could be inherited twice from a common ancestor. For example, individual I-2 is a heterozygote, *Cc*. The *c* allele could pass from I-2 to II-2 to III-2 and finally to IV-1 (see red lines in Figure 19.23). Likewise, the *c* allele could pass from I-2 to II-3 to III-3 and then to IV-1. Therefore, IV-1 has a chance of being homozygous because she inherited both copies of the *c* allele from a common ancestor to both of her parents. Inbreeding does not favor any particular allele—it does not favor *c* over *C*—but it does increase the likelihood that an individual will be homozygous for any given gene.

Although inbreeding by itself does not affect allele frequencies, it may have negative consequences with regard to recessive alleles. Rare recessive alleles that are harmful in the homozygous condition are found in nearly all populations. Such alleles do not usually pose a problem because heterozygotes carrying a rare recessive allele are also rare, making it very unlikely that two such heterozygotes will mate with each other. However, related individuals share some of their genes, including recessive alleles.

Therefore, if inbreeding occurs, homozygous offspring are more likely to be produced. For example, rare recessive diseases in humans are more frequent when inbreeding occurs.

19.6 Reviewing the Concepts

- Gene flow occurs when individuals migrate between populations with different allele frequencies. It reduces differences in allele frequencies between populations and enhances genetic diversity (Figure 19.22).
- Inbreeding, a form of nonrandom mating in which genetically related individuals have offspring with each other, tends to increase the proportion of homozygotes relative to heterozygotes (Figure 19.23).

19.6 Testing Your Knowledge

1. If the members of one population frequently migrate to a neighboring population and vice versa, which of the following would you expect to be correct?
   a. The two populations would tend to have similar allele frequencies.
   b. The two populations would tend to be more genetically diverse than if no migration had occurred.
   c. The two populations would be more susceptible to genetic drift.
   d. All of the above are correct.
   e. Only a and b are correct.

2. Populations that experience inbreeding may also experience
   a. a decrease in fitness due to an increased frequency of recessive genetic diseases.
   b. an increase in fitness due to increases in heterozygosity.
   c. very little genetic drift.
   d. no apparent change.
   e. increased mutation rates.

Assess and Discuss

Test Yourself

1. A change in one or more heritable characteristics of a population that occurs from one generation to the next is called
   a. natural selection.
   b. sexual selection.
   c. population genetics.
   d. evolution.
   e. inheritance of acquired characteristics.

2. An evolutionary change in which a population of organisms changes its characteristics over many generations in ways that make it better suited to its environment is
   a. natural selection.   d. evolution.
   b. an adaptation.   e. both a and c.
   c. an acquired characteristic.

3. Homology occurs because
   a. different species occupy similar environments.
   b. different species evolved from a common ancestor.
   c. new mutations modify existing structures.
   d. populations evolve from one generation to the next.
   e. both a and b.

4. Vestigial structures are anatomical structures that
   a. have more than one function.
   b. were functional in an ancestor but no longer have a useful function.
   c. look similar in different species but have different functions.
   d. have the same function in different species but have very different appearances.
   e. are all of the above.

5. Which of the following is an example of a developmental homology seen in human embryonic development and other vertebrate species that are not mammals?
   a. gill ridges   d. both a and c
   b. umbilical cord   e. all of the above
   c. tail

6. Population geneticists are interested in the genetic variation in populations. The most common type of genetic change that causes polymorphism in a population is
   a. a deletion of a gene sequence.
   b. a duplication of a region of a gene.
   c. a rearrangement of a gene sequence.
   d. a single-nucleotide substitution.
   e. an inversion of a segment of a chromosome.

7. In the Hardy-Weinberg equation, what portion of the equation would be used to calculate the frequency of individuals that do not exhibit a recessive disease but are carriers of a recessive allele?
   a. q d. q^2
   b. p^2 e. both b and d
   c. $2pq$

8. By itself, which of the following is not likely to have a major influence on allele frequencies?
   a. natural selection   d. inbreeding
   b. genetic drift   e. both c and d
   c. mutation

9. Which of the following statements is correct regarding mutations?
   a. Mutations are not important in evolution.
   b. Mutations provide the source for genetic variation, but other evolutionary factors are more important in determining allele frequencies in a population.
   c. Mutations occur at such a high rate that they promote major changes in the gene pool from one generation to the next.

   d. Mutations are of greater importance in smaller populations than in larger ones.
   e. Mutations are of greater importance in larger populations than in smaller ones.

10. The microevolutionary factor most sensitive to population size is
    a. mutation.   d. genetic drift.
    b. migration.   e. all of the above.
    c. natural selection.

Conceptual Questions

1. What is convergent evolution? How do the pairs of organisms shown in Figure 19.6 support the theory of descent with modification?

2. The percentage of individuals exhibiting a recessive disease in a population is 0.04, which is 4%. Based on a Hardy-Weinberg equilibrium, what percentage of individuals would be expected to be heterozygous carriers?

3. **PRINCIPLES**   A principle of biology is that *populations of organisms evolve from one generation to the next.* Explain how the homologous forelimbs of vertebrates indicate that populations evolve from one generation to the next.

Collaborative Questions

1. The term natural selection is sometimes confused with the term evolution. Discuss the meanings of these two terms. Explain how the terms are different and how they are related to each other.

2. Antibiotics are commonly used to combat bacterial and fungal infections. During the past several decades, however, antibiotic-resistant strains of microorganisms have become alarmingly prevalent. This has undermined the ability of physicians to treat many types of infectious disease. Discuss how the following processes that alter allele frequencies may have contributed to the emergence of antibiotic-resistant strains:
   a. random mutation
   b. genetic drift
   c. natural selection

Online Resource

www.brookerprinciples.com

Stay a step ahead in your studies with animations that bring concepts to life and practice tests to assess your understanding. Your instructor may also recommend the interactive eBook, individualized learning tools, and more.

Origin of Species and Macroevolution

Two different species of zebras. Grevy's zebra (*Equus grevyi*) is shown on the left, and Grant's zebra (*E. quagga boehmi*), which has fewer and thicker stripes, is shown on the right.

Chapter Outline

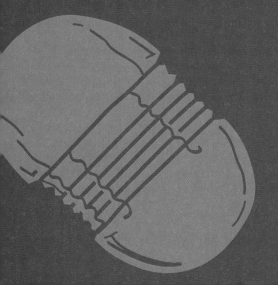

The origin of living organisms has been described by philosophers as the great "mystery of mysteries." Perhaps that is why so many different views have been put forth to explain the existence of living species. At the time of Aristotle (4th century B.C.E.), most people believed that some living organisms came into being by spontaneous generation—the idea that nonliving materials can give rise to living organisms. For example, it was commonly believed that worms and frogs could arise from mud, and mice could come from grain. By comparison, many religious teachings contend that species were divinely made and have remained the same since their creation. In contrast to these ideas, Charles Darwin proposed the scientific theory of evolution by descent with modification.

This chapter provides an exciting way to build on the information that we have considered in previous chapters. In Chapter 18, we examined how the first primitive cells in an RNA world could have evolved into prokaryotic cells and eventually eukaryotes. Chapter 19 surveyed the tenets on which the theory of evolution is built and explored **microevolution**—evolution on a small scale as it relates to allele frequencies in a population. In this chapter, we will consider evolution on a larger scale. **Macroevolution** refers to evolutionary changes that produce new species and groups of species.

To biologists, the concept of a **species** refers to a group of related organisms that share a distinctive set of attributes in nature. Members of the same species share an evolutionary history, which makes them more genetically similar to each other than they are to members of a different species. You may already have an intuitive sense of this concept. It is obvious that zebras and mice are different species. However, as discussed in the first section of this chapter, the distinction between different, closely related species is often blurred in natural environments. Two closely related species may look very similar, as the chapter-opening photo illustrates.

In this chapter, we will also focus on the mechanisms that promote the formation of new species, a phenomenon called **speciation**. Such macroevolution typically occurs by the accumulation of microevolutionary changes, those that occur in single genes. We will also consider how variations in the genes that control development play a role in the evolution of new species.

20.1 Identification of Species

Learning Outcomes:

1. Outline the characteristics that biologists use to distinguish different species.

2. Describe different species concepts.

How many different species are on Earth? The number is astounding. A study done by American biologist E. O. Wilson and colleagues in 1990 estimated the known number of species at approximately 1.4 million. Currently, about 1.3 million species have been identified and catalogued. However, a vast number of species have yet to be classified. This is particularly true among bacteria and archaea, which are difficult to categorize into distinct species. Also, new invertebrate and even vertebrate species are still being found in the far reaches of pristine habitats. Common estimates of the total number of species range from 5 to 50 million!

When studying natural populations, evolutionary biologists are often confronted with situations in which some differences between two populations are apparent, but it is difficult to decide whether the two populations truly represent separate species. When two or more geographically restricted groups of the same species display one or more traits that are somewhat different but not enough to warrant their placement into different species, biologists sometimes classify such groups as **subspecies**. Similarly, many bacterial species are subdivided into **ecotypes**. Each ecotype is a genetically distinct population adapted to its local environment. In this section, we will consider the characteristics that biologists examine when deciding if two groups of organisms constitute different species.

Each Species Is Established Using Characteristics and Histories That Distinguish It from Other Species

As mentioned, a species is a group of organisms that share a distinctive set of attributes in nature. In the case of sexually reproducing species, members of one species usually cannot successfully interbreed with members of other species. Members of the same species share an evolutionary history that is distinct from other species. Although this may seem like a reasonable way to characterize a given species, biologists would agree that distinguishing between species is a more difficult undertaking. What criteria do we use to distinguish species? How many differences must exist between two populations to classify them as different species? Such questions are often difficult to answer.

The characteristics that a biologist uses to identify a species depend, in large part, on the species in question. For example, the traits used to distinguish insect species are quite different from those used to identify different bacterial species. The relatively high level of horizontal gene transfer among bacteria presents special challenges in the grouping of bacterial species. Among bacteria, it is sometimes very difficult and perhaps arbitrary to divide closely related organisms into separate species.

The most commonly used characteristics for identifying species are morphological traits, the ability to interbreed, molecular

features, ecological factors, and evolutionary relationships. A comparison of these concepts will help you appreciate the various approaches that biologists use to identify the bewildering array of species on our planet.

Morphological Traits   One way to establish that a population constitutes a unique species is based on their physical characteristics. Organisms are classified as the same species if their anatomical traits appear to be very similar. Likewise, microorganisms can be classified according to morphological traits at the cellular level. By comparing many different morphological traits, biologists may be able to decide that certain populations constitute a unique species.

Although an analysis of morphological traits is a common way for biologists to establish that a particular group constitutes a species, this approach has drawbacks. First, researchers may have difficulty deciding how many traits to consider. In addition, quantitative traits, such as size and weight, that vary in a continuous way among members of the same species are not easy to analyze. Another drawback is that the degree of dissimilarity that distinguishes different species may not show a simple relationship. The members of the same species sometimes look very different, and conversely, members of different species sometimes look remarkably similar to each other. For example, Figure 20.1a shows two different frogs of the species *Dendrobates tinctorius*, commonly called the dyeing poison frog. This species exists in many different-colored morphs, which are individuals of the same species that have noticeably dissimilar appearances. In contrast, Figure 20.1b shows two different species of frogs, the Northern leopard frog (*Rana pipiens*) and the Southern leopard frog (*Rana utricularia*), which look fairly similar.

Reproductive Isolation   Why would biologists describe two species, such as the Northern leopard frog and Southern leopard frog, as being different if they are morphologically similar? One reason is that biologists have discovered that they are unable to breed with each other in nature. Therefore, a second way of identifying a species is by its ability to interbreed. In the late 1920s, geneticist Theodosius Dobzhansky proposed that each species is reproductively isolated from other species. Such **reproductive isolation** prevents one species from successfully interbreeding with other species. In 1942, German evolutionary biologist Ernst Mayr expanded on the ideas of Dobzhansky to provide a definition of a species. According to Mayr, a key feature of sexually reproducing species is that, in nature, the members of one species have the potential to interbreed with one another to produce viable, fertile offspring but cannot successfully interbreed with members of other species.

Reproductive isolation has been used to distinguish many plant and animal species, especially those that look alike but do not interbreed. Even so, this criterion suffers from four main problems. First, in nature, it may be difficult to determine if two populations are reproductively isolated, particularly if the populations have nonoverlapping geographic ranges. Second, biologists have noted many cases in which two different species can interbreed in nature yet consistently maintain themselves as separate species.

(a) Frogs of the same species

(b) Frogs of different species

Figure 20.1 Difficulties of using morphological traits to identify species. In some cases, members of the same species appear quite different. In other cases, members of different species look very similar. **(a)** Two frogs of the same species, the dyeing poison frog (*Dendrobates tinctorius*). **(b)** Two different species of frog, the Northern leopard frog (*Rana pipiens*, left) and the Southern leopard frog (*Rana utricularia*, right).

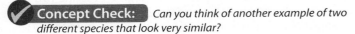 **Concept Check:** *Can you think of another example of two different species that look very similar?*

For example, different species of yucca plants, such as *Yucca pallida* and *Yucca constricta*, do interbreed in nature yet typically maintain populations with distinct characteristics. For this reason, they are viewed as distinct species. A third drawback of reproductive isolation is that it does not apply to asexual species such as bacteria and some species of plants and fungi. Finally, a fourth drawback is that it cannot be applied to extinct species. For these reasons, reproductive isolation has been primarily used to distinguish closely related species of modern animals and plants that reproduce sexually.

Molecular Features   Molecular features are now commonly used to determine if two different populations are different species. Evolutionary biologists often compare DNA sequences within genes, gene order along chromosomes, chromosome structure, and chromosome number in order to identify similarities and differences among different populations. For example, researchers may compare the DNA sequence of the *16S rRNA* gene between different bacterial populations as a way of determining if the two

populations represent different species. When the sequences are very similar, such populations would probably be judged as the same species. However, it may be difficult to draw the line when separating groups into different species. How much difference must be present for species to be considered separate? Is a 2% difference in their genome sequences sufficient to warrant placement into two different species, or do we need a 5% difference?

Ecological Factors   A variety of factors related to an organism's habitat are used to distinguish one species from another. For example, certain species of warblers are distinguished by the habitat in which they forage for food. Some species search the ground for food, others forage in bushes or small trees, and some species primarily forage in tall trees. Such habitat differences are used to distinguish different species that look morphologically similar.

Many bacterial species have been categorized as distinct based on ecological factors. Bacterial cells of the same species are likely to use the same types of resources (such as sugars and vitamins) and grow under the same types of conditions (such as temperature and pH). However, a drawback of this approach is that different groups of bacteria sometimes display very similar growth characteristics, and even the same species may show great variation in the growth conditions it will tolerate.

Evolutionary Relationships   In Chapter 21, we will examine the methods used to produce "evolutionary trees," diagrams that describe the relationships between ancestral species and modern species. In some cases, such relationships are based on an analysis of the fossil record. For example, we will consider how the fossil record was used to construct a tree that shows the ancestors that led to modern horse species. Alternatively, another way of establishing evolutionary relationships is by the analysis of DNA sequences. Researchers obtain samples of cells from different individuals and compare the genes within those cells to see how similar or different they are.

Biologists Have Proposed Different Species Concepts

A **species concept** is a way of defining the concept of a species and/or of providing an approach to distinguish one species from another. However, even Darwin realized the difficulty in defining a species. In 1859, he said, "No one definition [of species] has as yet satisfied all naturalists; yet every naturalist knows vaguely what he means when he speaks of a species." Since 1942, over 20 different species concepts have been proposed by a variety of evolutionary biologists. Let's consider a few of the more common ones.

- Ernst Mayr proposed one of the first species concepts, called the **biological species concept,** which defines a species as a group of individuals whose members have the potential to interbreed with one another in nature to produce viable, fertile offspring but cannot successfully interbreed with members of other species.

- According to the **evolutionary lineage concept** proposed by American paleontologist George Gaylord Simpson in 1961, species should be defined based on the separate evolution of lineages. A **lineage** is a series of species that forms a line of descent, with each new species the direct result of speciation from an immediate ancestral species.

- The **ecological species concept,** described by American evolutionary biologist Leigh Van Valen in 1976, defines each species based on an ecological niche, which is the unique set of habitat resources that a species requires, as well as its influence on the environment and other species.

- In 1998, American zoologist Kevin de Queiroz suggested that there is only a single general species concept, which concurs with Simpson's evolutionary lineage concept and includes all previous concepts. According to de Queiroz's **general lineage concept,** each species is a population of an independently evolving lineage. Each species has evolved from a specific series of ancestors and, as a consequence, forms a group of organisms with a particular set of characteristics. Multiple criteria are used to determine if a population is part of an independent evolutionary lineage, and thus a species, which is distinct from others. Because of its generality, the general lineage concept has received significant support.

20.1 Reviewing the Concepts

- A species is a group of related organisms that shares a distinctive set of attributes in nature. Speciation is the process by which new species are formed. Macroevolution refers to evolutionary changes that produce new species and groups of species.
- Different characteristics, including morphological traits, reproductive isolation, molecular features, ecological factors, and evolutionary relationships, are used to identify species (Figure 20.1).

20.1 Testing Your Knowledge

1. According to Mayr's biological species concept, a species is defined by
   a. ecological factors.
   b. morphological factors.
   c. the lineage to which it belongs.
   d. reproductive isolation.
   e. all of the above.

2. According to de Queiroz's general lineage concept, each species
   a. is a population of an independently evolving lineage.
   b. occupies its own niche.
   c. is reproductively isolated.
   d. is all of the above.
   e. is both a and b.

20.2 Reproductive Isolation

Learning Outcome:

1. Compare and contrast prezygotic and postzygotic isolating mechanisms.

Thus far we have considered various ways of differentiating species. In our discussion, you may have realized that the identification of a species is not always a simple matter. The phenomenon

of reproductive isolation has played a major role in the way biologists study plant and animal species, partly because it identifies a possible mechanism for the process of forming new species. For this reason, much research has been done to try to understand **reproductive isolating mechanisms,** the mechanisms that prevent interbreeding between different species. Why do reproductive isolating mechanisms occur? Populations do not intentionally erect these reproductive barriers. Rather, reproductive isolation is a consequence of genetic changes that usually occur because a species becomes adapted to its own particular environment. The view of evolutionary biologists is that reproductive isolation typically evolves as a by-product of genetic divergence. Over time, as a species evolves its own unique characteristics, some of those traits are likely to prevent breeding with other species.

Reproductive isolating mechanisms fall into two categories: **prezygotic isolating mechanisms,** which prevent the formation of a zygote, and **postzygotic isolating mechanisms,** which block the development of a viable and fertile individual after fertilization has taken place. **Figure 20.2** summarizes some of the more common ways that reproductive isolating mechanisms prevent reproduction between different species. When two species do produce offspring, such an offspring is called an **interspecies hybrid.**

Prezygotic Isolating Mechanisms We will consider five types of prezygotic isolating mechanisms.

1. **Habitat Isolation:** One obvious way to prevent interbreeding is for members of different species to never come in contact with each other. This phenomenon, called habitat isolation, may involve a geographic barrier to interbreeding.

2. **Temporal Isolation:** In temporal isolation, species happen to reproduce at different times of the day or year. In the northeastern U.S., for example, the two most abundant field crickets, *Gryllus veletis* and *Gryllus pennsylvanicus* (spring and fall field crickets, respectively), do not differ in song or habitat and are morphologically very similar (**Figure 20.3**). *G. veletis* matures in the spring, whereas *G. pennsylvanicus* matures in the fall, which minimizes interbreeding between the two species.

3. **Behavioral Isolation:** In the case of animals, mating behavior and anatomy often play key roles in promoting reproductive isolation. An example is found between the western meadowlark (*Sturnella neglecta*) and eastern meadowlark (*Sturnella magna*) (**Figure 20.4**). In the zone of overlap, very little interspecies mating takes place, largely due to differences in their songs, which enable meadowlarks to recognize potential mates as members of their own species.

4. **Mechanical Isolation:** Morphological features such as size or incompatible genitalia prevent two species from interbreeding. For example, male dragonflies use a pair of special appendages to grasp females during copulation. When a male tries to mate with a female of a different species, his grasping appendages do not fit her body shape.

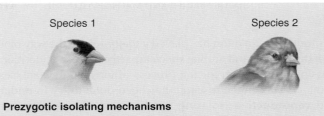

Species 1   Species 2

Prezygotic isolating mechanisms

Habitat isolation: Species occupy different habitats, so they never come in contact with each other.

Temporal isolation: Species have different mating or flowering seasons or times of day or become sexually mature at different times of the year.

Behavioral isolation: Sexual attraction between males and females of different animal species is limited due to differences in behavior or physiology.

Attempted mating

Mechanical isolation: Morphological features such as size and incompatible genitalia prevent 2 members of different species from interbreeding.

Gametic isolation: Gametic transfer takes place, but the gametes fail to unite with each other. This can occur because the male and female gametes fail to attract, because they are unable to fuse, or because the male gametes are inviable in the female reproductive tract of another species. In plants, the pollen of one species usually cannot generate a pollen tube to fertilize the egg cells of another species.

Fertilization

Postzygotic isolating mechanisms

Hybrid inviability: The egg of one species is fertilized by the sperm from another species, but the fertilized egg fails to develop past the early embryonic stages.

Hybrid sterility: An interspecies hybrid survives, but it is sterile. For example, the mule, which is sterile, is produced from a cross between a male donkey (*Equus asinus*) and a female horse (*Equus caballus*).

Hybrid breakdown: The F_1 interspecies hybrid is viable and fertile, but succeeding generations (F_2, and so on) become increasingly inviable. This is usually due to the formation of less-fit genotypes by genetic recombination.

Interspecies hybrid

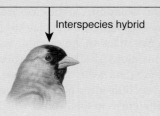

Figure 20.2 **Reproductive isolating mechanisms.** These mechanisms prevent successful breeding between different species. They can occur prior to fertilization (prezygotic) or after fertilization (postzygotic).

BioConnections: *Look back at Figure 19.18b. Is female choice an example of a prezygotic or postzygotic isolating mechanism?*

(a) Spring field cricket (*Gryllus veletis*)   **(b) Fall field cricket (*Gryllus pennsylvanicus*)**

Figure 20.3 **Temporal isolation.** Interbreeding between these two species of crickets does not usually occur because *Gryllus veletis* matures in the spring, whereas *Gryllus pennsylvanicus* matures in the fall.

 Concept Check: *Is this an example of a prezygotic or a postzygotic isolating mechanism?*

Biology Principle

Populations of Organisms Evolve from One Generation to the Next

One of the evolutionary changes that took place in these two species of meadowlarks is that their mating songs became different.

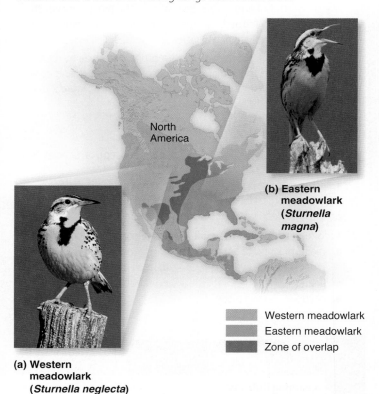

North America

(b) Eastern meadowlark (*Sturnella magna*)

Western meadowlark
Eastern meadowlark
Zone of overlap

(a) Western meadowlark (*Sturnella neglecta*)

Figure 20.4 **Behavioral isolation.** **(a)** The western meadowlark (*Sturnella neglecta*) and **(b)** eastern meadowlark (*Sturnella magna*) are very similar in appearance. The red region in this map shows where the two species' ranges overlap. However, very little interspecies mating takes place due to differences in their songs.

5. **Gametic Isolation:** Two species may attempt to interbreed, but the gametes fail to unite in a successful fertilization event. In flowering plants, gametic isolation is commonly associated with pollination. Plant fertilization is initiated when a pollen grain lands on the stigma of a flower and sprouts a pollen tube that ultimately reaches an egg cell. When pollen is released from a plant, it could be transferred to the stigma of many different plant species. In most cases, when a pollen grain lands on the stigma of a different species, it either fails to generate a pollen tube or the tube does not grow properly and cannot reach the egg cell.

Postzygotic Isolating Mechanisms   Let's now turn to postzygotic mechanisms of reproductive isolation of which there are three common types.

1. **Hybrid Inviability:** This occurs when an egg of one species is fertilized by a sperm from another species, but the fertilized egg cannot develop past early embryonic stages.

2. **Hybrid Sterility:** An interspecies hybrid may be viable but sterile. A classic example of hybrid sterility is the mule, which is produced by a mating between a male donkey (*Equus asinus*) and a female horse (*Equus ferus caballus*) (**Figure 20.5**). All male mules and most female mules are sterile. Why are mules usually sterile? Two reasons explain the sterility. Because the horse has 32 chromosomes per set and

a donkey has 31, a mule inherits 63 chromosomes (32 + 31). Due to the uneven number, not all of the chromosomes can pair evenly. Also, the chromosomes of the horse and donkey have structural differences, which either prevent them from pairing correctly or lead to chromosomal abnormalities if crossing over occurs during meiosis. For these reasons, mules usually produce inviable gametes.

3. **Hybrid Breakdown:** Interspecies hybrids may be viable and fertile, but the subsequent generation(s) may harbor genetic abnormalities that are detrimental. This third mechanism, called hybrid breakdown, can be caused by changes in chromosome structure. The chromosomes of closely related species may have structural differences from each other, such as inversions. In hybrids, a crossover may occur in the region that is inverted in one species but not the other. This will produce gametes with too little or too much genetic material. Such hybrids often have offspring with developmental abnormalities.

Postzygotic isolating mechanisms tend to be uncommon in nature compared with prezygotic mechanisms. Why are postzygotic mechanisms rare? One explanation is they are more costly in terms of energy and resources used. For example, a female mammal would use a large amount of energy to produce an offspring that is sterile. Evolutionary biologists hypothesize that natural selection has favored prezygotic isolating mechanisms because they do not waste a lot of energy.

20.2 Reviewing the Concepts

- Reproductive isolating mechanisms prevent two different species from breeding with each other (Figure 20.2).
- Prezygotic isolating mechanisms include habitat isolation, temporal isolation, behavioral isolation, mechanical isolation, and gametic isolation (Figures 20.3, 20.4).
- Postzygotic isolating mechanisms include hybrid inviability, hybrid sterility, and hybrid breakdown (Figure 20.5).

20.2 Testing Your Knowledge

1. A mechanism of reproductive isolation that does not prevent fertilization from happening is called
   a. a prezygotic isolating mechanism.
   b. a postzygotic isolating mechanism.
   c. both a and b.
   d. neither a or b.

2. Which of the following is *not* an example of a prezygotic isolating mechanism?
   a. Two species breed at different times of the year.
   b. An egg from one species is fertilized by the sperm of another, but the embryo dies at an early stage.
   c. Two different bird species have different mating calls.
   d. Two different species are geographically isolated from each other.
   e. All of the above are prezygotic isolating mechanisms.

 ×

Male donkey (*Equus asinus*)   **Female horse (*Equus ferus caballus*)**

Mule

Figure 20.5 Hybrid sterility. When a male donkey (*Equus asinus*) mates with a female horse (*Equus ferus caballus*), their offspring is a mule, which is usually sterile.

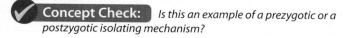 **Concept Check:**   *Is this an example of a prezygotic or a postzygotic isolating mechanism?*

20.3 Mechanisms of Speciation

Learning Outcomes:

1. Describe how allopatric speciation can occur and how it can lead to adaptive radiation.
2. Outline two different mechanisms of sympatric speciation.

Speciation, the formation of a new species, is caused by genetic changes in a particular group that make it different from the species from which it was derived. As discussed in Chapter 19, mutations in genes can be acted on by natural selection and other evolutionary mechanisms to alter the genetic composition of a population. New species commonly evolve in this manner. In addition, interspecies matings, changes in chromosome number, and horizontal gene transfer may also cause new species to arise. In all of these cases, the underlying cause of speciation is the accumulation of genetic changes that ultimately promote enough differences so we judge a population to constitute a unique species.

Even though genetic changes account for the phenotypic differences observed among living organisms, such changes do not fully explain the existence of many distinct species on our planet. Why does life often diversify into the more or less discrete populations that we recognize as species? Two main explanations have been proposed:

1. In some cases, speciation may occur due to abrupt events, such as changes in chromosome number, that cause reproductive isolation.
2. More commonly, species arise as a consequence of adaptation to different ecological niches. For sexually reproducing organisms, reproductive isolation is typically a by-product of that adaptation.

Depending on the species involved, one or both factors may play a dominant role in the formation of new species. In this section, we will consider how reproductive isolating mechanisms and adaptation to particular environments are critical aspects of the speciation process.

Geographic and Habitat Isolation Can Promote Allopatric Speciation

Cladogenesis is the splitting or diverging of a population into two or more species. In the case of sexually reproducing organisms, the process of cladogenesis requires that gene flow becomes interrupted between two or more populations, limiting or eliminating reproduction between members of different populations. **Allopatric speciation** (from the Greek *allos*, meaning other, and the Latin *patria*, meaning homeland) is the most prevalent way for cladogenesis to occur. This form of speciation occurs when a population becomes isolated from other populations and evolves into one or more species. Typically, this isolation may involve a geographic barrier such as a large area of land or body of water.

In some cases, geographic separation may be caused by slow geological events that eventually produce large geographic barriers. For example, a mountain range may emerge and split one species that occupies the lowland regions, or a creeping glacier may divide a population. **Figure 20.6** shows an interesting example in which geological separation promoted speciation. A fish called the Panamic porkfish (*Anisotremus taeniatus*) is found in the Pacific Ocean, whereas the porkfish (*Anisotremus virginicus*) is found in the Caribbean Sea. These two species were derived from an ancestral species whose population was split by the formation of the Isthmus of Panama about 3.5 mya. Before that event, the waters of the Pacific Ocean and Caribbean Sea mixed freely. Since the formation of the isthmus, the two populations have been geographically isolated and have evolved into distinct species.

Allopatric speciation can also occur when a small population moves to a new location that is geographically isolated from the main population. The Hawaiian Islands are a showcase of this type of allopatric speciation. The islands' extreme isolation coupled with their phenomenal array of ecological niches has enabled a small number of founding species to evolve into a vast assortment of different species. Biologists have investigated several examples of **adaptive radiation,** in which a single ancestral species has evolved into a wide array of descendant species that differ in their habitat, form, or behavior.

Biology Principle

All Species (Past and Present) Are Related by an Evolutionary History

These two species of fish look similar because they share a common ancestor that existed in the fairly recent past.

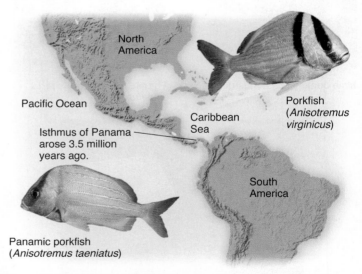

Figure 20.6   Allopatric speciation. An ancestral fish population was split into two by the formation of the Isthmus of Panama about 3.5 mya. Since that time, different genetic changes occurred in the two populations. These changes eventually led to the formation of different species: the Panamic porkfish (*Anisotremus taeniatus*) is found in the Pacific Ocean, and the porkfish (*Anisotremus virginicus*) is found in the Caribbean Sea.

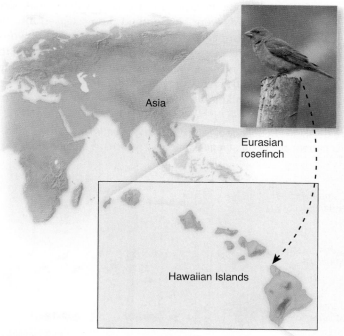

Asia

Eurasian
rosefinch

Hawaiian Islands

(a) Migration of ancestor to the Hawaiian Islands

Figure 20.7 **Adaptive radiation.** **(a)** The honeycreepers' ancestor is believed to be related to a Eurasian rosefinch that arrived on the Hawaiian Islands approximately 3–7 mya. Since that time, at least 54 different species of honeycreepers (Drepanidinae) have evolved on the islands. **(b)** Adaptations to feeding have produced honeycreeper species with notable differences in beak morphology.

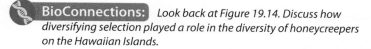

BioConnections: *Look back at Figure 19.14. Discuss how diversifying selection played a role in the diversity of honeycreepers on the Hawaiian Islands.*

Palila | Nihoa finch
Seed eaters

Maui Alauahio | Akikiki
Insect eaters

I'iwi | Akohekohe
Nectar feeders

(b) Examples of Hawaiian honeycreepers

As shown in Figure 20.7, an example of adaptive radiation is seen with a family of birds called honeycreepers (Drepanidinae). Researchers estimate that the honeycreepers' ancestor arrived in Hawaii 3–7 mya. This ancestor was a single species of finch, possibly a Eurasian rosefinch (genus *Carpodacus*) or, less likely, the North American house finch (*Carpodacus mexicanus*). At least 54 different species of honeycreepers, many of which are now extinct, evolved from this founding event to fill available niches in the islands' habitats. Natural selection resulted in the formation of many species with different feeding strategies. Seed eaters have stouter, stronger bills capable of cracking tough husks. Insect-eating honeycreepers have thin, warbler-like bills adapted for picking insects from foliage or strong, hooked bills to root out wood-boring insects. The curved bills of nectar-feeding honeycreepers enable them to extract nectar from the flowers of Hawaii's endemic plants.

FEATURE INVESTIGATION

Podos Found That an Adaptation to Feeding May Have Promoted Reproductive Isolation in Finches

In 2001, American evolutionary biologist Jeffrey Podos analyzed the songs of Darwin's finches on the Galápagos Islands to determine how environmental adaptation may contribute to reproductive isolation. As in honeycreepers, the differences in beak sizes and shapes among the various species of finches are adaptations to different feeding strategies. Podos hypothesized that changes in beak morphology could also affect the songs that the birds produce, thereby having the potential to affect mate choice. The components of the vocal tract of birds, including the trachea, larynx, and beak, work collectively to produce a bird's song. Birds actively modify the shape of their vocal tracts during singing, and beak movements are normally very rapid and precise.

Podos focused on two aspects of a bird's song. The first feature is the frequency range, which is a measure of the minimum and maximum frequencies in a bird's song, measured in kilohertz (kHz). The second feature is the trill rate. A trill is a series of notes or group of notes repeated in succession. **Figure 20.8** shows a graphical depiction of the songs of Darwin's finches. As you can see, the song patterns of these finches are quite different from each other.

To quantitatively study the relationship between beak size and song, Podos first captured male finches on Santa Cruz,

one of the Galápagos Islands, and measured their beak sizes (**Figure 20.9**). The birds were banded and then released into the wild. The banding provided a way of identifying the birds whose beaks had already been measured. After release, the songs of the banded birds were recorded on a tape recorder, and their range of frequencies and trill rate were analyzed. Podos then compared the data for the Galápagos finches to a large body of data that

Figure 20.8 **Differences in the songs of Galápagos finches.** These spectrograms depict the frequency of each bird's song over time, measured in kilohertz (kHz). The songs are produced in a series of trills that have a particular pattern and occur at regular intervals. Notice the differences in frequency and trill rate between different species of birds.

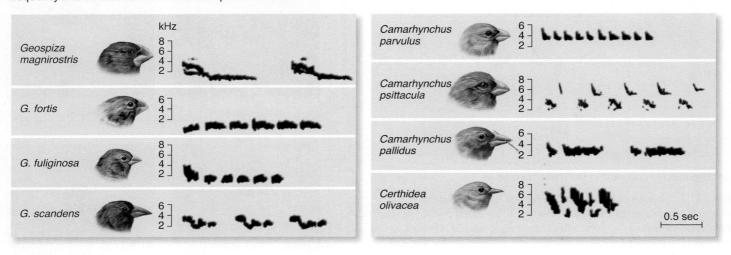

Figure 20.9 **Study by Podos investigating the effects of beak depth on song among different species of Galápagos finches.**

HYPOTHESIS Changes in beak morphology that are an adaptation to feeding may also affect the songs of Galápagos finches and thereby lead to reproductive isolation between species.

KEY MATERIALS This study was conducted on finch populations of the Galápagos Island of Santa Cruz.

	Experimental level	**Conceptual level**
1 Capture male finches and measure their beak depth. Beak depth is measured at the base of beak, from top to bottom.		This is a measurement of phenotypic variation in beak size.
2 Band the birds and release them back into the wild.	Band	Banding allows identification of birds with known beak depths.
3 Record the bird's songs on a tape recorder.		This is a measurement of phenotypic variation in song.

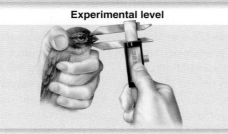
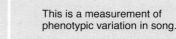

4 Analyze the songs with regard to frequency range and trill rate.

Time

The frequency range is the value between high and low frequencies. The trill rate is the number of repeats per unit time.

5   **THE DATA**

The data for the Galápagos finches were compared to a large body of data that had been collected on many other bird species. The relative constraint on vocal performance is higher if a bird has a narrower frequency range and/or a slower trill rate. These constraints were analyzed with regard to each bird's beak depth.

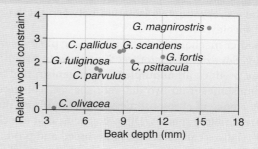

6   **CONCLUSION** Larger beak size, which is an adaptation to cracking open large, hard seeds, constrains vocal performance. This may affect mating song patterns and thereby promote reproductive isolation and, in turn, speciation.

7   **SOURCE** Podos, Jeffrey. 2001. Correlated evolution of morphology and vocal signal structure in Darwin's finches. *Nature* 409:185–188.

had been collected on many other bird species. This comparison was used to evaluate whether beak size, in this case, beak depth—the measurement of the beak from top to bottom, at its base—constrained either the frequency range and/or the trill rate of the finches.

The results of this comparison are shown in the data of Figure 20.9. As seen here, the relative constraint on vocal performance became higher as the beak depth became larger. This means that birds with larger beaks had a narrower frequency range and/or a slower trill rate. Podos proposed that as jaws and beaks became adapted for strength to crack open larger, harder seeds, they became less able to perform the rapid movements associated with certain types of songs. In contrast, the finches with smaller beaks adapted to probe for insects or eat smaller seeds had less constraint on their vocal performance. From the perspective of speciation, the changes observed in song patterns for the Galápagos finches could have played an important role in promot-

ing reproductive isolation, because song pattern is an important factor in mate selection in birds. Therefore, a by-product of beak adaptation for feeding is that it also appears to have affected song pattern, possibly promoting reproductive isolation and eventually the formation of distinct species.

Experimental Questions

1. What did Podos hypothesize regarding the effects of beak size on a bird's song? How could changes in beak size and shape lead to reproductive isolation among the finches?

2. How did Podos test the hypothesis that beak morphology caused changes in the birds' songs?

3. Did the results of Podos's study support his original hypothesis? Explain. What is meant by the phrase "by-product of adaptation," and how does it apply to this particular study?

Sympatric Speciation Occurs When Populations Are in Direct Contact

Sympatric speciation (from the Greek *sym*, meaning together) occurs when members of a species that are within the same range diverge into two or more different species even though there are no physical barriers to interbreeding. Although sympatric speciation is believed to be less common than allopatric speciation, particularly in animals, evolutionary biologists have discovered

several ways in which it can occur. These include polyploidy and adaptation to local environments.

Polyploidy   A type of genetic change that can cause immediate reproductive isolation is **polyploidy,** in which an organism has more than two sets of chromosomes. Plants tend to be more tolerant of changes in chromosome number than animals. For example, many crops and decorative species of plants are polyploid. How does polyploidy occur? One mechanism is complete nondisjunction of chromosomes, which increases the number of chromosome sets in a given species (autopolyploidy). Such changes can result in an abrupt sympatric speciation. For example, nondisjunction could produce a tetraploid plant with four sets of chromosomes from a species that was diploid with two sets. A cross between a tetraploid and a diploid produces a triploid offspring with three sets of chromosomes. Triploid offspring are usually sterile because an odd number of chromosomes cannot be evenly segregated during meiosis. This hybrid sterility causes reproductive isolation between the tetraploid and diploid species.

Another mechanism that leads to polyploidy is interspecies breeding. For example, interbreeding between two different species may produce an **allodiploid,** an organism that has one set of chromosomes from two different species. This term refers to the occurrence of chromosome sets (ploidy) from the genomes of different (allo-) species. Diploid species that are close evolutionary relatives can sometimes interbreed and produce allodiploid offspring. An organism containing two sets of chromosomes from two different species, for a total of four sets, is called an **allotetraploid.** An allotetraploid can occur as a result of nondisjunction in an allodiploid organism. This can also abruptly lead to reproductive isolation, because the allotetraploid would be reproductively isolated from related diploid species.

Polyploidy is so frequent in plants that it is a major mechanism of their speciation. In ferns and flowering plants, about 40–70% of the species are polyploid. By comparison, polyploidy can occur in animals, but it is much less common. For example, less than 1% of reptiles and amphibians are polyploids derived from diploid ancestors. The reason why polyploidy is not usually tolerated in animals is not understood.

Adaptation to Local Environments In some cases, populations occupying different local environments that are continuous with each other may diverge into different species. An early example of this type of sympatric speciation was described by American biologists Jeffrey Feder, Guy Bush, and colleagues. They studied the North American apple maggot fly (*Rhagoletis pomenella*). This fly originally fed on native hawthorn trees. However, the introduction of apple trees approximately 200 years ago provided a new local environment for this species. The apple-feeding populations of this species develop more rapidly because apples mature more quickly than hawthorn fruit. The result is partial temporal isolation, which is an example of prezygotic reproductive isolation. Although the two populations—those that feed on apple trees and those that feed on hawthorn trees—are considered subspecies, evolutionary biologists speculate they may eventually become distinct species due to reproductive isolation and the accumulation of independent mutations in the two populations.

American entomologist Sara Via and colleagues have studied the beginnings of sympatric speciation in pea aphids (*Acyrthosiphon pisum*), a small, plant-eating insect. Pea aphids in the same geographic area can be found on both alfalfa (*Medicago sativa*) and red clover (*Trifolium pratenae*) (**Figure 20.10**). Although pea

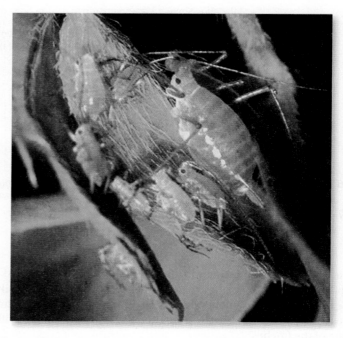

Biology Principle

Populations of Organisms Evolve from One Generation to the Next

Populations of pea aphids are evolving based on preference for different food sources—alfalfa or red clover. The populations may eventually evolve into separate species.

Figure 20.10 **Pea aphids, a possible example of sympatric speciation in progress.** Some pea aphids prefer alfalfa, whereas others prefer red clover. These two populations may be in the process of sympatric speciation.

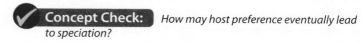

Concept Check: *How may host preference eventually lead to speciation?*

aphids on these two host plants look identical, they show significant genetic differences and are highly ecologically specialized. Pea aphids that are found on alfalfa exhibit a lower fitness when transferred to red clover, whereas pea aphids found on red clover exhibit a lower fitness when transferred to alfalfa. The same traits involved in this host specialization cause these two groups of pea aphids to be substantially reproductively isolated. Taken together, the observations of the North American apple maggot fly, pea aphids, and other insect species suggest that diversifying selection (described in Chapter 19) occurs because some members within the same range evolve to feed on a different host. This may be an important mechanism of sympatric speciation among insects.

20.3 Reviewing the Concepts

- Allopatric speciation occurs when a population becomes isolated from other populations and evolves into one or more new species. When speciation from a single ancestral species occurs multiple times, the process is called adaptive radiation (Figures 20.6, 20.7).
- Podos hypothesized that changes in beak depth, associated with adaptation to feeding, promoted reproductive isolation by altering the song pattern of finches (Figures 20.8, 20.9).
- Sympatric speciation involves the formation of different species in populations that are not geographically isolated from one another. Polyploidy and adaptation to local environments are mechanisms that promote sympatric speciation (Figure 20.10).

20.3 Testing Your Knowledge

1. Which of the following would be an example of allopatric speciation?
   a. A few birds fly to a distant island and after many generations a new bird species is formed.
   b. A diploid species becomes a new tetraploid species due to nondisjunction.
   c. A species diverges into two different species due to adaptation to local environments.
   d. All of the above are correct.

2. Which of the following would be the most likely to promote an abrupt speciation event?
   a. The formation of a new species on an island
   b. The adaptation of a species to local environments
   c. The formation of a polyploid species from a single diploid species
   d. The formation of an allotetraploid from two diploid species
   e. Both c and d

20.4 Evo-Devo: Evolutionary Developmental Biology

Learning Outcomes:

1. Describe how the spatial expression of genes, such as *BMP4* and *Gremlin*, affects pattern formation.
2. Explain the relationship between the number of *Hox* genes and the body plan of an animal species.
3. Outline how differences in the growth rates of body parts can change the characteristics of species.

In biology, **development** refers to a series of changes in the state of a cell, tissue, organ, or organism. Development is the process that gives rise to structures and functions of living organisms. In recent years, many evolutionary biologists have begun to investigate how genetic variation produces species and groups of species with novel shapes and forms. The underlying reasons for such changes are often rooted in the developmental pathways that control an organism's morphology.

Evolutionary developmental biology (referred to as **evo-devo**) is an exciting and relatively new field of biology that compares the development of different organisms in an attempt to understand ancestral relationships between organisms and the mechanisms that bring about evolutionary change. During the past few decades, developmental geneticists have gained a better understanding of biological development at the molecular level. Much of this work has involved the discovery of genes that control development in model organisms. As the genomes of more organisms have been analyzed, researchers have become interested in the similarities and differences that occur between closely related and distantly related species. The field of evolutionary developmental biology has arisen in response to this trend. In this section, we will see that proteins that control developmental changes, such as cell-signaling proteins and transcription factors, often play a key role in promoting the morphological changes that occur during evolution.

The Spatial Expression of Genes That Affect Development Has a Dramatic Effect on Phenotype

Genes that play a role in development influence cell division, cell migration, cell differentiation, and cell death. The interplay among these four processes produces an organism with a specific body pattern, a process called **pattern formation.** As you might imagine, developmental genes are very important to the phenotypes of individuals. They affect traits such as the shape of a bird's beak, the length of a giraffe's neck, and the size of a plant's flower. In recent years, the study of development has indicated that developmental genes are key players in the evolution of many types of traits. Changes in such genes affect traits that can be acted on by natural selection. Furthermore, variation in the expression of these genes may be commonly involved in the acquisition of new traits that promote speciation.

As an example, let's compare the formation of a chicken's foot with that of a duck. Developmental biologists have discovered that the morphological differences between a nonwebbed and a webbed foot are due to the differential expression of two different cell-signaling proteins called bone morphogenetic protein 4 (BMP4) and gremlin. The *BMP4* gene is expressed throughout the developing limb of both the chicken and duck; this is shown in **Figure 20.11a**, in which the BMP4 protein is stained purple. The BMP4 protein causes cells to undergo programmed cell death. The gremlin protein, which is stained brown in **Figure 20.11b**, inhibits the function of BMP4, thereby allowing cells to survive. In the developing chicken limb, the *Gremlin* gene is expressed throughout the limb, except in the regions between each digit. Therefore, in these regions, the cells die, and a chicken develops a nonwebbed foot (**Figure 20.11c**). By comparison, in the duck, *Gremlin* is expressed throughout the entire limb, including the interdigit

Chicken   Duck

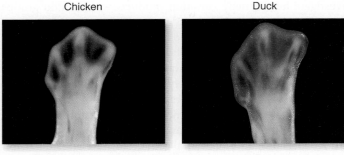

(a) BMP4 protein levels–similar expression in chicken and duck

Future interdigit regions

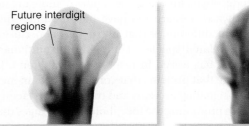

(b) Gremlin protein levels–not expressed in interdigit region in chicken

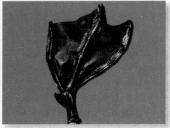

(c) Comparison of a chicken foot and a duck foot

Figure 20.11 **The role of cell-signaling proteins in the morphology of birds' feet.** This figure shows how changes in developmental gene expression can affect webbing between the toes. **(a)** Expression of the *BMP4* gene in the developing limbs. BMP4 protein is stained purple here and is expressed throughout the limb. **(b)** Expression of the *Gremlin* gene in the developing limbs. Gremlin protein is stained brown here. Note that *Gremlin* is not expressed in the interdigit regions of the chicken but is expressed in these regions of the duck. Gremlin inhibits BMP4, which causes programmed cell death. **(c)** Because BMP4 is not inhibited in the interdigit regions in the chicken, the cells in this region die, and the foot is not webbed. By comparison, inhibition of BMP4 in the interdigit regions in the duck results in a webbed foot.

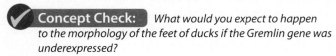 **Concept Check:** *What would you expect to happen to the morphology of the feet of ducks if the Gremlin gene was underexpressed?*

regions, and the duck develops a webbed foot. Interestingly, researchers have been able to introduce Gremlin protein into the interdigit regions of developing chicken limbs. This produces a chicken with webbed feet!

How are these observations related to evolution? During the evolution of birds, genetic variation arose such that some individuals expressed the *Gremlin* gene in the regions between each digit, but others did not. This variation determined whether or not a bird's feet were webbed. In terrestrial settings, having nonwebbed feet is an advantage because it enables the individual to hold onto perches, run along the ground, and snatch prey. Therefore, natural selection would favor nonwebbed feet in terrestrial environments. This process explains the occurrence of nonwebbed feet in chickens, hawks, crows, and many other terrestrial birds. In aquatic environments, however, webbed feet are an advantage because they act as paddles for swimming, so genetic variation that produced webbed feet in aquatic birds would have been acted on by natural selection. Over time, this gave rise to the webbed feet now found in a wide variety of aquatic birds, including ducks, geese, and penguins.

EVOLUTIONARY CONNECTIONS

The *Hox* Genes Have Been Important in the Evolution of a Variety of Body Plans

The study of developmental genes has revealed interesting trends among large groups of species. *Hox* genes are found in all animals, indicating they have originated very early in animal evolution. They specify the fate of a particular segment or region of the body. Developmental biologists have hypothesized that variation in the *Hox* genes has spawned the formation of many new body plans. As shown in **Figure 20.12**, the number and arrangement of *Hox* genes varies considerably among different types of animals. Sponges, the simplest of animals, have at least one gene that is homologous to *Hox* genes. Insects typically have nine or more *Hox* genes. In most cases, multiple *Hox* genes occur in a cluster in which the genes are close to each other along a chromosome. In mammals, *Hox* gene clusters have been duplicated twice during the course of evolution to form four clusters, all slightly different, containing a total of 38 genes.

Researchers propose that increases in the number of *Hox* genes have been instrumental in the evolution of many animal species with greater complexity in body structure. To understand how, let's first consider *Hox* gene function. All *Hox* genes encode transcription factors that act as master control proteins for directing the formation of particular regions of the body. Each *Hox* gene controls a hierarchy of many regulatory genes that regulate the expression of genes encoding proteins that ultimately affect the morphology of the organism. The evolution of complex body plans is associated with an increase not only in the number of regulatory genes—as evidenced by the increase in *Hox* gene complexity during evolution—but also in genes that encode proteins that directly affect an organism's form and function.

How would an increase in *Hox* genes enable more complex body forms to evolve? Part of the answer lies in the spatial expression of the *Hox* genes. Different *Hox* genes are expressed in different regions of the body along the body axis called the anteroposterior axis that runs from the head toward the abdomen (**Figure 20.13**). Therefore, an increase in the number of *Hox* genes allows each of these master control genes to become more spe-

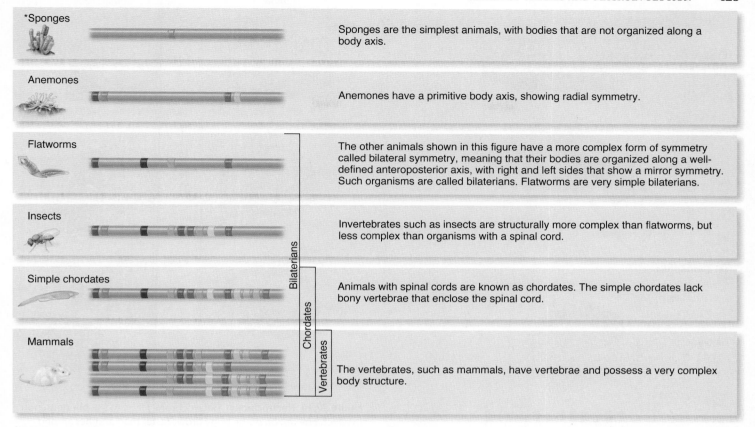

*Sponges — Sponges are the simplest animals, with bodies that are not organized along a body axis.

Anemones — Anemones have a primitive body axis, showing radial symmetry.

Flatworms — The other animals shown in this figure have a more complex form of symmetry called bilateral symmetry, meaning that their bodies are organized along a well-defined anteroposterior axis, with right and left sides that show a mirror symmetry. Such organisms are called bilaterians. Flatworms are very simple bilaterians.

Insects — Invertebrates such as insects are structurally more complex than flatworms, but less complex than organisms with a spinal cord.

Simple chordates — Animals with spinal cords are known as chordates. The simple chordates lack bony vertebrae that enclose the spinal cord.

Mammals — The vertebrates, such as mammals, have vertebrae and possess a very complex body structure.

Figure 20.12 *Hox* **gene number and body complexity in different types of animals.** Researchers speculate that the duplication of *Hox* genes and *Hox* gene clusters played a key role in the evolution of more complex body plans in animals. A correlation is observed between increasing numbers of *Hox* genes and increasing complexity of body structure. The different colors of *Hox* genes correspond to genes that are most closely related in different animal groups.

*Note: Sponges, which are the simplest animals with no true tissues, do not have true *Hox* genes, though they have an evolutionarily related gene called an *NK-like* gene. Some species of sponges have more than one copy of this gene.

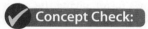 **Concept Check:** *What is the relationship between the total number of Hox genes in an animal species and its morphological complexity?*

cialized in the region that it controls. In fruit flies, one segment in the middle of the body can be controlled by a particular *Hox* gene and form wings and legs, whereas a segment in the head region can be controlled by a different *Hox* gene and develops antennae. Therefore, research suggests that one way for new, more complex body forms to evolve is by increasing the number of *Hox* genes, thereby making it possible to form many specialized parts of the body that are organized along a body axis.

Three lines of evidence support the idea that increases in *Hox* gene number have been instrumental in the evolution and speciation of animals with different body patterns. First, *Hox* genes are known to control the fate of regions along the anteroposterior axis. Second, as described in Figure 20.12, a general trend is observed in which animals with a more complex body structure tend to have more *Hox* genes and *Hox* clusters in their genomes than do the genomes of simpler animals. Third, a comparison of *Hox* gene evolution and animal evolution bears striking parallels. Researchers have analyzed *Hox* gene sequences among modern species and made estimates regarding the timing of past events. Using this type of approach, geneticists have estimated when the first

Hox gene arose by gene innovation. Though the date is difficult to precisely pinpoint, it is well over 600 mya. In addition, gene duplications of this primordial gene produced clusters of *Hox* genes in other species. Clusters such as those found in modern insects were likely to be present approximately 600 mya. A duplication of that cluster is estimated to have occurred around 520 mya.

Interestingly, these estimates of *Hox* gene origins correlate with major diversification events in the history of animals. As described in Chapter 18, the Cambrian period, which occurred from 543 to 490 mya, saw a great diversification of animal species. This diversification occurred after the *Hox* cluster was formed and was possibly undergoing its first duplication to produce two *Hox* clusters. Also, approximately 420 mya, a second duplication produced species with four *Hox* clusters. This event preceded the proliferation of tetrapods—vertebrates with four limbs—that occurred during the Devonian period, approximately 417–354 mya. Modern tetrapods have four *Hox* clusters. This second duplication may have been a critical event that led to the evolution of complex terrestrial vertebrates with four limbs, such as amphibians, reptiles, and mammals.

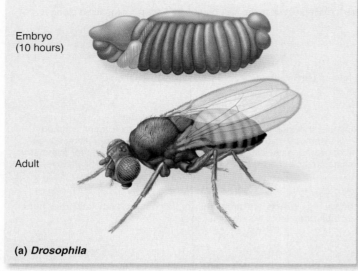

(a) *Drosophila*

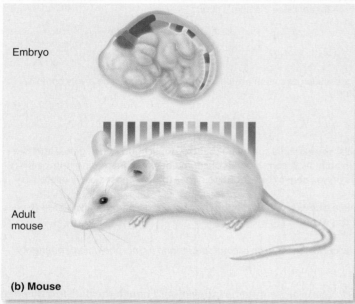

(b) Mouse

Figure 20.13 **Expression of *Hox* genes along the anteroposterior axis in animals.** The colors shown in this figure correspond to the gene colors in Figure 20.12, going from left to right.

Variation in Growth Rates Can Have a Dramatic Effect on Morphology

Another way that genetic variation can influence morphology is by controlling the relative growth rates of different parts of the body during development. The term **heterochrony** refers to evolutionary changes in the rate or timing of developmental events. The speeding up or slowing down of growth appears to be a common occurrence in evolution and leads to different species with striking morphological differences. With regard to the pace of evolution, such changes may rapidly lead to the formation of new species.

As an example, **Figure 20.14** compares the progressive growth of human and chimpanzee skulls. At the fetal stage, the size and shape of the skulls look fairly similar. However, after this stage,

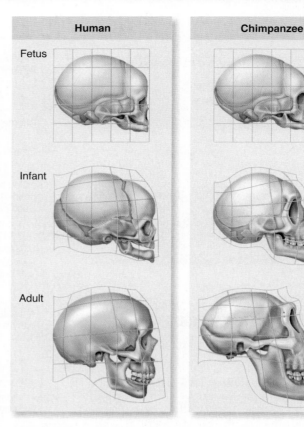

Figure 20.14 **Heterochrony.** Heterochrony refers to the phenomenon in which one region of the body grows faster than another among different species. The phenomenon explains why the skulls of adult chimpanzees and humans have different shapes even though their fetal skull shapes are quite similar.

the relative growth rates of certain regions become markedly different, thereby affecting the shape and size of the adult skull. In the chimpanzee, the jaw region grows faster, giving the adult chimpanzee a much larger and longer jaw. In the human, the jaw grows more slowly, and the region of the skull that surrounds the brain—the cranium—grows faster. The result is that adult humans have smaller jaws but a larger cranium.

20.4 Reviewing the Concepts

- Evolutionary developmental biology compares the development of different species in order to understand ancestral relationships and the mechanisms that bring about evolutionary change. These changes often involve variation in the expression of cell-signaling proteins and transcription factors.

- The spatial expression of genes that affect development can affect phenotypes dramatically, as shown by the expression of the *BMP4* and *Gremlin* genes in birds with nonwebbed or webbed feet (Figure 20.11).

- An increase in the number of *Hox* genes played an important role in the evolution of more complex body forms in animals (Figures 20.12, 20.13).

- A difference in the relative growth rates of body parts among different species, called heterochrony, can have a major effect on morphology (Figures 20.14).

20.4 Testing Your Knowledge

1. Which of the following species would you expect to have the most number of *Hox* genes?
   a. nematode worm
   b. fruit fly
   c. bird
   d. mammal
   e. All of the above would have the same number of *Hox* genes.

Assess and Discuss

Test Yourself

1. Macroevolution refers to evolutionary changes that
   a. occur in multicellular organisms.
   b. produce new species and groups of species.
   c. occur over long periods of time.
   d. cause changes in allele frequencies.
   e. occur in large mammals.

2. The ecological species concept classifies a species based on
   a. morphological characteristics.
   b. reproductive isolation.
   c. the niche the organism occupies in the environment.
   d. genetic relationships between an organism and its ancestors.
   e. both a and b.

3. Which of the following is considered an example of a postzygotic isolating mechanism?
   a. incompatible genitalia
   b. different mating seasons
   c. incompatible gametes
   d. mountain range separating two populations
   e. fertilized egg fails to develop normally

4. Hybrid breakdown occurs when interspecies hybrids
   a. do not develop past the early embryonic stages.
   b. have a reduced life span.
   c. are infertile.
   d. are fertile but produce offspring with reduced viability and fertility.
   e. produce offspring that express the traits of only one of the original species.

5. The evolution of one species into two or more species is called
   a. gradualism.   d. horizontal gene transfer.
   b. punctuated equilibrium. e. microevolution.
   c. cladogenesis.

6. A large number of honeycreeper species on the Hawaiian Islands is an example of
   a. adaptive radiation.   d. horizontal gene transfer.
   b. genetic drift.   e. microevolution.
   c. stabilizing selection.

7. A major mechanism of speciation in plants but not in animals is
   a. adaptation to new environments.
   b. polyploidy.
   c. hybrid breakdown.
   d. genetic changes that alter the organism's niche.
   e. both a and d.

8. The key difference between allopatric and sympatric speciation is
   a. how fast they occur.
   b. whether speciation involves geographic separation.
   c. the role of sexual selection in the speciation process.
   d. the role of reproductive isolation in the speciation process.
   e. all of the above.

9. Researchers suggest that an increase in the number of *Hox* genes
   a. caused reproductive isolation in all cases.
   b. could explain the evolution of color vision.
   c. facilitated the evolution of more complex body forms in animals.
   d. decreased the number of body segments in insects.
   e. did all of the above.

10. Evolutionary changes in the rate or timing of developmental events (heterochrony) explains
    a. why mammals are more complex that fruit flies.
    b. why human skulls and jaws are different sizes than those of chimpanzees.
    c. why some birds have webbed feet and others do not.
    d. how new species arise due to adaptation to local environments.
    e. how polyploidy can promote speciation.

Conceptual Questions

1. What is the key difference between prezygotic and postzygotic isolating mechanisms? Give an example of each type. Which type is more costly from the perspective of energy?

2. Compare and contrast different mechanisms of allopatric and sympatric speciation. How are genetic changes related to these two general forms of speciation?

3. **PRINCIPLES** A principle of biology is that *populations of organisms evolve from one generation to the next*. Describe one example in which genes that control development played an important role in the evolution of different species.

Collaborative Questions

1. What is a species? Discuss how geographic isolation can lead to speciation, and explain how reproductive isolation plays a role.

2. Discuss the type of speciation (allopatric or sympatric) that is most likely to occur under each of the following conditions:
   a. A pregnant female rat is transported by an ocean liner to a new continent.
   b. A meadow containing several species of grasses is exposed to a pesticide that promotes nondisjunction.
   c. In a very large lake containing several species of fishes, the water level gradually falls over the course of several years. Eventually, the large lake becomes subdivided into smaller lakes, some of which are connected by narrow streams.

Online Resource

www.brookerprinciples.com

Stay a step ahead in your studies with animations that bring concepts to life and practice tests to assess your understanding. Your instructor may also recommend the interactive eBook, individualized learning tools, and more.

21

Taxonomy and Systematics

Darwin's bark spider, *Caerostris darwini* (left side), which was discovered in 2010. The right side shows an example of the enormous web that a female spider of this species can weave.

Chapter Outline

New species are discovered on a regular basis. In 2010, researchers reported the discovery of a new species of spider in Madagascar, which they named Darwin's bark spider, *Caerostris darwini*. As seen in the chapter-opening photo, this species builds the largest orb-style webs that are known. Such webs have been found spanning rivers, streams, and lakes, reaching up to 25 m in length. The silk spun by these spiders is thought to be the toughest biological material ever studied. It is over 10 times stronger than Kevlar—the synthetic fiber used in bullet-proof vests, bicycle tires, and racing sails!

The rules for the classification of newly described species, such as Darwin's bark spider, are governed by the discipline of taxonomy (from the Greek *taxis*, meaning order, and *nomos*, meaning law). **Taxonomy** is the science of describing, naming, and classifying **extant** species, those that still exist today, as well as **extinct** species, those that have died out. Taxonomy results in the ordered division of species into groups based on similarities and dissimilarities in their characteristics. This task has been ongoing for over 300 years. In the mid- to late 1600s, naturalist John Ray made the first attempt to broadly classify all known forms of life. Ray's ideas were later extended by naturalist Carolus Linnaeus in the mid-1700s, which is considered by some to be the official birth of taxonomy.

Systematics is the study of biological diversity and the evolutionary relationships among organisms, both extant and extinct. In the 1950s, German entomologist Willi Hennig proposed that evolutionary relationships should be inferred from features shared by descendants of a common ancestor. Researchers now try to place new species into taxonomic groups based on evolutionary relationships with other species. In addition, previously established taxonomic groups are revised as new data shed light on evolutionary relationships.

In this chapter, we will begin with a discussion of taxonomy and the concept of taxonomic groups. We will then examine how biologists use systematics to determine evolutionary relationships among organisms, looking in particular at how those relationships are portrayed in diagrams called phylogenetic trees. We will then explore how analyses of morphological data and molecular genetic data are used to understand the evolutionary history of life on Earth.

21.1 Taxonomy

Learning Outcomes:

1. Identify the three domains of life.
2. Outline the hierarchy of groupings in taxonomy.
3. Explain how species are named using binomial nomenclature.

A hierarchy is a system of organization that classifies entities into successive levels. In biological taxonomy, every species is placed into several different nested groups within a hierarchy. For example, a leopard and a fruit fly are both classified into a large group known as animals, though they differ in many traits. By comparison, leopards and lions are placed together into a group with a smaller number of species called felines (more formally named Felidae), which are predatory cats. The felines are a subset of the animal group, which has species that share many similar traits. The species that are placed together into small taxonomic groups are likely to share many of the same characteristics. In this section, we will consider how biologists use a hierarchy to group similar species.

Living Species Are Subdivided into Three Domains of Life

Modern taxonomy places species into progressively smaller hierarchical groups. Each group at any level is called a **taxon** (plural, taxa). In the late 1970s, based on information in the sequences of genes, American biologist Carl Woese proposed the idea of creating a category called a **domain.** Under this system, all forms of life are grouped within three domains: **Bacteria, Archaea,** and **Eukarya** (**Figure 21.1**). The terms Bacteria and Archaea are capitalized when referring to the domains, but are not capitalized when referring to individual species. A single bacterial cell is called a bacterium, and a single archaeal cell is an archaeon.

The domain Eukarya formerly consisted of four kingdoms called Protista, Fungi, Plantae, and Animalia. Researchers later discovered that Protista is not a separate kingdom but instead is a very broad collection of species. Taxonomists now subdivide the eukaryotic domain into seven groups called supergroups. In the taxonomy of eukaryotes, a **supergroup** lies between a domain and a kingdom (Figure 21.1). As discussed in Chapter 22, all seven supergroups contain a distinctive group of protists. In addition, kingdoms Fungi and Animalia are within the supergroup Opisthokonta, because they are closely related to other protists in this supergroup. Kingdom Plantae is within the supergroup called Land plants and relatives. Green plants are closely related to green algae, which are protists in this supergroup. **Table 21.1** compares a variety of molecular and cellular characteristics among the domains Bacteria, Archaea, and Eukarya.

EVOLUTIONARY CONNECTIONS

Every Species Is Placed into a Taxonomic Hierarchy

Why is it useful to categorize species into groups? The three domains of life contain millions of different species. Subdividing them into progressively smaller taxonomic groups makes it easier for biologists to appreciate the relationships among such a large number of species. The order of hierarchy is:

domain > **supergroup** > **kingdom** > **phylum** (plural, phyla) > **class** > **order** > **family** > **genus** (plural, genera) > **species**

Each of these taxa contains progressively fewer species that are more similar to each other than they are to the members of the

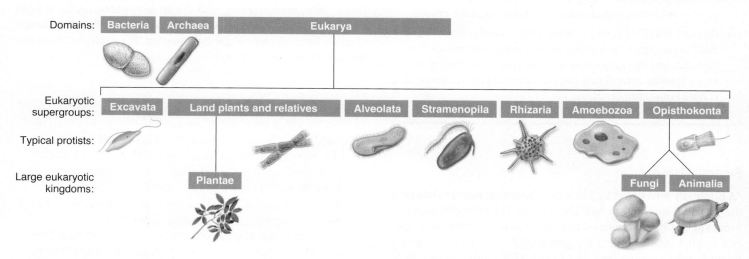

Figure 21.1 A classification system for living and extinct organisms. All organisms are grouped into three domains: Bacteria, Archaea, or Eukarya. Eukaryotes are divided into seven supergroups.

 **BioConnections:** *Look back at Figure 4.4. Which of the three domains contains organisms with prokaryotic cells?*

taxa above them in the hierarchy. For example, the taxon Animalia, which is at the kingdom level, has a larger number of fairly diverse species than does the class Mammalia, which contains fewer species that are relatively similar to each other.

To further understand taxonomy, let's consider the classification of a species such as the gray wolf (*Canis lupus*) **(Figure 21.2)**. The classification of this species is as follows:

- Domain Eukarya (several million species): The gray wolf is a eukaryote. See Table 21.1 for a description of eukaryotes.

- Supergroup Opisthokonta (over 1 million species): As described in Chapter 22, this supergroup includes the animal and fungal kingdoms and related protists.

- Kingdom Animalia (over 1 million species): Animals are multicellular and heterotrophic, which means they must consume other organisms or parts of other organisms to survive. Their cells lack a cell wall. Except for sponges, animal bodies contain tissues that have specialized cell types. Examples are muscle and nervous tissue.

- Phylum Chordata (~50,000 species): Animals in this group all have four common features at some stage of their development. These are a notochord (a cartilaginous rod that runs along the back), a tubular nerve or spinal cord located above the notochord, gill slits or arches, and a postanal tail.

- Class Mammalia (~5,000 species): Two distinguishing features are hair, which helps the body maintain a constant body temperature, and mammary glands, which produce milk to nourish the young.

- Order Carnivora (270 species): Carnivores typically have sharp claws, prominent canine teeth, and binocular vision. They usually follow a diet that primarily consists of meat.

- Family Canidae (34 species): All species in the family Canidae are doglike animals. This group is composed of different species of wolves, jackals, foxes, wild dogs, and the coyote.

- Genus *Canis* (7 species): Composed of closely related doglike species, which includes four species of jackals, the coyote, and two types of wolves. The species *Canis lupus* encompasses several subspecies, including the domestic dog (*Canis lupus familiaris*).

Binomial Nomenclature Is Used to Name Species

As originally advocated by Linnaeus, **binomial nomenclature** is the standard method for naming species. The scientific name of every species has two names, its genus name and its unique specific epithet. An example is the gray wolf, *Canis lupus*. The genus name is always capitalized, but the specific epithet is not. Both names are italicized. After the first mention, the genus name is often abbreviated to a single letter. For example, we would write that *Canis lupus* is the gray wolf, and in subsequent sentences, the species would be referred to as *C. lupus*.

Table 21.1	Distinguishing Cellular and Molecular Features of Domains Bacteria, Archaea, and Eukarya*		
Characteristic	**Bacteria**	**Archaea**	**Eukarya**
Chromosomes	Usually circular	Circular	Usually linear
Nucleosome structure	No	No	Yes
Chromosome segregation	Binary fission	Binary fission	Mitosis/meiosis
Introns in genes	Rarely	Rarely	Commonly
Ribosomes	70S	70S	80S
Initiator tRNA	Formyl-methionine	Methionine	Methionine
Operons	Yes	Yes	No
Capping of mRNA	No	No	Yes
RNA polymerases	One	Several	Three
Promoters of structural genes	-35 and -10 sequences	TATA box	TATA box
Cell compartmentalization	No	No	Yes
Membrane lipids	Ester-linked	Ether-linked	Ester-linked

*The descriptions in this table are meant to represent the general features of most species in each domain. Some exceptions are observed. For example, certain bacterial species have linear chromosomes, and operons occasionally are found in eukaryotes, such as the nematode worm *Caenorhabditis elegans*.

When naming a new species, genus names are always nouns or treated as nouns, whereas species epithets may be either nouns or adjectives. The names often have a Latin or Greek origin and refer to characteristics of the species or to features of its habitat. For example, the genus name of the gray wolf, *Canis,* is from the Latin, *canis,* meaning dog, and the species name, *lupus,* is from the Latin, *lupus,* meaning wolf. However, sometimes the choice of name for a species can be lighthearted. For example, there is a beetle named *Agra vation*.

21.1 Reviewing the Concepts

- Taxonomy is the field of biology that is concerned with describing, naming, and classifying living and extinct organisms. Systematics is the study and classification of evolutionary relationships among organisms through time.

- Taxonomy places all living organisms into progressively smaller hierarchical groups called taxa (sing., taxon). The broadest groups are the three domains, called Bacteria, Archaea, and Eukarya, followed by supergroups, kingdoms, phyla, classes, orders, families, genera, and species (Figures 21.1, 21.2, Table 21.1).

- Binomial nomenclature is a naming convention that provides each species with two names: its genus name and species epithet.

Biology Principle

All Species (Past and Present) Are Related by an Evolutionary History

A goal of taxonomy is to relate the diversity of species according to their evolutionary relationships.

Taxonomic group	Gray wolf found in	Number of species
Domain	Eukarya	~4–10 million
Supergroup	Opisthokonta	>1 million
Kingdom	Animalia	>1 million
Phylum	Chordata	~50,000
Class	Mammalia	~5,000
Order	Carnivora	~270
Family	Canidae	34
Genus	*Canis*	7
Species	*lupus*	1

Figure 21.2 A taxonomic classification of the gray wolf (*Canis lupus*).

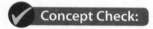 **Concept Check:** *Which group is broader, a phylum or a family?*

21.1 Testing Your Knowledge

1. The three domains of life are
   a. Animals, Bacteria, and Archaea.
   b. Eukarya, Prokaryotes, and Viruses.
   c. Eukarya, Bacteria, and Archaea.
   d. Protists, Animals, and Fungi.

2. Which of the following is a correct order of taxa?
   a. supergroup > domain > kingdom > phylum > class > order > family > genus > species
   b. domain > supergroup > kingdom > phylum > class > order > family > genus > species
   c. domain > supergroup > kingdom > class > phylum > order > family > genus > species
   d. supergoup > domain > kingdom > phylum > class > family > order > genus > species

21.2 Phylogenetic Trees

Learning Outcomes:

1. Explain the concept of phylogeny and its basis for the construction of phylogenetic trees.
2. Compare and contrast cladogenesis and anagenesis as patterns by which new species arise.
3. Describe how morphological and genetic homologies are used to construct phylogenetic trees.

As mentioned, systematics is the study of biological diversity and evolutionary relationships. By studying the similarities and differences among species, biologists can construct a **phylogeny**—the evolutionary history of a species or group of species. To propose a phylogeny, biologists use the tools of systematics. For example, the classification of the gray wolf described in Figure 21.2 is based on systematics. Therefore, one use of systematics is to place species into taxa and to understand the evolutionary relationships among different taxa.

In this section, we will consider the features of diagrams, or "trees," that describe the evolutionary relationships among various species, both extant and extinct. As you will learn, such trees are usually based on morphological or genetic data.

A Phylogenetic Tree Depicts Evolutionary Relationships Among Species

A **phylogenetic tree** is a diagram that describes the evolutionary relationships among various species, based on the information available to and gathered by systematists. A phylogenetic tree should be viewed as a hypothesis that is proposed, tested, and later refined as additional data become available. Let's look at what information a phylogenetic tree contains and the form in which it is presented. Figure 21.3 shows a hypothetical phylogenetic tree of the relationships among various flowering plant species, in which the species are labeled A through K. The vertical axis represents time, with the oldest species at the bottom.

New species can be formed by **anagenesis,** in which a single species evolves into a different species, or more commonly by **cladogenesis,** in which a species diverges into two or more

species. Some evolutionary biologists focus only on cladogenesis in the construction of their trees. The branch points in a phylogenetic tree, also called **nodes,** illustrate times when cladogenesis has occurred. For example, approximately 12 mya, species A diverged into species A and species B. Figure 21.3 also shows anagenesis in which species C evolved into species G. The tips of branches may represent species that became extinct in the past, such as species B and E, or living species, such as F, I, G, J, H, and K, which are at the top of the tree. Species A and D are also extinct but gave rise to species that are still in existence.

By studying the branch points of a phylogenetic tree, researchers can group species according to common ancestry. A **clade** consists of a common ancestral species and all of its descendant species. For example, the group highlighted in light green in Figure 21.3 is a clade derived from the common ancestral species labeled D. Likewise, the entire tree forms a clade, with species A as a common ancestor. Therefore, smaller and more recent clades are nested within larger clades that have older common ancestors.

A Central Goal of Systematics Is to Construct Taxonomic Groups Based on Evolutionary Relationships

A key goal of modern systematics is to create taxonomic groups that reflect evolutionary relationships. Systematics attempts to organize species into clades, which means that each group includes

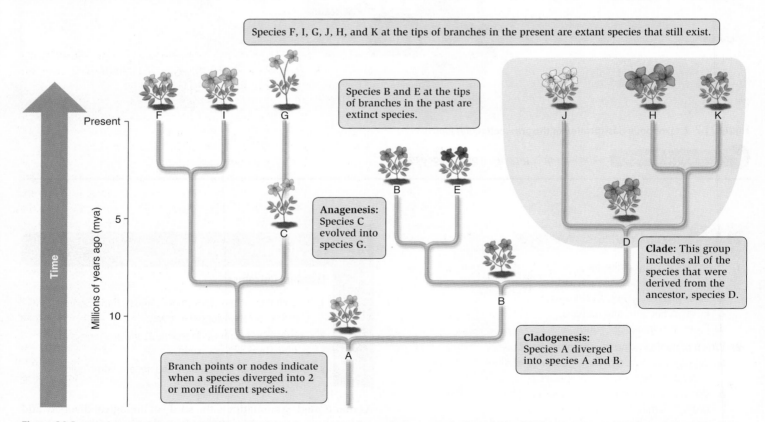

Species F, I, G, J, H, and K at the tips of branches in the present are extant species that still exist.

Species B and E at the tips of branches in the past are extinct species.

Anagenesis: Species C evolved into species G.

Clade: This group includes all of the species that were derived from the ancestor, species D.

Cladogenesis: Species A diverged into species A and B.

Branch points or nodes indicate when a species diverged into 2 or more different species.

Figure 21.3   How to read a phylogenetic tree. This hypothetical tree shows the proposed relationships between various plant species. Species are placed into clades, groups of organisms containing an ancestral organism and all of its descendants.

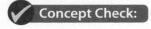 **Concept Check:**   *Can two different species have more than one common ancestor?*

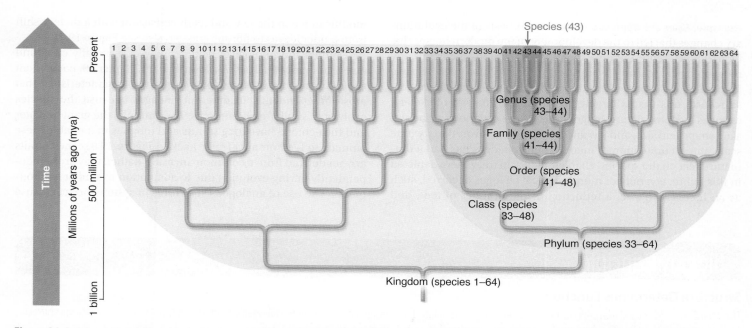

Figure 21.4 **Schematic relationship between a phylogenetic tree and taxonomy, when taxonomy is correctly based on evolutionary relationships.** The shaded areas highlight the kingdom, phylum, class, order, family, and genus for species number 43. All of the taxa are clades. Broader taxa, such as phyla and classes, are derived from more-ancient common ancestors. Smaller taxa, such as families and genera, are derived from more recent common ancestors. These smaller taxa are subsets of the broader taxa.

Concept Check: *Which taxon would have a more recent common ancestor, a phylum or an order?*

an ancestral species and all of its descendants. A **monophyletic group** is a taxon that is a clade. Ideally, every taxon, whether it is a domain, supergroup, kingdom, phylum, class, order, family, or genus, should be a monophyletic group.

What is the relationship between a phylogenetic tree and taxonomy? The relationship depends on how far back we go to identify a common ancestor. For broader taxa, such as a kingdom or phylum, the common ancestor existed a very long time ago, on the order of hundreds of millions or even billions of years ago. For smaller taxa, such as a family or genus, the common ancestor occurred much more recently, on the order of millions or tens of millions of years ago. This concept is shown in a very schematic way in **Figure 21.4.** This small, hypothetical kingdom is a clade that contains 64 living species. (Actual kingdoms are obviously larger and exceedingly more complex.) The diagram emphasizes the taxa that contain the species designated number 43. The common ancestor that gave rise to this kingdom of organisms existed approximately 1 bya. Over time, more recent species arose that subsequently became the common ancestors to the phylum, class, order, family, and genus that contain species number 43.

The Study of Systematics Is Usually Based on Morphological or Genetic Homology

As discussed in Chapter 19, the term **homology** refers to a similarity that occurs due to descent from a common ancestor. Such features are said to be homologous. For example, the arm of a human, the wing of a bat, and the flipper of a whale are homologous

structures (refer back to Figure 19.8). Similarly, genes found in different species are homologous if they have been derived from the same ancestral gene (refer back to Figure 19.9).

In systematics, researchers identify homologous features that are shared by some species but not by others, which allows them to group species based on their shared similarities. Researchers usually study homology by examining morphological features—those related to the structure of an organism—or they analyze genetic data. In addition, the data they gather are viewed in light of geographic data. Many organisms do not migrate extremely long distances. Species that are closely related evolutionarily are relatively likely to inhabit neighboring or overlapping geographic regions, though many exceptions are known to occur.

Analysis of Morphological Features The first studies in systematics focused on morphological features (also called anatomical features) of extinct and living species. Morphological traits continue to be widely used in systematic studies, particularly in those studies pertaining to extinct species and those involving groups that have not been extensively studied at the molecular level. To establish evolutionary relationships based on morphological features, many traits have to be analyzed to identify similarities and differences.

By studying morphological features of extinct species in the fossil record, paleontologists can propose phylogenetic trees that chart the evolutionary lineages of species, including those that still exist. In this approach, the trees are based on morphological features that change over the course of many generations. As an example, Figure 21.5 depicts a current hypothesis of the evolutionary changes that led to the development of the modern horse. This figure shows representative species from various genera. Many morphological features were used to create this tree. Because hard parts of the body are more commonly preserved in the fossil record, this tree is largely based on the analysis of skeletal changes in foot structure, lengths and shapes of various leg bones, skull shape and size, and jaw and teeth. Over an evolutionary time scale, the accumulation of many genetic changes has had a dramatic effect on the species' characteristics. In the genera depicted in this figure, a variety of morphological changes occurred, such as an increase in size, a reduction in the number of toes, and

modifications in the jaw and teeth consistent with a dietary shift from tender leaves to fibrous grasses (also see Figure 19.4).

Similar morphological features may occasionally confound an evolutionary analysis. As described in Chapter 19, convergent evolution results in analogous structures—characteristics that arose independently in different lineages because the species evolved in similar environments. For example, the giant anteater and the echidna have long snouts and tongues that enable these animals to feed on ants (refer back to Figure 19.6). These traits are not derived from a common ancestor. Rather, they arose independently during evolution due to adaptation to similar environments. The use of analogous structures in systematics can cause

Biology Principle

Structure Determines Function

The changes in structural features during horse evolution are related to changes in their functional needs. During this time, horse populations shifted from feeding on leaves in forested regions to feeding on abrasive grasses in more wide-open spaces.

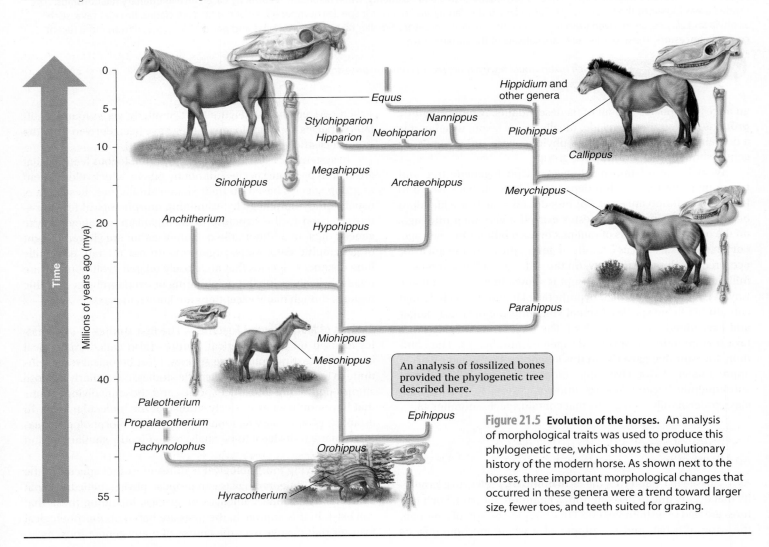

An analysis of fossilized bones provided the phylogenetic tree described here.

Figure 21.5 Evolution of the horses. An analysis of morphological traits was used to produce this phylogenetic tree, which shows the evolutionary history of the modern horse. As shown next to the horses, three important morphological changes that occurred in these genera were a trend toward larger size, fewer toes, and teeth suited for grazing.

errors if a researcher assumes that a particular trait arose only once and that all species having the trait are derived from a common ancestor.

Molecular Systematics The field of **molecular systematics** involves the analysis of genetic data, such as DNA sequences or amino acid sequences, to identify and study genetic homologies and propose phylogenetic trees. In 1963, Austrian biologist Emile Zuckerkandl and American chemist Linus Pauling were the first to suggest that molecular data could be used to establish evolutionary relationships. How can a comparison of genetic sequences help to establish evolutionary relationships? As discussed later in this chapter, DNA sequences change over the course of many generations due to the accumulation of mutations. Therefore, when comparing homologous sequences in different species, DNA sequences from closely related species are more similar to each other than they are to sequences from distantly related ones.

21.2 Reviewing the Concepts

- The evolutionary history of a species is its phylogeny. A phylogenetic tree is a diagram that describes the phylogeny of particular species and should be viewed as a hypothesis that is proposed, tested, and refined as more data become available (Figure 21.3).
- A central goal of systematics is to construct taxa and phylogenetic trees based on evolutionary relationships. Smaller taxa, such as families and genera, are derived from more recent common ancestors than are broader taxa such as kingdoms and phyla (Figure 21.4).
- Both morphological and genetic data are used to propose phylogenetic trees (Figure 21.5).

21.2 Testing Your Knowledge

1. A phylogenetic tree is
   a. a hypothesis about the evolutionary relationships among different species.
   b. a diagram that depicts the evolutionary relationships among different species.
   c. a diagram that should be organized according to the grouping of species into clades.
   d. all of the above.

2. Earlier in this chapter, we considered the taxonomy of the gray wolf. Which of the following taxa would have a common ancestor that is the oldest?
   a. Kingdom Animalia   c. Order Carnivora
   b. Phylum Chordata   d. Genus *Canis*

3. To construct a phylogenetic tree, a researcher compares the DNA sequence of a gene that encodes the cytoskeletal protein called tubulin among many different species. This would be an example of using
   a. morphological homology.   c. the fossil record.
   b. genetic homology.   d. both a and b.

21.3 Cladistics

Learning Outcomes:

1. Distinguish between shared primitive characters and shared derived characters.
2. Explain the use of cladistics to construct a phylogenetic tree.
3. Describe how the principle of parsimony is used to choose among phylogenetic trees.

Cladistics is the classification of species based on evolutionary relationships. A cladistic approach produces phylogenetic trees by considering the possible pathways of evolutionary changes that involve characteristics that are shared or not shared among various species. In this section, we will consider how the cladistic approach is used to produce phylogenetic trees known as **cladograms.**

Species Differ with Regard to Primitive and Derived Characters

A cladistic approach compares homologous features, also called **characters,** which may exist in two or more **character states.** For example, among different species, a front limb, which is a character, may exist in different character states such as a wing, an arm, or a flipper. The various character states are either shared or not shared by different species.

To understand the cladistic approach, let's take a look at a simplified phylogeny (**Figure 21.6**). We can place the living species that currently exist into two groups: D and E, and F and G. The most recent common ancestor to D and E is B, whereas species C is the most recent common ancestor to F and G. With these ideas in mind, let's focus on the front limbs (flippers versus legs) and eyes.

A character that is shared by two or more different taxa and inherited from ancestors older than their last common ancestor is called a **shared primitive character.** Such characters are viewed as being older—ones that occurred earlier in evolution. With regard to species D, E, F, and G, having two eyes is a shared primitive character. It originated prior to species B and C.

By comparison, a **shared derived character** is a character that is shared by two or more species or taxa and has originated in their most recent common ancestor. With regard to species D and E, having two front flippers is a shared derived character that originated in species B, their most recent common ancestor (Figure 21.6). Shared derived characters are more recent traits on an evolutionary timescale than are shared primitive characters. For example, among mammals, only some species have flippers, such as whales and dolphins. In this case, flippers were derived from the two front limbs of an ancestral species. The word "derived" indicates that evolution involves the modification of traits in pre-existing species. In other words, populations of organisms with new traits are derived from changes in pre-existing populations. The basis of the cladistic approach is to analyze many shared derived characters among groups of species to deduce the pathway that gave rise to those species.

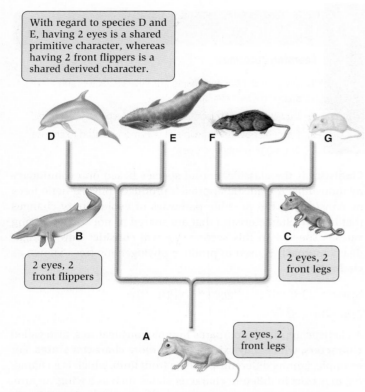

With regard to species D and E, having 2 eyes is a shared primitive character, whereas having 2 front flippers is a shared derived character.

D   E   F   G

B

C

2 eyes, 2 front flippers

2 eyes, 2 front legs

A

2 eyes, 2 front legs

Figure 21.6 A comparison of shared primitive characters and shared derived characters.

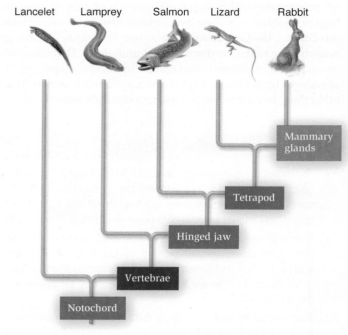

	Lancelet	Lamprey	Salmon	Lizard	Rabbit
Notochord	Yes	Yes	Yes	Yes	Yes
Vertebrae	No	Yes	Yes	Yes	Yes
Hinged jaw	No	No	Yes	Yes	Yes
Tetrapod	No	No	No	Yes	Yes
Mammary glands	No	No	No	No	Yes

(a) Characteristics among species

Lancelet   Lamprey   Salmon   Lizard   Rabbit

Mammary glands

Tetrapod

Hinged jaw

Vertebrae

Notochord

(b) Cladogram based on morphological traits

Figure 21.7 Using shared primitive characters and shared derived characters to propose a phylogenetic tree. **(a)** A comparison of characteristics among these species. **(b)** This phylogenetic tree illustrates both shared primitive and shared derived characters in a cladogram of five animal species.

Concept Check: *What shared derived character is common to the salmon, lizard, and rabbit, but not the lamprey?*

Note that the terms primitive and derived do not indicate the complexity of a character. For example, the flippers of a dolphin do not appear more complex than the front limbs of ancestral species A (see Figure 21.6), which were limbs with individual toes. Derived characters can be similar in complexity, less complex, or more complex than primitive characters.

A Cladistic Approach Produces a Cladogram Based on Shared Derived Characters

To understand how shared derived characters are used to propose a cladogram, Figure 21.7a compares several traits among five species of animals. The cladogram shown in Figure 21.7b is consistent with the distribution of shared derived characters among these species. A branch point is where two species differ in a character. The oldest common ancestor, which would now be extinct, had a notochord and was an ancestor to all five species. Vertebrae are a shared derived character of the lamprey, salmon, lizard, and rabbit, but not the lancelet, which is an invertebrate. By comparison, a hinged jaw is a shared derived character of the salmon, lizard, and rabbit, but not of the lamprey or lancelet.

In a cladogram, an **ingroup** is the group whose evolutionary relationships we wish to understand. By comparison, an **outgroup** is a species or group of species that is assumed to have diverged before the species in the ingroup. An outgroup lacks one or more shared derived characters that are found in the ingroup.

A designated outgroup can be closely related or more distantly related to the ingroup. In the tree shown in Figure 21.7, if the salmon, lizard, and rabbit are an ingroup, the lamprey would be an outgroup. The lamprey has a notochord and vertebrae but lacks a character shared by the ingroup, namely, a hinged jaw. Thus, for the ingroup, the notochord and vertebrae are shared primitive characters, whereas the hinged jaw is a shared derived character not found in the outgroup.

Likewise, the concept of shared derived characters can apply to molecular data, such as a gene sequence. Let's consider an example to illustrate this idea. Our example involves molecular data obtained from seven different hypothetical plant species

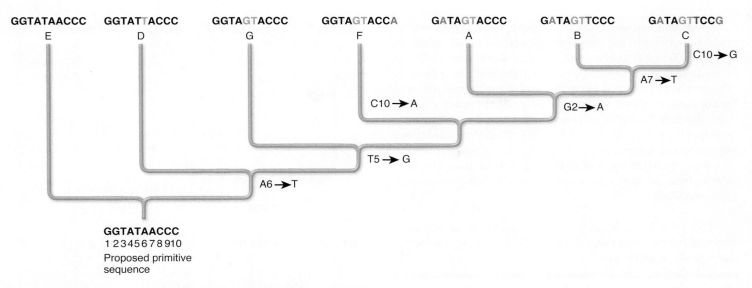

Figure 21.8 **The use of shared derived characters applied to molecular data.** This phylogenetic tree illustrates a cladogram involving homologous gene sequences found in seven hypothetical plant species. Mutations that alter a primitive DNA sequence are shared among certain species but not others. Note: A, T, G, and C refer to nucleotide bases, and the numbers refer to the position of the base in the nucleotide sequences. For example, A6 refers to an adenine at the sixth position.

✓ Concept Check: *What nucleotide change is a shared derived character for species A, B, and C, but not for species G?*

called A–G. In these species, a homologous region of DNA was sequenced as shown here:

```
    12345678910

A:  GATAGTACCC
B:  GATAGTTCCC
C:  GATAGTTCCG
D:  GGTATTACCC
E:  GGTATAACCC
F:  GGTAGTACCA
G:  GGTAGTACCC
```

The cladogram of **Figure 21.8** is a hypothesis of how these DNA sequences arose. In this case, a mutation that changes the sequence of nucleotides is comparable to a modification of a character. For example, let's designate plant species D as an outgroup and species A, B, C, F, and G as the ingroup. In this case, a G (guanine) at the fifth position is a shared derived character. The genetic sequence carrying this G is derived from an older primitive sequence.

In this textbook, most phylogenetic trees are rooted, which means that a single node at the bottom of the tree represents a common ancestor of all species or groups of species in the tree. A method for rooting trees is the use of a noncontroversial outgroup. Such an outgroup typically shares enough morphological traits and/or DNA sequence similarities with the members of the ingroup to allow a comparison between the ingroup and outgroup. Even so, the outgroup must be noncontroversial in that it shows enough distinctive differences with the ingroup to be considered a clear outgroup. For example, if the ingroup was a group of mammalian species, an outgroup could be a reptile.

Quantitative Analysis

THE PRINCIPLE OF PARSIMONY IS USED TO CHOOSE FROM AMONG POSSIBLE CLADOGRAMS

Although different methods may be used for choosing among possible cladograms, one commonly used approach is to assume that the best hypothesis is the one that requires the fewest number of evolutionary changes to explain the differences among observed characters. This concept, called the **principle of parsimony,** states that the preferred hypothesis is the one that is the simplest for all the characters and their states. For example, if two species possess a tail, we would initially assume that a tail arose once during evolution and that both species have descended from a common ancestor with a tail. Such a hypothesis is simpler, and more likely to be correct, than assuming that tails arose twice during evolution and that the tails in the two species are not due to descent from a common ancestor.

The principle of parsimony can also be applied to genetic data, in which case the most likely hypothesis is the one requiring the fewest base changes. Let's consider a hypothetical example involving a DNA sequence from four taxa (A–D), where A is presumed to be the outgroup.

```
    12345

A:  GTACA (outgroup)
B:  GACAG
C:  GTCAA
D:  GACCG
```

Given that B, C and D are the ingroup, three hypotheses for phylogenetic trees are shown in **Figure 21.9**, although more are possible. Tree 1 requires seven mutations, and tree 2 requires six, whereas tree 3 requires only five. Therefore, tree 3 requires the smallest number of mutations and is considered the most parsimonious. Based on the principle of parsimony, the tree with the fewest number of base changes would be the hypothesis that is the most likely to accurately reflect the evolutionary history of the ingroup in question. In practice, when researchers have multiple sequences that are longer than the ones shown here, computer programs are used to find the most parsimonious tree.

Crunching the Numbers: According to the principle of parsimony, which of these trees would you consider to be the least likely? Explain why.

21.3 Reviewing the Concepts

- In the cladistic approach to creating a phylogenetic tree, also called a cladogram, species are grouped together according to shared derived characters, characters shared by two or more species or taxa and originating in their most recent common ancestor (Figure 21.6).
- An ingroup is the group of interest, whereas an outgroup is a species or group of species that lacks one or more shared derived characters found in the ingroup. A comparison of the ingroup and outgroup is used to determine which character states are derived or primitive (Figures 21.7, 21.8).
- The cladistic approach produces many possible cladograms. The most likely phylogenetic tree may be chosen by the principle of parsimony (Figure 21.9).

21.3 Testing Your Knowledge

1. In a cladogram, the branch points or nodes are determined by differences in
  a. species complexity.
  b. shared derived characters.
  c. genetic homology but not molecular homology.
  d. molecular homology but not genetic homology.

2. With regard to choosing the most likely cladogram, explain how the principle of parsimony is used.
  a. The tree that has the minimum number of branch points is chosen.
  b. The tree that has the maximum number of branch points is chosen.
  c. The tree that has the fewest number of evolutionary changes is chosen.
  d. The tree that has the most number of evolutionary changes is chosen.

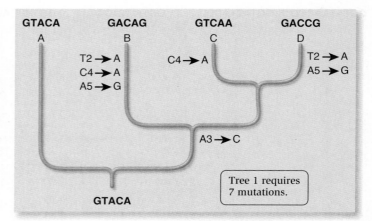

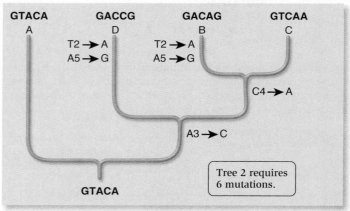

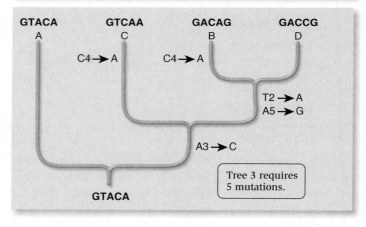

Figure 21.9 Using the principle of parsimony and molecular genetic data to choose a phylogenetic tree. Shown are three possible phylogenetic trees for the evolution of a short DNA sequence (although many more are possible). Changes in nucleotide sequence are indicated for each tree. For example, T2 → A means that the second base, a T, was changed to an A. According to the principle of parsimony, tree number 3 is the more likely choice because it requires only five mutations.

21.4 Molecular Clocks

Learning Outcomes:

1. Explain how molecular clocks are used in the dating of evolutionary events.
2. Compare and contrast the use of different genes to produce phylogenetic trees.

As we have seen, a phylogenetic tree describes the evolutionary relationships among various species. Researchers are interested not only in the most likely pathway of evolution (the branches of the trees), but also in the timing of evolutionary change (the lengths of the branches). How can researchers determine when different species diverged from each other in the past? As shown in Figure 21.5, the fossil record can sometimes help researchers apply a timescale to a phylogeny.

Another way to infer the timing of past events is by analyzing genetic sequences. The **neutral theory of evolution** proposes that most genetic variation that exists in populations is due to the accumulation of neutral mutations—changes in genes and proteins that are not acted upon by natural selection. The reasoning behind this concept is that favorable mutations are likely to be very rare, and detrimental mutations are likely to be eliminated from a population by natural selection. A large body of evidence supports the idea that much of the genetic variation observed in living species is due to the accumulation of neutral mutations. From an evolutionary point of view, if neutral mutations occur at a relatively constant rate, they can act as a **molecular clock** on which to measure evolutionary time. In this section, we will consider the concept of a molecular clock and its application in phylogenetic trees.

The Timing of Evolutionary Change May Be Inferred from Molecular Clock Data

Figure 21.10 illustrates the concept of a molecular clock. The graph's *y*-axis is a measure of the number of nucleotide differences in a homologous gene between different pairs of species. The *x*-axis plots the amount of time that has elapsed since each pair of species shared a common ancestor.

As an example, let's suppose a researcher compared a gene sequence that was 500 bp long. Between species A and species B, this sequence might differ at 10 places and be identical at 490 places. By comparison, the 500-bp sequence might differ at 20 places between species A and species C and be the same at 480 places. Such a result would be consistent with the idea that species A and species B shared a more recent common ancestor than do species A and species C. The explanation for this phenomenon is that the gene sequences of various species accumulate independent mutations after they have diverged from each other. A longer period of time since their divergence allows for a greater accumulation of mutations, which makes their sequences more different.

Figure 21.10 suggests a linear relationship between the number of nucleotide changes and the time of divergence. For

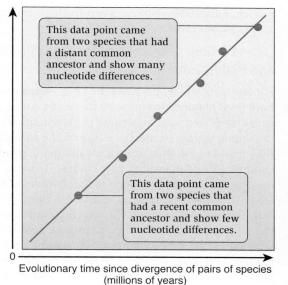

Figure 21.10 A molecular clock. According to the concept of a molecular clock, neutral mutations accumulate at a relatively constant rate over evolutionary time. When comparing homologous genes between species, those species that diverged more recently tend to have fewer differences than do those whose common ancestor occurred in the distant past.

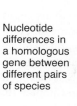 **BioConnections:** *Look back at Table 10.1, which shows the genetic code. Propose a mutation that would change the sequence of a codon and also be neutral.*

example, a linear relationship predicts that a pair of species that has, say, 20 nucleotide differences in a given gene sequence would have a common ancestor that is roughly twice as old as that of a pair showing 10 nucleotide differences. Although actual data sometimes show a relatively linear relationship over a defined time period, evolutionary biologists do not think that molecular clocks are perfectly linear over very long periods of time. Several factors can contribute to nonlinearity of molecular clocks. These include differences in the generation times of the species being analyzed and variation in the mutation rates of genes between different species.

To obtain reliable data, researchers must calibrate their molecular clocks. How much time does it take to accumulate a certain percentage of nucleotide changes? To perform such a calibration, researchers must have information regarding the date when two species diverged from a common ancestor. Such information could come from the fossil record, for instance. The genetic differences between those species are then divided by the amount of time since their last common ancestor to calculate a rate of evolutionary change. For example, fossil evidence suggests that humans and chimpanzees diverged from a common ancestor approximately 6 mya. The percentage of nucleotide differences between mitochondrial DNA of humans and chimpanzees is 12%. From these data, the molecular clock for changes in mitochondrial DNA sequences of primates is calibrated at roughly 2% nucleotide changes per million years.

Different Genes Are Analyzed to Study Phylogeny and Evaluate the Timing of Evolutionary Change

For evolutionary comparisons, the DNA sequences of many genes have been obtained from a wide range of sources. Many different genes have been used to propose phylogenetic trees and evaluate the timing of past events. For example, the gene that encodes an RNA found in the small ribosomal subunit (SSU rRNA) has been commonly used in evolutionary studies. As noted in Chapter 10, the gene for SSU rRNA is found in the genomes of all living organisms. Therefore, its function must have been established at an early stage in the evolution of life on this planet, and its sequence has changed fairly slowly. Furthermore, SSU rRNA is a rather large molecule, so it contains a large amount of sequence information. This gene has been sequenced from thousands of different species (see Figure 10.13). Slowly changing genes such as the gene that encodes SSU rRNA are useful for evaluating distant evolutionary relationships, such as comparing higher taxa. For example, SSU rRNA data can be used to place eukaryotic species into their proper phyla or orders.

Other genes have changed more rapidly during evolution because of a greater tolerance of neutral mutations. For example, the mitochondrial genome and DNA sequences within introns can more easily incur neutral mutations (compared to the coding sequences within exons), and so their sequences change frequently during evolution. More rapidly changing DNA sequences have been used to study recent evolutionary relationships, particularly among eukaryotic species such as large animals that have longer generation times and tend to evolve more slowly. In these cases, slowly evolving genes may not be very useful for establishing evolutionary relationships because two closely related species are likely to have identical or nearly identical DNA sequences for such genes.

Figure 21.11 shows a simplified phylogeny of closely related species of primates. This tree was proposed by comparing DNA sequence changes in the gene for cytochrome oxidase subunit II, one of several subunits of cytochrome oxidase, a protein located

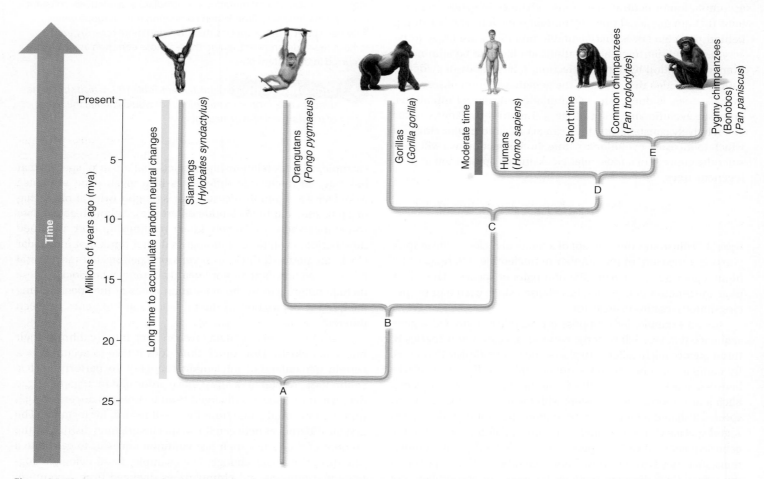

Figure 21.11   The use of DNA sequence changes to study primate evolution. This phylogenetic tree, which shows relationships among closely related species of primates, is based on a comparison of mitochondrial gene sequences encoding the protein cytochrome oxidase subunit II.

 **Concept Check:**   *Which pair of species would be expected to have fewer genetic differences: orangutans and gorillas or gorillas and humans?*

in the mitochondrial inner membrane that is involved in cellular respiration. This gene tends to change fairly rapidly on an evolutionary timescale. The vertical scale on Figure 21.11 represents time, and the branch points that are labeled with letters represent common ancestors. Let's take a look at three branch points (labeled A, D, and E) and relate them to the accumulation of neutral mutations.

- *Ancestor A:* This ancestor diverged into two species that ultimately gave rise to siamangs and the other five species. Since this divergence, there has been a long time (approximately 23 million years) for the siamang genome to accumulate a relatively high number of random neutral changes that would be different from the random changes that have occurred in the genomes of the other five species (see the yellow bar in Figure 21.11). Therefore, the gene in the siamangs is fairly different from the genes in the other five species.

- *Ancestor D:* This ancestor diverged into two species that eventually gave rise to humans and chimpanzees. This divergence occurred a moderate time ago, approximately 6 mya, as illustrated by the red bar. The differences in gene sequences between humans and chimpanzees are relatively moderate.

- *Ancestor E:* This ancestor diverged into two species of chimpanzees. Since the divergence of species E into two species, approximately 3 mya, the time for the molecular clock to "tick" (that is, accumulate random mutations) is relatively short, as depicted by the green bar in Figure 21.11. Therefore, the two existing species of chimpanzees have fewer differences in their gene sequences than between other primates.

21.4 Reviewing the Concepts

- The neutral theory of evolution proposes that most genetic variation in a population is due to neutral mutations. Assuming that neutral mutations occur at a relatively constant rate, genetic data can act as a molecular clock on which to measure evolutionary time (Figure 21.10).
- Slowly changing genes are useful for analyzing distant evolutionary relationships, whereas rapidly changing genes are used to analyze more recent evolutionary relationships, particularly among eukaryotes that have long generation times and evolve more slowly (Figure 21.11).

21.4 Testing Your Knowledge

1. When the same homologous gene is compared between closely related species (for example, a lion and a tiger) versus distantly related species (for example, a lion and a turtle),
   a. the genes between *closely* related species have *fewer* differences because their common ancestor occurred more recently.
   b. the genes between *distantly* related species have *fewer* differences because their common ancestor occurred more recently.
   c. the genes between *closely* related species have *more* differences because their common ancestor occurred more recently.
   d. the genes between *distantly* related species have *more* differences because their common ancestor occurred more recently.

2. An analysis of the number of neutral genetic changes among different species can be used to estimate the dates of past evolutionary events, such as the divergence of one species into two species. For this to be valid,
   a. researchers must have a way to calibrate their clock, such as using information from the fossil record.
   b. the rate of neutral mutations must be relatively constant over a given time period.
   c. the gene sequences that are analyzed must be relatively short.
   d. both a and b.

21.5 Horizontal Gene Transfer

Learning Outcome:

1. Explain how horizontal gene transfer affects evolution and the relationships among different taxa.

Thus far, we have considered various ways to propose phylogenetic trees, which describe the relationships between ancestors and their descendants. The type of evolution depicted in previous figures, which involves changes in groups of species due to descent from a common ancestor, is called vertical evolution. Since the time of Darwin, vertical evolution has been the traditional way that biologists view the evolutionary process. However, over the past couple of decades researchers have come to realize that evolution is not so simple. In addition to vertical evolution, horizontal gene transfer has also played a significant role in the phylogeny of living species.

Horizontal gene transfer is used to describe any process in which an organism incorporates genetic material from another organism without being the offspring of that organism. This phenomenon has reshaped the way that biologists view the evolution of species. Horizontal gene transfer has played a major role in the evolution of many species. As discussed in Chapter 15 (see Table 15.2), bacteria can transfer genes via conjugation, transformation, and transduction. Bacterial gene transfer can occur between strains of the same species or, occasionally, between cells of different bacterial species. The transferred genes may encode proteins that provide a survival advantage, such as resistance to antibiotics or the ability to metabolize an organic molecule in the environment. Horizontal gene transfer is also fairly common among certain unicellular eukaryotes. However, its relative frequency and importance in the evolution of multicellular eukaryotes remain difficult to evaluate.

Scientists have debated the role of horizontal gene transfer in the earliest stages of evolution, prior to the divergence of the bacterial and archaeal domains. The traditional viewpoint was that the three domains of life—Bacteria, Archaea, and Eukarya—arose from a single type of prokaryotic (or pre-prokaryotic) cell called the universal ancestor. However, genomic research has suggested that horizontal gene transfer may have been particularly common during the early stages of evolution on Earth, when all species were unicellular. Horizontal gene transfer may have been so prevalent that the universal ancestor may have actually been an ancestral community of cell lineages that evolved as a whole. If that were the case, the tree of life cannot be traced back to a single prokaryotic ancestor.

Figure 21.12 illustrates a schematic scenario for the evolution of life on Earth that includes the roles of both vertical evolution and horizontal gene transfer. This has been described as a "web of life" rather than a "tree of life." In this scenario, instead of a universal ancestor, a community of primitive cells frequently transferred genetic material in a horizontal fashion. Horizontal gene transfer was also prevalent during the early evolution of bacteria and archaea, and when eukaryotes first emerged as unicellular species. In living bacteria and archaea, it remains a prominent way to foster evolutionary change. By comparison, the region of the diagram that contains eukaryotic species has a more treelike structure. Researchers have speculated that multicellularity and sexual reproduction have presented barriers to horizontal gene transfer in most eukaryotes. For a gene to be transmitted to eukaryotic offspring, it would have to be transferred into a eukaryotic cell that is a gamete or a cell that gives rise to gametes. Horizontal gene transfer has become less common in eukaryotes, though it does occur occasionally.

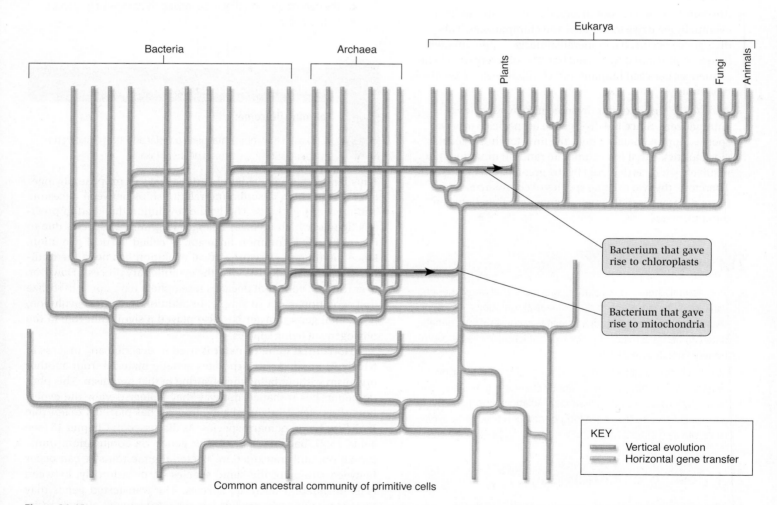

Figure 21.12 A web of life. This phylogenetic tree shows not only the vertical evolution of life on Earth but also the contribution of horizontal gene transfer. In this scenario, horizontal gene transfer was prevalent during the early stages of evolution, when all organisms were unicellular, and continues to be a prominent factor in the speciation of Bacteria and Archaea. Note: This tree is meant to be schematic. Also, while the introduction of chloroplasts into the eukaryotic domain is shown as a single event, such events have occurred multiple times and by different mechanisms.

✓ Concept Check: *How does the phenomenon of horizontal gene transfer muddle the concept of monophyletic groups?*

21.5 Reviewing the Concepts

- Horizontal gene transfer is the phenomenon in which an organism incorporates genetic material from another organism without being the offspring of that organism. Due to the prevalence of horizontal gene transfer, the tree of life may more accurately be described as a web of life (Figure 21.12).

21.5 Testing Your Knowledge

1. Which of the following would be an example of horizontal gene transfer?
   a. a mating between two different species, such as a horse and a donkey, to produce a mule
   b. the passage of genes from a mother cell to two daughter cells during cell division
   c. the transfer of an antibiotic resistance gene from one bacterial species to a different species
   d. both a and c

Assess and Discuss

Test Yourself

1. The study of biological diversity based on evolutionary relationships is
   a. paleontology.   c. systematics.   e. both a and b.
   b. evolution.   d. natural selection.

2. Which of the following is the correct order of the taxa used to classify organisms?
   a. kingdom, supergroup, domain, phylum, class, order, family, genus, species
   b. domain, supergroup, kingdom, class, phylum, order, family, genus, species
   c. supergroup, domain, kingdom, phylum, class, family, order, genus, species
   d. domain, supergroup, kingdom, phylum, class, order, family, genus, species
   e. kingdom, supergroup, domain, phylum, order, class, family, species, genus

3. When considering organisms within the same taxon, which level includes organisms with the greatest similarity?
   a. kingdom   c. order   e. genus
   b. class   d. family

4. Which of the following characteristics is not shared by bacteria, archaea, and eukaryotes?
   a. DNA is the genetic material.
   b. Messenger RNA encodes the information to produce proteins.
   c. All cells are surrounded by a plasma membrane.
   d. The cytoplasm is compartmentalized into organelles.
   e. Both a and d are correct.

5. The branch points or nodes in a phylogenetic tree depict which of the following?
   a. anagenesis   d. a and b only
   b. cladogenesis   e. b and c only
   c. horizontal gene transfer

6. The evolutionary history of a species is its
   a. domain.   c. evolution.   e. embryology.
   b. taxonomy.   d. phylogeny.

7. A taxon composed of all species derived from a common ancestor is referred to as
   a. a phylum.
   b. a monophyletic group or clade.
   c. a genus.
   d. an outgroup.
   e. all of the above.

8. A goal of modern taxonomy is to
   a. classify all organisms based on morphological similarities.
   b. classify all organisms into monophyletic groups.
   c. classify all organisms based solely on genetic similarities.
   d. determine the evolutionary relationships only between similar species.
   e. none of the above

9. The concept that the preferred hypothesis is the one that is the simplest is termed
   a. homology.   d. a molecular clock.
   b. cladistics.   e. both b and d.
   c. the principle of parsimony.

10. Research indicates that horizontal gene transfer is less prevalent in eukaryotes because of
   a. the presence of organelles.   d. all of the above.
   b. multicellularity.   e. b and c only.
   c. sexual reproduction.

Conceptual Questions

1. Explain how species' names follow a binomial nomenclature. Give an example.

2. What is a molecular clock? How is it used in depicting phylogenetic trees?

3. **PRINCIPLES** A principle of biology is that *populations of organisms evolve from one generation to the next.* What are some advantages and potential pitfalls of using changes in morphological features to construct phylogenetic trees?

Collaborative Questions

1. Discuss how taxonomy is useful. Make a list of some practical applications that are derived from taxonomy.

2. Discuss systematics and how it is used to propose a phylogenetic tree. Discuss the rationale behind using the principle of parsimony.

Online Resource

www.brookerprinciples.com

Stay a step ahead in your studies with animations that bring concepts to life and practice tests to assess your understanding. Your instructor may also recommend the interactive eBook, individualized learning tools, and more.

UNIT V
DIVERSITY

Biological diversity encompasses the variety of living things that exist on Earth now, as well as all the life-forms that lived in the past. Knowing about the many different kinds of modern organisms helps us to understand how life-forms are structured in ways that allow them to function differently in nature (described in Units VI and VII) and how species interact with each other and with their environments (described in Unit VIII—Ecology).

Unit V begins with microorganisms, which include bacteria, archaea, and diverse lineages of protists, Earth's oldest, simplest, and most numerous life-forms; Chapter 22 reveals the many ways that microorganisms influence our lives. In Chapter 23, we explore the diversification of plants, a process that explains the features and functions of the seed plants that are vital sources of human food, fiber, and medicine. The mysteries of the fungi, essential to the brewing and baking industries as well as ecological stability, are revealed in Chapter 24. The simplest animals, the invertebrates, are covered in Chapter 25. More complex animals, including humans and their closest relatives, are the focus of Chapter 26, which reveals how our species arose.

The following biology principles will be emphasized in this unit:

- **Cells are the simplest units of life.** *Most present and past microbial species have bodies consisting of only one or a few cells, whereas plants, animals, and many fungi display more complex bodies composed of many cells.*

- **Living organisms interact with their environment.** *Chapters 22 and 23 explain how ancient microorganisms and plants dramatically changed the composition of Earth's atmosphere, and how their modern descendants continue to influence today's atmosphere and climate.*

- **All species (past and present) are related by an evolutionary history.** *This concept, emphasized throughout the unit, helps us to comprehend how humans are related to other living things on Earth.*

- **Structure determines function.** *The chapters in this unit provide many examples of ways in which evolutionary change in molecular, cellular, or body structure has allowed organisms to achieve new and diverse functions.*

Microorganisms: The Archaea, Bacteria, and Protists

22

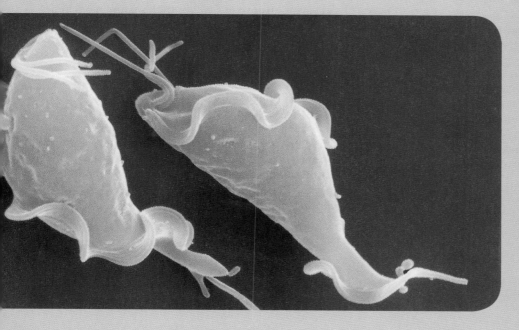

The protist *Trichomonas vaginalis* is one type of microorganism that causes infection of the human urogenital tract.

Chapter Outline

Millions of people around the world suffer from infections with urogenital tract microorganisms, which include prokaryotic bacteria as well as eukaryotic protists. *Trichomonas vaginalis*, for example, is a sexually transmitted protist that causes disease symptoms when it invades the human genitourinary tract. In this location *T. vaginalis* consumes bacteria and host epithelial and red blood cells, as well as carbohydrates and proteins released from damaged host cells. An estimated 170 million cases of infection with this organism occur each year around the globe, and infections can predispose humans to other diseases. *T. vaginalis* has an undulating membrane and flagella that allow it to move over mucus-coated skin (see chapter-opening photo). *Giardia intestinalis,* which infects the human intestinal tract, is another example of a protist whose flagella are critical to the ability to cause disease. Many types of disease-causing bacteria likewise move within the human body, including the urogenital and intestinal tracts, aided by motility structures.

These examples illustrate how knowledge of microbial diversity and structure is essential in medicine, but such knowledge is also important in comprehending the many ecological roles that Earth's microorganisms play. By influencing global environment, many microbes that do not cause disease nevertheless influence human health and sustainability. In this chapter we will survey microbial diversity, including the prokaryotic domain Archaea and domain Bacteria, as well as diverse phyla of eukaryotic protists.

22.1 Introduction to Microorganisms

Learning Outcomes:

1. Define the terms microorganism, archaea, bacteria, and protists.

2. Explain what microbiomes are and how they benefit hosts.

3. Draw a diagram that illustrates horizontal gene transfer and explain how it benefits the recipient organism.

Microorganisms, also known as microbes, are organisms that are typically so small in size that they can be seen only with the use of a microscope. Although some species of the Kingdom Fungi (Chapter 24) and a few animals are microscopic in size, most animals and many fungi grow large enough to see without a microscope. In this chapter we focus on groups that are primarily microscopic:

- the prokaryotic domain Archaea (informally known as archaea)

- the prokaryotic domain Bacteria (informally, bacteria)

- diverse phyla of protists having eukaryotic cells, which are classified in the domain Eukarya, together with animals, plants, and fungi

Recall that prokaryotic cells lack many of the features that occur in eukaryotic cells. Examples of distinctive eukaryotic cell features include nuclei having an envelope with complex pores, mitochondria, and other membrane-bound organelles. Comparative study of modern prokaryotic organisms and protists helps to reveal how eukaryotic cells first arose from prokaryotic ancestors.

Archaea and Bacteria Are Ancient Lineages That Continue to Be Abundant Today

The domains Archaea and Bacteria are both monophyletic groups, meaning they have a single common ancestor. Although archaea and bacteria together are sometimes referred to as the "prokaryotes," this combination does not represent a monophyletic group (Figure 22.1).

Archaea and bacteria include Earth's smallest known cells and are the most abundant organisms in the world. About half of

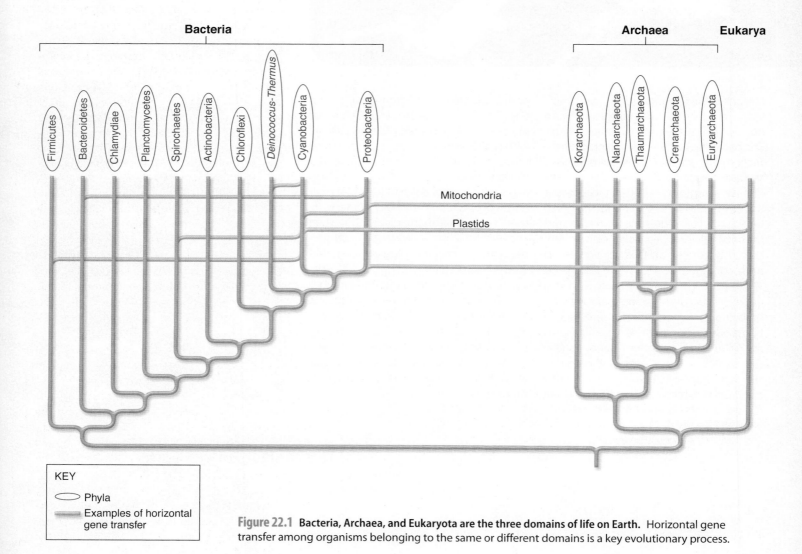

KEY

⬭ Phyla

▬ Examples of horizontal gene transfer

Figure 22.1 Bacteria, Archaea, and Eukaryota are the three domains of life on Earth. Horizontal gene transfer among organisms belonging to the same or different domains is a key evolutionary process.

Biology Principle

Cells Are the Simplest Units of Life

In the case of unicellular bacteria and archaea, a single cell represents an entire organism, but some bacteria have multicellular bodies.

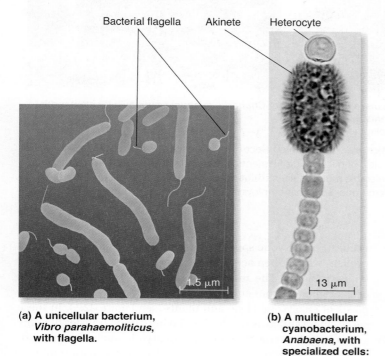

(a) A unicellular bacterium, *Vibro parahaemoliticus*, with flagella.

(b) A multicellular cyanobacterium, *Anabaena*, with specialized cells: heterocyte and akinete

Figure 22.2 **Bacterial cells.** **(a)** *Vibrio parahaemoliticus*, a unicellular bacterium that causes seafood poisoning, artificially colored. **(b)** *Anabaena*, a multicellular blue-green bacterium with specialized cells.

Earth's total biomass consists of an estimated 10^{30} individual bacteria and archaea. Just a pinch of garden soil can contain 2 billion prokaryotic cells, and about a million occur in 1 mL of seawater. Archaea and bacteria live in nearly every conceivable habitat, including extremely hot or salty waters that support no other life, and they are also Earth's most ancient organisms, having originated more than 3.5 bya. Their great age and varied habitats have resulted in extraordinarily high metabolic diversity. Such high metabolic diversity explains why modern archaea and bacteria play diverse ecological roles and can be used in many technological applications. Prokaryotic organisms are often single-celled (Figure 22.2a), though many achieve larger body size by aggregating cells into colonies or rows of cells known as **filaments.** Some bacteria display the defining features of true multicellularity, such as specialized cells (Figure 22.2b).

Protists Are Early-Diverging Eukaryotes Displaying Diverse Structural Types

The term protist comes from the Greek word *protos*, meaning first, reflecting the observation that protists were Earth's first eukaryotes. **Protists** are diverse eukaryotic organisms that cannot be classified into the Kingdoms Fungi, Plantae, or Animalia. Protists that lack chloroplasts are informally termed protozoa (Figure 22.3a) or fungus-like protists (Figure 22.3b), whereas protists having one or more chloroplasts are informally termed algae (Figure 22.3c). Although most protists are microscopic in size (see Figures 22.3a,b), many can be observed without using a microscope, examples being the multicellular marine photosynthetic protists commonly known as seaweeds (see Figure 22.3c).

Microbiomes Are Communities of Microbes That Associate with Host Organisms

Modern biologists use not only microscopes but also genetic technologies to understand that microorganisms occur nearly everywhere on Earth and are particularly abundant in moist places. Microorganisms often occur in communities of diverse species that inhabit a common habitat. The particular types of microbial communities known as **microbiomes** inhabit the bodies of plants, animals, and other organisms that function as hosts (Figure 22.4). Recent research has revealed the key medical and ecological importance of microbiomes.

The human microbiome occurs on the skin and in our digestive and reproductive systems. An estimated 10–100 trillion microbes normally live in the typical human colon alone! These microbes provide beneficial services using genetic traits that humans do not possess, and the diverse types of metabolism present in the microbiome have coevolved with human metabolism. Recent research has revealed that human gut microbiome communities contain hundreds of bacterial species and that gut microbiomes differ among healthy people, and between healthy people and those having different types of medical conditions. Although many people associate microorganisms primarily with disease, relatively few microbes cause diseases and many play beneficial roles. For example, certain bacteria normally present in the human gut supply us with vitamin K, and other microbiome components help defend against disease microbes. Such bacterial-host associations are examples of **symbioses,** close associations of two or more species, and mutualistic symbioses occur when all partners in a close association benefit. Microbiomes associated with humans and other organisms are currently of intense research interest because they reveal ways in which microbes and their hosts are interdependent.

Microbiomes Foster Horizontal Gene Transfer

Living closely together in microbiomes and other types of communities fosters the exchange of genetic material between microbial species, an important evolutionary process known as horizontal gene transfer. **Horizontal gene transfer** is the process in which an organism receives genetic material from another organism without being the offspring of that organism. This process contrasts with vertical gene transfer, which occurs from parent to progeny, and is increasingly recognized as an important evolutionary mechanism. Recipient organisms benefit from horizontal gene transfer by acquiring new metabolic capabilities.

Horizontal gene transfer is particularly common among archaea and bacteria (see Figure 22.1). For example, at least 17% of the genes present in the common human gut bacterium *Escherichia coli* came from other bacteria. The study of

Flagella

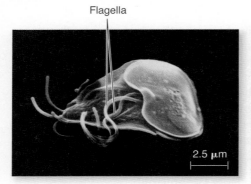

2.5 μm

(a) A single-celled protist, the flagellate protozoan, *Giardia*

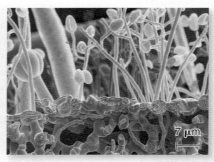

7 μm

(b) *Phytophthora infestans*, a fungus-like protist whose filaments grow within and emerge from a plant leaf

(c) *Chondrus crispus*, a multicellular algal protist

Figure 22.3 **Protist bodies take diverse forms that can be unicellular or multicellular.** **(a)** Scanning electron microscopic (SEM) view of the single-celled flagellate protozoan, *Giardia*, which infects the human gut. **(b)** SEM view of microscopic filaments produced by the fungus-like protist *Phytophthora infestans*, which causes disease of wild and crop plants, **(c)** an edible multicellular red alga that is conspicuous to the unaided eye, *Chondrus crispus*. Note: SEM images are made with a scanning electron microscope (SEM) that employs electrons rather than visible light, with the result that cellular structures do not normally appear in color.

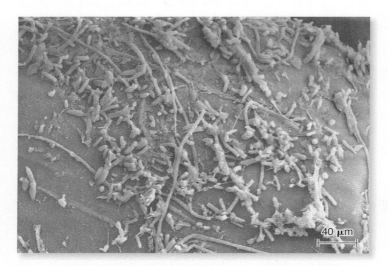

40 μm

Figure 22.4 **A microbiome.** This SEM shows some of the hundreds of bacterial species known to live on the surface of the green alga *Cladophora*. Together, these microbial species and their genes make up a microbiome that provides metabolic functions not present in the host and that can foster host growth. For example, associated bacteria produce vitamin B_{12} that the algal host needs.

nearly 200 genomes has revealed that about 80% of bacterial and archaeal genes have been involved in horizontal transfer at some point in their history. Genes also move among the bacterial, archaeal, and eukaryotic domains. For example, about a third of the genes present in the archaeal species *Methanosarcina mazei* originally came from bacteria, and the bacterial phylum Chlamydiae contributed at least 55 genes to plants.

Horizontal gene transfer can occur between different prokaryotic species via both transduction and transformation, as discussed in Chapter 15. Horizontal gene transfer also occurs by means of **endosymbiosis,** the process in which one species—the endosymbiont—lives in the body or cells of another species—the host. Endosymbiosis-based horizontal gene transfer is known to

occur in prokaryotic species, but is particularly common among protists, which often acquire new genes from bacterial or protist endosymbionts. The mitochondria present in most eukaryotic cells originated from endosymbiotic bacteria, as did the chloroplasts of eukaryotic algae and plants (see Figure 22.1). In these cases, endosymbiosis resulted in the horizontal transfer of many genes from bacterial genomes to eukaryotic nuclei. In this process, so many genes were transferred from the endosymbiont genome to the host nucleus that modern mitochondria and chloroplasts cannot reproduce outside host eukaryotic cells.

22.1 Reviewing the Concepts

- Prokaryotic Bacteria (informally bacteria) and Archaea (informally archaea) form two of the three domains of life. Prokaryotic species are often single-celled, though cellular aggregations are common, and examples of multicellularity occur (Figures 22.1, 22.2).

- Protists are classified into the domain Eukarya and occur as single eukaryotic cells or more complex bodies; multicellularity is common and some protists, such as seaweeds, are quite large (Figure 22.3).

- Many organisms, including humans, host communities of microbes known as microbiomes that confer additional metabolic capacities. Such close association among organisms fosters horizontal DNA transfer (Figure 22.4).

22.1 Testing Your Knowledge

1. Imagine that you have found a new type of organism that is composed of several cells but can only be observed by using a microscope. Is it possible that the cells of this organism have prokaryotic organization?
   a. Yes; although many prokaryotes are single-celled, some prokaryotes are multicellular.
   b. No; so far as is known, prokaryotes occur only as single cells.

2. What processes can serve as mechanisms of horizontal gene transfer between and among prokaryotic species and protists?

   a. viral transduction   **d.** all of the above

   b. transformation   **e.** none of the above

   c. endosymbiosis

22.2   Archaea

Learning Outcomes:

1. Describe the evolutionary and ecological importance of archaea.

2. List the features of archaea that enable them to grow in extreme habitats.

From an evolutionary perspective, archaea are important because they share a number of features with eukaryotes, suggesting common ancestry. For example, histone proteins are typically associated with the DNA of both archaea and eukaryotes, but such proteins are absent from most bacteria. Archaea and eukaryotes also share more than 30 ribosomal proteins that are not present in bacteria, and archaeal RNA polymerases are closely related to their eukaryotic counterparts. These similarities help evolutionary biologists learn how the information systems of eukaryotes evolved.

Archaea are also ecologically important. Though many archaea occur in soils and surface ocean waters of moderate conditions, diverse archaea occupy habitats with very high salt content, acidity, methane levels, or temperatures that would kill most bacteria and eukaryotes. Organisms that occur primarily in extreme habitats are known as **extremophiles** (meaning "lover of extreme conditions").

One example is *Methanopyrus*, which grows best at deep-sea thermal vent sites where the temperature is 98°C and is thus known as a hyperthermophile (meaning "lover of high temperatures"). At this temperature, the proteins of most organisms would denature, but those of *Methanopyrus* are resistant to such damage. Archaea help biologists to better understand the origin of life, the origin of eukaryotes, how life on Earth has evolved in extreme environments, and what kinds of extraterrestrial life might exist.

The domain Archaea includes five phyla: Korarchaeota, Nanoarchaeota, Thaumarchaeota, Crenarchaeota, and Euryarchaeota (see Figure 22.1). Early diverging Korarchaeota are primarily known from DNA sequences found in samples from hot springs. Nanoarchaeota includes the hyperthermophile *Nanoarchaeum equitans*, which associates with the deep-sea thermal vent crenarchaeote *Ignicoccus*. Thaumarchaeota species that oxidize ammonia are important in global nitrogen cycling. The Euryarchaeota includes some hyperthermophiles, diverse methane producers, and extreme halophiles—species able to grow in higher than usual salt concentrations.

Archaea possess distinctive membrane lipids, which are formed with ether bonds; in contrast, ester bonds characterize the membrane lipids of bacteria and eukaryotes (**Figure 22.5**). Ether-bonded membranes are resistant to damage by heat and other extreme conditions, which helps explain why many archaea are able to grow in extremely harsh environments. Also note that archaea use isoprene chains instead of fatty acid chains to build membranes. Although some archaea lack cell walls, most possess a wall composed of protein (which differs from the chemical composition of most bacterial cell walls described in Section 22.4).

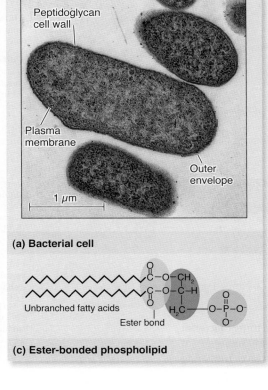

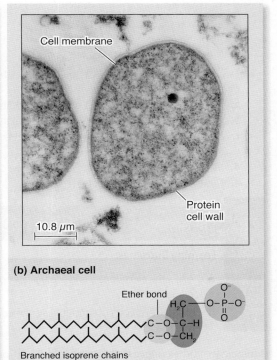

Figure 22.5   Archaea and Bacteria. **(a)** Bacteria and **(b)** archaea both have prokaryotic cell structure, but **(c)** bacterial membrane lipids are formed with ester linkages, whereas **(d)** archaeal membrane lipids feature ether linkages, which are thought to be more stable under extreme environmental conditions. As shown in transmission electron microscopic (TEM) images (a) and (b), most bacteria feature cell walls made of a material known as peptidoglycan that is often enclosed by an outer envelope, whereas archaea lack these features. Most archaea have outer coverings made of protein.

Archaea such as *Methanopyrus* are also ecologically important as producers of methane (CH_4)—the major component of natural gas. Methane is a greenhouse gas that increases global warming over 20 times more per molecule than does CO_2. In recent years the level of CH_4 has been increasing in Earth's atmosphere as the result of human activities. Several groups of anaerobic archaea convert CO_2, methyl groups, or acetate to CH_4 and release CH_4 from their cells into the atmosphere. Methane-producing archaea live in swampy wetlands, the bottoms of lakes, deep-sea habitats, or the digestive systems of animals such as cattle and humans.

22.2 Reviewing the Concepts

- Domain Archaea, which includes five phyla, is more closely related to Domain Eukarya than either is to Domain Bacteria (see Figure 22.1).
- Many representatives of Domain Archaea occur in extremely hot, salty, or acidic habitats. Ether-linked membrane lipids are among the features of archaea that enable their survival in extreme habitats (Figure 22.5).
- Several groups of archaea that occupy watery habitats generate the powerful greenhouse gas methane (CH_4).

22.2 Testing Your Knowledge

1. What features are characteristic of archaea but not bacteria?
   a. Archaea possess membrane lipids linked by ether bonds, not ester bonds as in bacteria.
   b. Archaea typically have cell walls composed of protein, not peptidoglycan as in the case of most bacteria.
   c. The DNA of archaea is bound to histone proteins, as in eukaryotes but not bacteria.
   d. All of the above statements are correct.
   e. None of the above statements is correct.

2. How does methane production by certain archaea contribute directly to global climate change?
   a. Methane has a cooling effect on Earth's climate.
   b. Methane in Earth's atmosphere increases rainfall.
   c. Methane is a powerful greenhouse gas that helps to warm Earth's climate.
   d. Methane in Earth's atmosphere increases the chance of fire.
   e. None of the above is correct.

22.3 Diversity of Bacterial Phyla

Learning Outcomes:

1. Explain the evolutionary and ecological importance of cyanobacteria.
2. List some examples of agriculturally or medically important proteobacteria.

Molecular studies suggest the existence of 50 or more bacterial phyla, though many are poorly known. Though some members of Domain Bacteria live in extreme environments, most favor moderate conditions. Many bacteria occur in the microbiome communities of eukaryotes and are thus of concern in medicine and agriculture. The characteristics of 10 prominent bacterial phyla (see Figure 22.1) are briefly summarized in **Table 22.1**. Among these, the Cyanobacteria and the Proteobacteria are particularly diverse and relevant to eukaryotic cell evolution, global ecology, and human affairs.

Table 22.1	Representative Bacterial Phyla
Phyla	**Characteristics**
Firmicutes	Diverse Gram-positive bacteria, some of which produce endospores. The disease-causing *Clostridium difficile* is an example.
Bacteroidetes	Includes representatives of diverse metabolism types; some are common in the human intestinal tract, and others are primarily aquatic.
Chlamydiae	Notably tiny, obligate intracellular parasites. Some cause eye disease in newborns or sexually transmitted diseases.
Planctomycetes	Reproduce by budding rather than binary fission; cell walls lack peptidoglycan; cytoplasm may contain nucleus-like bodies as in the case of *Gemmata obscuriglobus*.
Spirochaetes	Motile bacteria having distinctive corkscrew shapes, with flagella held close to the body. They include the pathogens *Treponema pallidum*, the agent of syphilis, and *Borrelia burgdorferi*, which causes Lyme disease.
Actinobacteria	Gram-positive bacteria producing branched filaments; many form spores. *Mycobacterium tuberculosis*, the agent of tuberculosis in humans, is an example. Actinobacteria are notable antibiotic producers; over 500 different antibiotics are known from this group.
Chloroflexi	Known as the green nonsulfur bacteria; conduct photosynthesis without releasing oxygen (anoxygenic photosynthesis).
Deinococcus-Thermus	Extremophiles. The genus *Deinococcus* is known for high resistance to ionizing radiation, and the genus *Thermus* inhabits hot springs. *Thermus aquaticus* has been used in commercial production of Taq polymerase enzyme used in the polymerase chain reaction (PCR), an important procedure in molecular biology laboratories.
Cyanobacteria	The oxygen-producing photosynthetic bacteria. Photosynthetic pigments include chlorophyll *a* and blue-green or red accessory pigments. Occur as unicells, colonies, unbranched filaments, and branched filaments. Many of the filamentous species produce specialized cells: dormant akinetes and heterocytes in which nitrogen fixation occurs. In waters having excess nutrients, cyanobacteria produce blooms and may release toxins harmful to the health of humans and wild and domesticated animals.
Proteobacteria	A very large group of Gram-negative bacteria, collectively having high metabolic diversity. Includes many species important in medicine, agriculture, and industry.

Cyanobacteria Are Photosynthetic Bacteria That Produce Oxygen and Play Other Important Ecological Roles

The phylum Cyanobacteria contains photosynthetic bacteria that are abundant in fresh waters, oceans, and wetlands and on the surfaces of arid soils. Cyanobacteria are named for blue-green (cyan) coloration conferred by photosynthetic pigments that help chlorophyll absorb light energy (see Figure 22.2b). Cyanobacteria are the only bacteria known to generate oxygen as a product of photosynthesis. Ancient cyanobacteria produced Earth's first oxygen-rich atmosphere, which allowed the eventual rise of eukaryotes. As previously noted, the chloroplasts of eukaryotic algae and plants evolved from cyanobacteria, a process that involved massive horizontal transfer of bacterial genes into eukaryotic nuclear genomes.

In phosphorus-rich bodies of water, some species of cyanobacteria grow rapidly into large, visible populations (blooms) that color the water blue-green, or cyan. The individual cells release small amounts of toxins that help to keep small aquatic animals from eating them, but when blooms occur, toxins can rise to levels that harm humans, pets, livestock, and wildlife. Consequently, public health authorities often warn people not to swim in waters with visible blue-green blooms nor to allow pets and livestock to drink such water. People can prevent the formation of cyanobacterial blooms by reducing the input of phosphorus-rich fertilizers, manure, and sewage into bodies of water.

Despite the harmful effects of some species, cyanobacteria provide important benefits to humans and other organisms, such as producing atmospheric oxygen. Many cyanobacteria also have the ability to convert abundant but inert atmospheric nitrogen gas into ammonia, which algae and plants can use to synthesize amino acids and proteins. This process, known as **nitrogen fixation,** enriches nutrient-poor soils, particularly wet paddy fields where rice is grown in many regions of the world, thereby helping to provide food for billions of people. Cyanobacteria illustrate the wide range of body diversity found among bacterial phyla:

- Unicells (Figure 22.6a) are single-celled bodies.
- Colonies are groups of cells held together by a thick gluey substance called mucilage (Figure 22.6b).
- Filaments are cells that are attached end-to-end (Figure 22.6c), some of which are branched (Figure 22.6d). Some filamentous cyanobacteria display the hallmarks of multicellularity that also mark multicellular plants and animals: cell-to-cell attachment, specialized cells, intercellular chemical communication, and programmed cell death.

Proteobacteria Do Not Produce Oxygen but Play Other Ecologically Important Roles

Though Proteobacteria share molecular and cell-wall features, this phylum displays amazing diversity of form and metabolism in five major classes:

- Alphaproteobacteria, which are closely related to the ancestry of mitochondria, include nitrogen-fixing species that associate with plants, thereby fostering plant growth (see Figure 29.11).
- Betaproteobacteria, such as the soil inhabitant *Nitrosomonas*, are important in the global nitrogen cycle.
- Gammaproteobacteria include human pathogens such as *Neisseria gonorrhoeae*, the agent of the sexually transmitted disease gonorrhea; *Vibrio cholerae,* which causes cholera epidemics when drinking water becomes contaminated with animal waste during floods and other natural disasters; and *Salmonella enterica* and *Escherichia coli* strain O157:H7, which can contaminate food and water, causing intestinal infections.
- Deltaproteobacteria include colony-forming myxobacteria and predatory bdellovibrios, which drill through the cell walls of other bacteria in order to consume them.
- Epsilonproteobacteria are represented by *Helicobacter pylori*, a risk factor for peptic ulcers and stomach cancer.

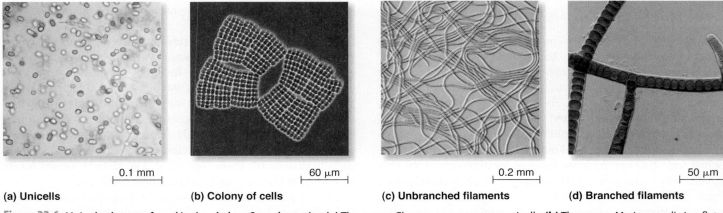

| 0.1 mm | 60 μm | 0.2 mm | 50 μm |

(a) Unicells   **(b) Colony of cells**   **(c) Unbranched filaments**   **(d) Branched filaments**

Figure 22.6 **Major body types found in the phylum Cyanobacteria. (a)** The genus *Chroococcus* occurs as unicells. **(b)** The genus *Merismopedia* is a flat colony of cells held together by mucilage. **(c)** The genus *Oscillatoria* is an unbranched filament. **(d)** The genus *Stigonema* is a branched filament having a mucilage sheath; sunscreen compounds that protect the cells from damage by ultraviolet (UV) radiation cause the brown color of the sheath.

22.3 Reviewing the Concepts

- The Domain Bacteria includes 50 or more phyla, including Cyanobacteria and Proteobacteria (Figure 22.1, Table 22.1).
- Cyanobacteria were ancestral to all modern chloroplasts, are the only prokaryotic organisms that produce oxygen as a result of photosynthesis, sometimes form harmful bloom populations in overly fertile waters, and illustrate prokaryotic body types (Figure 22.6).
- Proteobacteria were ancestral to mitochondria, do not produce oxygen, and include agriculturally and medically important species.

22.3 Testing Your Knowledge

1. What features of cyanobacteria can be harmful to humans and other animals?
   a. Oxygen production
   b. Toxin production
   c. Production of blue-green photosynthetic pigments
   d. Carbon fixation
   e. Nitrogen fixation

2. What essential role did early alphaproteobacteria play in the origin of eukaryotic cells?
   a. They were precursors of plastids.
   b. They were precursors of nuclei.
   c. Some evolved into mitochondria.
   d. Some evolved into the endomembrane system.
   e. None of the above is reasonable.

22.4 Diversity in Bacterial Cell Structure

Learning Outcomes:

1. Discuss cellular structural adaptations that have increased the complexity of prokaryotic cells.
2. Describe the structural differences between Gram-positive and Gram-negative bacterial cells.
3. Explain how mucilage influences bacterial behavior.
4. List the different means by which prokaryotic cells can move.

Even though bacteria have a much simpler cellular organization than do eukaryotes, many bacteria display structural adaptations that increase their complexity. Cyanobacteria and other photosynthetic bacteria, for example, are able to use light energy to produce organic compounds because their cells contain large numbers of thylakoids, flattened tubular membranes that grow inward from the plasma membrane (Figure 22.7a). The extensive membrane surface of the thylakoids bears large amounts of chlorophyll and other components required for photosynthesis. This explains why thylakoids are also abundant in plant chloroplasts, which descended from cyanobacterial ancestors. Thylakoids enable photosynthetic bacteria and chloroplasts to take maximum advantage of light energy in their environments.

In other bacteria, plasma membrane ingrowth has generated additional intriguing adaptations—magnetosomes and

nucleus-like bodies—that are sometimes described as bacterial organelles. Magnetosomes are tiny crystals of an iron mineral known as magnetite, each surrounded by a membrane. These structures occur in the bacterium *Magnetospirillum* and related genera (Figure 22.7b). In each cell, about 15 to 20 magnetosomes occur in a row, together acting as a compass needle that responds to the Earth's magnetic field. Magnetosomes help the bacteria to orient themselves in space and thereby locate the submerged, low-oxygen habitats they prefer. Plasma membrane ingrowths may also surround cellular DNA, producing nucleus-like structures within bacteria of the phylum Planctomycetes (Figure 22.7c). Common in aquatic habitats, such bacteria occur in microbiomes supported by protist hosts (see Figure 22.4), and are important to evolutionary biologists who are interested in the evolutionary origin of the eukaryotic nucleus.

Prokaryotic Cells Vary in Shape

Bacterial cells occur in five common shapes (Figure 22.8):

- Spheres, known as **cocci,** maximize surface area to volume ratio, thereby enhancing exchange of materials with the environment.
- Elongate rods, called **bacilli,** are able to store more nutrients than some other shapes.
- Comma-shaped cells are called **vibrios.**
- Spiral-shaped cells that are flexible are known as **spirochaetes.**
- Spiral-shaped cells that are rigid are termed **spirilli.**

Cytoskeletal proteins similar to those present in eukaryotic cells control these cell shapes. For example, helical strands of an actin-like protein are responsible for the rod shape of bacilli; if this protein is not produced, bacilli become spherical in shape.

Bacterial Cells Vary in Cell-Wall Structure

Most prokaryotic cells possess a rigid cell wall outside the plasma membrane. Cell walls maintain cell shape and help protect against attack by viruses or predatory bacteria. Cell walls also help bacteria and other microbes avoid lysing in hypotonic conditions, when the solute concentration is higher inside the cell than outside. The structure and composition of bacterial cell walls are medically important.

A polymer known as **peptidoglycan** is an important component of most bacterial cell walls. Peptidoglycan is composed of carbohydrates that are cross-linked by peptides. Bacterial cell walls occur in two major forms that differ in peptidoglycan thickness, presence or absence of a membrane occurring outside the peptidoglycan, staining properties, and response to antibiotics. Bacteria having these chemically different walls are called Gram-positive or Gram-negative bacteria, after the staining process used to distinguish them (Figure 22.9). The stain is named for its inventor, the Danish scientist Hans Christian Gram.

Gram-positive bacteria classified in the phyla Firmicutes and Actinobacteria have walls with a relatively thick peptidoglycan layer (Figure 22.10a). By contrast, the cell walls of Cyanobacteria, Proteobacteria, and other Gram-negative species have a thinner peptidoglycan layer and are enclosed by a thin, outer envelope

Thylakoids provide a greater surface area for chlorophyll and other molecules involved in photosynthesis.

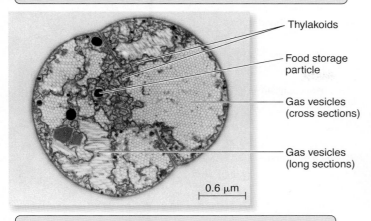

Thylakoids

Food storage particle

Gas vesicles (cross sections)

Gas vesicles (long sections)

0.6 μm

The gas vesicles buoy this photosynthetic organism to the lighted water surface, where it often forms conspicuous scums.

(a)

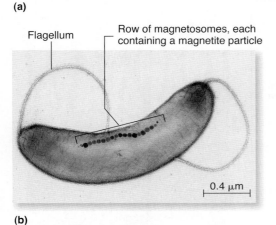

Flagellum

Row of magnetosomes, each containing a magnetite particle

0.4 μm

(b)

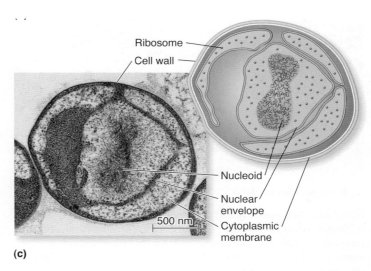

Ribosome

Cell wall

Nucleoid

Nuclear envelope

Cytoplasmic membrane

(c)

Figure 22.7 Bacterial cell structures that arise from infolded cell membrane. (a) Photosynthetic thylakoid membranes and numerous gas vesicles found in a cell of the aquatic cyanobacterial genus *Microcystis*. **(b)** Magnetosomes found in the spirillum *Magnetospirillum magnetotacticum*. An internal row of iron-rich magnetite crystals, each enclosed by a membrane derived from the plasma membrane. The row of magnetosomes functions like a compass needle, allowing this bacterium to detect the Earth's magnetic field. This feature allows *M. magnetotacticum* to orient itself in space and thereby locate its preferred habitat, low-oxygen subsurface waters. **(c)** A nucleus-like structure in *Gemmata obscuriglobus*, a genus of planctomycete bacteria. Although the nuclear envelope-like structure lacks pores, it encloses the bacterial cell's DNA, known as a nucleoid.

whose outer leaflet is rich in **lipopolysaccharides** (Figure 22.10b). This outer envelope of Gram-negative bacteria is a lipid bilayer, but is distinct from the plasma membrane. Peptidoglycan and lipopolysaccharides can affect disease symptoms, the composition of vaccines, and bacterial responses to antibiotics.

The lipopolysaccharide-rich outer membrane of Gram-negative bacteria helps them to resist the entry of some antibiotics and can contain proteins that help disease-causing bacteria to attach to target cells. However, this outer envelope also impedes the secretion of proteins from bacterial cells into the environment,

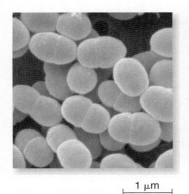

1 μm

Sphere-shaped cocci (*Lactococcus lactis*)

11.4 μm

Rod-shaped bacilli (*Lactobacillus plantarum*)

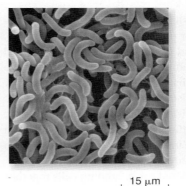

15 μm

Comma-shaped vibrios (*Vibrio cholerae*)

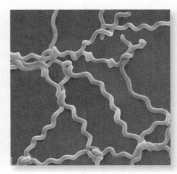

7.5 μm

Spiral-shaped spirochaetes (*Leptospira* sp.)

Figure 22.8 Major types of prokaryotic cell shapes. Scanning electron microscopic (SEM) views.

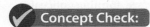 **Concept Check:** *Why are these images not colored?*

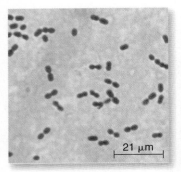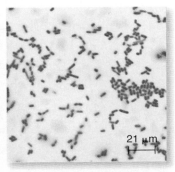

(a) Gram-positive bacteria   **(b) Gram-negative bacteria**

Figure 22.9 **Gram-positive and Gram-negative bacteria.**
(a) *Streptococcus pneumoniae*, a member of the phylum Firmicutes, stains positive (purple) with the Gram stain. **(b)** *Escherichia coli*, a member of the Proteobacteria, stains negative (pink) when the Gram stain procedure is applied.

a process that normally allows cells to communicate with each other. Gram-negative bacteria have adapted to the presence of an outer membrane by evolving several types of protein systems that function in secretion. In some disease-causing bacteria, these secretion systems have evolved into weapons used to attack plant or animal cells.

Distinguishing Gram-positive from Gram-negative bacteria is an important factor in choosing the best antibiotics for treating infectious diseases. For example, Gram-positive bacteria are typically more susceptible than Gram-negative bacteria to penicillin and related antibiotics because these antibiotics interfere with synthesis of peptidoglycan, which Gram-positive bacteria require in larger amounts. For this reason, penicillin or related antibiotics such as methicillin are widely used to treat infections caused by Gram-positive bacteria. However, it is of societal concern that some strains of Gram-positive bacteria have become resistant to some antibiotics, an example being methicillin-resistant *Staphylococcus aureus*, or MRSA. The evolution of antibiotic resistance in bacteria can often be traced to a horizontal gene transfer event.

Slimy Mucilage Often Coats Cellular Surfaces

Many bacteria exude a coat of slimy mucilage, also called a capsule, glycocalyx, or extracellular polymeric substance. Mucilage, which varies in consistency and thickness, is largely composed of hydrated polysaccharides and protein. A capsule helps some disease bacteria evade the defense system of their host. You may recall that Frederick Griffith discovered the transfer of genetic material while experimenting with capsule-producing pathogenic strains and capsule-less nonpathogenic strains of the bacterium *Streptococcus pneumoniae*. The immune system cells of mice are able to destroy this bacterium only if it lacks a capsule.

Mucilage plays many additional roles: holding cells together closely enough for chemical communication and DNA exchange to occur, helping aquatic species to float in water, binding mineral nutrients, helping cells to stick to surfaces where they may form coatings known as **biofilms** (see Figure 22.4), and repelling attack. Pigmented slime sheaths (see Figure 22.6d) coat some bacterial filaments, where they help to prevent UV damage.

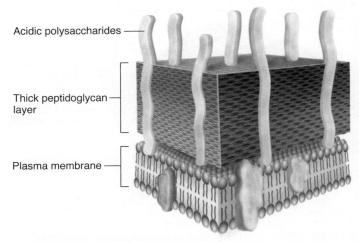

(a) Gram-positive: thick peptidoglycan cell wall layer, no outer envelope

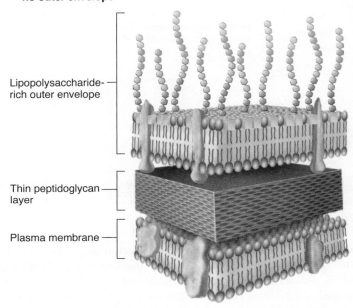

(b) Gram-negative: thinner peptidoglycan cell wall layer, with outer envelope

Figure 22.10 **Cell-wall structures of Gram-positive and Gram-negative bacteria. (a)** The structure of the cell wall of Gram-positive bacteria. **(b)** The structure of the cell wall and lipopolysaccharide envelope typical of Gram-negative bacteria.

Bacteria Move by a Variety of Cellular Adaptations

Many bacteria have structures at the cell surface or within cells that enable them to change position in their environment, a process known as motility. Motility allows bacterial and other microbes to respond to chemical signals emitted from other cells and to move to favorable conditions within gradients of light, gases, or nutrients.

- Internal buoyancy vesicles (see Figure 22.7a) help cyanobacteria to float into well-illuminated waters that allow photosynthesis to occur. Cyanobacteria filled with buoyancy vesicles can collect at the water surface, forming noticeable scums.

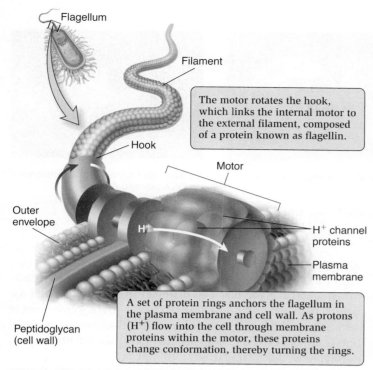

Figure 22.11 **Diagram of a prokaryotic flagellum, showing a filament, hook, and motor.**

The motor rotates the hook, which links the internal motor to the external filament, composed of a protein known as flagellin.

A set of protein rings anchors the flagellum in the plasma membrane and cell wall. As protons (H^+) flow into the cell through membrane proteins within the motor, these proteins change conformation, thereby turning the rings.

Concept Check: *Does the filament move more like the arms of a human swimmer or the shaft of a boat propeller?*

- Threadlike cell surface structures known as pili (singular, pilus) allow some species to twitch or glide across surfaces (and may also aid reproduction).
- Bacterial flagella (see Figure 22.2a) allow cells to move by twitching, gliding, or swimming in liquids at rates of more than 150 μm per second and thus can foster the spread of infection through an animal or plant body.

Bacterial flagella (singular, flagellum) differ from eukaryotic flagella in several ways. Although bacterial flagella are largely built of about 30 types of proteins, they lack a plasma membrane covering, an internal cytoskeleton of microtubules, and motor proteins—all features that characterize eukaryotic flagella. Unlike eukaryotic flagella, prokaryotic flagella do not repeatedly bend and straighten. Instead, prokaryotic flagella spin, propelled by molecular machines composed of a filament, hook, and motor that work together, somewhat like a boat's outboard motor and propeller (**Figure 22.11**). Lying outside the cell, the long, stiff, curved filament acts as a propeller. The hook links the filament with the motor that contains a set of protein rings at the cell surface. Hydrogen ions (protons), which have been pumped out of the cytoplasm, usually via the electron transport system, diffuse back into the cell through channel proteins within the motor. This proton flow powers the turning of the hook and filament at rates of hundreds of revolutions per second. (Archaea may have flagella that also rotate but are much thinner than bacterial flagella, composed of different proteins, and powered differently—by the hydrolysis of ATP.)

22.4 Reviewing the Concepts

- Intracellular structures such as thylakoids, magnetosomes, and nucleus-like organelles are examples of prokaryotic cell structure complexity (Figure 22.7).
- Major bacterial cell shape types are spherical cocci, rod-shaped bacilli, comma-shaped vibrios, and coiled spirochaetes and spirilli (Figure 22.8).
- Most bacterial cell walls contain peptidoglycan, which is composed of carbohydrates cross-linked by peptides. Gram-positive bacterial cells have thick peptidoglycan walls, whereas Gram-negative cells have less peptidoglycan in their walls and are enclosed by an outer lipopolysaccharide envelope (Figures 22.9, 22.10).
- Motility enables bacteria to change positions within their environment, which aids in locating favorable conditions for growth. Buoyancy vesicles, pili, and flagella are structures that enable motility (Figure 22.11).

22.4 Testing Your Knowledge

1. What structures that occur within some bacterial cells are produced by ingrowth of the plasma membrane?
   a. thylakoids in photosynthetic bacteria
   b. magnetosomes in bacteria that can sense and respond to Earth's magnetic field
   c. nucleus-like structures that enclose DNA
   d. all of the above
   e. none of the above

2. Which structures are associated with motility in one or more types of bacteria?
   a. pili   d. mucilage
   b. peptidoglycan   e. all of the above
   c. lipopolysaccharide envelope

22.5 Ecological and Medical Importance of Bacteria

Learning Outcomes:

1. Understand how populations of bacteria increase and how some bacteria survive under stressful conditions.
2. List the major modes of nutrition used by bacteria and different responses to oxygen.
3. Describe in basic terms the process of biological nitrogen fixation, why it is important, and how oxygen interferes with this process.

The small size of bacteria and relative simplicity of their genome allow many species to reproduce very quickly when nutritional resources are plentiful. Rapid reproduction can generate populations large enough to affect other organisms and indeed, our entire planet. Understanding bacterial reproduction is key to comprehending how microbes play key ecological and medical roles: producing and breaking down organic carbon, processing

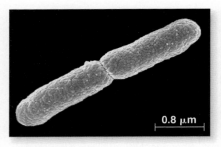

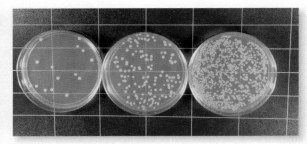

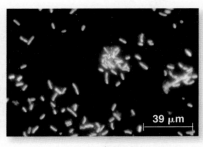

(a) Bacterium undergoing binary fission   **(b) Colonies developed from single cells**   **(c) Bacteria stained with fluorescent DNA-binding dye**

Figure 22.12 Bacteria can be visualized and counted by means of colonies formed by repeated binary fission or by using fluorescent dye.

minerals, serving as symbionts that benefit other organisms, and functioning as disease agents.

Bacterial Reproduction Helps to Explain Ecological Function

Bacteria lack eukaryote-type sexual reproduction involving specialized gametes, gamete fusion (syngamy), and meiosis, though they can exchange some genes by conjugation, transformation, and transduction (described in Chapter 15). Some bacteria reproduce asexually by budding, producing small progeny cells from larger parental cells. However, many bacteria reproduce asexually by division of a single cell into two equal progeny cells, a process known as **binary fission.**

Binary fission is the basis of a widely used method for detecting and counting bacteria in food, water samples, or patient fluids. Microbiologists who study the spread of disease need to quantify bacterial cells in samples taken from the environment. Medical technicians often need to count bacteria in body fluid samples to assess the likelihood of infection. However, because bacterial cells are small and often unpigmented, they are difficult to view and count directly. One way that microbiologists count bacteria is to place a measured volume of sample into plastic dishes filled with a semisolid nutrient medium. Bacteria in the sample undergo repeated binary fission to form colonies of cells visible to the unaided eye. Because each colony is assumed to represent a single cell that was present in the original sample, the number of colonies in the dish approximates the number of living bacteria in the original sample (**Figure 22.12**). Bacteria that cannot be cultivated in the laboratory can, however, be observed and counted with the use of a fluorescent dye that binds bacterial DNA (see Figure 22.12c).

Some Bacteria Survive Harsh Conditions as Akinetes or Endospores

Some bacteria produce thick-walled cells that are able to survive unfavorable conditions in a dormant state. These specialized cells develop when bacteria have experienced stress, such as low nutrients or unfavorable temperatures, and are able to germinate into metabolically active cells when conditions improve. For example, when winter approaches, aquatic filamentous cyanobacteria often produce **akinetes**—large, thick-walled, food-filled cells (see Figure 22.2b). Akinetes are able to survive winter at the bottoms of lakes, and they produce new filaments in spring when they are carried by water currents to the brightly lit surface. Persistence of such akinetes, followed by their growth into filaments by means of binary fission, explains how harmful cyanobacterial blooms can develop year after year in overly fertile lakes.

Endospores (**Figure 22.13**) are produced inside the cells of some bacterial species. DNA and other materials become enclosed within a tough coat and then are released when the enclosing cell dies and breaks down. Bacterial endospores can remain alive, though in a dormant state, for long periods, then reactivate when conditions are suitable. The ability to produce endospores allows some Gram-positive Firmicutes bacteria to cause serious diseases. For example, *Bacillus anthracis* causes the disease anthrax, a potential agent in bioterrorism and germ warfare. Most cases of human

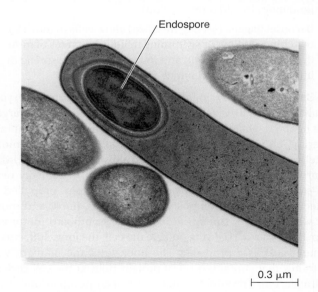

Endospore

0.3 μm

Figure 22.13 **Specialized bacterial cells capable of dormancy.** An endospore with a resistant wall develops within the cytoplasm of the pathogen *Clostridium difficile.*

✓ **Concept Check:** *How do endospores influence the ability of some bacteria to cause disease?*

anthrax result when endospores of *B. anthracis* enter breaks in the skin, causing skin infections that are relatively easily cured by antibiotic treatment. But sometimes the endospores are inhaled or consumed in undercooked, contaminated meat, potentially causing more serious illness or death. *Clostridium botulinum* can contaminate improperly canned food that has not been heated to temperatures high enough to destroy its tough endospores. When the endospores germinate and bacterial cells grow in the food, they produce a deadly toxin, as well as NH_3 and CO_2 gas, which causes can lids to bulge. If humans consume the food, the toxin causes botulism, a severe type of food poisoning that can lead to respiratory and muscular paralysis. The toxin is so potent that only 400 g of *C. botulinum* toxin would be sufficient to kill every human on Earth. That being the case, it is interesting that people use a commercial preparation of botulinum toxin in the form of Botox, which is injected into the skin to paralyze facial muscles, thereby reducing the appearance of wrinkles.

Clostridium tetani produces a nerve toxin that causes lockjaw, also known as tetanus, when bacterial cells or endospores from soil enter wounds. The ability of the genera *Bacillus* and *Clostridium* to produce resistant endospores helps to explain their widespread presence in nature and their effect on humans.

Microbes Are Classified by Type of Nutrition and Response to Oxygen

Microbes can be classified according to their energy source, carbon source, response to oxygen, and presence of specialized metabolic processes such as nitrogen fixation.

- **Autotrophs** (from the Greek, meaning self-feeders) are organisms that are able to produce all or most of their own organic compounds from inorganic sources. Autotrophs fall into two categories: photoautotrophs and chemolithoautotrophs.
- **Photoautotrophs** such as cyanobacteria use light as a source of energy for the synthesis of organic compounds from CO_2 and H_2O or from H_2S.
- **Chemolithoautotrophs** use energy obtained by chemical modifications of inorganic compounds to synthesize organic compounds. Such chemical modifications include nitrification (the conversion of ammonia to nitrate) and the oxidation of sulfur, iron, or hydrogen.
- **Heterotrophs** (from the Greek, meaning other feeders) are organisms that require at least one organic compound, and often more, from their environment.
- **Photoheterotrophs** are able to use light energy to generate ATP, but they must take in organic compounds from their environment as a source of carbon.
- **Chemoheterotrophs** must obtain organic molecules for both energy and as a carbon source. Among the many types of bacterial chemoheterotrophs is the Gram-positive species *Propionibacterium acnes*, which contributes to the skin condition acne, affecting up to 80% of adolescents in the U.S. The genome sequence of *P. acnes* has revealed numerous genes that allow it to break down skin cells and consume the products.

Microbial species also differ in their need for and responses to oxygen. These variations are important to the ecological or medical roles of microbes:

- **Obligate aerobes** require O_2 in order to survive.
- **Obligate anaerobes,** such as the Firmicutes genus *Clostridium*, are poisoned by O_2. People suffering from gas gangrene caused by *Clostridium perfringens* and related species are usually treated by placement in a chamber with a high oxygen content (called a hyperbaric chamber), which kills the organisms and deactivates the toxins.
- **Aerotolerant anaerobes** do not use O_2, but they are not poisoned by it either. These organisms obtain their energy by fermentation or anaerobic respiration, which uses electron acceptors other than oxygen in electron transport processes. Anaerobic metabolic processes include denitrification (the conversion of nitrate into N_2 gas) and the reduction of manganese, iron, and sulfate, which are all important in the Earth's cycling of minerals.
- **Facultative anaerobes** can use O_2 via aerobic respiration, obtain energy via anaerobic fermentation, or use inorganic chemical reactions to obtain energy, shifting between modes depending on environmental conditions.

Cyanobacteria and some other prokaryotic species are able to convert the abundant atmospheric nitrogen gas into a reduced form that algae and plants can use to produce amino acids and proteins. Oxygen poisons the principal enzyme involved in the nitrogen fixation process, so many cyanobacteria accomplish nitrogen fixation within specialized cells known as heterocytes, where oxygen concentrations are low (see Figure 22.2b). Some cyanobacteria that lack heterocytes accomplish nitrogen fixation at night, when photosynthetic oxygen production does not occur.

Cyanobacteria and other autotrophic bacteria, together with plants and algae, are important **producers,** organisms that use photosynthesis to synthesize the organic compounds used by other organisms for food. **Decomposers,** also known as saprobes, include heterotrophic microorganisms (as well as fungi and animals). These organisms break down dead organisms and organic matter, releasing minerals for uptake by living things. Certain bacteria known as methanotrophs (meaning "methane eaters") consume CH_4, thereby reducing its concentration in the atmosphere. In the absence of methanotrophs, Earth's atmosphere would be much richer in the greenhouse gas CH_4, which would substantially increase global temperatures. Methanotrophic bacteria require oxygen in order to oxidize methane, which explains why methanotrophs commonly associate with aquatic plants and algae; these photosynthetic organisms emit the needed oxygen.

Bacteria are also important in producing and degrading complex organic compounds. Astonishingly, many bacteria are able to break down antibiotics for use as a source of organic carbon, as discussed next.

FEATURE INVESTIGATION

Dantas and Colleagues Found That Many Bacteria Can Break Down and Consume Antibiotics as a Sole Carbon Source

Many microorganisms naturally secrete antibiotics, chemicals that inhibit the growth of other microorganisms. Antibiotic compounds are evolutionary adaptations that allow bacteria and other microbes to avoid attack or reduce competition for resources. People have taken advantage of high antibiotic production by certain bacteria, particularly species of the phylum Actinobacteria, to make commercial antibiotics in industrial processes.

In nature, many chemoheterotrophic bacteria have taken advantage of widespread natural antibiotic production by utilizing these organic compounds as a source of carbon. In 2008, Gautam Dantas, George Church, and their colleagues reported this conclusion after experimentally testing their hypothesis that soil bacteria might be able to metabolize antibiotics (**Figure 22.14**). The investigators first cultivated bacteria from 11 different soils in the laboratory, finding diverse phylogenetic types. Almost 90% of the cultured bacteria were Gram-negative Proteobacteria, some closely related to human pathogens, whereas 7% of the cultures

were Gram-positive Actinobacteria. These researchers then tested the ability of the bacteria cultured from different soils (isolates) to use various antibiotics as a sole carbon source. The 18 antibiotics tested included penicillin and related compounds, as well as widely prescribed ciprofloxacin (Cipro). Every antibiotic tested supported the growth of bacteria from soil. Importantly, each antibiotic-eating isolate was resistant to several antibiotics at concentrations used in medical treatment of infections.

In today's society, the widespread use of antibiotics in medicine and agriculture is of concern because it is thought to promote antibiotic resistance. The experiment by Dantas and associates revealed that natural evolutionary processes—the widespread development by diverse soil bacteria of metabolic processes to utilize many types of antibiotics as food—represent a previously unrecognized source of antibiotic resistance. The study also indicated that natural bacteria are a potential source of antibiotic-resistance genes that could be horizontally transferred to disease-causing bacteria.

Figure 22.14 Diverse bacteria isolated from different soils are able to grow on many types of antibiotics.

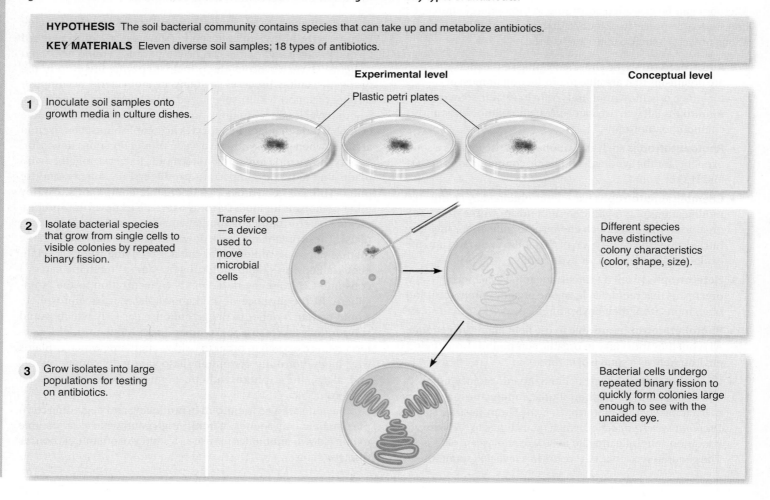

4 Inoculate each bacterial isolate onto replicate dishes containing a different antibiotic as the only food source.

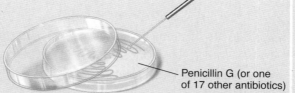

Penicillin G (or one of 17 other antibiotics)

Test the ability of each isolate to grow on a range of antibiotics.

5 Allow time for bacterial population growth; compare growth among dishes.

Strong growth of forest soil #1 bacterial isolate on penicillin G food.

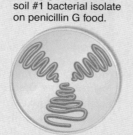

Poor growth of urban soil #3 bacterial isolate on dicloxacillin food.

Compare each isolate's ability to grow on different antibiotics.

6 THE DATA

Most soils tested contained bacterial species that were able to use antibiotics of many types for food and thus were resistant to those antibiotics.

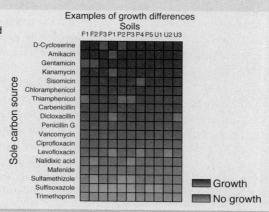

Examples of growth differences

Soils
F1 F2 F3 P1 P2 P3 P4 P5 U1 U2 U3

Sole carbon source:
D-Cycloserine
Amikacin
Gentamicin
Kanamycin
Sisomicin
Chloramphenicol
Thiamphenicol
Carbenicillin
Dicloxacillin
Penicillin G
Vancomycin
Ciprofloxacin
Levofloxacin
Nalidixic acid
Mafenide
Sulfamethizole
Sulfisoxazole
Trimethoprim

■ Growth
■ No growth

7 CONCLUSION Natural soils contain bacteria that are able to utilize antibiotics produced naturally by other species as food. Soil bacteria are a previously unrecognized source of antibiotic resistance genes that can be transferred to other species.

8 SOURCE Dantas, G., Sommer, M. O. A., Oluwasegun, R. D., and Church, G. M. 2008. Bacteria subsisting on antibiotics. *Science* 320:100–103.

Experimental Questions

1. What features of soil bacteria attracted the attention of researchers?

2. What processes did researchers use to test their hypothesis that soil bacteria might use antibiotics as a food source?

3. Why was it important to researchers to test the ability of soil bacteria to resist antibiotics in the same concentrations that physicians use to treat infections?

Pathogenic Bacteria Cause Some Forms of Disease

Microorganisms that cause disease in one or more types of host organism are known as **pathogens.** Cholera, leprosy, tetanus, pneumonia, whooping cough, diphtheria, Lyme disease, scarlet fever, rheumatic fever, typhoid fever, bacterial dysentery, and tooth decay are among the many examples of human diseases caused by bacterial pathogens. Bacteria also cause many plant diseases of importance in agriculture, including blights, soft rots, and wilts. Certain bacteria also attack other bacteria, protists, and fungi, thereby helping to control natural populations. In the mid- to late 1800s, the German physician Robert Koch established a series of four steps that even today are used to determine whether a particular organism causes a specific disease.

- First, the presence of the suspected pathogen must correlate with occurrence of symptoms in the host.
- Second, the pathogen must be isolated from an infected host and grown in pure culture if possible.
- Third, cells from the pure culture should cause disease when inoculated into a healthy host.
- Fourth and finally, one should be able to isolate the same pathogen from the second infected host.

Using these steps, known as **Koch's postulates,** Koch discovered the bacterial causes of anthrax, cholera, and tuberculosis. Subsequent investigators have used Koch's postulates to establish the identities of additional bacteria that cause other infectious diseases.

22.5 Reviewing the Concepts

- Populations of most bacteria and archaea enlarge by binary fission, a simple type of cell division that allows rapid population growth into colonies. Some bacteria are able to survive harsh conditions as dormant akinetes or endospores (Figures 22.12, 22.13).
- Bacteria and archaea can be grouped according to nutritional type, response to oxygen, or presence of distinctive metabolic features, such as methane consumption. Some bacteria consume antibiotics, a process linked to the evolution of antibiotic resistance (Figure 22.14).

22.5 Testing Your Knowledge

1. A toxic bloom of cyanobacteria occurs in the same lake during the summer, year after year, dying back each winter. How do the cyanobacteria generate new populations of cells each summer?
   a. Tough akinete cells survive over the winter and produce new populations by binary fission when conditions improve.
   b. Tough heterocytes survive over the winter in lake sediments and in spring generate new cells by means of mitosis.
   c. Toxic cyanobacteria invade the lake each year as airborne endospores that were produced in warmer climates.
   d. All of the above are involved.
   e. None of the above is accurate.

2. You have isolated a culture of a particular species of tissue-destroying, disease-causing bacteria from deep within a human patient's wound where the concentration of oxygen is relatively low and light does not penetrate. From this, what can you infer about the bacterial species' nutritional type?
   a. The bacterial species is an oxygen-producing photoautotroph.
   b. The bacterial species is a chemolithoautotroph.
   c. The bacterial species is photoheterotrophic.
   d. The bacterial species is an anaerobic chemoheterotroph.
   e. The bacterial species is methanotrophic.

22.6 Protist Classification by Habitat, Size, and Motility

Learning Outcomes:

1. List three features that define protists.
2. Distinguish among algae, protozoa, and fungus-like protists.
3. Define the terms phytoplankton, periphyton, flagellate, ciliate, and amoeba.

As earlier noted, the term protist comes from the Greek word *protos,* meaning first, reflecting the observation that protists were Earth's first eukaryotes, and protists are eukaryotes that are not classified in the plant, animal, or fungal kingdoms. Protists display two additional common characteristics: They are most abundant in moist habitats, and most of them are microscopic in size. Despite their small size, protists have a greater influence on global ecology and human affairs than most people realize. For example, the photosynthetic protists known as algae generate at least half of the oxygen in the Earth's atmosphere and produce organic compounds that feed marine and freshwater animals. The oil that fuels our cars and industry is derived from pressure-cooked algae that accumulated on the ocean floor over millions of years. Because fossil oil deposits are becoming depleted, algae are being engineered into systems for producing renewable biofuels that simultaneously clean pollutants from water and air.

Protists also include some parasites that cause serious human illnesses, as illustrated by the chapter-opening photo. Another example is the waterborne protist *Cryptosporidium parvum,* which in 1993 sickened 400,000 people in Milwaukee, Wisconsin, costing $96 million in medical expenses and lost work time. Species of the related protist *Plasmodium,* which is carried by mosquitoes in many warm regions of the world, cause the disease malaria. Every year, nearly 500 million people become ill with malaria, and more than 2 million die of this disease.

Protists Can Be Informally Labeled According to Their Ecological Roles

Protists are often labeled according to their ecological roles, which occur in three major types: algae, protozoa, and fungus-like protists (see Figure 22.3). All of these protists occur widely in aquatic habitats.

- **Algae** (singular, alga from the Latin, meaning "seaweeds") are protists that are generally photoautotrophic, meaning that most possess chlorophyll and other photosynthetic pigments and can produce organic compounds from inorganic sources by means of photosynthesis (**Figure 22.15**). In addition to organic compounds, photosynthetic algae produce oxygen. Despite the common occurrence of photosynthesis, algae do not form a monophyletic group descended from a single common ancestor.

- **Protozoa** (from the Greek, meaning first life) are diverse types of heterotrophic protists that cannot produce their own

Biology Principle

Living Organisms Use Energy

The organic components of the diatoms are digested by the ciliate and used as food, whereas the indigestible diatom walls are excreted.

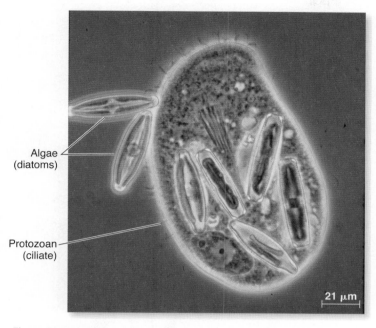

Algae
(diatoms)

Protozoan
(ciliate)

21 μm

Figure 22.15 **A heterotrophic protozoan feeding on photosynthetic algae.** The ciliate shown here has consumed several oil-rich, golden-pigmented, silica-walled algal cells known as diatoms. Diatom cells that have avoided capture glide nearby.

organic food and must obtain it by feeding. Protozoa feed by absorbing small organic molecules or by ingesting prey. For example, the protozoa known as ciliates consume smaller cells such as the single-celled photosynthetic algae known as diatoms (see Figure 22.15). Like the algae, the protozoa do not form a monophyletic group.

- **Fungus-like protists** are a nonmonophyletic assemblage of organisms having bodies, nutrition, or reproduction mechanisms similar to those of the true fungi (see Chapter 24). However, fungus-like protists are not closely related to fungi; their similar features represent cases of convergent evolution, in which species from different lineages have independently evolved similar characteristics. Water molds, some of which cause diseases of fish, and *Phytophthora infestans*, which causes diseases of many wild and crop plants, are examples of fungus-like protists (see Figure 22.3b).

Protists Can Be Informally Labeled According to Their Type of Motility

Microscopic protists have evolved diverse ways to propel themselves in moist environments of diverse types. Swimming by means of flagella, cilia, and amoeboid movement are major types of protist movements.

- **Flagellates** are the many types of photosynthetic and heterotrophic protists that are able to swim because they produce one or a few eukaryotic flagella (Figure 22.16a). Recall that eukaryotic flagella are cellular extensions whose movement is based on interactions between microtubules and the motor protein dynein. Eukaryotic flagella rapidly bend and straighten, thereby pulling or pushing cells through the water. Flagellates are typically composed of one or only a few cells and are small—usually from 2 to 20 μm long—because flagellar motion is not powerful enough to keep larger bodies from sinking. Some flagellate protists are sedentary, living attached to underwater surfaces. These protists use flagella to collect bacteria and other small particles for food. Macroalgae and other immobile protists often produce small, flagellate reproductive cells that allow these protists to mate and disperse to new habitats.

- **Ciliates** are protists that use many tiny hairlike surface extensions, known as **cilia,** to move. Cilia are structurally similar to eukaryotic flagella but are shorter and more abundant on cells (Figure 22.16b). Having many cilia allows ciliates to achieve larger sizes than flagellates yet still remain buoyant in water.

Flagellum

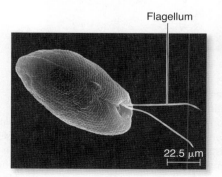

22.5 μm

(a) A cryptomonad with eukaryotic flagella

Cilia

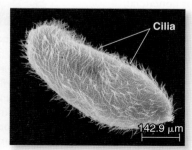

142.9 μm

(b) A protzoan ciliate covered by cilia

Pseudopod

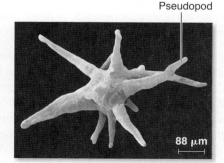

88 μm

(c) An amoeba extending many pseudopodia

Figure 22.16 **SEMs of a flagellate, a ciliate, and an amoeba.** **(a)** This cryptomonad, with two flagella, is an example of a flagellate. **(b)** The ciliate *Paramecium*, showing numerous cilia on the cell surface. **(c)** An amoeba of the genus *Pelomyxa*, showing pseudopodia.

- **Amoebae** are protists that move by extending cytoplasm into lobes, known as pseudopodia (from the Greek, meaning false feet) (Figure 22.16c). Once these pseudopodia move toward a food source or other stimulus, the rest of the cytoplasm flows after them, thereby changing the shape of the entire organism as it creeps along.

Protists Can Be Informally Labeled According to Their Habitats

Although protists occupy nearly every type of moist habitat, they are particularly common and diverse in oceans, lakes, wetlands, and rivers. Even extreme aquatic environments such as in Arctic and Antarctic ice and in acidic hot springs serve as habitats for some protists. In such places, protists may swim or float in open water or live attached to surfaces such as rocks or beach sand. As noted earlier, these different habitats influence protist structure and size. When humans pollute natural waters, harmful or nuisance growths of protists may result, but it is also the case that protists provide important ecological services.

- Planktonic protists swim or float in fresh or salt water, together with planktonic bacteria, viruses, and small animals. The photosynthetic protists in plankton are known as **phytoplankton** (plantlike plankton). Planktonic protists are necessarily quite small in size; otherwise they would readily sink to the bottom. Staying afloat is a particularly important characteristic of phytoplankton, which need light for photosynthesis, so planktonic protists are microscopic in size. Aquatic environments that have become polluted with too many nutrients such as phosphorus may foster the growth of red tides or other conspicuously large populations of harmful protists (Figure 22.17a).

- Periphytic protists attach themselves to underwater surfaces such as rocks, sand, and plants, where they occur in communities known as **periphyton** that also harbor attached prokaryotic species and fungi. Because sinking is not a problem for attached protists, their bodies can be larger than those of the plankton. In water that is polluted with too many nutrients such as phosphorus, growths of periphytic protists may become conspicuous (Figure 22.17b). Bushy periphyton growths can be considered a nuisance, but also provide ecological benefits such as habitat for beneficial microbes and small animals.

- Seaweeds, also known as macroalgae, are photosynthetic protists that are large enough to see with the unaided eye and that usually grow attached to underwater surfaces such as rocks, sand, docks, ship hulls, or offshore oil platforms. Seaweeds require sunlight and carbon dioxide for photosynthesis and growth, so most of them grow along coastal shorelines fairly near the water's surface (see Figure 22.3c). Kelp forests are communities dominated by tree-sized seaweeds that serve as refuges for aquatic animals such as sea otters, generate large amounts of organic carbon that enters aquatic food chains, and play additional important ecological roles (Figure 22.17c).

(a) Coastal red tide of phytoplankton

(b) Periphyton in shallow, nearshore water

(c) Offshore kelp forest

Figure 22.17 Protists can be classified according to habitats. **(a)** Swimming and floating protists occur in the plankton and photosynthetic plankton known as phytoplankton, sometimes forming large populations known as blooms, or red tides, that can be harmful. **(b)** Many types of protists occur as part of the periphyton, a diverse community of organisms that attach to substrata in shallow, nearshore waters. The green periphytic growths shown here are dominated by the common, abundant green alga *Cladophora*, which is associated with many other protists as well as bacteria, fungi, and small animals. **(c)** Kelp forests are extensive growths of tree-sized brown algae that grow in deeper offshore waters and harbor many other organisms.

22.6 Reviewing the Concepts

- Protists are eukaryotes that are not classified in the plant, animal, or fungal kingdoms; are abundant in moist habitats; and are mostly microscopic in size. Algae are mostly photosynthetic protists whereas fungus-like protists and protozoa are heterotrophic protists (Figure 22.15).

- Microscopic protists can be classified by propulsion method: flagella (flagellates), cilia (ciliates), or pseudopodia (amoebae) (Figure 22.16).

- Protists can also be labeled according to size and habitat: small planktonic species float or swim, larger periphytic protists live attached to shallow nearshore surfaces, and seaweeds are usually attached to the bottom in deeper, offshore ocean waters (Figure 22.17).

22.6 Testing Your Knowledge

1. Which group of protists listed below is monophyletic?
   - **a.** algae
   - **b.** protozoa
   - **c.** fungus-like protists
   - **d.** all of the above
   - **e.** none of the above

2. If you sampled living material from ocean shorelines, what types of protists could you likely find in the water?
   - **a.** flagellates, ciliates, and amoebae
   - **b.** algae, protozoa, and fungus-like protists
   - **c.** phytoplankton, periphytic protists, seaweeds
   - **d.** all of the above
   - **e.** none of the above

22.7 Eukaryotic Supergroups: Ecological and Medical Importance of Protists

Learning Outcomes:

1. Describe a distinctive structural characteristic for each of seven eukaryotic supergroups.

2. Draw a diagram showing at least four body types that occur among the protists.

At one time, protists were classified into a single kingdom. However, modern phylogenetic analyses based on comparative analysis of DNA sequences and cellular features reveal that protists do not form a monophyletic group (**Figure 22.18**). That is because some protists are more closely related to plants, animals, or fungi than to other protists. The relationships of some protists are uncertain or disputed, and new protist species are continuously being discovered. As a result, concepts of protist evolution and relationships have been changing as new information becomes available. For example, based on modern molecular analyses, an older concept of a supergroup known as the Chromalveolata has now been discarded.

Even so, molecular and cellular data reveal that many protist phyla can be classified within seven eukaryotic **supergroups** that each display distinctive features (see Figure 22.18). All of the eukaryotic supergroups include phyla of protists; some, in fact,

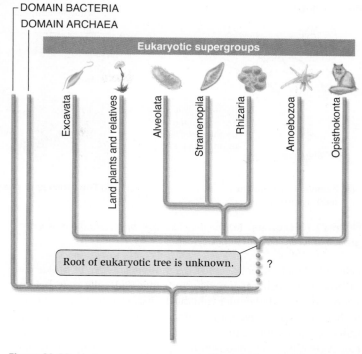

Figure 22.18 **Phylogenetic diagram showing relationships among seven major eukaryotic supergroups.** All eukaryotic supergroups include protists, and some supergroups include only protists.

contain only protist phyla. The supergroup Opisthokonta includes the multicellular animal and fungal kingdoms and related protists, whereas another supergroup includes the multicellular plant kingdom and the protists most closely related to it. The study of protists helps to reveal how multicellularity originated in animals, fungi, and plants. The following survey of eukaryotic supergroups reveals the medical and ecological importance of modern protists.

A Feeding Groove Characterizes Many Protists Classified in the Excavata

The protist supergroup known as the Excavata originated very early among eukaryotes, so this supergroup is important in understanding the early evolution of eukaryotes. The Excavata is named for a feeding groove "excavated" into the cells of many representatives, such as the genus *Jakoba* (**Figure 22.19**). The feeding groove is an important adaptation that allows these single-celled organisms (informally called excavates) to ingest small particles of food in their aquatic habitats. Once food particles are collected within the feeding groove, they are then taken into cells by a type of endocytosis known as **phagocytosis** (from the Greek, meaning cellular eating) (see Figure 22.19). During phagocytosis, a vesicle of plasma membrane surrounds each food particle and pinches off within the cytoplasm. Enzymes within these food vesicles break the food particles down into small molecules that, upon their release into the cytoplasm, can be used for energy.

Phagocytosis is also the basis for an important evolutionary process known as **endosymbiosis,** a symbiotic association in which a smaller species known as the **endosymbiont** lives within the body of a larger host species. Phagocytosis provides a way for protist

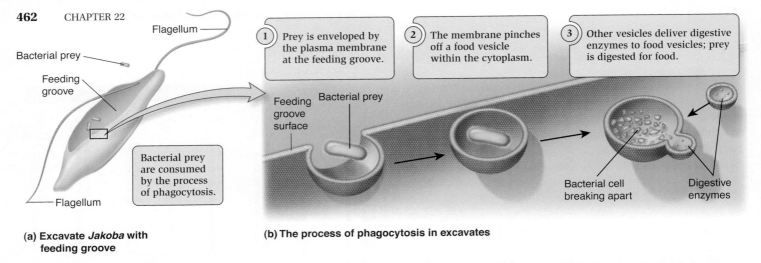

(a) Excavate *Jakoba* with feeding groove

(b) The process of phagocytosis in excavates

Figure 22.19 Excavata. (a) The flagellate *Jakoba intestinalis* is an example of an excavate protist. **(b)** Excavates display a characteristic feeding groove that functions in phagocytosis.

cells that function as hosts to take in diverse types of prokaryotic or eukaryotic cells. If not digested, ingested cells may become endosymbionts that confer valuable traits, as in the case of the proteobacteria that evolved into mitochondria. Most protists possess mitochondria, though these may be highly modified in some species. As earlier noted, endosymbiosis is a major way in which many new genes can be horizontally transferred into protist cells.

Excavate protists include euglenoid flagellates (**Figure 22.20**). Many euglenoids lack plastids, but others contain green plastids acquired by endosymbiosis. Photosynthetic euglenoids display conspicuous particles of carbohydrate and light-sensing systems that include red eyespots, which enable the cells to swim to favorable light environments (see Figure 22.20).

Some nonphotosynthetic excavate protists have become parasitic within animals, including human hosts. In addition to feeding by phagocytosis, parasitic species attack host cells and absorb food molecules released from them. *Trichomonas vaginalis* (see chapter-opening photo) is one example. *Giardia intestinalis* (previously known as *G. lamblia)*, another type of excavate protist, contains two active nuclei and produces eight flagella (Figure 22.3a). *G. intestinalis* causes giardiasis, an intestinal infection that can result from drinking untreated water or from unsanitary conditions in day-care centers. Nearly 300 million human

infections occur every year, and the disease also harms young farm animals, dogs, and cats, as well as wild animals. In the animal body, flagellate cells cause disease and also produce tough infectious stages known as cysts that are transmitted in feces and can survive several weeks outside a host. When an animal ingests as few as 10 of these cysts, within 15 minutes stomach acids induce the flagellate stage to develop and adhere to cells of the small intestine. *T. vaginalis* and *G. intestinalis* were once thought to lack mitochondria, but they are now known to possess simpler structures that are highly modified mitochondria.

Land Plants and Related Algae Share Similar Genetic Features

Genetic analyses indicate that the supergroup that includes land plants also encompasses several protist phyla, most of which are photosynthetic (**Figure 22.21**). Land plants and some closely related green algae together form one lineage (see Chapter 23), the phylum Chlorophyta includes most other green algae, a third phylum Rhodophyta is otherwise known as the red algae, and a fourth phylum (Cryptophyta) includes flagellates known as cryptomonads (see Figure 22.16a).

Green Algae Diverse structural types of green algae (**Figure 22.22**) occur in fresh water, the ocean, and on land. Some green algae are planktonic, some occur as attached periphyton, and others are more conspicuous seaweeds. Most of the green algae are photosynthetic, and their cells contain the same types of plastids and photosynthetic pigments that are present in land plants (which form the Kingdom Plantae as it is defined in this book). The green algae that are most closely related to land plants are known as streptophyte algae (see Chapter 23). Some green algae are responsible for harmful algal growths, but others are useful as food for aquatic animals and as model organisms. Many green algae possess flagella or the ability to produce them during the development of reproductive cells.

Red Algae Most species of red algae are multicellular marine seaweeds (see Figure 22.3c). The red appearance of these algae is caused by the presence of distinctive photosynthetic pigments

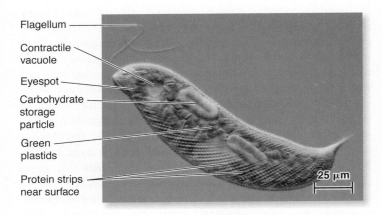

Figure 22.20 *Euglena,* a common excavate protist that contains plastids.

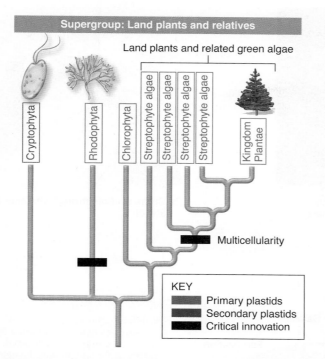

Figure 22.21 **One supergroup includes land plants and related protists.**

Membrane Sacs Lie at the Cell Periphery of Alveolata

The three supergroups Alveolata, Stramenopila, and Rhizaria cluster in recent phylogenetic studies (see Figure 22.18), a phylogenetic pattern that is not consistent with an older concept of a supergroup called Chromalveolata. Alveolata includes three important phyla: (1) the Ciliophora, or ciliates, which feed on bacteria and small algae (see Figures 22.15, 22.16b); (2) the Dinozoa, informally known as dinoflagellates (Figure 22.23a), recognized for their symbiotic relationships with reef-building corals and harmful red tide blooms that some species produce (see Figure 22.17a), and (3) the Apicomplexa, a medically important group of parasites. The Alveolata is named for saclike membranous vesicles known as alveoli that are present at the cell periphery in all of these phyla (Figure 22.23b).

About half of dinoflagellate species are heterotrophic, and half possess photosynthetic plastids of diverse types that originated by secondary or tertiary endosymbiosis. Tertiary endosymbiosis is the acquisition by hosts of plastids from cells that possessed secondary plastids (see Figure 22.25c). Species having tertiary plastids resulting from tertiary endosymbiosis have received genes by horizontal transfer from diverse endosymbiont genomes.

Apicomplexa include the protist genus that causes malaria, *Plasmodium*. About 40% of humans live in tropical regions of the world where malaria occurs, and millions of infections and human deaths result each year. Malaria is particularly deadly for young children. In addition to humans, the malarial parasite's alternate host is the mosquito classified in the genus *Anopheles*, which can also transmit malaria to the great apes. Though insecticides can be used to control mosquito populations and though antimalarial

that are absent from green algae or land plants. Red algae characteristically lack flagella—a feature that has strongly influenced the evolution of this group, resulting in unusually complex life cycles. Some classification schemes incorporate red and green algae into the Kingdom Plantae.

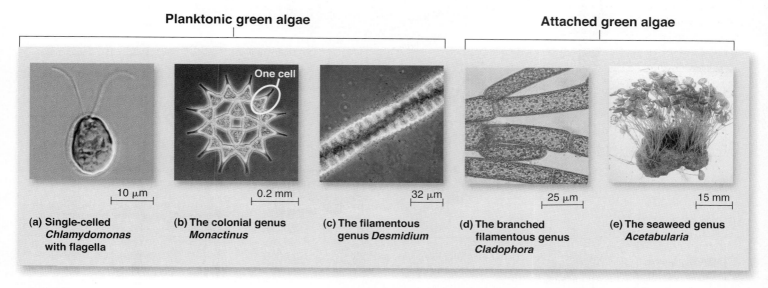

Figure 22.22 **Green algal body diversity fosters survival in aquatic habitats.** **(a)** The single-celled, swimming genus *Chlamydomonas* occurs in open water plankton, as do many other types of small, suspended microorganisms. **(b)** The genus *Monactinus* is composed of several cells that are associated to form a colony, whose lacy star shape helps to keep this photosynthetic protist afloat in brightly illuminated surface waters. Colonies can also avoid being eaten by predators that consume single-celled prey. **(c)** The filamentous genus *Desmidium* occurs as a twisted row of cells, another way to achieve larger body size while remaining afloat. **(d)** The large-celled, branched filamentous body of *Cladophora* is too large for most aquatic animals to consume, but is too heavy to float and so grows attached to nearshore rocks. **(e)** The seaweed genus *Acetabularia* represents many amazing species of tropical green algae whose bodies are the size of a dandelion plant or larger, yet are composed of only one extremely large cell.

Figure 22.23 Alveolata. (a) This single-celled dinoflagellate is a representative of the Alveolata. In this image made with a fluorescence microscope, cellulose wall pieces that occur within alveoli fluoresce blue, chlorophyll-containing plastids fluoresce red, and the cell nucleus fluoresces white. **(b)** Surface sacs called alveoli characterize the alveolate protists and are illustrated in this TEM of a dinoflagellate.

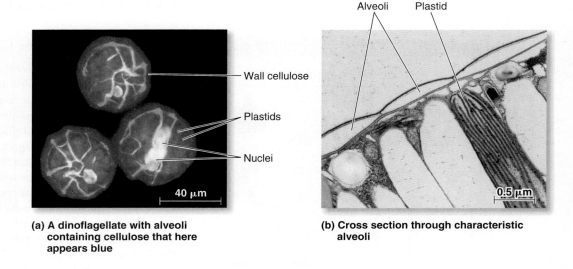

Wall cellulose
Plastids
Nuclei
40 μm

(a) A dinoflagellate with alveoli containing cellulose that here appears blue

Alveoli   Plastid

0.5 μm

(b) Cross section through characteristic alveoli

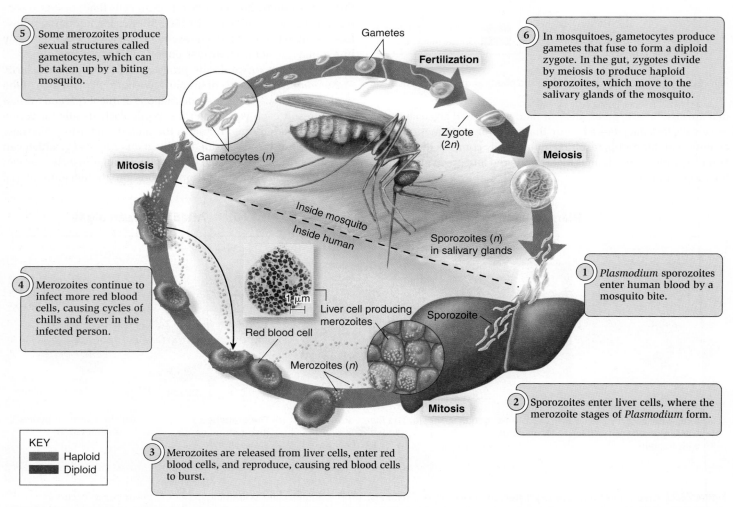

5 Some merozoites produce sexual structures called gametocytes, which can be taken up by a biting mosquito.

Gametes

Fertilization

6 In mosquitoes, gametocytes produce gametes that fuse to form a diploid zygote. In the gut, zygotes divide by meiosis to produce haploid sporozoites, which move to the salivary glands of the mosquito.

Zygote (2n)

Mitosis

Gametocytes (n)

Meiosis

Inside mosquito
Inside human

Sporozoites (n) in salivary glands

4 Merozoites continue to infect more red blood cells, causing cycles of chills and fever in the infected person.

1 μm

Liver cell producing merozoites

Sporozoite

Red blood cell

Merozoites (n)

1 *Plasmodium* sporozoites enter human blood by a mosquito bite.

Mitosis

2 Sporozoites enter liver cells, where the merozoite stages of *Plasmodium* form.

KEY
Haploid
Diploid

3 Merozoites are released from liver cells, enter red blood cells, and reproduce, causing red blood cells to burst.

Figure 22.24 Diagram of the life cycle of *Plasmodium falciparum*, a species that causes malaria. This life cycle requires two alternate hosts, humans (or great apes) and *Anopheles* mosquitoes. The inset is a TEM view of an infected human liver cell that contains numerous dark-stained merozoites. Such infected cells bud off groups of merozoites enclosed within a host-produced membrane. This membrane protects merozoites from being engulfed and destroyed by phagocytotic cells of the body's immune system.

✓ **Concept Check:** *In which of the hosts does sexual mating of P. falciparum gametes occur?*

drugs exist, malarial parasites can develop drug resistance. Experts are concerned that cases may double in the next 20 years.

When a mosquito bites a human or a great ape, *Plasmodium* enters the bloodstream as an asexual life stage known as a sporozoite (Figure 22.24). Upon reaching a victim's liver, sporozoites enter liver cells where they divide to form an asexual life stage known as merozoites. Hundreds of merozoites are produced within liver cells (see inset Figure 22.24), which then release into the bloodstream packages of merozoites enclosed by a host-derived cell membrane. This membrane protects merozoites from destruction by host immune cells, which would otherwise engulf merozoites by phagocytosis and then destroy the invaders. In the bloodstream, the protective host membranes disintegrate, releasing merozoites. The merozoites have protein complexes at their front ends, or apices, that allow them to invade human red blood cells. (The presence of these apical complexes gives rise to the phylum name Apicomplexa.)

Within red blood cells, merozoites release more than 200 proteins, which enable the parasites to commandeer these cells, causing many changes. For example, infected red blood cells form surface knobs that function like molecular Velcro, attaching cells to capillary linings. This process allows infected red blood cells to avoid being transported to the spleen, where they would be destroyed. The attachment of infected red blood cells to capillary linings disrupts circulation in the brain and kidney, a process that can cause death of the animal host.

While living within red blood cells, merozoites form rings, which can be visualized by staining and the use of a microscope, allowing diagnosis. The merozoites consume the hemoglobin in red blood cells, providing resources needed to reproduce asexually. Large numbers of new merozoites synchronously break out of red blood cells at intervals of 48 or 72 hours. These merozoite reproduction cycles correspond to cycles of chills and fever that an infected person experiences. Some merozoites produce sexual structures—gametocytes—which, along with blood, are transmitted to a female mosquito as she bites an infected person.

Within the mosquito's body, the gametocytes produce gametes and fertilization occurs, yielding a zygote, the only diploid cell in *Plasmodium*'s life cycle. Within the mosquito gut, the zygote undergoes meiosis, generating structures filled with many sporozoites, the stage that can be transmitted to a new human host. Sporozoites move to the mosquito's salivary glands, where they remain until they are injected into a human host when the mosquito feeds.

Plasmodium falciparum and some other apicomplexan protists possess plastids because they are descended from algal ancestors that had photosynthetic secondary plastids. About 550 (some 10%) of *Plasmodium*'s nuclear-encoded proteins are imported into a nonphotosynthetic plastid known as an apicoplast, where they are needed for fatty-acid metabolism and other processes. Because plastids are not present in mammalian cells, enzymes in apicoplast pathways are possible targets for development of drugs that will kill the parasite without harming the host. Mammals also lack calcium-dependent protein kinases (CDPKs), enzymes that are essential to merozoite release from red blood cells and the parasite's sexual development, offering another potential way to develop new antimalarial medicines.

EVOLUTIONARY CONNECTIONS

Primary Plastids and Primary Endosymbiosis

The plastids of red algae and green algae and land plants have an enclosing envelope composed of two membranes. Such plastids, known as **primary plastids,** are thought to have originated via a process known as **primary endosymbiosis** (Figure 22.25a). During primary endosymbiosis, heterotrophic host cells captured cyanobacterial cells via phagocytosis but did not digest them. These endosymbiotic cyanobacteria provided host cells with photosynthetic capability and other useful biochemical pathways and eventually evolved into primary plastids. Endosymbiotic acquisitions of plastids and mitochondria resulted in massive horizontal gene transfer from the endosymbiont to the host nucleus. As a result of such gene transfer, many of the proteins needed by plastids and mitochondria are synthesized in the host cytoplasm and then targeted to these organelles. All cells of plants, green algae, and red algae contain one or more primary plastids, and most of these organisms are photosynthetic. However, some species (or some of the cells within the multicellular bodies of photosynthetic species) are heterotrophic because photosynthetic pigments are not produced in the plastids. In these cases, plastids play other essential metabolic roles, such as producing amino acids and fatty acids.

Secondary Plastids and Secondary Endosymbiosis   In contrast to the primary plastids of plants and green and red algae, the plastids occurring in many other photosynthetic protists are derived from those of a photosynthetic red or green alga. Such plastids are known as **secondary plastids** because they originated by the process of **secondary endosymbiosis** (Figure 22.25b). Secondary endosymbiosis occurs when a eukaryotic host cell ingests and retains another type of eukaryotic cell that already has one or more primary plastids, a red or green alga. Such eukaryotic endosymbionts are often enclosed by endoplasmic reticulum (ER), explaining why secondary plastids typically have envelopes of more than two membranes. Although most of the endosymbiont's cellular components were lost over time, its plastids are retained, providing the host cell with photosynthetic capacity and other biochemical capabilities. Many of the alveolata, described next, possess secondary or tertiary plastids obtained from a eukaryotic alga.

Flagellar Hairs Distinguish Stramenopila

The supergroup Stramenopila (informally known as the stramenopiles) encompasses a wide range of algae, protozoa, and fungus-like protists that usually produce flagellate reproductive cells at some point in their lives. The Stramenopila (from the Greek *stramen*, meaning straw, and *pila*, meaning hair) is named for distinctive strawlike hairs that occur on the surfaces of flagella (Figure 22.26). These flagellar hairs function something like oars to greatly increase swimming efficiency.

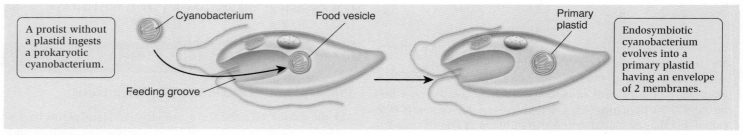

(a) Primary endosymbiosis

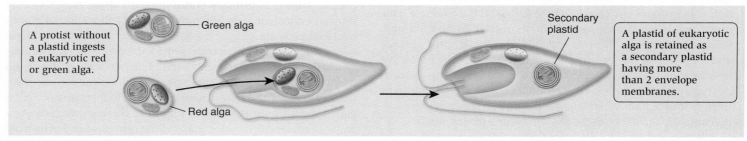

(b) Secondary endosymbiosis

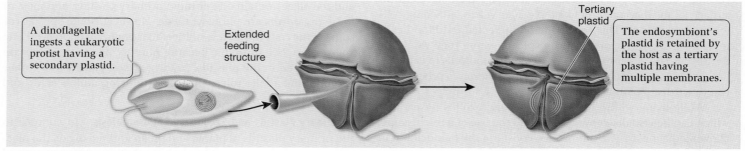

(c) Tertiary endosymbiosis

Figure 22.25 **Primary, secondary, and tertiary endosymbiosis.** **(a)** Primary endosymbiosis involves the acquisition of a cyanobacterial endosymbiont by a host cell without a plastid. During the evolution of a primary plastid, the bacterial cell wall is lost, and most endosymbiont genes are transferred to the host nucleus. **(b)** Secondary endosymbiosis involves the acquisition by a host cell of a eukaryotic endosymbiont that contains one or more primary plastids. During the evolution of a secondary plastid, most components of the endosymbiont cell are lost, but a plastid is often retained within an envelope of endoplasmic reticulum. **(c)** Tertiary endosymbiosis involves the acquisition by a host cell of a eukaryotic endosymbiont that possesses secondary plastids.

Heterotrophic stramenopiles include the fungus-like protist *Phytophthora infestans*, which causes the serious potato disease known as late blight that results in the loss of billions of dollars of crops every year (see Figure 22.3b). Photosynthetic stramenopiles include diatoms (Bacillariophyceae) (see Figure 22.15) and the brown algae known as giant kelps whose ecological importance has previously been emphasized (see Figure 22.17c).

Spiky Cytoplasmic Extensions Are Present on the Cells of Many Protists Classified in Rhizaria

Several groups of flagellates and amoebae that have thin, hairlike extensions of their cytoplasm—known as filose pseudopodia—are classified into the supergroup Rhizaria (from the Greek *rhiza*, meaning root) (Figure 22.27). Rhizaria includes the Radiolaria (Figure 22.27a) and Foraminifera (Figure 22.27b)—two phyla of ocean plankton that produce exquisite mineral shells. Radiolaria and foraminifera commonly shelter symbiotic algal cells that provide benefits to their nonphotosynthetic hosts.

Amoebozoa Includes Many Types of Amoebae with Pseudopodia

The supergroup Amoebozoa includes many types of amoebae that move by extension of pseudopodia (see Figure 22.16c). Several types of protists known as slime molds are classified in this supergroup. One example, *Dictyostelium discoideum*, is widely used as a model organism for understanding movement, communication among cells, and development. During reproduction, in response to starvation, single *Dictyostelium* amoebae aggregate into a multicellular slug that produces a cellulose-stalked structure containing many single-celled, asexual spores. In favorable conditions these spores produce new amoebae, which feed on bacteria.

A Single Flagellum Occurs on Swimming Cells of Opisthokonta

The supergroup Opisthokonta includes the animal and fungal kingdoms and related protists (Figure 22.28). This supergroup is named for the presence of a single posterior flagellum on

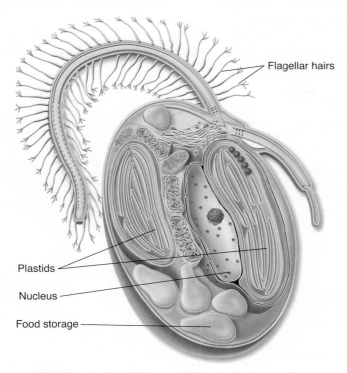

Figure 22.26 Stramenopila. Distinctive flagellar hairs occur on the flagellate cells of stramenopile protists.

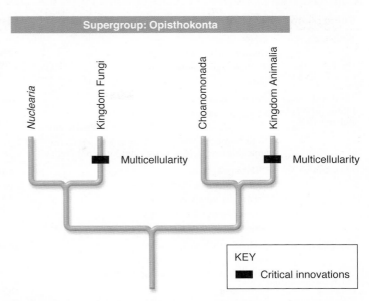

Figure 22.28 Supergroup Opisthokonta includes the kingdoms Fungi and Animalia and closely related protists.

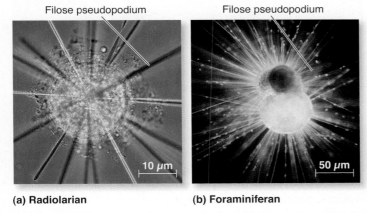

(a) Radiolarian   **(b) Foraminiferan**

Figure 22.27 Rhizaria. (a) The radiolarian, *Acanthoplegma* spp. **(b)** A foraminiferan showing long filose pseudopodia.

Biology Principle

All Species (Past and Present) Are Related by an Evolutionary History

Many more eukaryotic branches exist than are shown in the streamlined diagram of Figure 22.18 or that are listed in Table 22.2.

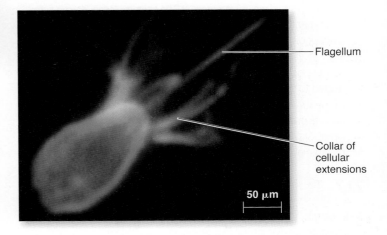

Figure 22.29 Opisthokonta, illustrated by a choanoflagellate with single flagellum. Choanoflagellates are the modern protists most closely related to the animal kingdom. Study of such protists helps to reveal how multicellularity evolved.

swimming cells. *Nuclearia* is an opisthokont genus that seems particularly closely related to the Kingdom Fungi. The more than 125 species of opisthokont protists known as choanoflagellates (formally, the Choanomonada) are single-celled or colonial protists featuring a distinctive collar surrounding the single flagellum (**Figure 22.29**). The collar is made of cytoplasmic extensions that filter bacterial food from water currents generated by flagellar motion. Among protists, choanoflagellates are believed to represent the closest living relatives of animals. The preceding survey of protists, summarized in **Table 22.2**, represents just some of the enormous diversity of protists on Earth.

Table 22.2 — Eukaryotic Supergroups and Examples of Constituent Kingdoms, Phyla, Classes, or Species

Supergroup	KINGDOMS, Phyla, classes, or *species*	Distinguishing features
Excavata	*Jakoba* spp. *Giardia intestinalis* *Trichomonas vaginalis* *Euglena*	Unicellular flagellates, often with feeding groove. The euglenoids (many of which are photosynthetic) and the kinetoplastids (some of which are pathogens) are also grouped with Excavata.
Land and Plant and Algal Relatives	**Rhodophyta** (red algae) **Chlorophyta** (most green algae) KINGDOM PLANTAE and close green algal relatives Note: Some classification systems group red and green algae with land plants into Kingdom Plantae.	Land plants, green algae, and red algae have primary plastids derived from cyanobacteria; such plastids have two envelope membranes. Cryptomonads (most of which possess secondary red plastids) and plastid-less relatives have recently been linked to this supergroup.

Alveolata	**Ciliophora** (ciliates)
	Apicomplexa (apicomplexans)
	  Plasmodium falciparum
	  Cryptosporidium parvum
	Dinozoa (dinoflagellates)
		Peripheral membrane sacs (alveoli)
		Apicomplexa often have nonphotosynthetic secondary plastids; some Dinozoa have secondary plastids derived from red algae, some have secondary plastids derived from green algae, and some have tertiary plastids.

Stramenopila	Bacillariophyceae (diatoms) Phaeophyceae (brown algae) *Phytophthora infestans* (fungus-like)	Strawlike flagellar hairs; secondary plastids (when present) derived from red algae.
Rhizaria	**Radiolaria** **Foraminifera**	Thin, cytoplasmic projections; symbiotic relationships between rhizaria and diverse types of algal cells are common.
Amoebozoa	**Dictyostelia** (a slime mold phylum) *Dictyostelium discoideum*	Amoeboid movement by pseudopodia
Opisthokonta	*Nuclearia* spp. KINGDOM FUNGI **Choanomonada** (choanoflagellates) KINGDOM ANIMALIA	Swimming cells possess a single posterior flagellum.

22.7 Reviewing the Concepts

- Modern phylogenetic analysis has revealed that many protists can be classified into one of seven major eukaryotic supergroups, each displaying one or more distinctive features (Figure 22.18).
- Primary, secondary, and tertiary endosymbiosis, all based on the cellular process of phagocytosis, has increased eukaryotic diversity (Figures 22.19, 22.20, 22.21, 22.22).
- Supergroup Alveolata, with peripheral sac (alveoli), includes dinoflagellates, ciliates, and apicomplexans. The apicomplexan *Plasmodium* is the agent of malaria and like most other apicomplexans possesses a nonphotosynthetic secondary plastid that was inherited from an algal ancestor (Figures 22.23, 22.24, 22.25).
- Stramenopiles featuring distinctively hairy flagella are closely related to spiky rhizaria and alveolates (Figure 22.26).
- Amoebozoa display cytoplasmic extensions known as pseudopods (Figure 22.27).
- Opisthokonts, whose motile cells bear only one flagellum, include the animal kingdom and related protists (Figures 22.28, 22.29).

22.7 Testing Your Knowledge

1–4. Match the four eukaryotic supergroups listed below with characteristic structural features.

1. Alveolata
2. Land plants and algal relatives
3. Opisthokonts
4. Stramenopiles

a. primary plastids
b. flagella occur singly
c. peripheral membrane-bound sacs
d. distinctive hairs occur on flagella

22.8 Technological Applications of Bacteria and Protists

Learning Outcome:

1. List some examples of ways in which bacteria and protists are used in human technology.

Bacteria and protists are used in diverse technological applications. Agriculture employs several species of the bacterium *Bacillus*, particularly *B. thuringiensis* (Bt). This species produces toxins, known as Bt toxins, that kill the insects that ingest the bacterial cells, but are harmless to many noninsect species. Tent caterpillars, potato beetles, gypsy moths, mosquitoes, and black flies are among the pests that can be controlled by the Bt toxin. Toxin genes from *B. thuringiensis* have been cloned and introduced into some crop plants to reduce conventional pesticide use and increase crop yields. Several industries have also harnessed the metabolic capabilities of microbes obtained from nature.

- The food industry uses bacteria to produce chemical changes in food that improve consistency or flavor. Cheese makers add pure cultures of certain bacteria to milk. The bacteria consume milk sugar (lactose) and produce lactic acid, which aids in curdling the milk.

- The chemical industry produces enzymes, vinegar, amino acids, vitamins, insulin, vaccines, antibiotics, and other useful pharmaceuticals by growing particular bacteria in giant vats. For example, the hot springs bacterial species *Thermus aquaticus* is a source of a form of DNA polymerase widely used in biology laboratories to amplify DNA in polymerase chain reaction (PCR). Industrially grown bacteria produce the antibiotics streptomycin, tetracycline, kanamycin, gentamycin, bacitracin, polymyxin-B, and neomycin.

- Vast accumulations of the silica-rich walls (see Figure 22.15) of ancient diatoms, known as diatomite or diatomaceous earth, are mined for use in reflective paint and other industrial products.

- Diverse, photosynthetic brown algae (Phaeophyceae) (see Figure 22.17c) are sources of polysaccharides known as alginates that are used to make many industrial products.

- Many red algae are harvested for extraction of food industry emulsifiers known as carageenan and for production of agar and agarose that are widely used in biology laboratories (see Figure 22.3c).

- Bacterial and algal cells can be used as chemical factories. By genetically modifying microbial genomes, microorganisms can be made to produce particular useful compounds, including pharmaceuticals and renewable biofuels.

- The ability of some microorganisms to break down organic compounds, precipitate metals from mine waste, or absorb water pollutants such as phosphorus makes them very useful in treating wastewater, industrial discharges, and oil spills. This process, known as bioremediation, is used to reduce levels of harmful materials in the environment.

22.8 Reviewing the Concepts

- Many bacteria and protists are useful in industrial and other applications to make food products, medicines, or renewable biofuels, or to clean up polluted environments.

22.8 Testing Your Knowledge

1–4. Match the bacteria or protists listed below with an appropriate technological application.

1. the stramenopiles known as diatoms
2. *Bacillus thuringiensis*
3. *Thermus aquaticus*
4. red algae

  a. source of genes for Bt toxin that kills insect pests
  b. source of commercial DNA polymerase
  c. ingredient in reflective paint
  d. agar is extracted for use in microbiology labs

Assess and Discuss

Test Yourself

1. The bacterial phylum that typically produces oxygen gas as the result of photosynthesis is
   a. the proteobacteria.
   b. the cyanobacteria.
   c. the Gram-positive bacteria.
   d. all of the listed choices.
   e. none of the listed choices.

2. The Gram stain is a procedure that microbiologists use to
   a. determine if a bacterial strain is a pathogen.
   b. determine if a bacterial sample can break down oil.
   c. infer the structure of a bacterial cell wall and bacterial response to antibiotics.
   d. count bacteria in medical or environmental samples.
   e. do all of the above.

3. Place the following steps in the correct order, according to Koch's postulates:
   I. Determine if pure cultures of bacteria cause disease symptoms when introduced to a healthy host.
   II. Determine if disease symptoms correlate with presence of a suspected pathogen.
   III. Isolate the suspected pathogen and grow it in pure culture, free of other possible pathogens.
   IV. Attempt to isolate pathogen from second-infected hosts.
   a. II, III, IV, I   c. III, II, I, IV   e. I, II, III, IV
   b. II, IV, III, I   d. II, III, I, IV

4. The structures that enable some Gram-positive bacteria to remain dormant for extremely long periods of time are known as
   a. akinetes.
   b. endospores.
   c. biofilms.
   d. lipopolysaccharide envelopes.
   e. pili.

5. By what means can bacterial cells or protists acquire new DNA?
   a. by transduction, the injection of viral DNA into cells
   b. by transformation, the uptake of DNA from the environment
   c. by endosymbiosis, the incorporation of another organism within the host cell
   d. all of the above

Conceptual Questions

1. Explain why many microbial populations grow rapidly, thereby influencing the rate of food spoilage, infection, and the formation of harmful blooms in aquatic habitats.

2. Explain how a bacterial cell entering through a wound could rapidly spread throughout the body of a plant or animal.

3. **PRINCIPLES**   A principle of biology is that *biology affects our society*. Why are the endospores produced by certain bacteria important in human life?

Collaborative Questions

1. Why might it be useful to catalog the microbial species that are closely associated with a host organism to form a microbiome?

2. Imagine that you are searching for new antibiotic compounds. Where in nature might be a good place to look?

Online Resource

www.brookerprinciples.com

Stay a step ahead in your studies with animations that bring concepts to life and practice tests to assess your understanding. Your instructor may also recommend the interactive eBook, individualized learning tools, and more.

23

Plant Evolution and Diversity

The drought-resistant water fern *Marsilea drummondii* in the Australian outback.

During an expedition to the desert outback of Australia in which the goal was to learn more about ancient events in the evolutionary history of land plants, a team of plant biologists was amazed to find extensive growths of the so-called water fern *Marsilea drummondii* (chapter-opening photo). They were surprised because most ferns live in relatively moist environments, including the humid interiors of buildings where ferns are often used as ornamentals. As indicated by their common name, most water ferns live in very moist places indeed. But some fern species, including *M. drummondii*, are so resistant to drying that they can live in arid places. This is possible because this fern's leaves are fuzzy with surface hairs that act like a blanket to retard drying and excessive heating. The leaves are also able to fold themselves, thereby reducing surface area from which water can evaporate. The plant can become so dry that it crunches underfoot; it is not dead, but is instead living in a state of reduced metabolism until sporadic rains stimulate active photosynthesis and growth. With these adaptations, *M. drummondii* is sufficiently abundant that aboriginal Australians, who call this plant "nardoo," have long gathered its small brown food-rich reproductive structures, using grinding stones to make flour for cakes.

Nardoo is just one of the hundreds of thousands of plants that have become adapted in diverse ways to life on land, even very arid places. As is illustrated by aboriginal Australians' use of nardoo and developed societies' reliance on agricultural crops, humans depend on this plant diversity for food and many other materials. In this chapter we will see how, in addition to their modern importance, ferns and many other types of plants have played dramatic roles in the Earth's past. Throughout their evolutionary history, diverse plants have influenced Earth's atmospheric chemistry, climate, and soils, and the evolution of many other groups of organisms.

23.1 Ancestry and Diversity of Land Plants

Learning Outcomes:

1. Name several characteristics unique to land plants.
2. Compare and contrast the features of vascular and nonvascular plants.
3. List adaptations that enable vascular plants to maintain stable water content.

Several hundred thousand modern species are formally classified into the Kingdom Plantae, informally known as the land plants or simply plants (**Figure 23.1**). Although some species live in watery places, plants can be defined as multicellular, mostly photosynthetic eukaryotes that are adapted in many ways for life on land. Molecular and other evidence indicates that the plant kingdom evolved from green algal ancestors similar to particular modern algae. Together, plants and their closest green algal relatives are known as **streptophytes** (from Latin words meaning twisted and plant) (**Figure 23.2**). Land plants are distinguished from closely related algae by the presence of traits that foster survival in terrestrial conditions, which are drier, sunnier, hotter, colder, and less physically supportive than aquatic habitats. Likewise, the first land animals had to acquire similar structural and reproductive adaptations.

Distinctive Features of the Land Plants

Land plants display distinctive features that represent early adaptations to the land habitat:

- The bodies of all land plants are primarily composed of **tissues,** defined as close associations of cells. Bodies composed of tissues have lower surface area-to-volume ratios than simpler green algal bodies and, thus, less readily lose water in dry air by evaporation.

- Land plant tissues arise from one or more actively dividing cells that occur at growing tips, forming **apical meristems.** The tissue-producing apical meristems of land plants produce relatively thick, robust bodies able to withstand drought and mechanical stress and produce tissues and organs with specialized functions. (Related green algae have simpler growth and body structure.)

- The life cycle of land plants, known as **alternation of generations** (or sporic life cycle), involves two types of multicellular bodies. A haploid generation known as the gametophyte produces eggs and/or sperm; a diploid generation known as the sporophyte produces spores by meiosis. (Related green algae possess a simpler zygotic life cycle in which a single-celled zygote is the only diploid stage.)

- Land plant embryos are young multicellular sporophytes that are produced by mitosis following fertilization of an egg cell and depend on maternal tissues for food during early development. Embryos are not present in related green algae, but are such a basic feature of land plants that the latter are also known as embryophytes.

Figure 23.1 A temperate rain forest containing diverse plant phyla in Olympic National Park in Washington State.

- Tough-walled plant **spores** allow land plants to disperse offspring through dry air. Plant spores are tough because their walls contain an impervious material known as **sporopollenin.** (Although related green algae incorporate sporopollenin into zygote walls, and algal zygotes undergo meiosis to produce spores, such algal spores don't contain sporopollenin in their walls and thus cannot survive long in air.)

- Specialized structures called **gametangia** generate, protect, and disperse land plant gametes; tough **sporangia** likewise produce, protect, and disperse the spores of land plants.

Modern Land Plants Can Be Classified into Nine Phyla

Plant systematists use molecular and structural information to classify plants into phyla and organize phyla into an evolutionary sequence (see Figure 23.2). The modern plant phyla are listed as follows, together with a brief description of evolutionary and ecological importance.

- Plants informally known as liverworts were the earliest to appear and thus serve as useful models of the earliest land plants.

- Mosses arose after liverworts, but prior to all other modern plant groups. Mosses play a particularly important role in stabilizing Earth's climate now and have likely been doing so for the past hundreds of millions of years.

- Hornworts are evolutionarily important because they are closely related to the lycophytes and other land plants that have a well-developed system for internal conduction of water, minerals, and organic compounds. As a consequence of their phylogenetic position, hornworts are useful in learning how plant conduction systems originated.

Biology Principle

All Species (Past and Present) Are Related by an Evolutionary History

This figure shows evolutionary divergence times indicated by molecular clock and some fossil evidence, suggesting when plant groups may first have arisen.

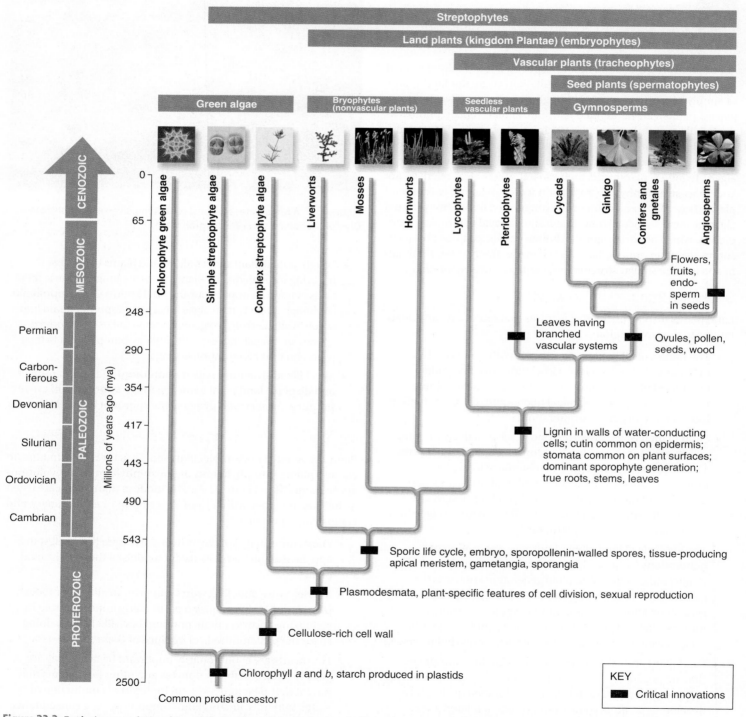

Figure 23.2 Evolutionary relationships of the modern plant phyla. Land plants gradually acquired diverse structural, biochemical, and reproductive adaptations to land that are known as critical innovations.

- Lycophytes are the earliest-divergent group of vascular land plants—those having conduction systems that also provide skeletal strength. In the ancient past, lycophytes were more abundant, much larger in size, and more diverse than are modern representatives.

- Ferns display many modern species, particularly in tropical habitats, and are valued for horticultural plantings. Lycophytes and ferns do not produce seeds, but display several adaptations that foster stable tissue-water content, a feature critical to the ability to survive through dry periods.

- Cycads are an early-diverging lineage of seed plants and so are important in understanding how seeds first evolved.

- Ginkgos are seed plants that were more diverse in the past than today. Modern ginkgos are valued as hardy and attractive street trees.

- Conifers, cone-bearing seed plants, are particularly important to humans as sources of wood and other commercial materials.

- Flowering plants, also known as angiosperms, are the plants upon which humans and many other animals most depend.

Liverworts, Mosses, and Hornworts Are the Simplest Land Plants

Liverworts, mosses, and hornworts (**Figures 23.3, 23.4**) are Earth's simplest land plants, and each forms a distinct, monophyletic group. There are about 6,500 species of modern liverworts, 12,000 or more species of mosses, and about 100 species of hornworts. Collectively, liverworts, mosses, and hornworts are known informally as the **bryophytes** (from the Greek *bryon,* meaning moss, and *phyton,* meaning plant). The bryophytes do not form a clade, but the term bryophyte is useful for expressing common structural, reproductive, and ecological features: bryophytes are all relatively small in stature and are most common and diverse in moist habitats. Bryophytes lack traits allowing them to grow tall or reproduce in dry places. Although many bryophytes possess a type of conducting tissue, bryophytes are unable to grow tall because such conducting tissues are not tough enough to also provide structural support. (In contrast, the tougher conducting tissues of vascular plants also provide support.)

Bryophytes require moist habitats in order to accomplish sexual reproduction because they produce flagellate sperm that must swim through water films to fertilize eggs. Recently, Todd Rosenstiel, Sarah Eppley, and associates discovered that at least some bryophytes emit perfume-like chemical attractants that lure small animals such as mites and springtails, which then help to disperse bryophyte sperm. This was a surprising discovery because animal-aided sexual reproduction was previously regarded as a seed plant trait.

Bryophytes are also distinctive in having a dominant (larger and longer-lived) gametophyte generation; the bryophyte sporophyte is a relatively small and short-lived life phase that

Figure 23.3 Liverwort, moss, and hornwort representatives. (a) The liverwort *Marchantia polymorpha* has a flat body that produces umbrella-shaped structures bearing egg-shaped sporophytes on the undersides. When sporophytes mature, they release tough-walled spores into the air. **(b)** The moss genus *Mnium* has a conspicuous, upright leafy green gametophyte that generates eggs and sperm and a less noticeable attached, unbranched sporophyte that bears a spore-producing sporangium at its tip. Inset: This SEM shows that the tips of moss sporangia often produce a number of tooth-shaped structures separated by spaces. Such tips function something like a salt shaker to sprinkle spores into the wind over a period of time, rather than releasing spores all at once. **(c)** Hornwort gametophytes grow close to the ground and produce upright sporophytes that release spores from tips into the air.

✔ **Concept Check:** *Why do you think liverworts, mosses, and hornworts produce their reproductive spores on raised structures?*

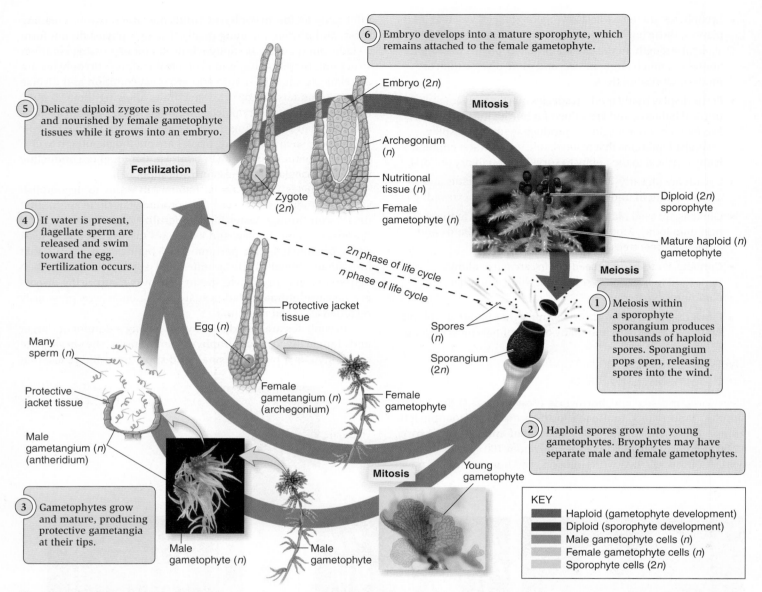

6 Embryo develops into a mature sporophyte, which remains attached to the female gametophyte.

Embryo (2n)

Mitosis

5 Delicate diploid zygote is protected and nourished by female gametophyte tissues while it grows into an embryo.

Archegonium (n)

Fertilization

Nutritional tissue (n)

Zygote (2n)

Female gametophyte (n)

Diploid (2n) sporophyte

Mature haploid (n) gametophyte

4 If water is present, flagellate sperm are released and swim toward the egg. Fertilization occurs.

Meiosis

2n phase of life cycle

n phase of life cycle

Protective jacket tissue

Egg (n)

Spores (n)

Sporangium (2n)

1 Meiosis within a sporophyte sporangium produces thousands of haploid spores. Sporangium pops open, releasing spores into the wind.

Many sperm (n)

Female gametangium (n) (archegonium)

Female gametophyte

Protective jacket tissue

Male gametangium (n) (antheridium)

2 Haploid spores grow into young gametophytes. Bryophytes may have separate male and female gametophytes.

Mitosis

Young gametophyte

3 Gametophytes grow and mature, producing protective gametangia at their tips.

Male gametophyte (n)

Male gametophyte

KEY

	Haploid (gametophyte development)
	Diploid (sporophyte development)
	Male gametophyte cells (n)
	Female gametophyte cells (n)
	Sporophyte cells (2n)

Figure 23.4 The life cycle of the early-diverging peat moss genus *Sphagnum*. The life cycle of this common peat moss illustrates reproductive adaptations commonly found in bryophytes that were also present in early land plants.

does not branch (see Figure 23.3b, Figure 23.4). By contrast, as described next, vascular land plants possess a dominant sporophyte generation that branches, giving rise to a larger body, whereas the gametophyte generation is relatively small and inconspicuous.

Lycophytes and Ferns Are Vascular Plants That Do Not Produce Seeds

Vascular plants, which include all groups of modern plants except bryophytes, possess a conduction system that also provides structural support. Vascular plants have been important to Earth's ecology for several hundreds of millions of years. Fossils indicate that the first vascular plants appeared later than the earliest bryophytes and that several early vascular plant lineages once existed

but became extinct. Molecular data demonstrate that the lycophytes are the oldest phylum of living vascular plants and that ferns are the next oldest living plant phylum (see Figure 23.2). In the past, lycophytes were very diverse and included tall trees, but now only about 1,000 relatively small species exist (Figure 23.5a). Ferns diversified more recently, and there are about 12,000 modern species, including horsetails, whisk ferns, and other ferns (Figure 23.5b–d). Because the lycophytes and ferns diverged prior to the origin of seeds, they are informally known as seedless vascular plants. Gymnosperms and angiosperms are the seed-producing vascular plants.

Together, lycophytes, ferns, and seed-producing vascular plants are also known as the **tracheophytes,** named for **tracheids,** a type of specialized conducting cell. Tracheids occur in specialized tissues known as **xylem** that conduct water and

Figure 23.5 Representative seedless vascular plants. (a) The lycophyte *Lycopodium obscurum*. The sporophyte stems bear many tiny leaves, and leaves bearing sporangia generally occur in club-shaped clusters. For this reason, lycophytes are informally known as club mosses or spike mosses, though they are not true mosses. The gametophytes of lycophytes are small structures that often occur underground, where they are better protected from drying. **(b)** The leafless, rootless green stems of the whisk fern (*Psilotum nudum*) branch by forking and bear many clusters of yellow sporangia that disperse spores via wind. The gametophyte of this plant is a tiny pale structure that lives underground in a symbiotic partnership with fungi. **(c)** The giant horsetail (*Equisetum telmateia*) displays branches in whorls around the green stems. The leaves of this plant are tiny, light brown structures that encircle branches at intervals. This plant produces spores in cone-shaped structures, and the wind-dispersed spores grow into small green gametophytes. **(d)** The early-diverging fern *Botrychium lunaria*, showing a green photosynthetic leaf with leaflets and a modified leaf that bears many round sporangia.

(a) Club moss

(b) A whisk fern

(c) The giant horsetail

(d) An early-diverging fern

minerals throughout the plant body. The xylem also provides structural support, allowing vascular plants to grow taller than nonvascular plants. This support function arises from the presence of a compression and decay-resistant waterproofing material known as **lignin,** which occurs in the cell walls of tracheids and some other types of plant cells. A second type of vascular tissue known as **phloem** conducts a watery sap containing organic molecules such as sugar throughout the plant body. Xylem and phloem, together known as **vascular tissues,** occur in the major plant organs: stems, roots, and leaves.

Tracheophyte **stems** are branching organs that bear reproductive sporangia and leaves. Most vascular plants also produce **roots**—branching organs specialized for uptake of water and minerals from the soil—and **leaves** that generally have a

photosynthetic function. Like stems, roots and leaves contain both xylem- and phloem-conducting tissues. Together, the branching vascular tissues of the stem, roots, and leaves are known as the vascular system. The vascular system of a plant functions much like the vascular system of an animal; both systems carry nutrients and other materials throughout the body.

In relatively dry habitats, lycophytes, ferns, and other vascular plants are able to grow to larger sizes and remain metabolically active for longer periods than can bryophytes. Vascular plants have this advantage because they are better able to maintain stable internal water content by means of several adaptations, including a vascular system, a waxy cuticle, and stomata. A vascular system allows water and minerals taken up by roots to move through stems and leaves and allows sugar produced in leaves (and sometimes stems) to move into locations where the sugar is respired to produce ATP. A protective waxy **cuticle** present on most plant surfaces contains a polyester polymer known as cutin that deters pathogen attack and wax that helps to prevent drying (Figure 23.6a). The surface tissue of vascular plant stems and leaves contains many **stomata** (singular, stoma or stomate)—pores that can open and close (Figure 23.6b). Stomata allow plants to take in the carbon dioxide needed for photosynthesis and release oxygen to the air, while conserving water. When the environment is moist, the pores open, allowing photosynthetic gas exchange to occur. When the environment is very dry, the pores close, thereby reducing water loss by evaporation into the air. In vascular plants, a conducting system, a waxy cuticle, and stomata function together to maintain moisture homeostasis, allowing tracheophytes to exploit a wide spectrum of land habitats. Additional information about the function of angiosperm vascular systems and stomata can be found in Chapter 29.

Lycophytes and ferns have a life cycle dominated by the diploid sporophyte, which is large enough to produce many spores. Clusters of sporangia are often visible on the undersides of fern leaves (Figure 23.7). The fern gametophyte is small, but can be seen with the unaided eye and so is widely used in biology classes to demonstrate the plant life cycle. By contrast, seed plants produce both spores and seeds, and seed plant gametophytes are microscopic in size.

Gymnosperms and Angiosperms Are the Modern Seed Plants

Among the vascular plants, the seed plant phyla known as gymnosperms and angiosperms dominate most modern landscapes. Because both groups produce seeds, gymnosperms and angiosperms are together known as the **spermatophytes. Seeds** are complex structures having specialized tissues that protectively enclose embryos and contain stores of carbohydrate, lipid, and protein that enable embryos to grow and develop. Seed plants produce **pollen,** small air- or animal-borne spores that contain and protect microscopic male gametophytes. The ability to produce seeds and pollen helps to free seed plants from reproductive limitations experienced by the seedless plants, revealing why seed plants are the dominant plants on Earth today.

The modern seed plant phyla commonly known as cycads, ginkgos, conifers (including a group known as the gnetophytes) are collectively known as gymnosperms (Figure 23.8 a–c). The term **gymnosperm** comes from the Greek, meaning naked seeds, reflecting the observation that gymnosperm seeds are not enclosed within fruits. Though gymnosperms produce pollen and seeds, they lack flowers, fruits, and endosperm.

The **angiosperms** (Figure 23.8d) produce seeds and pollen, but are distinguished from gymnosperms by the presence of flowers, fruits, and a specialized seed tissue known as endosperm. A **flower** is a short stem bearing reproductive organs that are specialized in ways that enhance seed production. **Fruits** are structures that develop from flowers, enclose seeds, and foster seed dispersal in the environment. The term angiosperm comes from the Greek, meaning enclosed seeds, reflecting the observation that the flowering plants produce seeds within fruits. **Endosperm**

Biology Principle

Living Organisms Maintain Homeostasis

The structures illustrated in this figure explain how vascular land plants maintain homeostasis in water content.

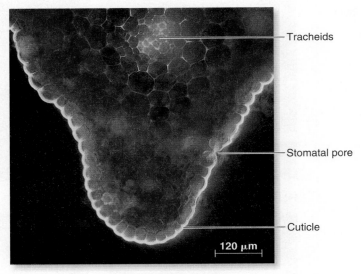

Tracheids

Stomatal pore

Cuticle

120 μm

(a) Stem showing tracheophyte adaptations

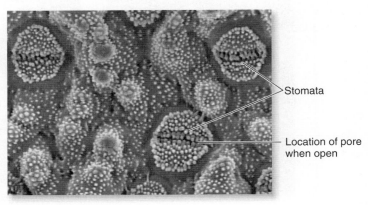

Stomata

Location of pore when open

(b) Close-up of stomata

Figure 23.6 **A fern stem showing tracheophyte adaptations for transporting and conserving water.** **(a)** A cross section through a stem of the whisk fern *Psilotum nudum*. When viewed with fluorescence microscopy and illuminated with violet light, an internal core of xylem tracheids glows yellow, as does the surface cuticle. **(b)** Surface pores associated with specialized cells—the complexes known as stomata—allow for gas exchange between plant and atmosphere. This photo naturally lacks color because it was made with a scanning electron microscope (SEM), which uses electrons rather than visible light to form magnified images.

is a nutritive seed tissue that increases the efficiency with which food is stored in the seeds of flowering plants, and contributes a large proportion of human food such as cereal crops. Flowers, fruits, and endosperm are defining features of the angiosperms, and they are integral components of the diet of many animals.

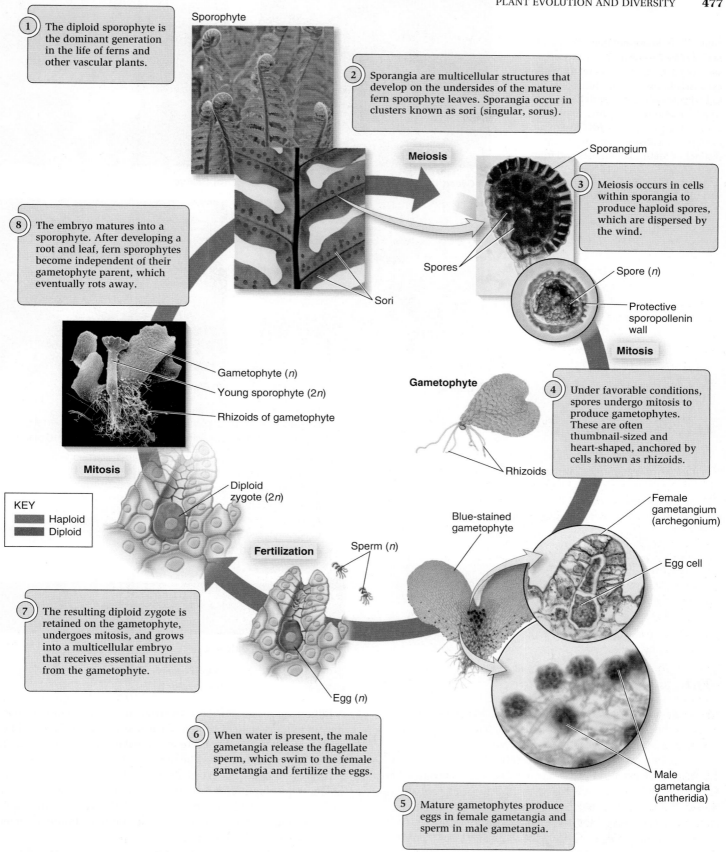

① The diploid sporophyte is the dominant generation in the life of ferns and other vascular plants.

Sporophyte

② Sporangia are multicellular structures that develop on the undersides of the mature fern sporophyte leaves. Sporangia occur in clusters known as sori (singular, sorus).

Meiosis

Sporangium

③ Meiosis occurs in cells within sporangia to produce haploid spores, which are dispersed by the wind.

⑧ The embryo matures into a sporophyte. After developing a root and leaf, fern sporophytes become independent of their gametophyte parent, which eventually rots away.

Spores

Sori

Spore (*n*)

Protective sporopollenin wall

Mitosis

Gametophyte (*n*)
Young sporophyte (2*n*)
Rhizoids of gametophyte

Gametophyte

④ Under favorable conditions, spores undergo mitosis to produce gametophytes. These are often thumbnail-sized and heart-shaped, anchored by cells known as rhizoids.

Rhizoids

Mitosis

Diploid zygote (2*n*)

KEY
Haploid
Diploid

Female gametangium (archegonium)

Blue-stained gametophyte

Egg cell

Fertilization

Sperm (*n*)

⑦ The resulting diploid zygote is retained on the gametophyte, undergoes mitosis, and grows into a multicellular embryo that receives essential nutrients from the gametophyte.

Egg (*n*)

⑥ When water is present, the male gametangia release the flagellate sperm, which swim to the female gametangia and fertilize the eggs.

Male gametangia (antheridia)

⑤ Mature gametophytes produce eggs in female gametangia and sperm in male gametangia.

Figure 23.7 The life cycle of a typical fern. The fern life cycle is often used to illustrate plant alternation of generations because both sporophyte and gametophyte are large enough for people to see with the unaided eye.

Figure 23.8 **Representative seed plants.**
(a) Palmlike foliage and conspicuous seed-producing cones are features of most cycads. **(b)** *Ginkgo biloba* has leaves with forked veins and seeds with fleshy, foul-smelling seed coats. **(c)** An example of a conifer, the pine (*Pinus*). **(d)** Citrus is an example of a flowering plant, showing the distinctive features of flowers and fruits.

(a) Cycad

(b) *Ginkgo*

(c) Conifer

(d) Flowering plant

23.1 Reviewing the Concepts

- Plants are multicellular eukaryotic organisms that are mostly photosynthetic and display many adaptations to life on land. The modern plant kingdom consists of nine phyla, informally known as the liverworts, mosses, hornworts, lycophytes, ferns, cycads, ginkgos, conifers, and angiosperms (Figures 23.1, 23.2).
- The monophyletic liverwort, moss, and hornwort phyla are together known informally as the bryophytes (Figures 23.3, 23.4).
- Lycophytes, ferns, and other vascular plants (tracheophytes) generally possess stems, roots, and leaves having vascular systems composed of conductive phloem and xylem (Figures 23.5, 23.6, 23.7).
- Cycads, ginkgos, conifers (the gymnosperms), and flowering plants (the angiosperms) are the seed plants (Figure 23.8).

23.1 Testing Your Knowledge

1. Which of the following descriptions most accurately represents how the plant gametophyte has changed through time?
   a. The first plant gametophytes were, like those of modern bryophytes, larger than the earliest plant sporophytes.
   b. The first plant gametophytes were, like modern bryophytes, the same size as the earliest plant sporophytes.
   c. The first plant gametophytes were, like those of modern bryophytes, smaller than the earliest plant sporophytes.
   d. The earliest type of plant life cycle, represented by modern bryophytes, was similar to that of related green algae; the only diploid cells produced by early land plants were zygotes, so a multicellular sporophyte generation was lacking.

   e. The earliest type of plant life cycle involved the dispersal of small gametophytes within pollen, as in modern seed plants.

2. Place the plant structures in correct order, starting with earliest evolved and ending with most recently evolved.
   a. flower, seed, embryo, tracheid
   b. tracheid, embryo, seed, flower
   c. embryo, tracheid, seed, flower
   d. embryo, seed, tracheid, flower
   e. seed, embryo, tracheid, flower

23.2 An Evolutionary History of Land Plants

Learning Outcome:

1. Describe two major events in plant history and how they affected other life on Earth.

A billion years ago, Earth's terrestrial surface was comparatively devoid of life. Green or brown crusts of cyanobacteria most likely grew in moist places, but there would have been very little soil, no plants, and no animal life. The origin of the first land plants was a pivotal event in the history of life on Earth because the first plants enabled development of the first substantial soils and the evolution of modern plant communities. Had early land plants not played these key roles, animals would not have found sufficient food and shelter to allow land colonization.

How can we know about events such as the origin and diversification of land plants? One line of information comes from comparing molecular and other features of modern plants. For example, the genome sequence of the moss *Physcomitrella patens*, first reported in 2007, reveals the presence of genes that aid heat and drought tolerance, which are especially useful in the terrestrial habitat. Plant fossils, the preserved remains of plants that lived in earlier times, provide another line of information. Tough plant materials such as sporopollenin, cutin, and lignin do not readily decay and therefore foster the fossilization of plant parts that contain these tough materials (**Figure 23.9**). The study of fossils and the molecular, structural, and functional features of modern plants have revealed an amazing story—how plants gradually acquired adaptations, allowing them to conquer the land.

Past and Present Seedless Plants Have Transformed Earth's Ecology

Past and present bryophytes have played important ecological roles by storing CO_2 as decay-resistant organic compounds. The abundant modern moss genus *Sphagnum* (see Figure 23.4) is widely harvested from natural wetlands for use as a garden soil conditioner because this moss does not easily decay and so adds valuable organic material that improves plant growth (see Chapter 29). *Sphagnum* moss contains so much decay-resistant mass that in many places, dead moss has accumulated over thousands of years, forming deep peat deposits. By storing very large amounts of organic carbon for long periods, *Sphagnum* helps to keep Earth's climate steady. Under cooler than normal conditions, *Sphagnum* grows more slowly and thus absorbs less CO_2, allowing atmospheric CO_2 to rise a bit, warming the climate a little. As the climate warms, *Sphagnum* grows faster and sponges up more CO_2, storing it in peat deposits. Such a reduction in atmospheric CO_2 returns the climate to slightly cooler conditions. In this way, ancient and modern peat mosses have helped to keep the world's climate from changing dramatically. Today, experts are concerned that large regions currently dominated by peat mosses are being affected by land use alterations, over-harvesting of moss peat, and global environmental changes that could reduce the ability of peat moss to moderate Earth's climate.

Fossils tell us that extensive forests dominated by tree-sized lycophytes, ferns, and early seed plants occurred in widespread swampy regions during the warm, moist Carboniferous period (354–290 mya) (**Figure 23.10**). Plants that died and fell into oxygen-poor sediments didn't completely decay and were eventually transformed into coal. Much of today's coal is derived from the abundant remains of ancient plants, explaining why the Carboniferous is commonly known as the Coal Age. During this period, plants and coal stored so much carbon dioxide as organic carbon that Earth's atmospheric CO_2 fell dramatically and oxygen rose to the highest known level. This large increase in the oxygen content of Earth's atmosphere fostered the evolution of giant insects (see Figure 28.10). In today's lower atmospheric oxygen levels, these

Figure 23.9 Fossil of *Pseudosalix handleyi*, an angiosperm.

Concept Check: *What biochemical components of plants favor the formation of fossils?*

Giant dragonfly

Giant horsetail (pteridophyte) Giant lycophyte

Figure 23.10 **Reconstruction of a Carboniferous (Coal Age) forest.** This ancient swampy forest was dominated by tree-sized lycophytes and ferns, which later contributed to the formation of large coal deposits.

Concept Check: *Why did giant dragonflies occur during the Carboniferous, but not now?*

insects' modern relatives have a harder time obtaining sufficient oxygen and so are smaller.

An Ancient Cataclysm Marked the Rise of Angiosperms

Diverse phyla of gymnosperms dominated Earth's vegetation through the Mesozoic era (248–65 mya), which is sometimes called the Age of Dinosaurs. In addition, fossils provide evidence that early mammals and flowering plants existed in the Mesozoic. Gymnosperms and early angiosperms were probably sources of food for early mammals as well as for herbivorous dinosaurs.

One fateful day about 65 mya, disaster struck from the sky, causing a dramatic change in the types of plants and animals that dominated terrestrial ecosystems. That day, at least one large meteorite crashed into the Earth near the present-day Yucatán Peninsula in Mexico. This episode is known as the K/T event because it marks the end of the Cretaceous (sometimes spelled with a K) period and the beginning of the Tertiary (T) period. The impact, together with substantial volcanic activity that also occurred at this time, is thought to have produced huge amounts of ash, smoke, and haze that dimmed the Sun's light long enough to kill many of the world's plants. Many types of plants became extinct, though some survived and their descendants persist to the present time. With a severely reduced food supply, most dinosaurs were also doomed, the exceptions being their descendants, the birds. The demise of the dinosaurs left room for birds and mammals to expand into many kinds of terrestrial habitats formerly inhabited by dinosaurs.

After the K/T event, ferns dominated long enough to leave huge numbers of fossil spores, and then surviving groups of flowering plants began to diversify into the space left by the extinction of previous plants. The rise of angiosperms fostered the diversification of beetles and other types of insects that associate with modern plants. Because most mammals, including humans, rely directly or indirectly upon food that angiosperms produce, the rise of angiosperms was also key to the evolutionary diversification of humans and other mammals. Diversification of angiosperms was also critical to the origin of agriculture, upon which most modern humans depend for food, shelter, and many other materials.

23.2 Reviewing the Concepts

- Paleobiologists and plant evolutionary biologists infer the history of land plants by analyzing the molecular features of modern plants and by comparing the structural features of fossil and modern plants (Figure 23.9).
- Ancient and modern plants transformed Earth's ecology by altering atmospheric chemistry and climate, and by influencing the evolutionary diversification of animals (Figure 23.10).

23.2 Testing Your Knowledge

1. Plants lack bones, but they have left many fossils. What decay-resistant plant materials are largely responsible for the occurrence of plant fossils?
   a. lignin in the xylem of the plant conducting system
   b. cutin produced on plant surfaces
   c. sporopollenin produced on spore surfaces
   d. all of the above
   e. none of the above

2. How have plants influenced the evolution of animals?
   a. The earliest land plants generated substantial soils, thereby fostering the growth of later plants that provided earliest land animals with food and shelter.
   b. Plant evolutionary diversification generated many different types of habitat, thereby influencing the evolutionary diversification of animals.
   c. The photosynthetic activity and fossilization of abundant Coal Age plants decreased the amount of CO_2 and increased the amount of O_2 in Earth's atmosphere, thereby affecting insect size and causing global climate change.
   d. The diversification of angiosperms following the K-T event fostered the diversification of modern mammals and other animal lineages.
   e. All of the above are correct.

23.3 Diversity of Modern Gymnosperms

Learning Outcome:

1. List three gymnosperm phyla and describe their importance to humans.

Figure 23.11 shows our current understanding of the relationships among modern seed plants, the flowering plants (angiosperms), and three phyla of gymnosperms. Gymnosperms appear to have originated from ancestral plants that had the capacity to produce wood, a tough material composed of xylem tissue, allowing such plants to grow to tree height. Tall height allows trees to gain an advantage in capturing light energy for photosynthesis. Consequently, wood is a common trait in gymnosperms. Following the early diversification of gymnosperms, an unknown, extinct gymnosperm lineage gave rise to the angiosperms—the flowering plants. Angiosperms inherited many traits from gymnosperm ancestors, including the capacity to produce seeds and wood. **Table 23.1** provides a summary of the characteristics of modern seed plants.

Cycads Are Endangered in the Wild But Are Widely Used as Ornamentals

Cycads (see Figure 23.8a) are regarded as the earliest diverging modern gymnosperm phylum, originating more than 300 mya. Although cycads are an ancient group, molecular clock analyses indicate that modern cycad species are about 12 million years old. Nearly 300 cycad species occur today, primarily in tropical and subtropical regions. However, many species of cycads are rare, and their tropical forest homes are increasingly threatened by human activities. Many cycads are listed as endangered, and commercial trade in cycads is regulated by CITES (Convention on International Trade in Endangered Species of Wild Fauna and

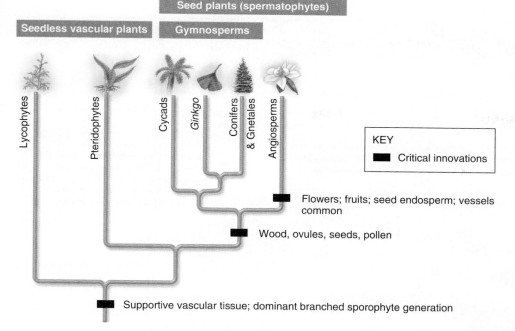

Seed plants (spermatophytes)

Seedless vascular plants | Gymnosperms

Lycophytes | Pteridophytes | Cycads | *Ginkgo* | Conifers & Gnetales | Angiosperms

KEY
■ Critical innovations

Flowers; fruits; seed endosperm; vessels common

Wood, ovules, seeds, pollen

Supportive vascular tissue; dominant branched sporophyte generation

Figure 23.11 A phylogeny of modern seedless and seed plants.

conelike structures that produce either pollen or **ovules,** structures that contain female gametophyte tissues, including egg cells (see Figure 23.8a). When mature, both types of reproductive structures emit odors that attract beetles. These insects carry pollen to ovules, where the pollen produces tubes that deliver sperm to eggs. Fertilization of an egg to form a zygote triggers development of the ovule into a seed.

Ginkgo biloba Is the Last Survivor of a Once-Diverse Group

The beautiful tree *Ginkgo biloba* (see Figure 23.8b) is the single remaining species of a phylum that was much more diverse during the Age of Dinosaurs. Today, *G. biloba* may be nearly extinct in the wild; widely cultivated modern *Ginkgo* trees are descended from seeds produced by a tree found in a remote Japanese temple garden and brought to Europe by 17th-century explorers.

G. biloba trees are widely planted along city streets because they are ornamental and also tolerate cold, heat, and pollution better than many other trees. In addition, these trees are long-lived—individuals can live for more than a thousand years and grow to 30 m in height. Individual trees have sex chromosomes much like those of humans, and so produce either ovules and seeds or pollen. Seed embryos are protected by a fleshy,

Flora), a voluntary international agreement between governments to protect such species.

The structure of cycads is so interesting and attractive that many species are cultivated for use in outdoor plantings or as houseplants. Cycads display spreading, palmlike leaves (*cycad* comes from a Greek word, meaning palm). Mature leaves of the African cycad *Encephalartos laurentianus* can reach an astounding 8.8 m in length! Individual cycad plants produce conspicuous

Table 23.1	Distinguishing Features of Modern Streptophyte Algae and Land Plants

Streptophyte Algae
Primarily aquatic habitat; zygotic life cycle; embryos and tough-walled spores absent

LAND PLANTS (EMBRYOPHYTES)
Primarily terrestrial habitat; alternation of two multicellular generations—diploid sporophyte and haploid gametophyte; multicellular embryos are nutritionally dependent on maternal gametophyte for at least some time during development; spore-producing sporangia; gamete-producing gametangia; tough-walled spores
Nonvascular plants (Bryophytes) (**liverworts, mosses, hornworts**)
Dominant gametophyte generation; supportive, lignin-containing vascular tissue absent; true roots, stems, leaves absent; sporophytes unbranched and unable to grow independently of gametophytes

VASCULAR PLANTS (TRACHEOPHYTES) (lycophytes, ferns, spermatophytes)
Dominant sporophyte generation; lignin-walled water-conducting tissue—xylem; specialized organic food-conducting tissue—phloem; sporophytes branched and eventually become able to grow independently of gametophytes; all have stems; most also have leaves and roots
Lycophytes Leaves generally small with a single, unbranched vein (lycophylls); sporangia borne on sides of stems

FERNS + SEED PLANTS
Ferns Leaves relatively large with extensively branched vein system; sporangia borne on leaves; seeds absent

SEED PLANTS (SPERMATOPHYTES)
Seeds present; leaves have branched vein systems

GYMNOSPERMS (**cycads, ginkgos, conifers**)
Flowers and fruits absent; seed food stored in female gametophyte, endosperm absent
Angiosperms (**flowering plants**)
Flowers and fruit present; seed food stored after fertilization in endosperm formed by double fertilization

Key: **Phyla**; LARGER MONOPHYLETIC CLADES (synonyms). All other classification terms are not clades.

Biology Principle

Living Organisms Grow and Develop

This diagram illustrates the entire seed-to-seed growth and development cycle of conifers.

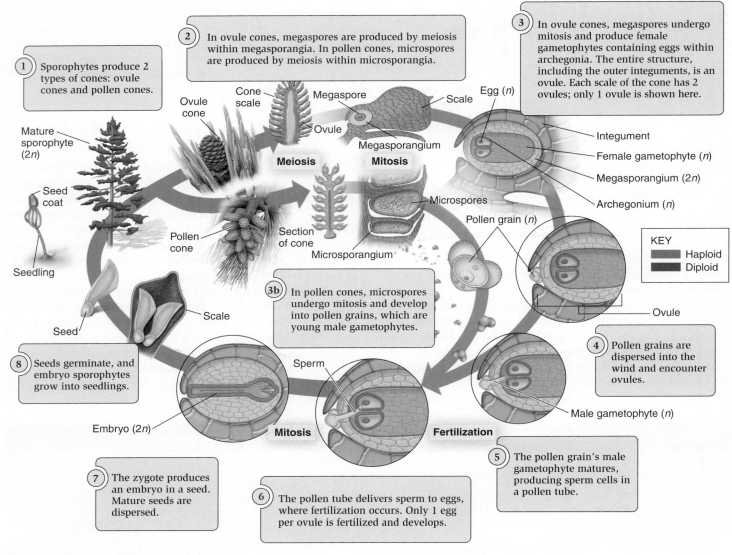

1. Sporophytes produce 2 types of cones: ovule cones and pollen cones.

2. In ovule cones, megaspores are produced by meiosis within megasporangia. In pollen cones, microspores are produced by meiosis within microsporangia.

3. In ovule cones, megaspores undergo mitosis and produce female gametophytes containing eggs within archegonia. The entire structure, including the outer integuments, is an ovule. Each scale of the cone has 2 ovules; only 1 ovule is shown here.

3b. In pollen cones, microspores undergo mitosis and develop into pollen grains, which are young male gametophytes.

4. Pollen grains are dispersed into the wind and encounter ovules.

5. The pollen grain's male gametophyte matures, producing sperm cells in a pollen tube.

6. The pollen tube delivers sperm to eggs, where fertilization occurs. Only 1 egg per ovule is fertilized and develops.

7. The zygote produces an embryo in a seed. Mature seeds are dispersed.

8. Seeds germinate, and embryo sporophytes grow into seedlings.

KEY
Haploid
Diploid

Figure 23.12 The life cycle of the genus *Pinus.*

bad-smelling outer seed coat and a hard, inner seed coat. For street-side or garden plantings, people usually select the pollen-producing trees to avoid the stinky seeds.

Conifers Are the Most Diverse Modern Gymnosperm Lineage

The conifers (see Figure 23.8c) are a lineage of trees named for their seed cones, of which pinecones are familiar examples. Modern conifer families include more than 50 genera. Conifers are particularly common in mountain and high-latitude forests and are important sources of wood and paper pulp.

Conifers produce simple pollen cones and more complex ovule-bearing cones (Figure 23.12). The pollen cones of conifers bear many leaf-like structures, each bearing a sporangium in which meiosis occurs and pollen grains develop. This pollen-producing sporangium is called a microsporangium because the pollen grains develop from small spores known as microspores. The ovule cones are composed of many short branch systems that bear ovules, within which female gametophyte tissues produce eggs.

When conifer pollen is mature, it is released into the wind, which transports pollen to ovules. When released from pollen tubes, sperm fuse with eggs, generating zygotes that grow into the embryos within seeds. Altogether, it takes nearly 2 years for pine (the genus *Pinus*) to complete the processes of male and female gamete development, fertilization, and seed development. The seeds of pine and some other conifers develop wings that aid in wind dispersal. Other conifers, such as yew and juniper, produce seeds or cones with bright-colored, fleshy coatings that are attractive to birds, which help to disperse the seeds.

Many conifers occur in cold climates and thus display numerous adaptations to such environments. Their conical shapes and flexible branches help conifer trees shed snow, preventing heavy snow accumulations from breaking branches. People who use conifers in landscape plantings also value these traits. Conifer leaf shape and structure are adapted to resist damage from drought that occurs in both summer and winter, when liquid water is scarce. Conifer leaves are often scalelike or needle-shaped; these shapes reduce the area of leaf surface from which water can evaporate. A thick, waxy cuticle coats conifer leaf surfaces, retarding water loss and preventing attack by disease organisms. Many conifers are evergreen; that is, their leaves live for more than 1 year before being shed and are not all shed during the same season. Retaining leaves through winter helps conifers start up photosynthesis earlier than deciduous trees, which in spring must replace leaves lost during the previous autumn. Evergreen leaves thus provide an advantage in the short growth season of alpine or high-latitude environments.

The conifer phylum also includes the Gnetales, an order of three genera, *Gnetum*, *Ephedra*, and *Welwitschia*, that feature distinctive adaptations:

- *Gnetum* is unusual among modern gymnosperms in having broad leaves similar to those of many tropical plants (Figure 23.13a). Such leaves foster light capture in the dim forest habitat. More than 30 species of the genus *Gnetum* occur as vines, shrubs, or trees in tropical Africa or Asia.

- *Ephedra*, native to arid regions of the southwestern U.S., has tiny brown scalelike leaves and green, photosynthetic stems (Figure 23.13b). These adaptations help to conserve water by preventing water loss that would otherwise occur from the surfaces of larger leaves. Like all plants, *Ephedra* produces **secondary metabolites**, compounds that are not essential for basic cellular structure and growth, but that aid plant structure, protection, or reproduction. Plant secondary compounds influence humans in many ways (see Section 23.4), and *Ephedra*'s secondary compounds have long been known to affect humans. For example, early settlers of the western U.S. used *Ephedra* to treat colds and other medical conditions. The modern decongestant drug pseudoephedrine is based on the chemical structure of ephedrine, which was named for and originally obtained from *Ephedra*. Pseudoephedrine sales are now restricted in many places because this compound can be used as a starting point for the synthesis of illegal drugs. Ephedrine has also been used to enhance sports performance, a practice that has elicited medical concern.

- *Welwitschia* has only one living representative species. *Welwitschia mirabilis* is a strange-looking plant that grows in the coastal Namib Desert of southwestern Africa, one of the driest places on Earth (Figure 23.13c). A long taproot anchors a stubby stem that barely emerges from the ground. Two very

(a) Genus *Gnetum*

(b) *Ephedra californica*

(c) *Welwitschia mirabilis*

Figure 23.13 Gnetales. **(a)** A tropical plant of the genus *Gnetum*, displaying broad leaves and reproductive structures. **(b)** *Ephedra californica* growing in deserts of North America, showing minuscule brown leaves on green, photosynthetic stems and reproductive structures. **(c)** *Welwitschia mirabilis* growing in the Namib Desert of southwestern Africa, showing long, wind-shredded leaves and reproductive structures.

long leaves grow from the stem but are rapidly shredded by the wind into many strips. The plant is thought to obtain most of its water from coastal fog that accumulates on the leaves, explaining how *W. mirabilis* can grow and reproduce in such a dry place.

23.3 Reviewing the Concepts

- The seed plants (also called spermatophytes) consist of the gymnosperms, with exposed seeds, and the angiosperms, with seeds enclosed in fruits (Figures 23.11, 23.12, Table 23.1).
- The diversity of modern gymnosperms includes three modern phyla that are all important to human life: cycads, *Ginkgo biloba*, and the conifers (including Gnetales; Figure 23.13).

23.3 Testing Your Knowledge

1. In what way are gymnosperms different from angiosperms?
   a. Gymnosperms possess embryos.
   b. Gymnosperms possess lignified xylem.
   c. Gymnosperms possess seeds.
   d. Gymnosperms possess wood.
   e. Gymnosperms lack flowers, fruit, and seed endosperm.

2. Which of the following plant traits represent examples of plant adaptations that are useful to humans?
   a. lignin-walled xylem   d. secondary metabolites
   b. stems, leaves, and roots   e. all of the above
   c. seed endosperm

23.4 Diversity of Modern Angiosperms

Learning Outcomes:

1. List four flower organs and their functions, and explain how each flower part may have first evolved.
2. Describe how diversification of flowers and fruits enhances seed production and dispersal.
3. Name three major types of angiosperm secondary metabolites and how these affect animals.

The flowering plants, including hundreds of thousands of species, are the most diverse group of modern land plants. The evolutionary success of angiosperms is based upon traits that are absent or rare in other plants—flowers, fruits, and endosperm. Recall that a flower is a short stem bearing reproductive organs, fruits develop from flowers, and endosperm is a nutritive seed tissue. Flowers foster seed production, fruits favor seed dispersal, and endosperm food helps embryos within seeds grow into seedlings. Angiosperms also possess more efficient water conducting systems than do other plants. In addition to tracheids, most angiosperms also possess water-conducting **vessels,** which are wider than tracheids and therefore increase the efficiency of water flow through plants. Though similar structures occur in some seedless plants and gymnosperms, these are thought to have evolved independently. Angiosperms also possess vascular systems that branch more densely than do those of other plants, a trait that allows flowering plants to more effectively conduct materials through the body.

More than 124 mya, an extinct group of gymnosperms gave rise to the angiosperms—the flowering plants. Charles Darwin famously referred to the origin of the flowering plants as "an abominable mystery," one that has not been fully solved even today. Modern plant evolutionary biologists continue to study the evolutionary origin of distinctive angiosperm traits, such as the flower, that help to explain why flowering plants are so diverse.

Flowers Include Stamens and/or Carpels, and Often Also Petals and Sepals

Flowers are produced at stem tips and may contain four types of organs: sepals, petals, pollen-producing stamens, and ovule-producing carpels (**Figure 23.14**). These flower organs are supported by tissue located at the tip of a flower stem. The functioning of several genes that control flower organ development explains why carpels are the most central flower organs, why stamens surround carpels, and why petals and sepals are the outermost flower organs.

Many flowers produce attractive **petals** that play a role in **pollination,** the transfer of pollen among flowers of similar type. **Sepals** of many flowers are green and form the outer layer of flower buds. The sepals of some flowers, such as tulip and lily, look similar to petals, in which case both sepals and petals are known as tepals. All of a flower's sepals and petals are collectively known as the perianth. Most flowers produce one or more **stamens,** the structures that produce and disperse pollen. Most flowers also contain a single or multiple **carpels,** structures that produce ovules. Some flowers produce only a single carpel, others display several separate carpels, and many possess several carpels that are fused together into a compound structure. Both a single carpel and fused carpels are referred to as a **pistil** (from the Latin *pistillum*, meaning pestle) because it resembles the device people use to grind materials to powder in a mortar (see Figure 23.14). Pistil structure can be divided into three regions having distinct functions. A topmost portion of the pistil, known as the stigma, receives and recognizes pollen of the appropriate species or genotype. The elongate middle portion of the pistil is called the style. The lowermost portion of the pistil is the ovary, which encloses and protects ovules.

During the flowering plant life cycle (**Figure 23.15**), the stigma allows pollen of appropriate genetic type to germinate, producing

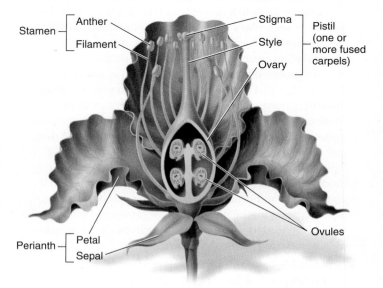

Figure 23.14 **Generalized flower structure.** Although flowers are diverse in size, shape, and color, they commonly have the parts illustrated here.

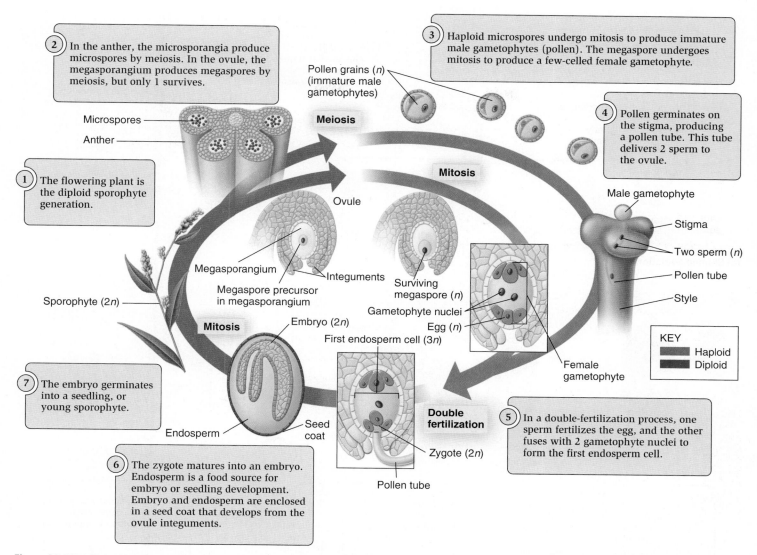

2 In the anther, the microsporangia produce microspores by meiosis. In the ovule, the megasporangium produces megaspores by meiosis, but only 1 survives.

3 Haploid microspores undergo mitosis to produce immature male gametophytes (pollen). The megaspore undergoes mitosis to produce a few-celled female gametophyte.

4 Pollen germinates on the stigma, producing a pollen tube. This tube delivers 2 sperm to the ovule.

1 The flowering plant is the diploid sporophyte generation.

5 In a double-fertilization process, one sperm fertilizes the egg, and the other fuses with 2 gametophyte nuclei to form the first endosperm cell.

6 The zygote matures into an embryo. Endosperm is a food source for embryo or seedling development. Embryo and endosperm are enclosed in a seed coat that develops from the ovule integuments.

7 The embryo germinates into a seedling, or young sporophyte.

Pollen grains (*n*) (immature male gametophytes)

Meiosis

Microspores

Anther

Mitosis

Ovule

Megasporangium

Integuments

Megaspore precursor in megasporangium

Surviving megaspore (*n*)

Gametophyte nuclei

Egg (*n*)

Male gametophyte

Stigma

Two sperm (*n*)

Pollen tube

Style

Sporophyte (2*n*)

Mitosis

Embryo (2*n*)

First endosperm cell (3*n*)

Female gametophyte

Endosperm

Seed coat

Zygote (2*n*)

Pollen tube

Double fertilization

KEY
Haploid
Diploid

Figure 23.15 **The life cycle of a flowering plant, illustrated by the genus *Polygonum*.** Flowering plant life cycles differ in length of the cycle and the number of cells and nuclei occurring in the female gametophyte, the seven-celled, eight-nuclei of *Polygonum* being common.

a long pollen tube that grows through the style. The pollen tube delivers two sperm cells to ovules. In the distinctive angiosperm process known as **double fertilization,** one sperm nucleus fuses with the egg nucleus to form a zygote, and the other sperm nucleus fuses with the nuclei of other haploid cells of the female gametophyte. The latter is the first step in the development of a characteristic angiosperm nutritive tissue known as endosperm. Fed by the endosperm, the zygote develops into an embryo, and the ovule develops into a seed. Ovaries (and sometimes additional flower parts) develop into fruits.

EVOLUTIONARY CONNECTIONS

Flower Organs Evolved from Leaflike Structures

Petals and sepals are often similar to leaves in shape and structure of the vascular system, features that suggest the evolution

of petals and sepals from leaves. Structural comparison and molecular data indicate that stamens and pistils likewise originated from leaflike structures. Angiosperm stamens resemble leaflike structures of gymnosperms that produce the microspores that develop into pollen. Plant evolutionary biologists hypothesize that over time, the microspore-producing tissues became restricted to the stamen tips, generating anthers on a supporting filament (**Figure 23.16a**). Plant evolutionary biologists likewise hypothesize that carpels are homologous to leaflike structures of gymnosperms that bear ovules on their surfaces. The carpels of some early-diverging modern plants are leaflike structures that fold over ovules, with the carpel edges stuck together by secretions (**Figure 23.16b**). Most modern flowers produce carpels whose edges have fused together into a tube whose lower portion (ovary) encloses and protects ovules, improving plant fitness. The first flowers arose when early stamens, carpels, and perianth parts aggregated into a single structure.

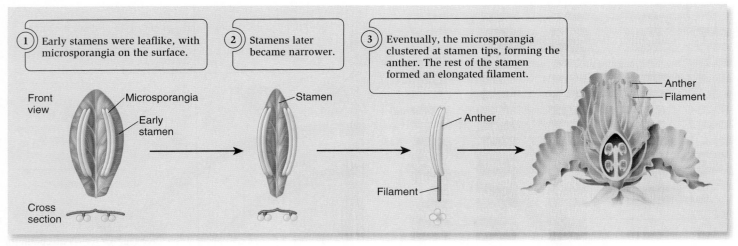

(a) Stamen evolution

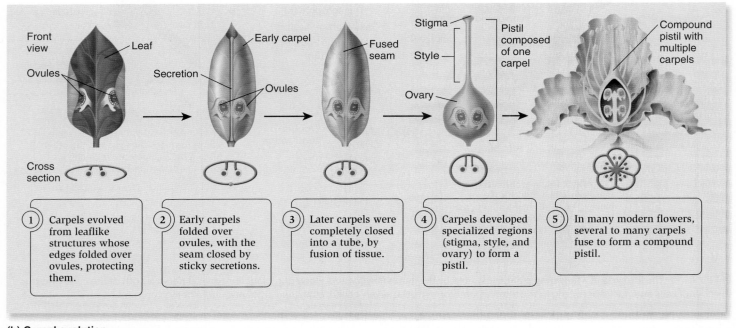

(b) Carpel evolution

Figure 23.16 **Hypothetical evolutionary origin of stamens, carpels, and pistils.** Plant biologists test these models by searching for new fossils or generating additional molecular data.

Flowering Plants Diversified into Several Lineages, Including Monocots and Eudicots

Figure 23.17 presents our current understanding of the relationships among modern angiosperm groups. According to gene-sequencing studies, the earliest-diverging modern angiosperms are represented by a single species called *Amborella trichopoda*, a shrub that lives in forests on the South Pacific island of New Caledonia. Later-diverging groups of angiosperms include water lilies, the star anise plant, and other close relatives (see Figure 23.17). Magnoliids, represented by the genus *Magnolia*, are the next-diverging group. Magnoliids are closely related to two very large and diverse angiosperm lineages: the **monocots** and the **eudicots.**

Monocots and eudicots are named for differences in the number of embryonic leaves called cotyledons. Monocot embryos possess one cotyledon, whereas eudicots possess two cotyledons. Also, monocots typically have petals, stamens, or other floral parts numbering three or some multiple of three, whereas eudicot flower parts tend to occur in fours, fives, or a multiple of four or five. Tulips, daffodils, and irises are examples of monocots, whereas roses, snapdragons, and daisies are examples of dicots.

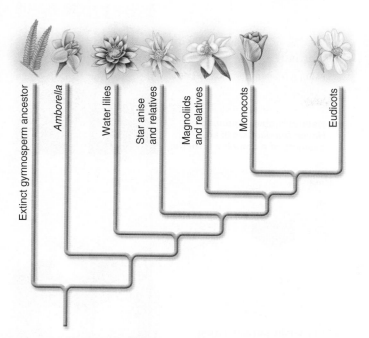

Figure 23.17 **A phylogeny showing the major modern angiosperm lineages.**

Flower Diversification Has Fostered Efficient Seed Production

During the diversification of flowering plants, flower evolution has involved several types of changes that foster the transfer of pollen from one plant to another. Effective pollination is essential to efficient seed production because it minimizes the amount of energy plants must expend to accomplish sexual reproduction.

Fusion of flower organs, clustering of flowers into groups, and reducing the perianth are some examples of changes leading to effective pollination.

- Many flowers have fused petals that form floral tubes. Such tubes tend to accumulate sugar-rich nectar that provides a reward for **pollinators,** animals that transfer pollen among plants. The diameters of floral tubes vary among flowers and are evolutionarily tuned to the feeding structures of diverse animals, which range from the narrow tongues of butterflies to the wider bills of nectar-feeding birds (**Figure 23.18**). Nectar-feeding bats stick their heads into even larger tubular flowers to lap up nectar with their tongues.

- Many plants produce **inflorescences,** groups of flowers tightly clustered together, which occur in several types. The zinnia features a type of inflorescence in which many small flowers are clustered into a head (see Figure 23.18a). The flowers at the center of a sunflower head function in reproduction and lack showy petals, but flowers at the rim have showy petals that attract pollinators. Flower heads allow pollinators to transfer pollen among a large number of flowers at the same time.

- The grass family features flowers with few or no perianths, which explains why grass flowers are not showy. This adaptation fosters pollination by wind, since petals would get in the way of such pollen transfer. Since grasses often grow in dense populations, wind pollination can be very effective.

Diverse Types of Fruits Function in Seed Dispersal

Fruits are structures that develop from ovary walls in diverse ways that aid the dispersal of enclosed seeds. Seed dispersal helps to prevent seedlings from competing with their larger parents for

(a) Zinnia flower and butterfly **(b) Hibiscus flower and hummingbird** **(c) Saguaro cactus flower and bat**

Figure 23.18 **Flowers whose perianths form nectar-containing floral tubes of different widths that accommodate different pollinators.** **(a)** This zinnia is composed of an outer rim of showy flowers and a central disc of narrow tubular flowers that produce nectar. Butterflies, but not other pollinators, are able to reach the nectar by means of narrow tongues. **(b)** The hibiscus flower produces nectar in a floral tube whose diameter corresponds to the dimensions of a hummingbird bill. **(c)** The saguaro cactus (*Carnegiea gigantea*) flower forms a floral tube that is wide enough for nectar-feeding bats to get their heads inside. The cactus flower has been drawn here as if it were transparent, to illustrate bat pollination.

(a) A fleshy fruit (cherry)

(b) An aggregate fruit (strawberry)

(c) A multiple fruit (pineapple)

(d) Legumes with dry pods (peas)

Figure 23.19 **Representative fruit types.** **(a)** The cherry is an example of a fleshy fruit that is adapted to attract animals that consume the fruits and excrete the seeds. **(b)** Strawberry is an aggregate fruit, consisting of many tiny, single-seeded fruits produced by a single flower. The fruits are embedded in the surface of tissue that originally supported the flower. **(c)** Pineapple is a large multiple fruit formed by the aggregation of smaller fruits, each produced by one of the flowers in an inflorescence. **(d)** Peas produce legumes, fruits that open on two sides to release seeds.

scarce resources such as water and light. Dispersal of seeds also allows plants to colonize new habitats.

- Many mature angiosperm fruits, such as cherries, are attractively colored, soft, juicy, and tasty (Figure 23.19a). Such fruits are adapted to attract animals that consume the fruits, digest the outer portion as food, and eliminate the seeds after traveling some distance, thereby dispersing them. Hard seed coats prevent such seeds from being destroyed by the animal's digestive system.

- Strawberries are aggregate fruits, many fruits that all develop from a single flower having multiple pistils (Figure 23.19b). The ovaries of these pistils develop into tiny, single-seeded yellow fruits on a strawberry surface; the fleshy, red, sweet portion of a strawberry develops from tissue that supported the flower. Aggregate fruits allow a single animal consumer, such as a bird, to disperse many seeds at the same time.

- Pineapples (Figure 23.19c) are juicy multiple fruits that develop when many ovaries of an inflorescence fuse together. Such multiple fruits are larger and attract relatively large animals that have the ability to disperse seeds over long distances.

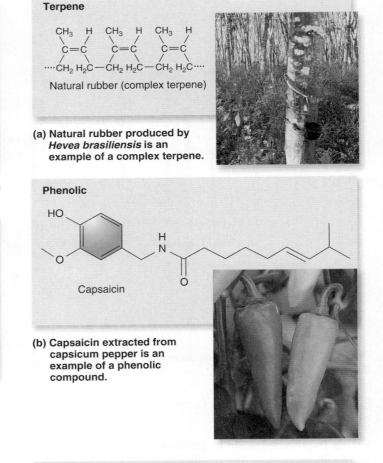

(a) Natural rubber produced by *Hevea brasiliensis* is an example of a complex terpene.

(b) Capsaicin extracted from capsicum pepper is an example of a phenolic compound.

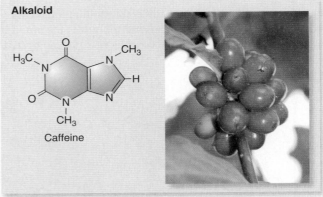

(c) Caffeine produced by *Coffea arabica* is an example of an alkaloid.

Figure 23.20 **Major types of plant secondary metabolites.** Note that the chemistry of plant secondary metabolites differs from that of the primary compounds produced by all cells. The production by plants of terpenes, phenolics, and alkaloids helps to explain how plants survive and reproduce, and why plants are useful to humans in so many ways.

- The plant family informally known as legumes is named for its distinctive fruits, dry pods that split open down both sides when seeds are mature, thereby releasing them (Figure 23.19d).

- Nuts and grains are additional examples of dry fruits. Grains are the characteristic single-seeded fruits of cereal grasses such as rice, corn (maize), barley, and wheat. Other plants produce dry fruits with surface burrs that attach to animal fur.

Angiosperms Produce Diverse Secondary Metabolites That Play Important Roles in Structure, Reproduction, and Protection

As noted in discussion of the gymnosperm *Ephedra* (see Section 22.3), secondary metabolites are organic compounds that are not essential for basic cell structure and growth but aid survival, structure, and reproduction. Certain prokaryotes, protists, and fungi, as well as some animals and all plants, produce secondary metabolites, but these compounds are most diverse in the angiosperms. Most of the 100,000 or so known types of secondary metabolites are produced by flowering plants. The diversification of these compounds has strongly influenced flowering plant evolution, as well as everyday human life. Three major classes of plant secondary metabolites occur: (1) terpenes and terpenoids; (2) phenolics; and (3) alkaloids (Figure 23.20).

- About 25,000 types of plant terpenes and terpenoids are derived from different arrangements of the simple hydrocarbon gas isoprene. Taxol, used in the treatment of cancer, is a terpene, as are citronella and a variety of other compounds that repel insects. Rubber, turpentine, rosin, and amber are complex terpenoids that likewise serve important roles in plant biology as well as having useful human applications.

- Phenolic compounds are responsible for some flower and fruit colors as well as the distinctive flavors of cinnamon, nutmeg, ginger, cloves, chilies, and vanilla. Phenolics absorb ultraviolet radiation, thereby preventing damage to cellular DNA. They also help to defend plants against insects and disease microbes. Some phenolic compounds found in tea, red wine, grape juice, and blueberries are antioxidants that detoxify free radicals, highly reactive by-products of normal metabolism. Such phenolics thereby prevent cellular damage in the plant as well as animals that consume them.

- Alkaloids are nitrogen-containing secondary metabolites that often have potent effects on the animal nervous system. Plants produce at least 12,000 types of alkaloids, and certain species produce many alkaloids. Caffeine, nicotine, morphine, ephedrine, cocaine, and codeine are examples of alkaloids that influence the physiology and behavior of humans and so their use and abuse are of societal concern. Like flowers and fruit structures, secondary metabolites are useful in distinguishing among Earth's hundreds of thousands of flowering plant species.

FEATURE INVESTIGATION

Hillig and Mahlberg Analyzed Secondary Metabolites to Explore Species Diversification in the Genus *Cannabis*

The genus *Cannabis* has long been a source of hemp fiber used for ropes and fabric. People have also used *Cannabis* (also known as marijuana) in traditional medicine and as a hallucinogenic drug. *Cannabis* produces THC (tetrahydrocannabinol), a type of alkaloid called a cannabinoid. THC and other cannabinoids are produced in glandular hairs that cover most of the *Cannabis* plant's surface but are particularly rich in leaves located near the flowers. THC mimics compounds known as endocannabinoids, which are naturally produced and act in the animal brain and elsewhere in the body. THC affects humans by binding to receptor proteins in plasma membranes in the same way as natural endocannabinoids. Cancer and AIDS patients sometimes choose to use cannabis to reduce nausea and stimulate their appetite, counteracting side effects of cancer treatment and the wasting that accompanies both diseases.

Because humans have subjected cultivated *Cannabis* plants to artificial selection for so long, plant biologists have been uncertain how cultivated *Cannabis* species are related to those in the wild. In the past, plants cultivated for drug production were often identified as *Cannabis indica*, whereas those grown for hemp were typically known as *Cannabis sativa*. However, these species are difficult to distinguish on the basis of structural features, and the relevance of these names to wild cannabis was unknown. At the same time, species identification has become important for biodiversity studies, agriculture, and law enforcement. For these reasons, plant biologists Karl Hillig and Paul Mahlberg hypothesized that ratios of THC to another cannabinoid known as CBD (canna<u>bid</u>iol) might aid in defining *Canna-*

bis species and identifying plant samples at the species level, as shown in Figure 23.21.

To test their hypothesis, the investigators began by collecting *Cannabis* fruits from nearly a hundred diverse locations around the world and then growing these plants from seed under uniform conditions in a greenhouse. The investigators next extracted cannabinoids, analyzed them by means of gas chromatography (a laboratory technique used to identify components of a mixture), and determined the ratios of THC to CBD. The results, published in 2004, suggested that the wild and cultivated *Cannabis* samples evaluated in this study could be classified into two species: *C. sativa*, displaying relatively low THC levels, and *C. indica*, having relatively high THC levels. As a result of this work, ecologists, agricultural scientists, and forensic scientists can reliably use ratios of THC to CBD to classify samples. Similar studies of plant secondary metabolites offer the benefit of uncovering potential new medicinal compounds or other applications of significance to humans.

Experimental Questions

1. In Figure 23.21, note that investigators obtained nearly 100 *Cannabis* fruit samples from around the world. Why were so many samples needed?

2. Why did Hillig and Mahlberg grow plants in a greenhouse before conducting the cannabinoid analysis?

3. Why did Hillig and Mahlberg collect samples from the leaves growing nearest the flowers?

Figure 23.21 Hillig and Mahlberg's analysis of secondary metabolites in the genus *Cannabis*.

GOAL To determine if cannabinoids aid in distinguishing *Cannabis* species.

KEY MATERIALS *Cannabis* fruits obtained from nearly 100 different worldwide sources.

	Experimental level	Conceptual level
1	Grow multiple *Cannabis* plants from seeds under standard conditions in a greenhouse.	Eliminates differential environmental effects on cannabinoid content.

2	Extract cannabinoids from leaves surrounding flowers.	Extracts were made from tissues richest in cannabinoids; this reduces the chance that cannabinoids present in lower levels would be missed.

3 Analyze cannabinoids by gas chromatography. Determine ratios of THC (tetrahydrocannabinol) to CBD (cannabidiol) in about 200 *Cannabis* plants.

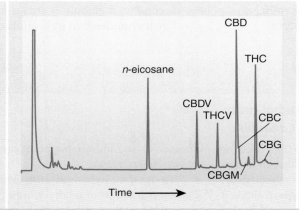

Previous data suggested that ratios of THC to CBD might be different in separate species.

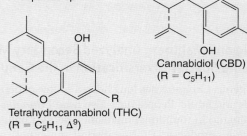

Cannabidiol (CBD) $(R = C_5H_{11})$

Tetrahydrocannabinol (THC) $(R = C_5H_{11} \; \Delta^9)$

4 THE DATA

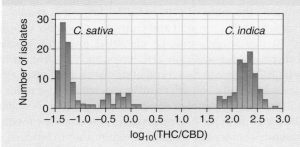

Cannabis plants isolated from diverse sources worldwide formed 2 groups—those having relatively high THC to CBD ratios and those having lower THC to CBD ratios.

Plants having low THC to CBD ratios, often used as hemp fiber sources, corresponded to the species *C. sativa*.

Plants having high THC to CBD ratios, often used as drug sources, corresponded to the species *C. indica*.

5 CONCLUSION Differing cannabinoid ratios support a concept of 2 *Cannabis* species.

6 SOURCE Hillig, K.W., and Mahlberg, P.G. 2004. A chemotaxonomic analysis of cannabinoid variation in *Cannabis* (Cannabaceae). *American Journal of Botany* 91:966–975.

23.4 Reviewing the Concepts

- Flowers foster seed production and are adapted in various ways that aid pollination. Flower parts likely evolved from leaflike structures (Figures 23.14, 23.15, 23.16).
- The two largest and most diverse lineages of flowering plants are the monocots and eudicots (Figure 23.17).
- Flower diversification involved evolutionary changes such as fusion of petals, clustering of flowers into inflorescences, and reduced perianth that improve pollination effectiveness and seed production (Figure 23.18).
- Fruits are structures that enclose seeds and aid in their dispersal (Figure 23.19).
- Angiosperms produce three main groups of secondary metabolites: (1) terpenes and terpenoids; (2) phenolics; and (3) alkaloids, which play essential roles in plant structure, reproduction, and defense, respectively (Figures 23.20, 23.21).

23.4 Testing Your Knowledge

1. A plant produces very small, petal-less flowers that are clustered into a dangling inflorescence. Among the choices given, which pollination agent is most likely?
   a. butterfly   c. bat   e. water
   b. hummingbird   d. wind

2. A plant produces juicy, sweet red fruits having relatively small seeds. Among the choices given, which seed dispersal agent is most likely in nature?
   a. butterfly   c. bear   e. water
   b. bird   d. wind

23.5 Human Influences on Angiosperm Diversification

Learning Outcome:

1. Understand how humans created the domesticated wheat, corn, and rice grain crops widely planted around the world today.

By means of the process known as **domestication,** which involves artificial selection for traits desirable to humans, ancient humans transformed wild plant species into new crop species. Cultivated bread wheat (*Triticum aestivum*) was probably among the earliest food crops, having originated more than 8,000 years ago in what is now southeastern Turkey and northern Syria. Bread wheat originated by a series of steps from wild ancestors (*Triticum boeoticum* and *Triticum dicoccoides*). Among the earliest changes that

occurred during wheat domestication was the loss of shattering, the process by which ears of wild grain crops break apart and disperse their grains (a type of fruit). A mutation probably caused the ears of some wheat plants to remain intact, a trait that is disadvantageous in nature but beneficial to humans. Nonshattering ears would have been easier for humans to harvest than normal ears. Early farmers probably selected seed stock from plants having nonshattering ears and other favorable traits such as larger grains. These ancient artificial selection processes, together with modern breeding efforts, explain why cultivated wheat differs from its wild relatives in shattering and other properties. The accumulation of these trait differences explains why cultivated and wild wheat plants are classified as different species.

About 9,000 years ago, people living in what is now Mexico domesticated a native grass known as teosinte (of the genus *Zea*), producing a new species, *Zea mays*, known as corn or maize. The evidence for this pivotal event includes ancient ears that were larger than wild ones and distinctive fossil pollen. Modern ears of corn are much larger than those of teosinte, with many more rows and larger and softer corn grains, and modern corn ears do not shatter, as do those of ancestral teosinte (**Figure 23.22**).

Biology Principle

Biology Affects Our Society

The domestication of corn from a wild grass to one of the world's largest production crops is an amazing feat of artificial selection.

Immature ear of teosinte   Grain

Mature, shattered ear of teosinte

Nonshattering ear of *Z. mays*

Figure 23.22 Ears and grains of modern corn and its ancestor, teosinte. This illustration shows that domesticated corn ears are much larger than those of the ancestral grass teosinte. In addition, corn fruits are softer and more edible than the grains of teosinte, which are enclosed in a hard casing.

 **Concept Check:** *In what other way do corn ears differ from those of teosinte?*

Molecular analyses indicate that domesticated rice (*Oryza sativa*) originated from ancestral wild species of grasses (*Oryza nivara* and/or *Oryza rufipogon*). As in the cases of wheat and corn, domestication of rice involved loss of ear shattering, in this case resulting from a key amino acid substitution. Ancient humans might have unknowingly selected for this mutation while gathering rice from wild populations, because the mutants would not so easily have shed grains during the harvesting process. Eventually, the nonshattering mutant became a widely planted crop throughout Asia, and today it is the food staple for millions of people. Although humans generated these and other new plant species, in modern times humans have caused the extinction of plant species as the result of habitat destruction and other threats to species. Protecting biodiversity will continue to challenge humans as populations and demands on the Earth's resources increase.

23.5 Reviewing the Concepts

- Humans have produced new crop species by domesticating wild plants. The process of domestication involved artificial selection for traits such as nonshattering ears of wheat, corn, and rice (Figure 23.22).

23.5 Testing Your Knowledge

1. What features of wild food did humans alter during crop domestication?
 a. fruit size
 b. fruit softness
 c. seed dispersal
 d. all of the above

Assess and Discuss

Test Yourself

1. The simplest and most ancient phylum of modern land plants is probably
 a. the ferns.
 b. the cycads.
 c. the liverworts.
 d. the angiosperms.
 e. none of the listed choices.

2. Plants possess a life cycle that involves alternation of two multicellular generations: the gametophyte and
 a. the lycophyte.
 b. the bryophyte.
 c. the spermatophyte.
 d. the lignophyte.
 e. the sporophyte.

3. The seed plants are also known as
 a. bryophytes.
 b. ferns.
 c. lycophytes.
 d. spermatophytes
 e. none of the above.

4. A waxy cuticle is an adaptation that
 a. helps to prevent water loss from tracheophytes.
 b. helps to prevent water loss from algae.
 c. helps to increase water loss from tracheophytes.
 d. aids in water transport within the bodies of vascular plants.
 e. does all of the above.

5. Vascular plant photosynthesis transformed a very large amount of carbon dioxide into organic compounds that were incompletely degraded and transformed into coal, thereby causing a dramatic decrease in atmospheric carbon dioxide levels during the geological period known as the
 a. Cambrian.
 b. Ordovician.
 c. Carboniferous.
 d. Permian.
 e. Pleistocene.

6. Which phylum among the plants listed has vascular tissue?
 a. liverworts
 b. hornworts
 c. mosses
 d. ferns
 e. none of the above

7. Which sequence of critical adaptations reflects the order of their appearance in time?
 a. embryos, vascular tissue, seeds, flowers
 b. vascular tissue, embryos, flowers, seeds
 c. vascular tissue, seeds, embryos, flowers
 d. seeds, embryos, flowers, vascular tissue
 e. seeds, vascular tissue, embryos, flowers

8. The primary function of a fruit is to
 a. provide food for the developing seed.
 b. provide food for the developing seedling.
 c. foster pollen dispersal.
 d. foster seed dispersal.
 e. none of the above.

Conceptual Questions

1. How have flowering plants been able to diversify into so many species?

2. Why are some fruits useful for human food?

3. **PRINCIPLES**   A principle of biology is that *living organisms maintain homeostasis.* Explain how several structural features help vascular plants to maintain stable internal water content.

Collaborative Questions

1. Discuss at least one difference in environmental conditions experienced by Coal Age plants as compared to modern plants.

2. List as many plant adaptations to land as you can.

Online Resource

www.brookerprinciples.com

Stay a step ahead in your studies with animations that bring concepts to life and practice tests to assess your understanding. Your instructor may also recommend the interactive eBook, individualized learning tools, and more.

Fungi

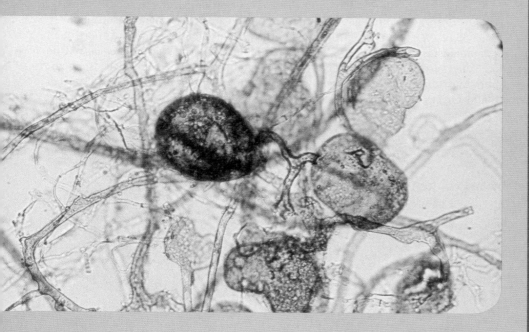

Fossil fungus that is 460 million years old. This fossil is one of the oldest known fossils of ancient fungi and aids in understanding ancient Earth environments.

Chapter Outline

24.1 Evolutionary Relationships of the Kingdom Fungi

24.2 Fungal Bodies and Feeding

24.3 Fungal Asexual and Sexual Reproduction

24.4 The Importance of Fungi in Ecology and Medicine

24.5 Biotechnological Applications of Fungi

Assess and Discuss

One of the requirements of Robin's introductory biology course was to do a short research project. As a double major in biology and geology, Robin decided to use knowledge and skills learned in both fields to look for fossil organisms in ancient rocks. She used her geology knowledge to locate, collect, and cut up rocks of known age, then dissolved the rock minerals with acid, making organic materials visible. Then she spent hours in a biology professor's lab, using a microscope to find and study materials likely to be of biological origin. During this process, Robin found fossils of early-diverging fungi, which at about 460 million years of age are among the oldest fossil fungi known. By collaborating with experts, she determined that the fossil fungi closely resembled species that today help plants obtain sufficient minerals for growth. Her work demonstrated that fungi, which play essential ecological roles today, have been doing so for hundreds of millions of years.

Modern fungi are all around us, but are relatively inconspicuous, often occurring within soil or other materials. Fungi become more conspicuous when reproductive portions such as mushrooms extend above the soil's surface. Though often inconspicuous, fungi play essential roles in the Earth's environment; are associated in diverse ways with other organisms, including humans; and have many applications in biotechnology. In this chapter, we will explore the distinctive features of fungal evolution, structure, growth, nutrition, and reproduction. In the process, you will learn how fungi are connected to medicine, forest growth, food production, and other topics of great importance to humans.

24.1 Evolutionary Relationships of the Kingdom Fungi

Learning Outcomes:

1. Describe the evolutionary relationships of fungi.
2. Identify seven fungal lineages described in this chapter.

The eukaryotes known as fungi are so distinct from other organisms that they are placed in their own kingdom, the kingdom Fungi, also known as the true fungi (Figure 24.1). Fungi diverged from Animalia more than a billion years ago, during the Middle Proterozoic era.

Fungi are closely related to the protist genus *Nuclearia*—an amoeba that feeds by ingesting algal and bacterial cells. Such closely related protists, the kingdom Fungi, and the kingdom Animalia (also known as Metazoa) are included in a eukaryotic supergroup known as Opisthokonta. Several types of nonopisthokont protists such as slime molds and disease-causing oomycetes resemble fungi in some ways (see Chapter 22), but are not regarded as true fungi.

The true fungi form a monophyletic group of more than 100,000 species. In this chapter we discuss seven lineages of true fungi, using their informal names: cryptomycota, chytrids, microsporidia, zygomycetes, AM fungi, ascomycetes, and basidiomycetes (Figure 24.2a–f) (Table 24.1).

Biology Principle

All Species (Past and Present) Are Related by an Evolutionary History

More than 15 fungal phyla occur, but their relationships and names are still being determined.

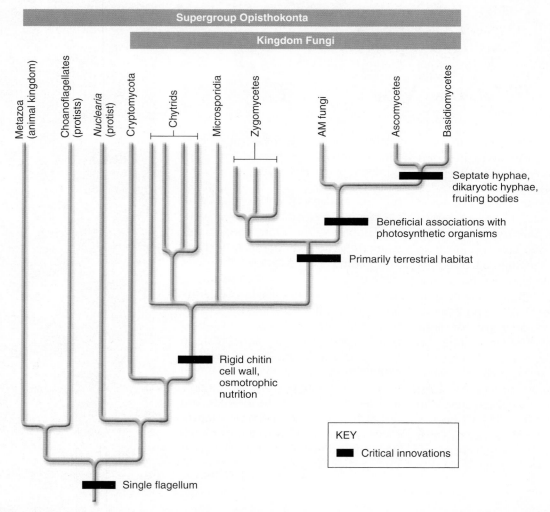

Figure 24.1 Evolutionary relationships of the fungi. The kingdom Fungi arose from a protist ancestor similar to the modern genus *Nuclearia*. Seven informal fungal groups are described in this chapter: cryptomycota, chytrids, microsporidia, zygomycetes, AM fungi, ascomycetes, and basidiomycetes.

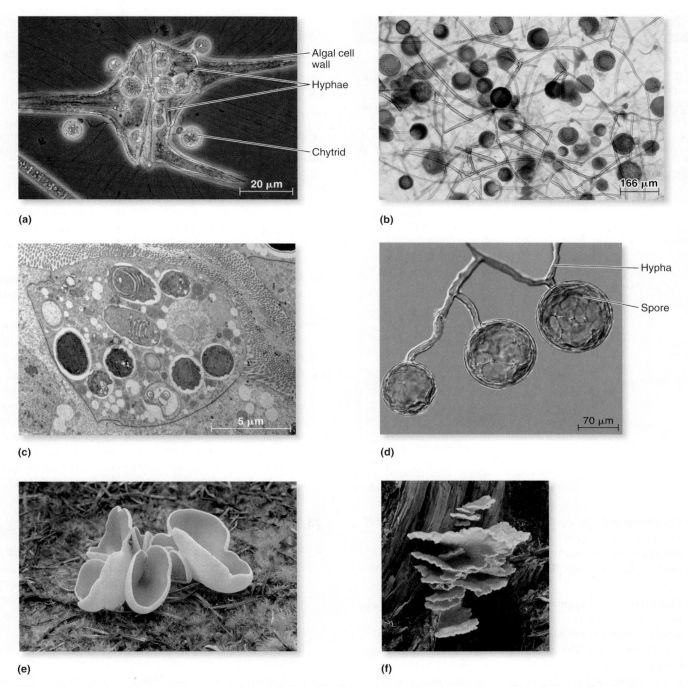

Figure 24.2 **Representatives of six fungal lineages.** **(a)** The colorless chytrids produce hyphae that penetrate the cellulose cell walls of the aquatic dinoflagellate *Ceratium hirundinella*, absorbing organic materials. Chytrids use these materials to produce spherical flagellate reproductive cells called spores that swim away to attack other algal cells. **(b)** The black bread mold *Rhizopus stolonifer,* a representative zygomycete, showing brown hyphae and green-stained reproductive structures. **(c)**The microsporidian fungus *Nosema ceranae*. **(d)** The genus *Glomus*, an example of an AM fungus. These fungi are found in and near the roots of many types of plants, aiding them in acquiring water and nutrients. AM fungi produce distinctive large, multinucleate reproductive spores (compare to chapter-opening photo of similar ancient fossils). **(e)** Fruiting structures of the edible ascomycetes commonly known as morels. **(f)** Shelf fungi, such as this *Laetiporus sulphureus*, are the fruiting bodies of basidiomycete fungi that have infected trees.

Table 24.1	Major Fungal Groups		
Informal name	**Habitat**	**Ecological role**	**Reproduction**
Cryptomycota	Water and soil	Unknown	Flagellate cells
Chytrids	Water and soil	Mostly decomposers; some parasites	Flagellate spores or gametes
Microsporidia	Animal cells	Parasites, pathogens	Nonflagellate spores
Zygomycetes	Mostly terrestrial	Decomposers and pathogens	Nonflagellate asexual spores produced in sporangia; resistant sexual zygospores
AM Fungi	Terrestrial	Form mutually beneficial mycorrhizal associations with plants	Distinctively large, nonflagellate, multinucleate asexual spores
Ascomycetes	Mostly terrestrial	Decomposers; pathogens; many form lichens; some are mycorrhizal	Asexual conidia; nonflagellate sexual spores (ascospores) in sacs (asci) on fruiting structures (ascocarps)
Basidiomycetes	Terrestrial	Decomposers; many are mycorrhizal; less commonly form lichens	Several types of asexual spores; nonflagellate sexual spores (basidiospores) on club-shaped basidia on fruiting structures (basidiocarps)

- **Cryptomycota.** The earliest-diverging fungi are classified as cryptomycota, which occur in diverse genetic types in soil and water. Cryptomycota have the genetic capacity to produce flagella and unlike other fungi, seem to lack a cell wall.

- **Chytrids.** Several aquatic lineages of microscopic species, informally known as chytrids, display cell walls made of a tough nitrogen-containing carbohydrate known as **chitin** (see Figure 24.2a). The chitin cell wall is present in all fungal lineages except the cryptomycota. Presence of a chitin wall enables fungi to resist high osmotic pressure that results when they feed by absorbing small organic molecules, a process known as osmotrophy. Chytrids produce flagellate reproductive cells, which are absent from other fungi except cryptomycota. The loss of flagella is linked to ecological transition from aquatic habitats to land, where the chitin cell wall is also advantageous.

- **Microsporidia.** Microsporidia are named for their very small size (1–4 μm) and occurrence as single-celled, chitin-walled spores (see Figure 24.2b). The strong chitin wall helps microsporidia to survive in the environment until they enter the bodies of animals; microsporidia are pathogens that can

only reproduce inside the cells of an animal host. Some are linked to honeybee decline (see Figure 24.2b).

- **Zygomycetes.** Familiar black bread molds represent one of several lineages of terrestrial fungi known as zygomycetes named for their distinctive large zygotes known as zygospores (the suffix *mycetes* derives from a Greek word for fungus) (see Figure 24.2c).

- **AM Fungi.** The <u>a</u>rbuscular <u>m</u>ycorrhizal fungi, abbreviated AM fungi, are well known for their close associations with plant roots (see Figure 24.2d). In these associations, the fungus provides the plant with mineral fertilizers and the plant provides organic food to the fungus. Ancient fossils similar to modern AM fungi (see chapter-opening paragraph) and other fossil evidence suggest that early plants may likewise have depended on associations with fungi.

- **Ascomycetes.** The name ascomycetes derives from unique reproductive structures known as asci (singular, ascus) from the Greek *asco*, meaning bags or sacs. Ascomycetes are ecologically important as decomposers and disease-causing organisms. Edible truffles and morels are the reproductive structures of particular ascomycetes (see Figure 24.2e).

- **Basidiomycetes.** The name given to the basidiomycetes derives from basidia, club-shaped reproductive cells. An estimated 30,000 modern basidiomycete species are known and are very important as decomposers and in associations with plants. Reproductive structures occur as mushrooms, puffballs, stinkhorns, shelf fungi, rusts, and smuts (see Figure 24.2f). Ascomycetes and basidiomyces are the two most recently diverged fungal lineages (see Figure 24.1).

24.1 Reviewing the Concepts

- Fungi form a monophyletic kingdom that is part of the eukaryotic supergroup Opisthokonta. The origin of a rigid chitin cell wall is associated with the origin of fungal dependence on osmotrophy, which is feeding by importing small organic compounds. Loss of ability to produce flagella is associated with change from aquatic to terrestrial habitat (Figure 24.1).

- At least seven major lineages of fungi occur: the early-diverging cryptomycota, chytrids, microsporidia, zygomycetes, and AM fungi, and the most recently diverged ascomycetes and basidiomycetes (Figure 24.2).

24.1 Testing Your Knowledge

1. If you were asked to draw a diagram that shows the relationships of fungi to animals and the protist *Nuclearia*, which of the following features should be included?
   a. Fungi and their closest protist relatives should be clustered with animals and their closest protist relatives to form a clade.
   b. *Nuclearia* should be clustered with fungi.

c. Oomycetes and other fungus-like nonopisthokont protists should not be clustered with fungi.

d. All of the above are correct.

e. None of the above is correct.

2. How did the origin of a chitin cell wall influence the diversification of true fungi?

a. Having a chitin cell wall allowed fungal cells to cope with high internal osmotic pressure.

b. Chitin cell walls fostered survival of fungi on land as well as in aquatic habitats.

c. All of the above are correct.

d. None of the above is correct.

24.2 Fungal Bodies and Feeding

Learning Outcomes:

1. Explain how fungi are similar to animals and how they differ.

2. Discuss how fungal feeding is related to fungal growth.

Because fungi are closely related to the animal kingdom, fungi and animals display some common features. For example, both animals and fungi are heterotrophic, meaning that they cannot produce their own food but must obtain it from the environment. Fungi use an amazing array of organic compounds as food, which is termed their substrate. The substrate could be the soil, a rotting log, a piece of bread, a living tissue, or a wide array of other materials. Fungi are also like animals in having **absorptive nutrition.** Both fungi and the cells of animal digestive systems secrete enzymes that break down complex organic materials and absorb the resulting small organic food molecules. In addition, both fungi and animals store surplus food as the carbohydrate glycogen in their cells. Despite these nutritional commonalities, fungal body structure, growth, and reproduction differ from those in animals.

Fungi Have a Unique Body Form

Most fungi have a distinctive type of body known as a **mycelium** (plural, mycelia), which is composed of individual microscopic, branched filaments known as **hyphae** (singular, hypha) (**Figure 24.3**). Hyphae and mycelia evolved even before fungi made the transition from aquatic to terrestrial habitats. The hyphae of ascomycetes and basidiomycetes are septate, that is, divided into smaller cellular units by cross walls known as septa. Other fungal hyphae are not septate.

A fungal mycelium may be very extensive, but is often inconspicuous because the component hyphae are so tiny and spread out in the substrate. The diffuse form of the fungal mycelium makes sense because most hyphae function to absorb organic food from the substrate. By spreading out, hyphae can absorb food from a large volume of substrate. The absorbed food is used for mycelial growth and for reproduction by means of fruiting structures, also known as **fruiting bodies,** such as mushrooms. Fruiting structures are often the more conspicuous parts of fungal bodies because they typically emerge from substrata (see Figure 31.2e,f). A fungal mycelium that has not yet produced fruiting structures represents a complete fungal body, but can be quite inconspicuous.

Fruiting structures are composed of densely packed hyphae that have undergone a sexual mating process. During mating, hyphae of different, but compatible individuals are attracted to each other and fuse. The resulting mated hyphae differ genetically and biochemically from unmated hyphae. When environmental conditions are right, mated hyphae pack together and enlarge to produce mature fruiting structures that emerge from the substrate. Sexual reproduction generates new allele combinations that may allow fungi to colonize new types of habitats.

Amazingly diverse in form, color, and odor, mature fruiting structures are specialized to produce and disperse chitin-walled reproductive cells known as **spores.** Produced by the processes of meiosis or mitosis and protected by tough walls, spores reflect a major adaptation to the terrestrial habitat. (Tough-walled spores also appeared early in the evolution of the land plants, described in Chapter 23.) Like plant spores, fungal spores are generally adapted for transport by wind or by animals that move around above the substrate. When fungal spores settle in places where conditions are favorable for growth, they produce new mycelia. When the new mycelia undergo sexual reproduction, they produce new fruiting structures and spores, completing the fungal life cycle (see Figure 24.3).

Fungi Have Distinctive Growth Processes

If you have ever watched bread or ripe fruit become increasingly moldy over the course of several days, you have observed fungal growth. When a food source is plentiful, fungal mycelia can grow rapidly at their tips, adding as much as a kilometer of new hyphae per day! The mycelia grow at their edges as the fungal hyphae extend their tips through the undigested substrate. The narrow dimensions and extensive branching of hyphae provide a very high surface area for absorption of organic molecules, water, and minerals.

Hyphal Tip Growth   Cytoplasmic streaming and osmosis are important cellular processes in hyphal growth. Recall that osmosis (see Chapter 5) is the diffusion of water through a membrane, from a solution with a lower solute concentration into a solution with a higher solute concentration. Water enters fungal hyphae by means of osmosis because their cytoplasm is rich in sugars, ions, and other solutes. Water entry swells the hyphal tip, producing the force necessary for tip extension. Masses of tiny vesicles carrying enzymes and cell-wall materials made in the Golgi apparatus collect in the hyphal tip (**Figure 24.4**). The vesicles then fuse with the plasma membrane. Some vesicles release enzymes that digest materials in the environment, releasing small organic molecules that are taken up as food. Other vesicles deliver cell-wall materials to the hyphal tip, allowing it to extend.

Variations in Mycelium Growth Form   Fungal hyphae grow rapidly through a substrate from areas where the food has become depleted to food-rich areas. In nature, mycelia may take an irregular shape, depending on the distribution of the food substrate. A fungal mycelium may extend into food-rich areas for

Biology Principle

Living Organisms Grow and Develop

After a mating process occurs, mated hyphae produce fruiting bodies whose form fosters spore production and dispersal. In suitable sites, spores may germinate, producing new mycelia.

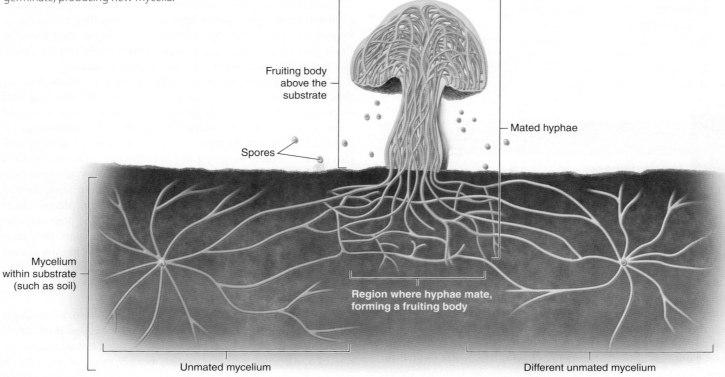

Fruiting body above the substrate

Mated hyphae

Spores

Mycelium within substrate (such as soil)

Region where hyphae mate, forming a fruiting body

Unmated mycelium

Different unmated mycelium

Figure 24. 3 Fungal body structure and life cycle. A young fungus consists of haploid food-gathering hyphae that grow and branch from a central point to form a diffuse mycelium within a food substrate, such as soil. When compatible mates are present, a sexual reproduction process generates a mycelium composed of mated hyphae that can produce a conspicuous fruiting structure (such as a mushroom). Cells at the surface of the fruiting structure contain diploid zygote nuclei that undergo meiosis, thereby producing haploid spores of diverse genetic types. Spore dispersal allows fungi to colonize new habitats.

great distances. In liquid laboratory media, fungi will grow as a spherical mycelium that resembles a cotton ball floating in water (**Figure 24.5a**). Grown in flat laboratory dishes, the mycelium assumes a more two-dimensional growth form (**Figure 24.5b**). Sometimes cells or hyphae of different fungal species fuse, forming hybrid mycelia whose traits may differ from those of the parents.

24.2 Reviewing the Concepts

- Fungal bodies, known as mycelia, are composed of microscopic branched filaments known as hyphae that feed and grow at their tips (Figures 24.3, 24.4).
- Mycelial shape depends on the distribution of nutrients in the environment (Figure 24.5).

24.2 Testing Your Knowledge

1. If you were asked to draw a diagram of a complete fungal body and label distinctive parts, which of the following would be an adequate representation?
   a. A drawing that shows (labeled) mycelium growing inside a rotting orange.
   b. A drawing of a forest mushroom (labeled "fruiting structure") that shows only aboveground structures.
   c. A drawing of the surface of a leaf that is infected by a fungus whose conspicuous fruiting structures are labeled.
   d. A drawing of the surface of a human foot that is infected by a fungus.
   e. All of the above.

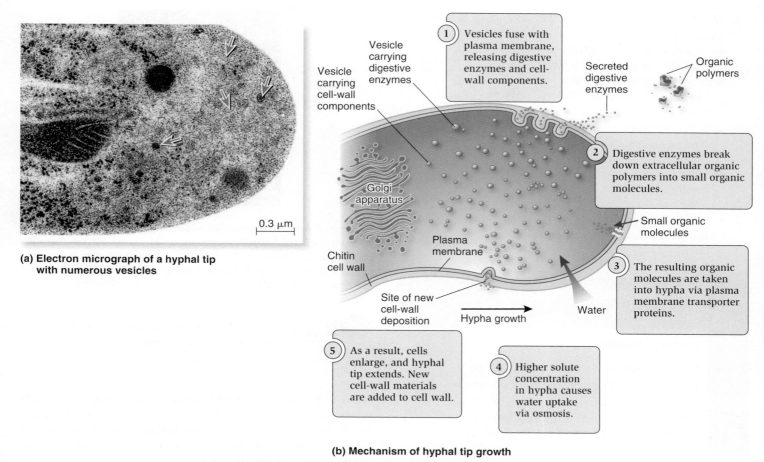

(a) Electron micrograph of a hyphal tip with numerous vesicles

(b) Mechanism of hyphal tip growth

Figure 24.4 Hyphal tip growth and absorptive nutrition. (a) TEM showing the hyphal tip of *Aspergillus nidulans*, a fungus commonly used as a genetic model organism. The tip is filled with membrane-bound vesicles that fuse with the plasma membrane. Purple arrowheads show dark-stained vesicles carrying digestive enzymes; green arrowheads point out light-stained vesicles carrying cell-wall materials. **(b)** Diagram of a hyphal tip, with vesicles of the same two types, showing the steps of hyphal tip growth.

✔ **Concept Check:**   *What do you think would happen to fungal hyphae that begin to grow into a substrate with a higher solute concentration? How might your answer be related to food preservation techniques such as drying or salting?*

(a) Mycelium growing in liquid medium

(b) Mycelium growing on flat, solid medium

Figure 24.5 Fungal shape shifting. (a) When a mycelium, such as that of this *Rhizoctonia solani*, is surrounded by food substrate in a liquid medium, it will grow into a spherical form. **(b)** When the food supply is limited to a two-dimensional supply, as shown by *Neotestudina rosatii* in a laboratory dish, the mycelium will form a disc. Likewise, distribution of the food substrate determines the mycelium shape in nature.

2. Why do fungal fruiting structures commonly emerge from the substrate?

a. To produce spores, most fruiting structures, such as a mushroom, require light as a source of energy.

b. To produce spores, most fruiting structures, such as a mushroom, require atmospheric carbon dioxide as a carbon source.

c. To disperse spores, most fruiting structures, such as a mushroom, take advantage of wind or animals that move around above the substrate.

d. Chemical features of the substrate prevent the development of most fruiting structures within the substrate itself.

e. Physical features of the substrate prevent the development of most fruiting structures within the substrate itself.

24.3 Fungal Asexual and Sexual Reproduction

Learning Outcomes:

1. Give examples of fungal asexual reproduction.

2. Identify some of the distinctive sexual reproductive processes in fungi.

3. Explain why people may safely consume some fungal fruiting structures, whereas other fungi produce substances that are toxic to humans.

In addition to reproduction by spores generated from a sexual mating, many fungi can also reproduce asexually by means of spores, each of which can grow into a new adult. In the absence of new mutations, the progeny arising from asexual reproduction are genetically identical to each other and to the parent fungus. Many fungi reproduce only asexually. Asexual reproduction is a natural cloning process; it produces genetically identical organisms. Production of asexual spores allows fungi that are well adapted to a particular environment to disperse to similar, favorable places. By contrast, as previously noted, sexual reproduction generates new allele combinations that give fungi the potential to colonize new types of habitats.

Fungi Reproduce Asexually by Dispersing Specialized Cells

Asexual reproduction is particularly important to fungi, allowing them to spread rapidly. To reproduce asexually, fungi do not need to find compatible mates or expend resources on fruiting-body formation and meiosis. More than 17,000 fungal species reproduce primarily or exclusively by asexual means. DNA-sequencing studies have revealed that many types of modern fungi that reproduce only asexually have evolved from ancestors that had both sexual and asexual reproduction.

Many fungi produce asexual spores known as **conidia** (from the Greek *konis*, meaning dust) at the tips of hyphae (**Figure 24.6**).

Figure 24.6 Asexual reproductive cells of fungi. SEM of the asexual spores (conidia) of *Aspergillus versicolor*, which causes skin infections in burn victims and lung infections in AIDS patients. Each of these small cells is able to detach and grow into an individual that is genetically identical to the parent fungus and so is able to grow in similar conditions.

✓ **Concept Check:** *How might you try to protect a burn patient from infection by a conidial fungus?*

When they land on a favorable substrate, conidia germinate into a new mycelium that produces many more conidia. The green molds that form on citrus fruits are familiar examples of conidial fungi. A single fungus can produce as many as 40 million conidia per hour over a period of 2 days.

Because they can spread so rapidly, asexual fungi are responsible for costly fungal food spoilage, allergies, and diseases. Medically important fungi that reproduce primarily by asexual means include the athlete's foot fungus (*Epidermophyton floccosum*) and the infectious yeast (*Candida albicans*). **Yeasts** are unicellular fungi of various lineages. Asexual reproduction in some yeasts occurs by budding, the production of a new cell on the surface of a larger parental cell (**Figure 24.7**).

Fungi Have Distinctive Sexual Reproductive Processes

As is typical for eukaryotes, the fungal sexual reproductive cycle involves the union of gametes, the formation of zygotes, and the process of meiosis. In contrast to plants, whose life cycle is an alternation of haploid and diploid generations, and diploid-dominant animals, the fungal life cycle is more-or-less haploid-dominant, as is the life cycle for many protists. The sexually produced spores dispersed by many fungi are haploid, as is also the case for plants (see Chapter 23). However, some aspects of fungal sexual reproduction, including the function of hyphal branches as gametes and the development of fruiting bodies, are unique.

Fungal Gametes and Mating Early-diverging fungi that live in the water produce flagellate sperm that swim to nonmotile eggs, as do animals and many protists and plants. By contrast, the gametes

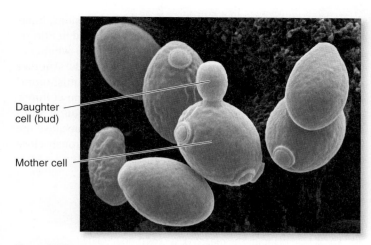

Figure 24.7 **The budding yeast *Saccharomyces cerevisiae*.** In budding, a small daughter cell is formed on the surface of a larger mother cell, eventually pinching off and forming a new cell.

BioConnections: *Look back at Table 17.2, which shows the genome characteristics of some model organisms. How does the genome of* S. cerevisiae *compare with genomes of other model organisms?*

of terrestrial fungi are cells of hyphal branches rather than distinguishable male and female gametes. Fungal mycelia occur in multiple mating types that differ biochemically, controlled by particular genes. During fungal sexual reproduction, hyphal branches of different, but compatible mycelia are attracted to each other by secreted peptides, and when hyphae have grown sufficiently close, they fuse. The mating of hyphal branches represents an adaptation to terrestrial life.

Fruiting Structures As we have seen, under appropriate environmental conditions, such as seasonal change, a mated mycelium may produce a fruiting structure such as a mushroom (see Figure 24.3). Fruiting structures typically disperse haploid spores that can grow into haploid mycelia. If a haploid mycelium encounters hyphae of an appropriate mating type, hyphal branches will fuse and start the sexual cycle over again. The structures of fruiting bodies vary in ways that reflect different adaptations that foster spore dispersal by wind, rain, or animals.

- Mature puffballs have delicate surfaces upon which just a slight pressure causes the spores to puff out into wind currents (Figure 24.8a). Birds' nest fungi form characteristic egg-shaped spore clusters. Raindrops splash on these clusters and disperse the spores.

- The fruiting bodies of stinkhorn fungi smell and look like rotting meat (Figure 24.8b), which attracts carrion flies. The flies land on the fungi to investigate the potential meal and then fly away, in the process dispersing spores that stick to their bodies.

(a) **Fruiting bodies adapted for dispersal of spores by wind**

Spores in a sticky matrix

(b) **Fruiting body adapted for dispersal of spores by insects**

(c) **The black truffle *Tuber melanosporum*, an ascomycete fungus, highly valued for its taste.**

Figure 24.8 **Fruiting structure adaptations that foster spore dispersal. (a)** When disturbed by wind gusts or animal movements, spores puff from fruiting structures of the puffball fungus (*Lycoperdon perlatum*). **(b)** The fruiting structures of stinkhorn fungi, such as this *Phallus impudicus*, smell and look like dung or rotting meat. This attracts flies, which come into contact with the sticky fungal spores, thereby dispersing them. (c) The black truffle *Tuber melanosporum,* an ascomycete fungus, produces fruiting structures underground. The smell of mature truffle fruiting structures attracts animals that dig them up, thereby dispersing spores.

- The fruiting bodies of fungal truffles (Figure 24.8c) are unusual in being produced underground. Truffles have evolved a spore dispersal process that depends on animals that eat fungi. Mature truffles emit an odor that attracts wild pigs and dogs, which break up the fruiting structures while digging for them, thereby dispersing the spores. Collectors use trained leashed pigs or dogs to locate valuable truffles from forests for the market.

(a) *Amanita*   (b) *Claviceps*

Figure 24.9 Toxic or hallucinogenic fruiting structures. (a) Common in conifer forests, *A. muscaria* is both toxic and hallucinogenic. Ancient people used this fungus to induce spiritual visions and to reduce fear during raids. This fungus produces a toxin, amanitin, which specifically inhibits RNA polymerase II of eukaryotes. **(b)** The fungus *Claviceps purpurea* infects rye and other grasses, producing hard masses of mycelia known as ergots in place of some of the grains (fruits). Ergots such as the one illustrated produce alkaloids related to LSD and thus cause psychotic delusions in humans and animals that consume products made with infected rye.

BioConnections: *Look back at Figure 11.12, which illustrates the cellular role of RNA polymerase II in eukaryotes. What effect would the amanitin toxin have on human cells?*

Many fungal fruiting bodies such as truffles and morels are edible, and several species of edible fungi are cultivated for human consumption. However, the bodies of many other fungi produce toxic substances that may deter animals from consuming them. For example, several fungi that attack stored grains, fruits, and spices produce aflatoxins that cause liver cancer and are a major health concern worldwide. The forest mushroom *Amanita virosa* (**Figure 24.9a**), known as the "destroying angel," contains a powerful toxin that can cause liver failure so severe that death may ensue unless a liver transplant is performed. Each year, many people in North America are poisoned when they consume similarly toxic mushrooms gathered in the wild. There is no reliable way for nonexperts to distinguish poisonous from nontoxic fungi; it is essential to receive instruction from an expert before foraging for mushrooms in the woods. Therefore, many authorities recommend that it is better to search for mushrooms in the grocery store than in the wild.

Several types of fungal fruiting structures produce hallucinogenic or psychoactive substances. As in the case of fungal toxins, fungal hallucinogens may have evolved as herbivore deterrents, but humans have inadvertently experienced their effects. For example, *Claviceps purpurea*, which causes a disease of rye crops and other grasses known as ergot, produces a psychogenic compound related to LSD (lysergic acid diethylamide) (**Figure 24.9b**).

Some experts speculate that cases of hysteria, convulsions, infertility, and a burning sensation of the skin that occurred in Europe during the Middle Ages and that were attributed to witchcraft resulted from ergot-contaminated rye used in foods. Another example of a hallucinogenic fungus is the "magic mushroom" *Psilocybe*, which is used in traditional rituals in some cultures. Like ergot, the magic mushroom produces a compound similar to LSD. Consuming hallucinogenic fungi is risky because the amount used to achieve psychoactive effects is dangerously close to a poisonous dose.

24.3 Reviewing the Concepts

- Fungi spread rapidly by means of spores produced by asexual or sexual reproduction (Figures 24.6, 24.7).
- The life cycle of fungi is haploid-dominant. Most nonreproductive fungal cells are haploid, haploid hyphal branches function as gametes, and the meiotic division of diploid zygotes generates haploid spores (look back to Figure 24.3).
- Fungi produce diverse types of fruiting bodies that foster spore dispersal by wind, water, or animals. Although many fungal fruiting bodies are edible, many others produce defensive toxins or hallucinogens (Figures 24.8, 24.9).

24.3 Testing Your Knowledge

1. How does asexual reproduction benefit fungi?
   a. Asexual reproduction allows fungi to spread rapidly in a favorable environment, without expending resources required for mating and the formation of fruiting structures.
   b. Asexual reproduction fosters genetic diversity.
   c. Asexual reproduction allows fungi to produce fruiting structures in which meiosis occurs.
   d. Asexual reproduction does not benefit fungi.
   e. None of the above is correct.

2. Which of the following sequences most accurately represents the necessary order of events to allow for a fungal fruiting structure to form in a terrestrial environment?
   a. An unmated fungal mycelium produces conidia that grow into fungal fruiting structures.
   b. Two haploid spores each grow into mycelia of differing but compatible mating types, and when hyphal branches of the two types meet, they function as gametes to produce mated hyphae that may develop into a fungal fruiting structure.
   c. Unmated fungal mycelia produce flagellate sperm that under moist conditions swim to eggs and fertilize them; the resulting diploid zygote grows into a diploid fruiting structure in which meiosis occurs, producing haploid spores.
   d. Unmated diploid mycelia undergo meiosis to produce haploid hyphae that mate, then the resulting mated hyphae generate a fruiting structure that disperses diploid spores.

The Importance of Fungi in Ecology and Medicine

Learning Outcomes:

1. Identify the ecological roles of decomposer and disease fungi.
2. Give examples of fungal diseases of plants and animals, including humans.
3. Explain how mycorrhizae and lichens represent beneficial associations of fungi with other organisms.

Fungi play important ecological roles as decomposers of organic matter, predators that consume animal prey, and pathogens that cause diseases of plants and animals. Many fungi live in beneficial associations with plants and algae, and some fungi have beneficial associations with animals.

Decomposer and Predatory Fungi Play Important Ecological Roles

Decomposer fungi are essential components of the Earth's ecosystems. Together with bacteria, they decompose dead organisms and wastes, preventing the buildup of organic debris in ecosystems. For example, only certain bacteria and fungi can break down cellulose and lignin, the main components of wood. Decomposer fungi and bacteria are Earth's recycling engineers. They release CO_2 into the air and other minerals into the soil and water, making these essential nutrients available to plants and algae.

More than 200 species of predatory soil fungi use special adhesive or nooselike hyphae to trap tiny soil animals, such as nematodes, and absorb nutrients from their bodies (**Figure 24.10**). Such fungi help to control populations of nematodes, some of which attack plant roots. Other fungi obtain nutrients by attacking insects, and certain of these species have been used as biological control agents to kill black field crickets, red-legged earth mites, and other pests.

Pathogenic Fungi Cause Plant and Animal Diseases

One of the most important ways in which fungi affect humans is by causing diseases of wild and crop plants and animals. Five thousand fungal species are known as plant pathogens because they cause serious crop diseases. Pathogenic fungi use the organic compounds absorbed from plants to grow, attack additional plant cells, and produce reproductive spores capable of infecting more plants. Wheat rust is an example of a common crop disease caused by fungi (**Figure 24.11**). Rusts are named for the reddish spores that emerge from the surfaces of infected plants. Agricultural customs inspectors closely monitor the entry of plants, soil, foods, and other materials that might harbor plant pathogenic fungi.

Athlete's foot and ringworm are common human skin diseases caused by several types of fungi that are known as dermatophytes because they colonize the human epidermis. *Pneumocystis jiroveci* and *Cryptococcus neoformans* are fungal pathogens that infect individuals with weakened immune systems, such as those with AIDS, sometimes causing death. *Blastomyces dermatitidis*, which causes the disease blastomycosis; *Coccidioides immitis*, the cause of coccidioidomycosis; and *Histoplasma capsulatum*, the agent of histoplasmosis, are fungal pathogens that affect the lungs and may spread to other parts of the body, causing severe illness. Though fungal diseases that attack humans and domesticated animals are of societal concern, in nature, fungal pathogens play an important ecological role in controlling population growth of other organisms.

Fungi Form Beneficial Associations with Other Species

Symbioses are close associations of two or more species, and mutualism is a symbiotic interaction in which all partners in the association benefit. Fungi form several types of mutualisms with animals, plants, algae, bacteria, and even viruses. For example,

Biology Principle

Biology Affects Our Society

Recent analyses indicate that environmental changes linked to human activities correlate with increases in the incidence of new fungal pathogen infestations that threaten human health and agricultural sustainability.

Wheat leaf tissue

Puccinia graminis spores

0.1 mm

Figure 24.11 Wheat rust. The plant pathogenic fungus *Puccinia graminis* grows within the tissues of wheat plants, using plant nutrients to produce rusty streaks of red spores that erupt at the stem and leaf surface where spores can be dispersed. Red spore production is but one stage of a complex life cycle involving several types of spores. Rusts infect many other crops in addition to wheat, causing immense economic damage.

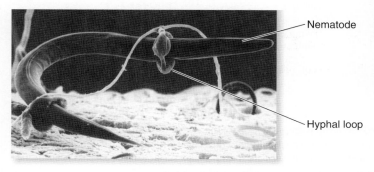

Nematode

Hyphal loop

Figure 24.10 A predatory fungus. The fungus *Arthrobotrys anchonia* traps nematode worms in hyphal loops that suddenly swell in response to the animal's presence. Fungal hyphae then grow into the worm's body and digest it.

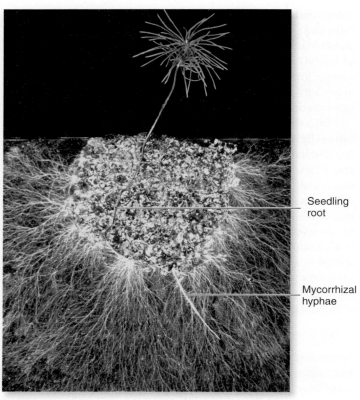

Figure 24.12 **Tree seedling with mycorrhizal fungi.** Hyphae of a mycorrhizal fungus extend farther into the soil than do the seedling's roots, helping the plant to obtain mineral nutrients.

leaf-cutting ants, certain termites and beetles, and the salt marsh snail (*Littoraria irrorata*) cultivate particular fungi for food—much as human mushroom growers do. We focus next on two types of fungi—mycorrhizal fungi and lichen fungi—that are beneficially associated with photosynthetic organisms.

Mycorrhizae Mutualisms between the hyphae of certain fungi and the roots of most seed plants are known as **mycorrhizae** (from the Greek, meaning fungus roots). Similar associations also occur between fungi and bryophytes, which lack roots, suggesting that fungi have been key to plant success on land from the beginning. Modern fungus-root associations are very important in nature and agriculture; more than 80% of terrestrial plants form mycorrhizae. Plants that have mycorrhizal partners receive an increased supply of water and mineral nutrients, primarily phosphate, copper, and zinc. They do so because an extensive fungal mycelium is able to absorb minerals from a much larger volume of soil than can roots alone (Figure 24.12). Added together, all the branches of a fungal mycelium in 1 m³ of soil can reach 20,000 km in total length. Experiments have shown that mycorrhizae greatly enhance plant growth compared with plants lacking fungal partners. In return, plants provide fungi with organic food molecules, sometimes contributing as much as 20% of their photosynthetic products.

The two most common types of mycorrhizae are endomycorrhizae, which occur within root tissue, and ectomycorrhizae, which coat roots. **Endomycorrhizae** (from the Greek *endo*, meaning inside) are partnerships between plants and fungi in which the fungal hyphae penetrate the spaces between root cell walls and plasma membranes and grow along the outer surface of the plasma membrane. In such spaces, endomycorrhizal fungi often form highly branched, bushy arbuscules (from the word "arbor," referring to tree shape). As the arbuscules develop, the root plasma membrane also expands. Consequently, the arbuscules and the root plasma membranes surrounding them have a very high surface area that facilitates rapid and efficient exchange of materials: Minerals flow from fungal hyphae to root cells, while organic food molecules move from root cells to hyphae. These fungus-root associations are known as **arbuscular mycorrhizae,** abbreviated **AM** (Figure 24.13; see also Figure 24.2d). AM fungi are associated with apple and peach trees, coffee shrubs, and many

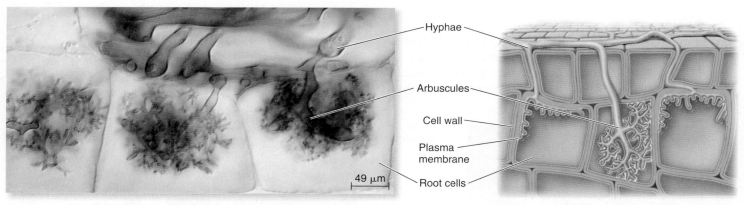

(a) Micrograph of arbuscular mycorrhizae

(b) Hyphae growing between cell walls and plasma membranes

Figure 24.13 **Endomycorrhizae.** **(a)** Light micrograph showing black-stained AM fungi within the roots of the forest herb *Asarum canadensis*. Endomycorrhizal fungal hyphae penetrate plant root cell walls, and then branch into the space between root cell walls and plasma membranes. **(b)** Diagram showing the position of highly branched arbuscules. Hyphal branches or arbuscules are found on the surface of the plasma membrane, which becomes highly invaginated. The result is that both hyphae and plant membranes have very high surface areas.

 **Concept Check:** *What fungal phylum consists entirely of endomycorrhizal fungi that are completely dependent upon plant hosts?*

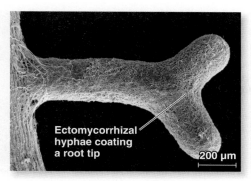

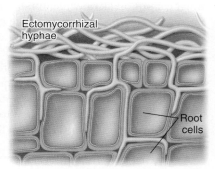

(a) Ectomycorrhizal fruiting body   **(b) SEM of ectomycorrhizal hyphae**   **(c) Hyphae invading intercellular spaces**

Figure 24.14 Ectomycorrhizae. (a) The fruiting structure of the common forest fungus *Laccaria bicolor*. This is an ectomycorrhizal fungus that is associated with tree roots. **(b)** SEM showing ectomycorrhizal fungal hyphae of *L. bicolor* covering the surfaces of young *Pinus resinosa* root tips. **(c)** Diagram showing that the hyphae of ectomycorrhizal fungi do not penetrate root cell walls but grow within intercellular spaces. In this location, fungal hyphae are able to obtain organic food molecules produced by plant photosynthesis.

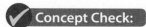 **Concept Check:**   *What benefits do plants obtain from the association with fungi?*

herbaceous plants, including legumes, grasses, tomatoes, and strawberries.

Ectomycorrhizae (from the Greek *ecto*, meaning outside) are mutualistic symbioses between temperate forest trees and soil fungi, particularly basidiomycetes. The fungi that engage in such associations are known as ectomycorrhizal fungi (Figure 24.14a). The hyphae of ectomycorrhizal fungi coat tree-root surfaces (Figure 24.14b) and grow into the spaces between root cells but do not penetrate the cell membrane (Figure 24.14c). Some species of oak, beech, pine, and spruce trees will not grow unless their ectomycorrhizal partners are also present. Mycorrhizae are thus essential to the success of commercial nursery tree production and reforestation projects. New genetic information has illuminated how ectomycorrhizal fungi originated during the diversification of basidiomycete metabolism.

EVOLUTIONARY CONNECTIONS

Comparison of Genomes Reveals How Basidiomycete Metabolism Diversified

Genomic sequences have been obtained for many of the basidiomycete fungi. Comparison of these genomes reveals how basidiomycete fungi acquired diverse metabolic pathways that allow them to utilize organic carbon produced by plants.

- Some basidiomycete fungi decompose cellulose and lignin, which are major structural components of woody plants that are very abundant (see Chapter 23). Such basidiomycetes are thus able to break down dead trees, woody debris, leaf litter, and compost, using these organic materials as food.

- Certain dung-destroying relatives break down similar dead organic materials that have passed intact through the guts of animals.

- Other basidiomycete species have evolved ectomycorrhizal associations with living plants that enable the fungi to acquire plant-produced soluble carbohydrates. Ectomycorrhizal fungi do not destroy the structural components of the living plants upon which they depend.

White-rot fungi, such as *Phanerochaete chrysosporium*, decompose both the cellulose and lignin present in wood, leaving white-colored remains. These fungi employ complex enzymatic pathways to break down the many types of chemical bonds present in tough lignin. Such complex pathways are energetically expensive to produce, but allow the fungi ready access to cellulose embedded within a lignin matrix. The lignin-degrading enzymes produced by white-rot fungi are useful in biotechnological applications, such as degrading harmful wastes arising from industrial paper production and removing lignin from plant biomass used to produce renewable biofuels.

Molecular clock analyses indicate that white-rot fungal metabolism first arose about 300 mya during the Carboniferous period, consistent with fossils of white rot fungi known from somewhat later times. You may recall that the Carboniferous period is named for the vast amount of organic carbon, composed largely of plant-produced lignin that was stored in sediments at this time and ultimately generated large coal deposits. The evolution of enzymatic pathways capable of breaking down lignin allowed fungi to take advantage of a resource that had not previously been available to them. The timing of this evolutionary event explains why less plant-produced organic carbon has been stored in sediments since the end of the Carboniferous period (see Chapter 23).

Other fungi, such as *Serpula lacrymans*, are known as brown-rot fungi because they obtain energy by breaking down the cellulose contained in wood, leaving brown-colored lignin. Genomic comparisons have revealed that brown-rot fungi such as *S. lacrymans* evolved from white-rot ancestors by loss of protein families involved in lignin degradation. Consequently the brown-rot fungi cannot break down lignin, but save the energy they would need to expend in this process. The enzymes produced by these cellulose degraders are industrially useful for converting cellulose to sugars for production of bioethanol or other renewable biofuels. In nature, the lignin that brown-rot fungi leave behind contributes a substantial amount of organic carbon to forest soils, thereby enhancing soil fertility. Genomic comparisons suggest that brown-rot ancestors gave rise to common ectomycorrhizal fungi, which can gain nutrients from living plants.

Lichens   Partnerships formed by particular fungi and certain photosynthetic green algae and/or bacteria are known as **lichens.** There are at least 25,000 lichen species, but these did not all descend from a common ancestor. DNA-sequencing studies suggest that lichens evolved independently in at least five separate fungal lineages.

Lichen partnerships take one of three major forms:

- Crustose lichens are flat and adhere tightly to an underlying surface (**Figure 24.15a**).
- Foliose lichens are flattened and leaflike (**Figure 24.15b**).
- Fruticose lichens grow upright (**Figure 24.15c**) or hang down from tree branches.

In a lichen partnership, photosynthetic green algae or cyanobacteria typically occur in a distinct layer close to the lichen's surface, with fungal hyphae making up the rest (**Figure 24.15d**). Lichen structure differs dramatically from that of the fungal component grown separately, demonstrating that the photosynthetic components influence lichen form.

The photosynthetic partners provide lichen fungi with organic food molecules and oxygen, and in turn receive carbon dioxide, water, and minerals from the fungal partner. Lichen fungi also protect their photosynthetic partners from environmental stress. For example, lichens that occupy exposed habitats of high light intensity often produce bright yellow, orange, or red-colored compounds that absorb excess light, thereby helping to prevent damage to the photosynthetic components of the photosynthetic partner (see Figure 24.15a). Lichen fungi also produce distinctive organic acids and other compounds that deter animal and microbial attacks.

Lichens often grow on rocks, buildings, tombstones, tree bark, soil, or other surfaces that easily become dry. When water is not available, the lichens lie dormant until moisture returns. Thus, lichens may spend much of their time in an inactive state, and for this reason, they often grow very slowly. However, because they can persist for long periods, lichens can be very old; some are estimated to be more than 4,500 years old. Lichens occur in diverse types of habitats, and a number grow in some of the most extreme, forbidding terrestrial sites on Earth—deserts, mountaintops, and the Arctic and Antarctic—places where most plants cannot survive. In these locations, lichens serve as a food source for reindeer and other hardy organisms. Though unpalatable, lichens are not toxic to humans and have also served as survival foods for indigenous peoples in times of shortages.

(a) Crustose lichen   **(b) Foliose lichen**

(c) Fruticose lichen   **(d) Microscopic view of a cross section of a lichen**

Figure 24.15 Lichen structure. (a) An orange-colored crustose lichen grows tightly pressed to the substrate. **(b)** The flattened, leaf-shaped genus *Umbilicaria* is a common foliose lichen. **(c)** The highly branched genus *Cladonia* is a common fruticose lichen. **(d)** A handmade thin slice of *Umbilicaria* viewed with a light microscope reveals that the photosynthetic algae occur in a thin upper layer. Fungal hyphae make up the rest of the lichen.

Soil building is another important lichen function. Lichen acids help to break up the surfaces of rocks, beginning the process of soil development. Lichens having nitrogen-fixing cyanobacterial partners (see Chapter 22) can also increase soil fertility. One study showed that such lichens released 20% of the nitrogen they fixed into the environment, where it is available for uptake by plants.

24.4 Reviewing the Concepts

- Fungi play important roles in nature as decomposers, predators, and pathogens, and by forming beneficial associations with other organisms (Figures 24.10, 24.11).
- Mycorrhizae are symbiotic associations between fungi and plant roots. Endomycorrhizae commonly form highly branched arbuscules in the spaces between root cell walls and plasma membranes. Ectomycorrhizae coat root surfaces, extending into root intercellular spaces (Figures 24.12, 24.13, 24.14).
- Comparative genomic studies reveal how basidomycete fungi diversified in metabolic pathways.

- Lichens are multispecies partnerships between fungi, photosynthetic green algae, and bacteria that play important ecological roles (Figure 24.15).

24.4 Testing Your Knowledge

1. If you were asked to draw diagrams of plant roots that show how endomycorrhizal fungi and ectomycorrhizal fungi differ in location, which of the following would be accurate?
   a. You draw endomycorrhizal fungi inside the cytoplasm of the root cells.
   b. You draw endomycorrhizal fungi on the outside surface of the plant root.
   c. You draw ectomycorrhizal fungi between the cell wall and the cell membrane of root cells, but not on the root surface.
   d. All of the above would be correct.
   e. None of the above would be correct.

2. What is the major way in which lichens benefit plant growth?
   a. Lichens that grow on plant surfaces produce carbon dioxide that plants are able to utilize in respiration.
   b. Some lichens contain bacteria that are able to fix nitrogen and release a considerable amount to the environment, where the fixed nitrogen is available for use by plants.
   c. Lichen algae produce oxygen that can be taken up by plants for use in photosynthesis.
   d. All of the above are correct.
   e. None of the above is correct.

24.5 Biotechnological Applications of Fungi

Learning Outcome:

1. List several technological uses of fungi or lichens.

The ability of fungi and lichens to grow on many types of substrata and produce many types of organic compounds reflects their diverse ecological adaptations. Humans have harnessed fungal and lichen biochemistry in many types of biotechnology applications.

- A variety of industrial processes use fungi to convert inexpensive organic compounds into valuable materials such as citric acid used in the food industry; glycerol; antibiotics such as penicillin; and cyclosporine, a drug widely used to prevent rejection of organ transplants.
- Enzymes extracted from fungi are used to break down plant materials for renewable bioenergy production.
- In the food industry, fungi are used to produce the distinctive flavors of blue cheese and other cheeses.
- Other fungi secrete enzymes that are used in the manufacture of protein-rich tempeh and other food products from soybeans.

- The brewing and winemaking industries find yeasts essential, and the baking industry depends on the yeast *Saccharomyces cerevisiae* (see Figure 24.7) for bread production.
- *S. cerevisiae* is also widely used as a model organism for fundamental biological studies. Yeasts are useful in the laboratory because they have short life cycles, they are easy and safe for lab workers to maintain, and their genomes are similar to those of animals.
- Lichens are useful as air-quality monitors because they are particularly sensitive to air pollutants such as sulfur dioxide. Air pollutants severely injure their photosynthetic components, causing death of the lichens. The disappearance of lichens serves as an early warning sign of air-pollution levels that are also likely to affect humans. Lichens can also be used to monitor atmospheric radiation levels because they accumulate radioactive substances from the air.

24.5 Reviewing the Concepts

- Fungi are useful in the chemical, food-processing, waste-treatment, renewable biofuel, brewing, and baking industries.
- Lichens are useful as monitors of air pollution and atmospheric radiation levels.

24.5 Testing Your Knowledge

1. Which of the following statements best explains the diverse technological uses of the kingdom fungi?
   a. The metabolic diversity of fungi includes the ability to conduct photosynthesis as well as to break down and respire many types of organic compounds.
   b. Most fungi are predators; they consume many types of microscopic animals, so as a group, the fungi display diverse metabolic pathways involved in breaking down complex animal tissues.
   c. Being heterotrophic, during their evolutionary diversification, fungi have taken advantage of many types of organic substrata as food sources and consequently have evolved many metabolic pathways.
   d. All of the above are correct.
   e. None of the above is correct.

Assess and Discuss

Test Yourself

1. Fungal cells differ from animal cells in that fungal cells
   a. lack ribosomes, though these are present in animal cells.
   b. lack mitochondria, though these occur in animal cells.
   c. have chitin cell walls, whereas animal cells lack rigid walls.
   d. lack cell walls, whereas animal cells possess walls.
   e. none of the above

2. Conidia are
   a. cells produced by some fungi as the result of sexual reproduction.
   b. fungal asexual reproductive cells produced by the process of mitosis.
   c. structures that occur in septal pores.
   d. the unspecialized gametes of fungi.
   e. none of the above.

3. What are mycorrhizae?
   a. the bodies of fungi, composed of hyphae
   b. fungi that attack plant roots, causing disease
   c. fungal hyphae that are massed together into stringlike structures
   d. fungi that have symbiotic partnerships with algae or cyanobacteria
   e. mutually beneficial associations of particular fungi and plant roots

4. Which fungi are examples of hallucinogen producers?
   a. *Claviceps* and *Psilocybe*
   b. *Epidermophyton* and *Candida*
   c. *Pneumocystis jiroveci* and *Histoplasma capsulatum*
   d. *Saccharomyces cerevisiae* and *Phanerochaete chrysosporium*
   e. *Cryphoenectria parasitica* and *Ventura inaequalis*

5. What forms do lichens take?
   a. crusts, flat bodies
   b. foliose, leaf-shaped bodies
   c. fruticose, erect or dangling bodies
   d. single cells
   e. a, b, and c

6. Lichens consist of a partnership between fungi and what other organisms?
   a. red algae and brown algae
   b. green algae and bacteria
   c. the roots of vascular plants
   d. choanoflagellates and *Nuclearia*
   e. none of the above

7. Which group of organisms listed is most closely related to the kingdom Fungi?
   a. the animal kingdom   d. the bacteria
   b. the green algae   e. the archaea
   c. the land plants

Conceptual Questions

1. Explain three ways that fungi are like animals and two ways in which fungi resemble plants.

2. Explain why some fungi produce toxic or hallucinogenic compounds.

3. **PRINCIPLES**   A principle of biology is that *living organisms interact with their environment*. Describe two ways in which fungi function as beneficial partners with autotrophs and what benefit the fungi receive from the partnerships.

Collaborative Questions

1. Think about the natural habitats closest to you. Where can you find fungi, and what roles do these fungi play?

2. Imagine that you are helping to restore the natural vegetation on a piece of land that had long been used to grow crops. You are placed in charge of planting pine seedlings (*Pinus resinosa*) and fostering their growth. In what way could you consider using fungi?

Online Resource

www.brookerprinciples.com

Stay a step ahead in your studies with animations that bring concepts to life and practice tests to assess your understanding. Your instructor may also recommend the interactive eBook, individualized learning tools, and more.

Animal Diversity: Invertebrates

Scarab beetles have been revered in Egyptian culture for millennia. Invertebrate animals have tremendous impacts on human societies.

Chapter Outline

There are more beetles (about 400,000 species) than any other type of organism on Earth. When the British biologist J. B. S. Haldane was asked by a group of theologians what one could conclude about the nature of the Creator, he is said to have replied, "An inordinate fondness for beetles."

The dung beetle, or scarab beetle, shown in the chapter-opening photograph, is found in the area surrounding the Mediterranean Sea. Many scarab beetles feed exclusively on dung. In some species, males form the dung into a ball and roll it to a place where they bury it. Males can roll balls up to 50 times their own body weight. The female lays an egg in the dung ball, and when the egg hatches, the larva feeds on the dung surrounding it. After a period of weeks to months, the larva completely changes its form to a fully formed beetle and emerges. Scarabs feature prominently in ancient Egyptian culture. The Egyptians saw the rolling of balls of dung across the ground as a symbol of the forces moving the Sun across the sky, and considered the scarab beetle to be sacred. The apparent self-creation of the beetles from a dung ball buried underground and the mummy-like appearance of the pupa all conveyed the ideas of transformation and resurrection from an underground tomb.

Animals constitute the most species-rich kingdom. Many different kinds of animals and their products are part of our diet. In addition, humans enjoy many animal species as companions and depend on other species to test lifesaving drugs. However, other animals threaten our food supply and transmit deadly diseases.

Since the time of Carolus Linnaeus in the 1700s, scientists have classified animals based on their morphology, that is, on their physical structure. In the 1990s, animal classifications based on similarities in DNA and rRNA sequences became more common. Quite often, traditional classifications based on morphology and those based on molecular data were similar, but some important differences arose. In this chapter, we will begin by defining the key characteristics of animals and then take a look at the major types of invertebrates. In Chapter 26, we will look specifically at the vertebrates, animals more familiar to us, including fish, amphibians, reptiles, and mammals. Throughout both chapters, we will explore how new molecular data have enabled scientists to revise and refine the animal phylogenetic tree.

25.1   Characteristics of Animals

Learning Outcome:

1. List the key characteristics of animals that distinguish them from others organisms.

The Earth contains a dazzling diversity of animal species, living in environments from the deep sea to the desert and exhibiting an amazing array of characteristics. Most animals move and eat multicellular prey, and therefore, they are loosely differentiated from species in other kingdoms. However, coming up with a firm definition of an animal can be tricky because animals are so diverse that biologists can find exceptions to nearly any given characteristic. Even so, the following features can help us broadly characterize the group we call animals.

Cell Structure

- Animals are multicellular; however, animal cells lack cell walls and are flexible. This flexibility facilitates movement.
- Animal cells gain structural support from an extensive extracellular matrix (ECM) that forms strong fibers outside the cell (refer back to Figure 4.27).
- A group of unique cell junctions—anchoring, tight, and gap junctions—play an important additional role in holding animal cells in place and allowing communication between cells (refer back to Section 5.7).

Mode of Nutrition

- Animals are heterotrophs; that is, they ingest other organisms or their products to sustain life. Many different modes of feeding exist among animals, including suspension feeding—filtering food out of the surrounding water; bulk feeding—eating large food pieces; and fluid feeding—sucking plant sap or animal body fluids (Figure 25.1).

Movement

- Muscle tissue is unique to animals, and most animals are capable of some type of locomotion in order to acquire food or escape predators.
- Nervous tissue is also unique to animals, and a nervous system coordinates movement.

Genomes

- All animals possess *Hox* genes, which function in patterning the body axis (see Figure 20.12, 20.13)
- Animals have very similar genes that encode for RNA of small ribosomal subunit (SSU) rRNA (see Figure 10.13).

Reproduction and Development

- Nearly all members of the animal kingdom reproduce sexually, whereby a small, mobile sperm generally unites with a much larger egg to form a fertilized egg, or zygote. Fertilization can occur internally, which is common in terrestrial species, or externally, which is more common in aquatic species.
- Similarly, embryos develop inside the mother or outside in the mother's environment. A particularly unusual developmental phenomenon is the occurrence of **metamorphosis,** by which an organism changes from a juvenile to an adult form, for example, when a caterpillar changes into a butterfly or when a scarab larva changes into an adult scarab beetle.

25.1   Reviewing the Concepts

- Animals constitute a very species-rich kingdom, with a number of characteristics that distinguish them from other organisms, including multicellularity, an extracellular matrix (ECM), and unique cell junctions, in addition to heterotrophic feeding, internal digestion, and the possession of nervous and muscle tissues.
- Many different feeding modes exist among animals, including suspension feeding, bulk feeding, and fluid feeding (Figure 25.1).

25.1   Testing Your Knowledge

1. Which of the following is *not* a distinguishing characteristic of animals?
   a. the capacity to move at some point in their life cycle
   b. possession of cell walls
   c. multicellularity
   d. heterotrophy
   e. All of the above are characteristics of animals.

  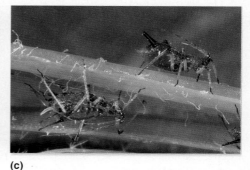

(a)   (b)   (c)

Figure 25.1   Modes of animal nutrition.   (a) Suspension feeders, such as this tube worm, filter food particles from the water column. **(b)** Bears and other bulk feeders tear off large pieces of their food and chew it or swallow it whole. **(c)** Fluid feeders, such as this aphid, suck fluid from their food source.

25.2 Animal Classification

Learning Outcomes:

1. Discuss why choanoflagellates are believed to be the closest living relatives of animals.

2. Describe how the presence of tissues, symmetry, germ layers, and embryonic development form the basis of animal classification.

3. Describe how differences in body cavities and segmentation may also be used to distinguish groups of animals.

Although animals constitute an extremely diverse kingdom, most biologists agree that the kingdom is monophyletic, meaning that all taxa have evolved from a single common ancestor. Today, scientists recognize about 35 animal phyla. At first glance, many of these phyla seem so distantly related to one another (for example, chordates and jellyfish) that making sense of this diversity with a classification scheme seems nearly impossible. However, over the course of centuries, scientists have come to some basic conclusions about the evolutionary relationships among animals. In this section, we explore the major features of animal body plans that form the basis of animal phylogeny (Figure 25.2).

Biology Principle

All Species (Past and Present) Are Related by an Evolutionary History

All animals are believed to be derived from a choanoflagellate-like ancestor.

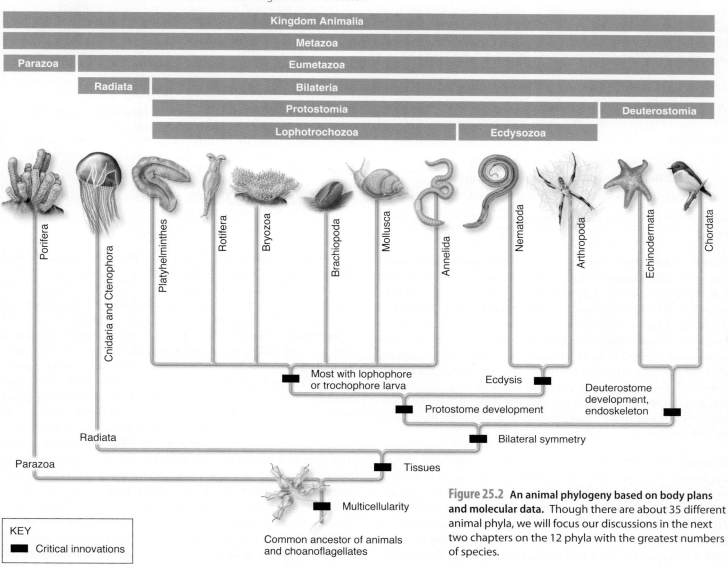

Figure 25.2 An animal phylogeny based on body plans and molecular data. Though there are about 35 different animal phyla, we will focus our discussions in the next two chapters on the 12 phyla with the greatest numbers of species.

KEY

■ Critical innovations

Animals Evolved from a Choanoflagellate-Like Ancestor

The history of animal life on Earth has evolved over hundreds of millions of years. Some scientists suggest that changing environmental conditions, such as a buildup of dissolved oxygen and minerals in the ocean or an increase in atmospheric oxygen, eventually permitted higher metabolic rates and increased the activity of a wide range of animals. Others suggest that with the development of sophisticated locomotor skills, a wide range of predators and prey evolved, leading to an evolutionary "arms race" in which predators evolved powerful weapons and prey evolved more powerful defenses against them. Such adaptations would have led to a proliferation of different lifestyles and taxa. Finally, the evolution of *Hox* genes may have resulted in an increase in diversity.

With the monophyletic nature of the animal kingdom in mind, scientists have attempted to characterize the organism from which animals most likely evolved. According to research, the closest living relative of animals is believed to be a flagellated protist known as a choanoflagellate. Choanoflagellates are tiny, single-celled or colonial organisms, each with a single flagellum surrounded by a collar composed of cytoplasmic tentacles (Figure 25.3a; look back to Figure 22.16h). As shown in Figure 25.3b, colonial choanoflagellate cells bear a striking similarity to cell types called choanocytes, which are found in sponges—the simplest animals.

Animal Classification Is Based Mainly on Body Plans

Biologists traditionally classified animal diversity in terms of these three main morphological and developmental features of animal body plans:

1. Presence or absence of different tissue types
2. Type of body symmetry and number of germ layers
3. Specific features of embryonic development

We will discuss each of these major features of animal body plans next.

Tissues   Collectively, animals are known as **Metazoa.** Animals can be divided into two subgroups based on whether or not they have specialized types of tissues, that is, groups of cells that have a similar structure and function. The **Parazoa** (from the Greek, meaning alongside animals) are not generally thought to possess specialized tissue types or organs, although they may have several distinct types of cells. The Parazoa consist of a single phylum, Porifera (sponges) (Figure 25.4a). In contrast, the **Eumetazoa** (from the Greek, meaning true animals) have one or more types of tissue and, for the most part, have different types of organs—a collection of two or more tissues performing a specific function or set of functions.

Symmetry and Germ Layers   The Eumetazoa are divided according to their type of symmetry. Symmetry refers to the existence of balanced proportions of the body on either side of a median plane. Radially symmetric animals, the **Radiata,** can be divided equally by any longitudinal plane passing through the central axis (Figure 25.4b). Such animals are often circular or tubular in shape, with a mouth at one end, and include the animals called cnidarians and ctenophores (jellyfish and related species).

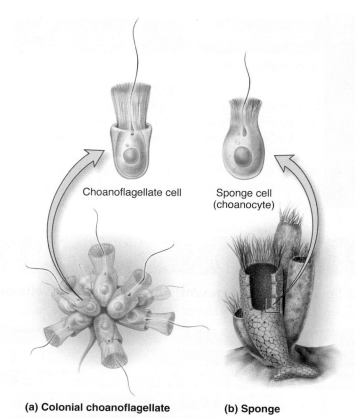

(a) Colonial choanoflagellate   **(b) Sponge**

Figure 25.3   Early animal characteristics: A comparison of a colonial choanoflagellate and a sponge. Both types of organisms have very similar types of cells. The structure of sponges and in particular the sponge cell called the choanocyte is described later (look ahead to Figure 25.11).

✓ Concept Check: *Why are sponges considered animals but simple choanoflagellates are not?*

Bilaterally symmetric animals, the **Bilateria,** can be divided along a vertical plane at the midline to create two halves (Figure 25.4c). Thus, a bilateral animal has a left side and a right side, which are mirror images, as well as a **dorsal** (upper) and a **ventral** (lower) side, which are not identical, and an **anterior** (head) and a **posterior** (tail) end. Bilateral symmetry is strongly correlated with both the ability to move through the environment and with **cephalization**—the localization of sensory structures at the anterior end of the body. Such abilities allow animals to encounter their environment initially with their head, which is best equipped to detect and consume prey and to detect and respond to predators and other dangers. Most animals are bilaterally symmetric.

Fertilization of an egg by a sperm creates a diploid zygote. The zygote then undergoes **cleavage**—a succession of rapid cell divisions with no significant growth that produces a hollow sphere of cells called a **blastula.** In all animals except the sponges, the growing zygote develops different layers of cells during a process known as **gastrulation** (Figure 25.5). In gastrulation, an area in the blastula folds inward, or invaginates, creating in the process a structure called a **gastrula.** The inner layer of cells becomes the **endoderm,** which lines the primitive digestive tract. The outer

(a) Parazoa: no tissue types

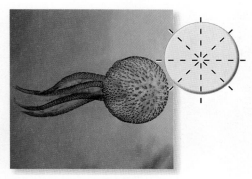

(b) Eumetazoa: two tissue types
Radiata: radial symmetry

(c) Eumetazoa: three tissue types
Bilateria: bilateral symmetry

Figure 25.4 **Early divisions in the animal phylogeny.** Animals can be categorized based on **(a)** the absence of different tissue types (Parazoa; the sponges) or **(b, c)** the presence of tissues (Eumetazoa; all other animals). Further categorization is based on the presence of **(b)** radial symmetry (Radiata; the cnidarians and ctenophores) or **(c)** bilateral symmetry (Bilateria; all other animals).

layer, or **ectoderm,** covers the surface of the embryo and differentiates into the epidermis and nervous system.

A key difference between the Radiata and Bilateria is that radially semetric animals have only these two embryonic cell layers, called **germ layers.** The Bilateria develop a third layer of cells, termed the **mesoderm,** between the ectoderm and endoderm. Mesoderm forms the muscles and most other organs between the digestive tract and the ectoderm (look ahead to Figure 40.17). Because the Bilateria have these three distinct germ layers, they are often referred to as **triploblastic,** whereas the Radiata, which have only ectoderm and endoderm, are termed **diploblastic.**

Specific Features of Embryonic Development   The most fundamental feature of embryonic development concerns the development of a mouth and anus (**Figure 25.6a**). In gastrulation, the endoderm forms an indentation, the **blastopore,** which is the opening of

the digestive tract to the outside. In **protostomes** (from the Greek *protos*, meaning first, and *stoma*, meaning mouth), the blastopore becomes the mouth. If an anus is formed in a protostome, it develops from a secondary opening. In contrast, in **deuterostomes** (from the Greek *deuteros*, meaning second), the blastopore becomes the anus, and the mouth develops from a secondary opening.

In addition, protostomes and deuterostomes differ in some other embryonic features. In the early stages of embryonic development, repeated cell divisions occur without cell growth, a process known as cleavage. Protostome development is generally characterized by so-called **determinate cleavage,** in which the fate of each embryonic cell is determined very early (**Figure 25.6b**). If one of the cells is removed from a four-cell protostome embryo, neither the single cell nor the remaining three-cell mass can form viable embryos, and development is halted. In contrast, most deuterostome development is characterized by **indeterminate cleavage,**

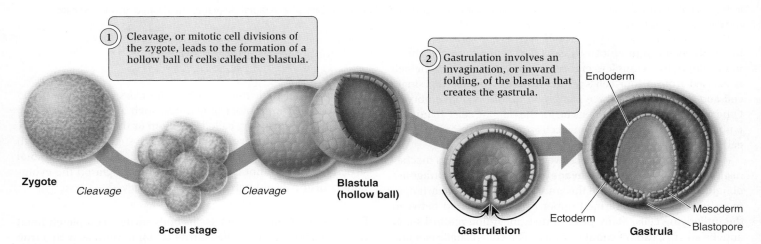

① Cleavage, or mitotic cell divisions of the zygote, leads to the formation of a hollow ball of cells called the blastula.

② Gastrulation involves an invagination, or inward folding, of the blastula that creates the gastrula.

Zygote   *Cleavage*   **8-cell stage**   *Cleavage*   **Blastula (hollow ball)**   **Gastrulation**   Endoderm   Ectoderm   **Gastrula**   Mesoderm   Blastopore

Figure 25.5 **Formation of germ layers.** Note: Radially symmetric animals (Radiata) do not form mesoderm.

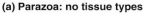 **BioConnections:** *Look back to Figure 21.7. Is the existence of three layers in the Bilateria a shared primitive character or a shared derived character?*

③ In the gastrula, the layer of cells lining the primitive digestive tract becomes the endoderm. The cells on the outside of the blastula form the ectoderm. In the Bilateria, a middle layer termed the mesoderm develops between the ectoderm and endoderm.

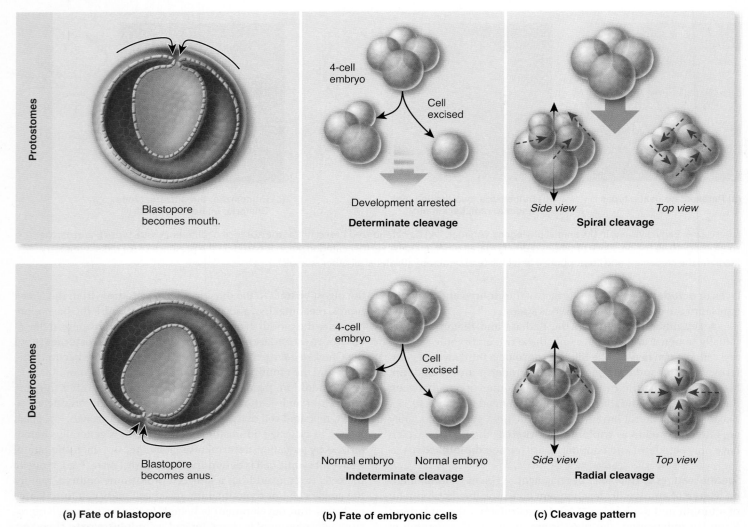

Figure 25.6 Differences in embryonic development between protostomes and deuterostomes. **(a)** In protostomes, the blastopore becomes the mouth. In deuterostomes, the blastopore becomes the anus. **(b)** Protostomes have determinate cleavage, whereas deuterostomes have indeterminate cleavage. **(c)** Many protostomes have spiral cleavage, and all deuterostomes have radial cleavage. The dashed arrows indicate the direction of cleavage.

in which each cell produced by early cleavage retains the ability to develop into a complete embryo. For example, when one cell is excised from a four-cell sea urchin embryo, both the single cell and the remaining three can go on to form viable embryos. Other embryonic cells compensate for the missing cells. In human embryos, if individual embryonic cells separate from one another early in development, identical twins can result.

In the developing zygote, cleavage may occur by two mechanisms (**Figure 25.6c**). In **spiral cleavage,** the planes of cell cleavage are oblique to the vertical axis of the embryo, resulting in an arrangement in which newly formed upper cells lie centered between the underlying cells. Many protostomes, including mollusks and annelid worms, exhibit spiral cleavage. The coiled shells of some mollusks result from spiral cleavage. In **radial cleavage,** the cleavage planes are either parallel or perpendicular to the vertical axis of the egg. This results in tiers of cells, one directly above the other. All deuterostomes exhibit radial cleavage, as do insects and nematodes, suggesting it may have been an ancestral condition.

Additional Morphological Criteria Are Used to Classify Animals

In older phylogenetic trees of animal life, classification was based on additional morphological features, such as the possession of a fluid-filled body cavity called a **coelom** or the presence of body segmentation. More recent molecular data suggest that although these features are helpful in describing differences in animal structure, they are not as useful in shedding light on the evolutionary history of animals as previously believed.

Body Cavity In many animals, the body cavity is completely lined with mesoderm and is called a true coelom. Animals with a true coelom, such as annelids, arthropods, and chordates, are termed **coelomates** (**Figure 25.7a**). If the fluid-filled cavity is not completely lined by tissue derived from mesoderm, it is known as a pseudocoelom (**Figure 25.7b**). Animals with a pseudocoelom, including rotifers and nematodes, are termed **pseudocoelomates.** Some

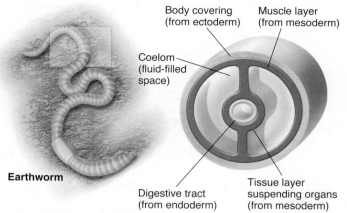

Body covering (from ectoderm)

Muscle layer (from mesoderm)

Coelom (fluid-filled space)

Earthworm

Digestive tract (from endoderm)

Tissue layer suspending organs (from mesoderm)

(a) Coelomate

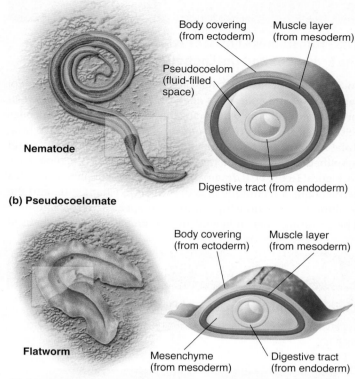

Body covering (from ectoderm)

Muscle layer (from mesoderm)

Pseudocoelom (fluid-filled space)

Nematode

Digestive tract (from endoderm)

(b) Pseudocoelomate

Figure 25.7 **The three basic body cavities of bilaterally symmetric animals.** Cross sections of each animal are shown on the right.

✔ **Concept Check:** *What advantages does a coelom confer for movement?*

animals, such as flatworms, lack a fluid-filled body cavity and are termed **acoelomates** (Figure 25.7c). Instead of fluid, this region contains mesenchyme, a tissue derived from mesoderm.

In some soft-bodied invertebrates, such as earthworms, the coelom functions as a **hydrostatic skeleton**—a fluid-filled body cavity surrounded by muscles that gives support and shape to the body of organisms. Muscle contractions at one part of the body push this fluid toward another part of the body. This type of movement can best be observed in an earthworm. In some organisms, such as insects and mollusks, the fluid in the body cavity also acts as a simple circulatory system. Finally, the fluid is relatively incompressible and therefore cushions internal organs such as the heart and intestinal tract in all coelomate animals, helping to prevent injury from external forces.

Segmentation   Another well-known feature of the animal body plan is the presence or absence of segmentation. In segmentation, the body is divided into regions called segments. Segmentation

Flatworm

Body covering (from ectoderm)

Muscle layer (from mesoderm)

Mesenchyme (from mesoderm)

Digestive tract (from endoderm)

(c) Acoelomate

is most obvious in the annelids, or segmented worms, but it is also evident in arthropods and chordates (Figure 25.8). In annelids, each segment contains the same set of blood vessels, nerves, and muscles. Some segments may differ, such as those containing the brain or the sex organs, but many segments are very similar. In chordates, we can see segmentation in the backbone and muscles. The advantage of segmentation is that it allows specialization of body regions and the appendages used for movement. Many insects have wings and three pairs of legs, whereas centipedes have no wings and many legs. Crabs, lobsters, and shrimp have highly specialized thoracic appendages that aid in movement and feeding (look forward to Figure 25.30).

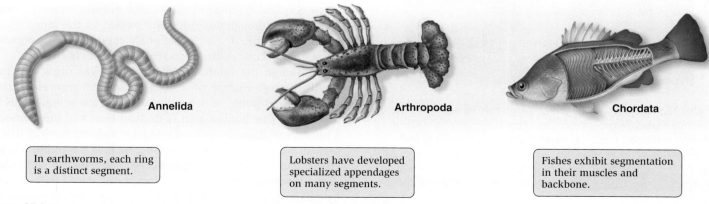

Annelida

Arthropoda

Chordata

In earthworms, each ring is a distinct segment.

Lobsters have developed specialized appendages on many segments.

Fishes exhibit segmentation in their muscles and backbone.

Figure 25.8 **Segmentation.** Annelids, arthropods, and chordates all exhibit segmentation.

EVOLUTIONARY CONNECTIONS

The Protostomes Consist of Two Major Clades—the Ecdysozoa and the Lophotrochozoa

In 1997, American molecular biologists Anna Marie Aguinaldo, James Lake, and colleagues analyzed the relationships between protostome clades by sequencing the complete gene that encodes SSU (small subunit) rRNA from a variety of representative taxa. Total genomic DNA was isolated using standard techniques and amplified by the polymerase chain reaction (PCR; refer back to Figure 16.6). PCR fragments were then subjected to DNA sequencing, a technique also described in Chapter 16, and the evolutionary relationships among 50 species were examined. The resulting data indicated the existence of a new clade of

Biology Principle

Living Organisms Grow and Develop

For animals with exoskeletons, growth and development necessitate molting.

Figure 25.9 Ecdysis. The dragonfly, shown here emerging from a discarded exoskeleton, is a member of the Ecdysozoa—a clade of animals exhibiting ecdysis, the periodic shedding (molting) and re-formation of the exoskeleton.

 **Concept Check:** *What are the main members of the Ecdysozoa?*

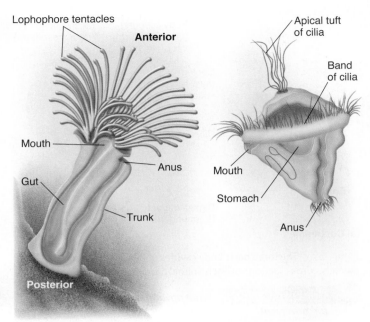

(a) Lophophore of a phoronid worm (b) Trochophore larva

Figure 25.10 Characteristics of the Lophotrochozoa. (a) A lophophore, a crown of ciliated tentacles, generates a current to bring food particles into the mouth. **(b)** The trochophore larval form is found in several animal lineages.

molting animals, the **Ecdysozoa** (pronounced ek-die-so-zo-ah), consisting of the nematodes and arthropods. This study represented a scientific breakthrough because it underscored the value of molecular phylogenies. According to molecular evidence, the other major protostome clade is the **Lophotrochozoa** (pronounced low-fo-tro-ko-zo-ah), which encompasses the mollusks, annelids, and several other phyla (see Figure 25.2). When some morphologists reviewed their data in light of this new information, they found there was also morphological support for these new groupings.

The Ecdysozoa is so named because all of its members secrete a nonliving cuticle, an external skeleton (exoskeleton); think of the hard shell of a beetle or that of a crab. As these animals grow, the exoskeleton becomes too small, and the animal molts, or breaks out of its old exoskeleton, and secretes a newer, larger one (**Figure 25.9**) This molting process is called **ecdysis;** hence the name Ecdysozoa. Although this group was named for this morphological characteristic, it was first strongly supported as a separate clade by molecular evidence such as similarities in DNA.

Although the Lophotrochozoa clade was organized primarily through analysis of molecular data, its name also stems from two morphological features seen in many organisms of this clade. The "lopho" part is derived from the **lophophore,** a horseshoe-shaped crown of tentacles used for feeding that is present on some phyla in this clade, such as the rotifers, bryozoans, and brachiopods (**Figure 25.10a**). The "trocho" part refers to the **trochophore larva,** a distinct larval stage characterized by a band of cilia around its middle that is used for swimming (**Figure 25.10b**). Trochophore larvae are found in several Lophotrochozoa phyla, such as annelid worms and mollusks, indicating their similar ancestry. Other members of the clade, such as the platyhelminthes, have neither of these morphological features and are classified as lophotrochozoans based strictly on molecular data.

25.2 Reviewing the Concepts

- Animals can be categorized according to the absence of different types of tissues (the Parazoa or sponges) and the presence of tissues (Eumetazoa or all other animals). The Eumetazoa can also be divided according to their type of symmetry, whether radial (Radiata, the cnidarians and ctenophores) or bilateral (Bilateria, all other animals) (Figure 25.4).
- The Radiata have two embryonic cell layers (germ layers): the endoderm and the ectoderm. The Bilateria have a third germ layer termed the mesoderm, which develops between the endoderm and the ectoderm (Figure 25.5).
- Animals are also classified according to patterns of embryonic development. In protostomes, the blastopore becomes the mouth; in deuterostomes, the blastopore becomes the anus (Figure 25.6). Most protostomes have spiral cleavage and all deuterostomes have radial cleavage.
- Recent molecular studies propose a division of the protostomes into two major clades: the Ecdysozoa and the Lophotrochozoa. Members of the Ecdysozoa secrete and periodically shed a nonliving cuticle, typically an exoskeleton, or external skeleton (Figure 25.9). Most members of the Lophotrochozoa are distinguished by two morphological features: the lophophore, a crown of tentacles used for feeding, and the trochophore larva, a distinct larval stage (Figure 25.10).

25.2 Testing Your Knowledge

1. In protostomes
   a. the blastopore becomes the mouth.
   b. the blastopore becomes the anus.
   c. development is characterized by indeterminate cleavage.
   d. a and c.
   e. b and c.
2. In triploblastic animals, the inner lining of the digestive tract is derived from the
   a. ectoderm.
   b. mesoderm.
   c. endoderm.
   d. pseudocoelom.
   e. coelom.

3. Pseudocoelomates
   a. lack a fluid-filled cavity.
   b. have a fluid-filled cavity that is completely lined with mesoderm.
   c. have a fluid-filled cavity that is partially lined with mesoderm.
   d. have a fluid-filled cavity that is not lined with mesoderm.
   e. have an air-filled cavity that is partially lined with mesoderm.

25.3 Parazoa: Sponges, the First Multicellular Animals

Learning Outcomes:

1. Outline the body plan and unique characteristics of sponges.
2. Describe how sponges defend themselves against predators.

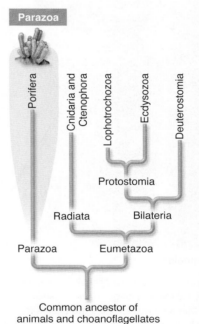

Common ancestor of animals and choanoflagellates

The Parazoa consist of one phylum, Porifera (from the Latin, meaning pore bearers), whose members are commonly referred to as sponges. Sponges lack true tissues—groups of cells that have a similar structure and function. However, sponges are multicellular and possess several types of cells that perform different functions. Biologists have identified approximately 8,000 species of sponges, the vast majority of which are marine. Sponges range in size from only a few millimeters across to more than 2 m in diameter. Smaller sponges may be radially symmetric, but most have no apparent symmetry. Some sponges have a low encrusting growth form, whereas others grow tall and erect (**Figure 25.11a**). Although adult sponges are sessile, that is, anchored in place, the larvae are free-swimming.

Choanocytes Help Circulate Water

The body of a sponge looks similar to a vase pierced with small holes or pores (**Figure 25.11b**). Water is drawn through these pores into a central cavity, and flows out through the large opening at the top, called the osculum. The water enters the pores by the beating action of the flagella of the **choanocytes,** or collar cells, that line the central cavity (**Figure 25.11c**). In the process, the choanocytes trap and eat small particulate matter and tiny plankton.

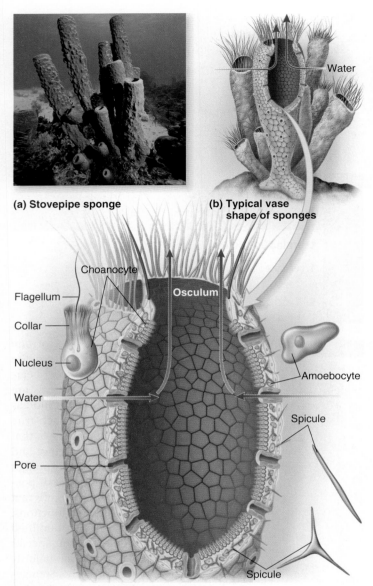

(a) Stovepipe sponge

(b) Typical vase shape of sponges

Choanocyte

Flagellum

Collar

Nucleus

Water

Pore

Osculum

Amoebocyte

Spicule

Spicule

Water

(c) Cross section of sponge morphology

Figure 25.11 **(a)** The stovepipe sponge (*Aplysina archeri*) is a common sponge found on Caribbean reefs. **(b)** Many sponges have a vaselike shape. **(c)** A cross section reveals that sponges are truly multicellular animals, having various cell types but no distinct tissues.

✓ Concept Check: *Since sponges are soft and sessile, why aren't they eaten by other organisms?*

As noted in Section 25.1, because of striking morphological and molecular similarities between choanocytes and choanoflagellates, a group of modern protists having a single flagellum, scientists believe that sponges originated from a choanoflagellate-like ancestor. Also lining the central cavity are mobile cells called amoebocytes that absorb food from choanocytes, digest it, and carry the nutrients to other cells. Sponges are unique among the major animal phyla in using intracellular digestion, the uptake of food particles by cells, as a mode of feeding.

Sponges Have Mechanical and Chemical Defenses Against Predators

Some amoebocytes can also form tough skeletal fibers that support the body. In many sponges, this skeleton consists of sharp **spicules** formed of protein, calcium carbonate, or silica. For example, some deep-ocean species, called glass sponges, are distinguished by needle-like silica spicules that form elaborate lattice-like skeletons. The presence of such tough spicules may help explain why there is not much predation of sponges. Other sponges have fibers of a tough protein called **spongin** that lend skeletal support. Spongin skeletons are still commercially harvested and sold as bath sponges. Many species produce toxic defensive chemicals, some of which are thought to have possible antibiotic and anti-inflammatory effects in humans.

Sponges Reproduce Sexually and Asexually

Sponges reproduce through both sexual and asexual means. Most sponges are **hermaphrodites** (from the Greek, for the Greek god Hermes and the goddess Aphrodite), individuals that can produce both sperm and eggs. Gametes are derived from amoebocytes or choanocytes. Sperm are released into the water and carried by water currents to fertilize the eggs of neighboring sponges. Zygotes develop into flagellated swimming larvae that eventually settle on a suitable substrate to become sessile adults. In asexual reproduction, a small fragment or bud may detach and form a new sponge.

25.3 Reviewing the Concepts

- Invertebrates, or animals without a backbone, make up more than 95% of all animal species. An early lineage—the Parazoa—consists of one phylum, the Porifera, or sponges. Although sponges lack true tissues, they are multicellular animals possessing several types of cells (Figure 25.11).

25.3 Testing Your Knowledge

1. How do sponges protect themselves from predators?
   a. They are protected by silica spicules.
   b. They are protected by toxic defensive chemicals.
   c. They are eaten, and the leftover cells reaggregate into new, smaller sponges.
   d. a and b are correct.
   e. a, b, and c are correct.

2. Choanocytes are
   a. a group of protists that are believed to have given rise to animals.
   b. specialized cells of sponges that function to trap and eat small particles.
   c. cells that make up the gelatinous layer in sponges.
   d. cells of sponges that function to transfer nutrients to other cells.
   e. cells that form spicules in sponges.

25.4 Radiata: Jellyfish and Other Radially Symmetric Animals

Learning Outcomes:

1. Compare and contrast the two body forms of cnidarians.
2. Describe how cnidarians defend themselves.
3. Outline the unique features of ctenophores

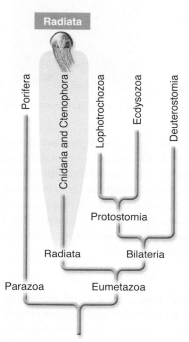

The Radiata consists of two closely related phyla: the Cnidaria (from the Greek *knide*, meaning nettle, and *aria*, meaning related to; pronounced nid-air'-e-ah) and the Ctenophora (from the Greek *ktenos*, meaning comb, and *phora*, meaning bearing; pronounced teen-o-for'-ah). Members of the Radiata phyla, or radiates, are mostly found in marine environments, although a few are freshwater species. The Cnidaria includes hydra, jellyfish, box jellies, sea anemones, and corals; and the Ctenophora consists of the comb jellies. The Radiata have only two embryonic germ layers: the ectoderm and the endoderm. A gelatinous substance called the **mesoglea** connects the two layers. In jellyfish, the mesoglea is enlarged and forms a transparent jelly, whereas in hydra and corals, the mesoglea is very thin (Figure 25.12). The Radiata is the first clade with true tissues.

Both cnidarians and ctenophores possess a body cavity with a single opening to the external environment, called a **gastrovascular cavity,** where extracellular digestion takes place. Extracellular digestion, the breakdown of large molecules, takes place outside of the cell, allows the ingestion of larger food particles, and represents a major increase in complexity over the sponges, which use only intracellular digestion. Most radiates have tentacles around the mouth that aid in food detection and capture. Radiates also have true nerve cells arranged as a **nerve net** consisting of interconnected neurons with no central control organ (look ahead to Figure 32.17a). In nerve nets, nerve impulses pass in either direction along a given neuron.

The Cnidarians Exist in Two Different Body Forms

Most cnidarians exist as two different body forms and associated lifestyles: the sessile **polyp** or the motile **medusa** (Figure 25.12b). For example, corals exhibit only the polyp form, and jellyfish exist predominantly in the medusa form.

Biology Principle

Structure Determines Function

The inverted, umbrella-shaped medusae are free-swimming, whereas the tubular, polyp forms are sedentary.

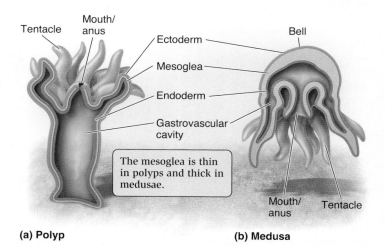

The mesoglea is thin in polyps and thick in medusae.

(a) Polyp   **(b) Medusa**

Figure 25.12 Polyp and medusa forms of cnidarians. Both **(a)** polyp and **(b)** medusa forms have two layers of cells: an outer (ectoderm) and an inner (endoderm). In between is a layer of mesoglea, which is thin in polyps and thick in medusae.

✓ **Concept Check:** *What are the dominant life stages of the following types of cnidarians: jellyfish, sea anemone, and Portuguese man-of-war?*

The polyp form has a tubular body with an opening at the oral (top) end that is surrounded by tentacles and functions as both mouth and anus (see Figure 25.12a). The aboral (bottom) end is attached to the substrate. Polyps exist colonially, as they do in corals, or alone, as in sea anemones. Corals take dissolved calcium and carbonate ions from seawater and precipitate them as limestone underneath their bodies. In some species, this leads to a buildup of limestone deposits. As each successive generation of polyps dies, the limestone remains in place, and new polyps grow on top. Thus, huge underwater limestone deposits called coral reefs are formed (look ahead to Figure 43.23b). The largest of these is Australia's Great Barrier Reef, which stretches over 2,300 km. Many other extensive coral reefs are known, including the reef system along the Florida Keys, all of which occur in warm water, generally between 20°C and 30°C.

The free-swimming medusa form has an umbrella-shaped body with an opening that serves as both mouth and anus on the concave underside that is surrounded by tentacles (see Figure 25.12b). Medusae possess simple sense organs near the bell margin, including organs of equilibrium called statocysts and photosensitive organs known as ocelli. When one side of the bell tips upward, the statocysts on that side are stimulated, and muscle contraction is initiated to reorient the medusa so the tentacles

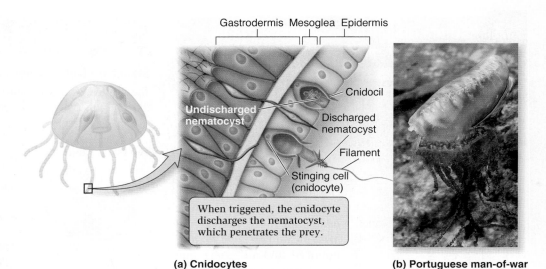

Figure 25.13 **Specialized stinging cells of cnidarians, called cnidocytes.** **(a)** Cnidocytes, which contain stinging capsules called nematocysts, are situated in the tentacles. **(b)** The Portuguese man-of-war (*Physalia physalis*) employs cnidocytes that can be lethal to humans.

When triggered, the cnidocyte discharges the nematocyst, which penetrates the prey.

(a) Cnidocytes

(b) Portuguese man-of-war

are pointing downward. The ocelli allow medusae to position themselves in particular light levels.

The phylum Cnidaria consists of four classes: Hydrozoa (including the Portuguese man-of-war), Scyphozoa (jellyfish), Anthozoa (sea anemones and corals), and Cubozoa (box jellies). The distinguishing characteristics of these classes are shown in **Table 25.1**.

Cnidarians Have Specialized Stinging Cells

One of the unique and characteristic features of the cnidarians is the existence of stinging cells called **cnidocytes,** which function in defense or the capture of prey (**Figure 25.13a**). Cnidocytes contain **nematocysts,** powerful capsules with an inverted coiled and barbed thread. Each cnidocyte has a hairlike trigger called a **cnidocil** on its surface. When the cnidocil is touched or

a chemical stimulus is detected, the nematocyst is discharged, and its filament penetrates the prey and injects a small amount of toxin. Small prey are immobilized and passed into the mouth by the tentacles. After discharge, the cnidocyte is absorbed, and a new one grows to replace it. The nematocysts of most cnidarians are not harmful to humans, but those on the tentacles of the larger jellyfish and the Portuguese man-of-war (**Figure 25.13b**) can be extremely painful and even fatal.

The Ctenophores Have a Complete Gut

Ctenophores, also known as comb jellies, are a small phylum of fewer than 100 species, all of which are marine and look very much like jellyfish (**Figure 25.14**). They have eight rows of cilia on their surfaces that resemble combs. The coordinated beating of the cilia propels the ctenophores. Averaging about 1–10 cm in length, comb jellies are probably the largest animals to use cilia for locomotion.

Comb jellies possess two long tentacles but lack stinging cells. Instead, they have cells on the tentacles that secrete a sticky substance onto which small prey adhere. The tentacles are then drawn over the mouth. As with cnidarians, digestion occurs in a gastrovascular cavity, but waste and water are eliminated through two anal pores. Thus, the comb jellies possess the first complete gut. Prey are generally small and may include tiny crustaceans called copepods and small fishes. Comb jellies are often transported around the world in ships' ballast water. *Mnemiopsis leidyi*, a ctenophore species native to the Atlantic coast of North and South America, was accidentally introduced into the Black and Caspian seas in the 1980s. With a plentiful food supply and a lack of predators, *Mnemiopsis* underwent a population explosion and ultimately devastated the local fishing industries.

All ctenophores are hermaphroditic, possessing both ovaries and testes, and gametes are shed into the water to eventually form a free-swimming larva that grows into an adult. There is no polyp stage. Nearly all ctenophores exhibit **bioluminescence,** a phenomenon that results from chemical reactions that give off light rather than heat. Individuals are particularly evident at night, and ctenophores that wash up on shore can make the sand or mud appear luminescent.

Table 25.1	Main Classes and Characteristics of the Cnidaria	
	Class and examples (est. # of species)	**Class characteristics**
	Hydrozoa: Portuguese man-of-war, hydra, some corals (2,700)	Mostly marine; exist in polyp stage; often colonial
	Scyphozoa: jellyfish (200)	All marine; exist in medusa stage; large (up to 2 m)
	Anthozoa: sea anemones, sea fans, most corals (6,000)	All marine; exist in polyp stage; many are colonial
	Cubozoa: box jellies, sea wasps (20)	All marine; exist in medusa stage; box-shaped

Figure 25.14 A ctenophore. Ctenophores are called comb jellies because the eight rows of cilia on their surfaces resemble combs.

25.4 Reviewing the Concepts

- The Radiata consists of two phyla: the Cnidaria (hydra, jelly-fish, box jellies, sea anemones, and corals) and the Ctenophora (comb jellies). Radiata have only two embryonic germ layers: the ectoderm and endoderm, with a gelatinous substance (meso-glea) connecting the two layers.

- Cnidarians exist in two forms: polyp or medusa. A characteristic feature of cnidarians is their stinging cells, or cnidocytes, which function in defense and prey capture. Ctenophores possess the first complete gut, and nearly all exhibit bioluminescence (Figures 25.12–25.14, Table 25.1).

25.4 Testing Your Knowledge

1. Cnidarians defend themselves using
  a. a nerve net.   **d.** medusa.
  b. bioluminescence.   **e.** cnidocils.
  c. nematocysts.

2. Ctenophores are unique among the Radiata in possessing
  a. nematocysts.   **d.** cnidocils.
  b. a gastrovascular cavity.   **e.** mesoglea.
  c. a complete gut.

25.5 Lophotrochozoa: The Flatworms, Rotifers, Bryozoans, Brachiopods, Mollusks, and Annelids

Learning Outcomes:

1. Describe the unique features of platyhelminthes, rotifers, bryozoans, and brachiopods.

2. Outline the main biological features and list the main classes of the mollusks.

3. List the advantages of segmentation in the annelids.

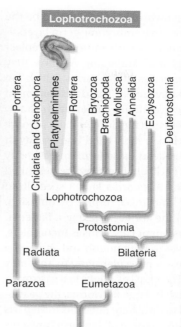

As we noted earlier, morphological and molecular data suggest that there are three clades of bilateral animals: the Lophotrochozoa and the Ecdysozoa (collectively known as the Protostomia, or protostomes) and the Deuterostomia (deuterostomes). In this section, we explore the distinguishing characteristics of the Lophotrochozoa, a diverse group that includes taxa that possess either a lophophore (a crown of ciliated tentacles, Bryozoa and Brachiopoda) or a distinct larval stage called a trochophore (Mollusca and Annelida). Also included in this clade are the Platyhelminthes (some of which have trochophore-like larvae) and the Rotifera (which have a lophophore-like feeding device), both of which share molecular similarities with the other members of the Lophotrochozoa.

The Phylum Platyhelminthes Consists of Flatworms with No Coelom

Platyhelminthes (from the Greek *platy*, meaning flat, and *helminth*, meaning worm), or flatworms, were among the first animals to develop an active predatory lifestyle. Platyhelminthes, and indeed most animals, possess mesoderm and are bilaterally symmetric, with a head bearing sensory appendages, a feature called cephalization (**Figure 25.15**).

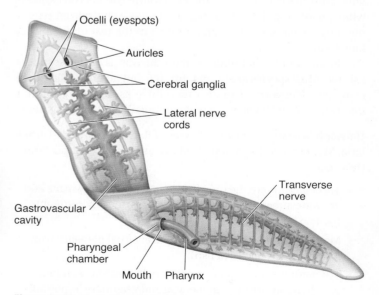

Figure 25.15 Body plan of a flatworm. Flatworm morphology is represented by a planarian, a member of the class Turbellaria.

 **Concept Check:** *How do flatworms breathe?*

Development of Mesoderm   The flatworms are believed to be the first animals to develop three distinctive embryonic germ layers—ectoderm, endoderm, and mesoderm—with mesoderm replacing the simpler gelatinous mesoglea of cnidarians. As such, they are said to be triploblastic. The muscles in flatworms, which are derived from mesoderm, are well developed. The development of mesoderm was therefore a critical evolutionary innovation in animals, leading to complex movement and the development of more sophisticated organs. Flatworms lack a fluid-filled body cavity in which the gut is suspended, and instead mesoderm fills the body spaces around the gastrovascular cavity; hence, they are described as acoelomates (see Figure 25.7c). Flatworms lack a specialized respiratory or circulatory system and must respire by diffusion. Thus, no cell can be too far from the surface, making a flattened shape necessary. The digestive system of flatworms is incomplete, with only one opening, which serves as both mouth and anus, as in cnidarians. Most flatworms possess a muscular pharynx that may be extended through the mouth. The pharynx opens to a gastrovascular cavity, where food is digested. In large flatworms, the gastrovascular cavity is highly branched to distribute nutrients to all parts of the body. The incomplete digestive system of flatworms prevents continuous feeding. Some flatworms are predators, but many species invade other animals as parasites.

Cephalization   At the anterior end of some free-living flatworms are light-sensitive eyespots, called ocelli, as well as chemoreceptive and sensory cells that are concentrated in organs called auricles. A pair of **cerebral ganglia,** which are clusters of nerve cell bodies, receives input from photoreceptors in eyespots and sensory cells. From the ganglia, a pair of lateral nerve cords running the length of the body allows rapid movement of information from anterior to posterior. In addition, transverse nerves form a nerve net on the ventral surface, similar to that of cnidarians. Thus, flatworms retain the cnidarian-style nervous system, while possessing the beginnings of the more centralized type of nervous system seen throughout much of the rest of the animal kingdom.

In all the Platyhelminthes, reproduction is either sexual or asexual. Most species are hermaphroditic but do not fertilize their own eggs. Flatworms can also reproduce asexually by splitting into two parts, with each half regenerating the missing fragment.

Flatworm Diversity   The four classes of flatworms are the Turbellaria, Monogenea, Trematoda (flukes), and Cestoda (tapeworms) (**Table 25.2**).

- Turbellarians are the only free-living class of flatworms and are widespread in lakes, ponds, and marine environments (**Figure 25.16a**).

- Monogeneans are relatively simple external parasites with just one host species (a fish).

- Trematodes and cestodes are internally parasitic in humans and therefore are of great medical and veterinary importance. They possess a variety of organs of attachment, such as hooks and suckers, that enable them to remain embedded within their hosts. For example, cestodes attach to their

Table 25.2	Main Classes and Characteristics of Platyhelminthes	
	Class and examples (est. # of species)	**Class characteristics**
	Turbellaria: planarian (3,000)	Mostly marine; free-living flatworms; predators or scavengers
	Monogenea: fish flukes (1,000)	Marine and freshwater; usually external parasites of fish; simple life cycle (no intermediate host)
	Trematoda: flukes (11,000)	Internal parasites of vertebrates; complex life cycle with several intermediate hosts
	Cestoda: tapeworms (5,000)	Internal parasites of vertebrates; complex life cycle, usually with one intermediate host; no digestive system; nutrients absorbed across epidermis

host by means of an organ at the head end called a scolex (**Figure 25.16b**). They have no mouth or gastrovascular cavity and absorb nutrients across the body surface.

Flatworm life cycles can be complex. Cestodes often require two separate vertebrate host species: one host, such as pigs or cattle, to begin their life cycle and another host, a primate such as a human, to complete their development. Behind the scolex in cestodes is a long ribbon of identical segments called proglottids (see Figure 25.16b). These are essentially segments of sex organs that develop thousands of eggs. The proglottids are continually shed in the host's feces. Human feces passed out into the ground are eaten with grass by pigs or cattle. Many tapeworms are then ingested by humans when they consume undercooked, infected meat—hence the value of thoroughly cooking meat.

The life history of trematodes is even more complex than that of cestodes, involving multiple hosts. The first host, called the intermediate host, is usually a mollusk, and the final host, or definitive host, is usually a vertebrate, but often a second or even a third intermediate host is involved (**Figure 25.17**).

Because the flukes multiply in each host, prodigious numbers of offspring can be produced. Blood flukes are the most common parasitic trematodes infecting humans; they cause the disease known as schistosomiasis. Over 200 million people worldwide, primarily in tropical Asia, Africa, and South America, are infected with this disease. The inch-long adult flukes can live for years in human hosts, and the release of eggs may cause chronic inflammation and blockage in many organs. Untreated schistosomiasis can lead to severe damage to the liver, intestines, and lungs and can eventually lead to death. Sewage treatment and access to clean water can greatly reduce infection rates.

Biology Principle

Biology Affects Our Society

About 1% of U.S. cattle are infected by beef tapeworms. Consuming beef that is not sufficiently well cooked can lead to infection by these parasites.

(a)   (b)

Figure 25.16 Flatworms. (a) Many free-living marine turbellarians are brightly colored such as this racing stripe flatworm, *Pseudoceros bifurcus*, from Bali, Indonesia, **(b)** The tapeworm *Taenia pisiformis* is a member of the class Cestoda. Note the tiny hooks and suckers that make up the scolex. Each segment is a proglottid, replete with eggs.

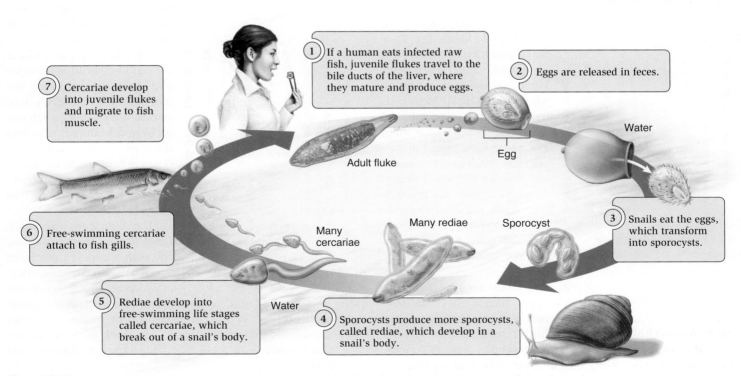

Figure 25.17 The complete life cycle of a trematode. This figure shows the life cycle of the Chinese liver fluke (*Clonorchis sinensis*).

Quantitative Analysis

HOW MANY FLUKES?

Many parasites face the challenge of reproducing and having their offspring find a new host. How can offspring relocate to a new host when their parent is locked up inside the host's body? As noted previously, in tapeworms each proglottid contains thousands of eggs. This ensures that vast numbers of eggs pass out of the host's body in the hope of finding a new host. Flukes, such as Chinese liver fluke (*Clonorchis sinensis*), have multiple host species. Eggs, on release from the human host, pass into water, where snails eat them (see Figure 25.17, step 2). Eggs develop into sporocysts inside the snail, and each sporocyst produces more sporocysts, called rediae. The rediae produce cercariae, which break out of the snail's body to attach to fish. The cercariae eventually lodge in fish muscles, which are then consumed by humans. The chances of infection at each of these stages are very low, so flukes produce huge numbers of offspring to compensate. We can appreciate the vast reproductive effort involved by calculating the number of offspring at each stage:

- Average number of eggs produced per fluke per day = 28,000
- Average length of life of adult fluke = 1,800 days (about 5 years)
- Number of sporocysts produced per lifetime = 28,000 × 1,800 = about 50 million
- Average number of cercariae produced per sporocyst = 200
- Total number of cercariae produced per lifetime = 200 × 50 million = 10 billion

Crunching the Numbers: If tapeworms shed about 5 proglottids per day, each proglottid contains about 50,000 eggs, and most tapeworms live in colonies of about 10 per host, how many eggs are shed by each host per day?

Members of the Phylum Rotifera Have a Pseudocoelom and a Ciliated Crown

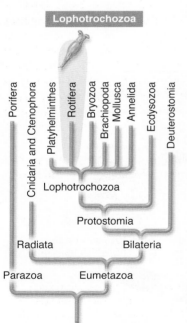

Members of the phylum Rotifera (from the Latin *rota*, meaning wheel, and *fera*, meaning to bear) get their name from their ciliated crown, or **corona,** which, when beating, looks similar to a rotating wheel (**Figure 25.18**). Most rotifers are microscopic animals, usually less than 1 mm long, and some have beautiful colors. The corona creates water currents that propel the animal through the water and that also waft small planktonic organisms or decomposing organic material toward the mouth. Rotifers have an alimentary canal, a digestive tract with a separate mouth and anus, which means they can feed continuously. There are about 2,000 species of rotifers, most of which inhabit fresh water, with a few marine and terrestrial species. Most often they are bottom-dwelling organisms, living on the pond floor or along lakeside vegetation.

Bryozoa and Brachiopoda Are Closely Related Phyla

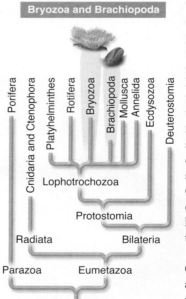

The Bryozoa and the Brachiopoda both possess a lophophore, a ciliary feeding device (see Figure 25.10a), and a true coelom (see Figure 25.7a). The lophophore is a circular fold of the body wall bearing tentacles that draw water toward the mouth. Because a thin extension of the coelom penetrates each tentacle, the tentacles also serve as a respiratory organ. Gases diffuse across the tentacles and into or out of the coelomic fluid and are carried throughout the body.

The bryozoans (from the Greek *bryon*, meaning moss, and *zoon*, meaning animal) are small colonial animals, most of which are less than 0.5 mm long, that can be found encrusted on rocks in shallow aquatic environments (**Figure 25.19a**). For this reason, bryozoans have been important reef-builders. Bryozoans date back to the Paleozoic era, and thousands of fossil forms have been discovered and identified.

Figure 25.18 *Philodina roseola*, a common rotifer, showing the crown of cilia (corona).

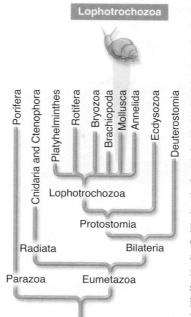

classification of about 35,000 fossil species. Mollusks have a considerable economic, aesthetic, and ecological importance to humans. Many, including scallops, oysters, clams, and squids, serve as sources of food. A significant industry involves the farming of oysters to produce cultured pearls, and rare and beautiful mollusk shells are extremely valuable to collectors. Snails and slugs can damage vegetables and ornamental plants, and boring mollusks can penetrate wooden ships and wharfs. Mollusks are intermediate hosts to many parasites, and several exotic species have become serious pests. For example, populations of the zebra mussel (*Dreissena polymorpha*) have been introduced into North America from Asia via ballast water from transoceanic ships. Since their introduction, they have spread rapidly throughout the Great Lakes and an increasing number of inland waterways, adversely affecting native organisms and clogging water intake valves to municipal water-treatment plants around the lakes.

Brachiopods (from the Greek *brachio*, meaning arm, and *podos*, meaning foot) are small, 1–8 cm bottom-dwelling marine organisms with two shell halves, much like clams (**Figure 25.19b**). Although they are now a relatively small group, with about 300 living species, brachiopods flourished in the Paleozoic and Mesozoic eras—about 30,000 fossil species have been identified.

The Mollusca Is a Large Phylum Containing Snails, Slugs, Clams, Oysters, Octopuses, and Squids

Mollusks (from the Latin *mollis*, meaning soft) constitute a very large phylum, with over 100,000 living species, including organisms as diverse as snails, clams and oysters, octopuses and squid, and chitons. They are an ancient group, as evidenced by the

The Mollusk Body Plan   One common feature of the mollusks is their soft body, which in many species exists under a protective external shell. Most mollusks are marine, although some have colonized fresh water. Many snails and slugs have moved onto land, but survive only in humid areas and where the calcium necessary for shell formation is abundant in the soil. The ability to colonize freshwater and terrestrial habitats has led to a diversification of mollusk body plans. Thus, in the amazing diversity of mollusks we see how organismal diversity is related to environmental diversity.

Although great variation in morphology occurs between classes, mollusks have a basic body plan consisting of three parts (**Figure 25.20**).

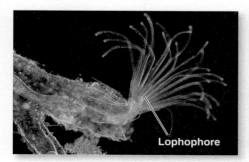

(a) A bryozoan

(b) A brachiopod, the northern lamp shell

Figure 25.19 Bryozoans and brachiopods. **(a)** Bryozoans are colonial animals that reside inside a nonliving case. **(b)** Brachiopods, such as this northern lamp shell (*Terebratulina septentrionalis*), in Nova Scotia, Canada, have dorsal and ventral shells.

 **Concept Check:**   *What are the two main functions of the lophophore?*

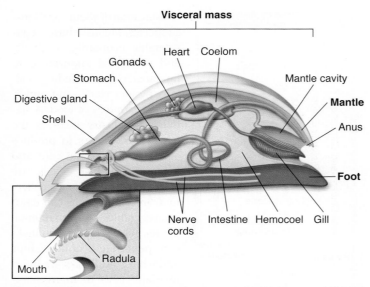

Figure 25.20 The mollusk body plan. The generalized body plan of a mollusk includes the characteristic foot, mantle, and visceral mass.

- A muscular **foot** is usually used for movement, and a **visceral mass** containing the internal organs rests atop the foot.
- The **mantle,** a fold of skin draped over the visceral mass, secretes a shell in those species that form shells.
- The **mantle cavity** houses delicate **gills,** filamentous organs that are specialized for gas exchange. A continuous current of water, often induced by cilia present on the gills or by muscular pumping, flushes out the wastes from the mantle cavity and brings in new oxygen-rich water.

Mollusks have an **open circulatory system** with a heart that pumps body fluid called hemolymph through vessels and into sinuses. Sinuses are the open, fluid-filled cavities between the internal organs. The organs and tissues are therefore continually bathed in hemolymph. The sinuses coalesce to form an open cavity known as the hemocoel (blood cavity). From these sinuses, the hemolymph drains into vessels that take it to the gills and then back to the heart.

The mollusk's mouth may contain a **radula,** a unique, protrusible, tonguelike organ that has many teeth and is used to eat plants, scrape food particles off rocks, or, if the mollusk is predatory, bore into shells of other species and tear flesh (see inset Figure 25.20). Other mollusks, particularly bivalves, have lost their radula and are filter feeders that strain water brought in by ciliary currents.

Mollusk Reproduction Most mollusks have separate sexes, although some are hermaphroditic. Gametes are usually released into the water, where they mix and fertilization occurs. In some snails, however, fertilization is internal, with the male inserting sperm directly into the female. Internal fertilization was a key evolutionary development, enabling some snails to colonize land,

and can be considered a critical innovation that fostered extensive adaptive radiation. In many species, reproduction involves the production of a trochophore larva that develops into a free-swimming larva that has a rudimentary foot, shell, and mantle.

The Major Molluscan Classes The four most common molluscan classes are the Polyplacophora (chitons), Gastropoda (snails and slugs), Bivalvia (clams and mussels), and Cephalopoda (octopuses, squids, and nautiluses) **(Table 25.3)**. Chitons are marine mollusks with a shell composed of eight separate plates **(Figure 25.21a)**. Chitons are common in the intertidal zone, an area above water at low tide and under water at high tide. The class Gastropoda (from the Greek *gaster*, meaning stomach, and *podos*, meaning foot) is the largest group of mollusks and encompasses about 75,000 living species, including snails, periwinkles, limpets, and other shelled members **(Figure 25.21b)**. The class also includes species such as slugs and nudibranchs, whose shells have been greatly reduced or completely lost during their evolution **(Figure 25.21c)**. Most gastropods are marine or freshwater species, but some species, including snails and slugs, have also colonized land. Most gastropods are slow-moving animals that are weighed down by their shell. Unlike bivalves, gastropods have a one-piece shell, into which the animal can withdraw to escape predators. Bivalves are marine or freshwater mollusks with two halves to their shell. Most are filter feeders using their gills to strain food particles from the water **(Figure 25.21d)**.

The 780 species of Cephalopoda (from the Greek *kephalo*, meaning head, and *podos*, meaning foot) are the most morphologically complex of the mollusks and indeed among the most complex of all invertebrates. Most are fast-swimming marine predators that range from organisms just a few centimeters in

Table 25.3	Main Classes and Characteristics of Mollusks	
	Class and examples (est. # of species)	**Class characteristics**
	Polyplacophora: chitons (860)	Marine; eight-plated shell
	Gastropoda: snails, slugs, nudibranchs (75,000)	Marine, freshwater, or terrestrial; most with coiled shell, but shell absent in slugs and nudibranchs; radula present
	Bivalvia: clams, mussels, oysters (30,000)	Marine or freshwater; shell with two halves or valves; primarily filter feeders with siphons
	Cephalopoda: octopuses, squids, nautiluses (780)	Marine; predatory, with tentacles around mouth, often with suckers; shell often absent or reduced; closed circulatory system; jet propulsion via siphon

(a) A chiton, class Polyplacophora

(b) A snail, class Gastropoda

(c) A sea slug, class Gastropoda

(d) A Quahog clam, class Bivalvia

(e) A blue-ringed octopus, class Cephalopoda

Figure 25.21 Mollusks. (a) A chiton (*Tonicella lineata*), a polyplacophoran with a shell made up of eight separate plates. **(b)** A gastropod tree snail (*Liguus fasciatus*) from the Florida Everglades, showing its characteristic coiled shell. **(c)** A nudibranch (*Chromodoris kuniei*). The nudibranchs are a gastropod subclass whose members have lost their shell altogether. **(d)** A bivalve shell, class Bivalvia, with growth rings. Quahog clams (*Mercenaria mercenaria*) can live over 20 years. **(e)** The highly poisonous blue-ringed octopus (*Hapalochlaena lunulata*) is a cephalopod.

 **BioConnections:** *In what period did mollusks arise? Look back to Figure 18.8.*

size to the colossal squid (*Mesonychoteuthis hamiltoni*), which is known to reach over 13 m in length and 495 kg (1,091 lb) in weight. A cephalopod's mouth is surrounded by many long arms commonly armed with suckers. All cephalopods have a beaklike jaw that allows them to bite their prey, and some, such as the blue-ringed octopus (*Hapalochlaena lunulata*), deliver a deadly poison through their saliva (**Figure 25.21e**).

The foot of some cephalopods has become modified into a muscular siphon. Water drawn into the mantle cavity is quickly expelled through the siphon, propelling the organisms forward or backward in a kind of jet propulsion. Such vigorous movement requires powerful muscles and a very efficient circulatory system to deliver oxygen and nutrients to the muscles. Cephalopods are the only mollusks with a **closed circulatory system,** in which blood flows throughout an animal entirely within a series of vessels. One of the advantages of this type of system is that the heart can pump blood through the tissues rapidly, making oxygen more readily available. The blood of cephalopods contains the copper-rich protein hemocyanin for transporting oxygen. Less efficient than the iron-rich hemoglobin of vertebrates, hemocyanin gives the blood a blue color.

The Phylum Annelida Consists of the Segmented Worms

Annelids are a large phylum with about 15,000 described species. Its members include free-ranging marine worms, tube worms, the familiar earthworm, and leeches. They range in size from less than 1 mm to enormous Australian earthworms that can reach a size of 3 m.

The Annelid Body Plan   If you look at an earthworm, you will see little rings all down its body. Indeed, the phylum name Annelida is derived from the Latin *annulus*, meaning little ring. Each ring is a distinct segment of the annelid's body, with each segment separated from the one in front and the one behind by septa (**Figure 25.22**). All annelids except the leeches have chitinous bristles, called **setae,** on each segment. In some, these are situated on fleshy, footlike **parapodia** (from the Greek, meaning almost feet) that are pushed into the substrate to provide traction during movement. In others, the setae are held closer to the body. Many annelid species burrow into soil or into muddy marine sediments and extract nutrients from ingested soil or mud. Some annelids also feed on dead or living vegetation, whereas others are predatory or parasitic.

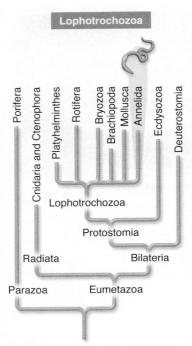

Lophotrochozoa

Annelids have a double transport system. Both the circulatory system and the coelomic fluid carry nutrients, wastes, and respiratory gases, to some degree. Annelids have a closed circulatory system, with dorsal and ventral vessels connected by pairs of pulsating vessels (look ahead to Figure 36.1b). The blood of most annelid species contains the respiratory pigment hemoglobin. Respiration occurs directly through the permeable skin surface, which restricts annelids to moist environments. The digestive system is complete and unsegmented, with many specialized regions: mouth, pharynx, esophagus, crop, gizzard, intestine, and anus. Annelids have a relatively sophisticated nervous system involving a pair of cerebral ganglia that connect to a large ventral nerve cord running down the entire length of the body. The ventral nerve is unusual because it contains a few very large nerve cells called **giant axons** that facilitate high-speed nerve conduction and rapid responses to stimuli.

Sexual reproduction involves two individuals, often of separate sexes, but sometimes hermaphrodites, which exchange sperm via internal fertilization. In some species, asexual reproduction by fission occurs, in which the posterior part of the body breaks off and forms a new individual.

The Major Annelid Groups   Recent evidence published by German evolutionary biologist Torsten Struck and colleagues in 2011 suggests that the phylum Annelida contains two major groups: the Errantia, active free-ranging worms, and the Sedentaria, which are burrowers or parasites.

Members of the Errantia have many long setae bristling out of their body and are supported on footlike parapodia (**Figure 25.23a**). Most of them are free-ranging predators with well-developed eyes and powerful jaws. Many are brightly colored. In turn, most species are important prey for fishes and crustaceans.

In the Sedentaria, setae are in close proximity to the body wall, which facilitates better anchorage in tubes and burrows. Their more sedentary lifestyle is associated with reductions in head appendages. Within the Sedentaria, three types of lifestyles are apparent. Tube worms are marine sedentarians that exhibit beautiful tentacle crowns for filtering food items, such as plankton, from the water column (**Figure 25.23b**). The bulk of these worms remain hidden in a tube deep in the mud or sand.

Earthworms ingest soil and leaf tissue to extract nutrients and in the process create burrows in the Earth (**Figure 25.23c**). As plant material and soil pass through the earthworm's digestive system,

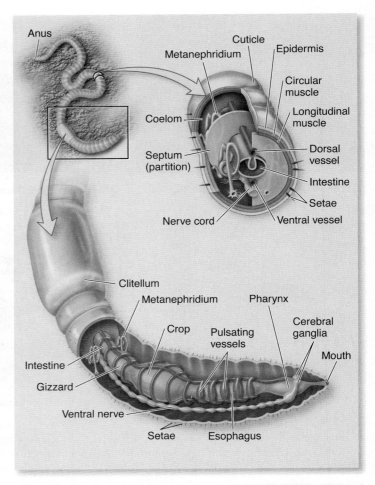

Figure 25.22 The segmented body plan of an annelid, as illustrated by an earthworm. The segmented nature of the worm is apparent internally as well as externally. Individual segments are separated by septa.

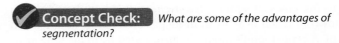 **Concept Check:**   *What are some of the advantages of segmentation?*

they are finely ground in the gizzard into smaller fragments. The biologist Charles Darwin, who penned the first detailed study of earthworm ecology, wrote, "All the fertile areas of this planet have at least once passed through the bodies of earthworms."

Leeches are primarily found in freshwater environments, but there are also some marine species as well as terrestrial species that inhabit warm, moist areas such as tropical forests. Leeches have a fixed number of segments, usually 34, though in most species the septa have disappeared. Most leeches feed as blood-sucking parasites of vertebrates. They have powerful suckers at both ends of the body, and the anterior sucker is equipped with razor-sharp jaws that can bore or slice into the host's tissues. The salivary secretion of leeches (hirudin) acts as an anticoagulant to stop the prey's blood from clotting and an anesthetic to numb the pain. Leeches can suck up to several times their own weight in blood. They were once used in the medical field in the practice of bloodletting, the withdrawal of often considerable quantities of blood from a patient in

(b) Tube worm

(d) Leech

(a) Marine worm

(c) Earthworm

Figure 25.23 Annelids. (a) This free-ranging marine worm from Indonesia is a member of the group Errantia. Members of the group Sedentaria include **(b)** tube worms, **(c)** earthworms, and **(d)** leeches. This species, *Hirudo medicinalis*, is sucking blood from a hematoma, a swelling of blood that can occur after surgery.

the erroneous belief that this would prevent or cure illness and disease. Even today, leeches may be used after surgeries (Figure 25.23d). In these cases, the blood vessels are not fully reconnected and excess blood accumulates, causing a swelling called a hematoma. The accumulated blood blocks the delivery of new blood and stops the formation of new vessels. The leeches remove the accumulated blood, and new capillaries are more likely to form.

25.5 Reviewing the Concepts

- Most Lophotrochozoa include taxa that possess either a lophophore or trochophore larva. Platyhelminthes, or flatworms, are regarded as the first animals to have the organ-system level of organization (Figure 25.15, Table 25.2). Flukes and tapeworms are internally parasitic, with complex life cycles (Figures 25.16, 25.17).
- The bryozoa and brachiopods both possess a lophophore, a ciliary feeding structure (Figure 25.19).
- The mollusks, which constitute a large phylum with over 100,000 diverse living species, have a basic body plan with three parts—a foot, a visceral mass, and a mantle—and an open circulatory system (Figures 25.20, 25.21). The four most common mollusk classes are the polyplacophora (chitons), gastropoda (snails and slugs), bivalvia (clams and mussels), and cephalopoda (octopuses, squids, and nautiluses) (Table 25.3).
- Annelids are a large phylum with two main groups: Errantia, which includes free-ranging marine worms, and Sedentaria, which includes tube worms, earthworms, and leeches (Figure 25.23). Segmentation, in which the body is divided into compartments, is a critical evolutionary innovation in the annelids.

25.5 Testing Your Knowledge

1. Platyhelminthes possess
   a. a lophophore.   d. a muscular foot.
   b. a coelom.   e. giant axons.
   c. mesoderm.
2. All mollusks possess
   a. a radula.   d. an external shell.
   b. an open circulatory system.   e. segmentation.
   c. a soft body.
3. What is an advantage of segmentation in annelids?
   a. It allows specialization of body regions and appendages.
   b. It allows sexual reproduction.
   c. It allows for radial symmetry.
   d. It is correlated with cephalization.
   e. It permits the development of a complete gut.

25.6 Ecdysozoa: The Nematodes and Arthropods

Learning Outcomes:

1. List the distinguishing characteristics of nematodes.
2. Describe the arthropod body plan and its major features.
3. Give examples of the arthropod subphyla Chelicerata, Myriapoda, Hexapoda, and Crustacea.
4. List the features that help account for the diversity of insect species.

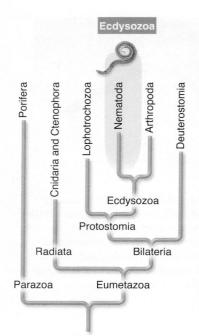

The Ecdysozoa is the sister group to the Lophotrochozoa. Although the separation is supported by molecular evidence, the Ecdysozoa is named for a morphological characteristic, the physical phenomenon of ecdysis, or the periodic molting of the exoskeleton (see Figure 25.9). All ecdysozoans possess a **cuticle,** a nonliving cover that serves to both support and protect the animal. Once formed, however, the cuticle typically cannot increase in size, which restricts the growth of the animal inside. The solution for growth is the formation of a new, softer cuticle under the old one. The old one then splits open and is sloughed off, allowing the new, soft cuticle to expand to a bigger size before it hardens. Where the cuticle is thick, as in arthropods, it impedes the diffusion of oxygen across the skin. Such species acquire oxygen by lungs, gills, or a set of branching, air-filled tubes called tracheae. A variety of appendages specialized for locomotion evolved in many species, including legs for walking or swimming and wings for flying. The ability to shed the cuticle opened up developmental options for the ecdysozoans. For example, many species undergo a complete metamorphosis, changing from a wormlike larva into a winged adult. Another significant adaptation is the development of internal fertilization, which permitted species to live in dry environments.

Because of these innovations, ecdysozoans are an incredibly successful group. Here, we will consider the two most common ecdysozoan phyla: the nematodes and arthropods. The grouping of nematodes and arthropods is a relatively new concept supported by molecular data and implies that the process of molting arose only once in animal evolution. In support of this, certain hormones that stimulate molting have been discovered to exist only in both nematodes and arthropods.

The Phylum Nematoda Consists of Small Pseudocoelomate Worms Covered by a Tough Cuticle

The nematodes (from the Greek *nematos*, meaning thread), also called roundworms, are small, thin worms that range from less than 1 mm to about 5 cm (**Figure 25.24**), although some parasitic species measuring 1 m or more have been found in the placenta of sperm whales. Nematodes are ubiquitous organisms that exist in nearly all habitats, from the poles to the tropics. They are found in the soil, in both freshwater and marine environments, and inside plants and animals as parasites. A shovelful of soil may contain a million nematodes. Over 20,000 species are known, but there are probably at least five times as many undiscovered species.

Figure 25.24 Scanning electron micrograph of a nematode within a plant leaf.

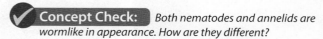

Concept Check: *Both nematodes and annelids are wormlike in appearance. How are they different?*

The Nematode Body Plan   Nematodes have several distinguishing characteristics. A tough cuticle covers the body. The cuticle is secreted by the epidermis and is made primarily of **collagen,** a structural protein also present in vertebrates (see Figure 4.27). The cuticle is shed periodically as the nematode grows. The pseudocoelom functions as both a fluid-filled skeleton and a circulatory system. Diffusion of gases occurs through the cuticle. Roundworms have a complete digestive tract composed of a mouth, pharynx, intestine, and anus. The mouth often contains sharp, piercing organs called **stylets,** and the muscular pharynx functions to suck in food.

Nematode Reproduction   Nematode reproduction is usually sexual, with separate males and females, and fertilization takes place internally. Females can produce prodigious numbers of eggs, in some cases, over 100,000 per day. Development in some nematodes is easily observed because the organism is transparent and the generation time is short. For these reasons, the small, free-living nematode *Caenorhabditis elegans* has become a model organism for researchers to study. This nematode has 1,090 somatic cells, but 131 die, leaving exactly 959 cells. The cells die via genetically controlled programmed cell death, or apoptosis. Many diseases in humans, including acquired immunodeficiency syndrome (AIDS), cause extensive apoptosis, whereas others, such as cancer and autoimmune diseases, reduce apoptosis so that cells that should die do not. Researchers are studying the process of apoptosis in *C. elegans* in the hope of finding treatments for these and other human diseases.

Parasitic Nematodes   A large number of nematodes are parasitic in humans and other vertebrates. The large roundworm *Ascaris lumbricoides* is a parasite of the small intestine that can reach up to 30 cm in length. Over a billion people worldwide carry this parasite, although infections are most prevalent in tropical or developing countries. Eggs pass out in feces and can remain

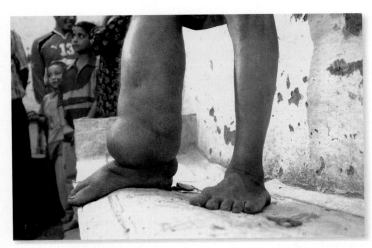

Figure 25.25 Elephantiasis in a human leg. The disease is caused by the nematode parasite *Wuchereria bancrofti*, which lives in the lymphatic system and blocks the flow of lymph.

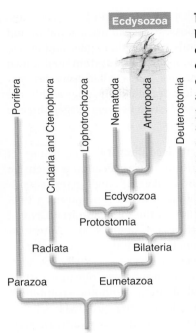

viable in the soil for years, although they require ingestion before hatching into an infective stage. Hookworms (*Necator americanus*), so named because their anterior end curves dorsally like a hook, are also parasites of the human intestine. The eggs pass out in feces, and recently hatched hookworms can penetrate the skin of a host's foot to establish a new infection. In areas with modern plumbing, these diseases are uncommon.

Pinworms (*Enterobius vermicularis*), although a nuisance, have relatively benign effects on their hosts. The rate of infection in the U.S., however, is staggering: 30% of children and 16% of adults are believed to be hosts. Adult pinworms live in the large intestine and migrate to the anal region at night to lay their eggs, which causes intense itching. The resultant scratching can spread the eggs from the hand to the mouth. In the tropics, some 250 million people are infected with *Wuchereria bancrofti*, a fairly large (100 mm) worm that lives in the lymphatic system, blocking the flow of lymph, and, in extreme cases, causing elephantiasis, an extreme swelling of the legs and other body parts (**Figure 25.25**). Females release tiny, live young called microfilariae, which are transmitted to new hosts via mosquitoes.

The Phylum Arthropoda Contains the Spiders, Millipedes and Centipedes, Insects, and Crustaceans—Species with Jointed Appendages

The arthropods (from the Greek *arthron*, meaning joint, and *podos*, meaning foot) constitute perhaps the most successful phylum on Earth. About three-quarters of all described living species present on Earth are arthropods, and scientists have estimated they are also numerically common, with an estimated 10^{18} (a billion billion) individual organisms. The huge success of the arthropods, in terms of their sheer numbers and diversity, is related to features that permit these animals to live in all the major biomes on Earth, from the poles to the tropics, and from marine and freshwater habitats to dry land. Such features include an exoskeleton, segmentation, and jointed appendages.

The Arthropod Body Plan The body of a typical arthropod is covered by a hard cuticle, an **exoskeleton** (external skeleton), made of layers of chitin and protein. The exoskeleton provides protection and also a point of attachment for muscles, all of which are internal. It is also relatively impermeable to water, a feature that may have enabled many arthropods to conserve water and colonize land. From this point of view, the development of a hard cuticle was a critical innovation. It also reminds us that the ability to adapt to diverse environmental conditions can lead to increased organismal diversity.

Arthropods are segmented, and many of the segments bear jointed appendages, which are used for such functions as walking, swimming, sensing, breathing, food handling, or reproduction. In many orders, the body segments have become fused into functional units, or **tagmata,** such as the head, thorax, and abdomen of an insect (**Figure 25.26**). Cephalization is extensive, and arthropods have well-developed sensory organs, including organs of sight, touch, smell, hearing, and balance.

Like most mollusks, arthropods have an open circulatory system (look ahead to Figure 36.1a), in which hemolymph is pumped from a tubelike heart into the aorta or short arteries and then into open sinuses from where the gases and nutrients diffuse into tissues. The hemolymph flows back into the heart via pores, called ostia, that are equipped with valves.

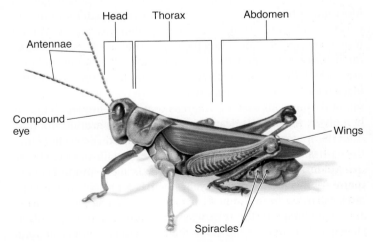

Figure 25.26 Body plan of an arthropod, as represented by a grasshopper.

Because the cuticle impedes the diffusion of gases through the body surface, arthropods possess special organs that permit gas exchange. Aquatic arthropods have feathery gills, and terrestrial species have a highly developed **tracheal system** (look ahead to Figure 37.6). On the body surface, pores called **spiracles** provide openings to a series of finely branched air tubes within the body called trachea. The tracheal system delivers oxygen directly to tissues and cells.

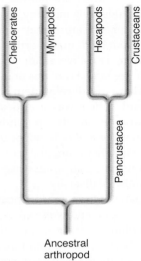

Ancestral
arthropod

Arthropod Diversity

The history of arthropod classification is extensive and active. Although many classifications have been proposed, a 1995 study of the mitochondrial DNA of arthropod species by American geneticist Jeffrey Boore and colleagues suggests a phylogeny with five main subphyla: one now-extinct subphylum, Trilobita (trilobites), and four living subphyla: Chelicerata (spiders and relatives), Myriapoda (millipedes and centipedes), Hexapoda (insects and relatives), and Crustacea (crabs and relatives) **(Table 25.4)**. Molecular evidence thus suggests insects are more closely related to crustaceans than they are to spiders or millipedes and centipedes.

Subphylum Chelicerata: Spiders and Relatives

The Chelicerata consists mainly of the class Arachnida, which contains predatory spiders and scorpions as well as the ticks and mites, some of which are blood-sucking parasites that feed on vertebrates. All species have a body consisting of two tagmata: a fused head and thorax (called a cephalothorax) and an abdomen. All species also possess six pairs of appendages: the chelicerae, or fangs; a pair of pedipalps, which have various sensory, predatory, or reproductive functions; and four pairs of walking legs.

Spider fangs are supplied with venom from poison glands. Most spider bites are harmless to humans, although they are very effective in immobilizing and/or killing their insect prey. Venom from some species, including the black widow (*Latrodectus mactans*) **(Figure 25.27a)** and the brown recluse (*Loxosceles reclusa*), are potentially, although rarely, fatal to humans. The toxin of the black widow is a neurotoxin, which interferes with the functioning of the nervous system, whereas that of the brown recluse is hemolytic, meaning it destroys red blood cells around the bite. After the spider has subdued its prey, it pumps digestive fluid into the tissues via the fangs and sucks out the partially digested meal.

Spiders have abdominal silk glands, called spinnerets, and many spin webs to catch prey. The silk is a protein that stiffens after extrusion from the body because the mechanical shearing causes a change in the organization of the amino acids. Silk is stronger than steel of the same diameter and more elastic than Kevlar, the material used in bulletproof vests. Each spider family constructs a characteristic size and style of web and can do it

Table 25.4	Main Subphyla and Characteristics of Arthropods	
	Subphyla and examples (est. # of species)	**Class characteristics**
	Chelicerata: spiders, scorpions, mites, ticks, horseshoe crabs, and sea spiders (74,000)	Body usually with cephalothorax and abdomen only; six pairs of appendages, including four pairs of legs, one pair of fangs, and one pair of pedipalps; terrestrial; predatory or parasitic
	Myriapoda: millipedes and centipedes (13,000)	Body with head and highly segmented trunk. In millipedes, each segment with two pairs of walking legs; terrestrial; herbivorous. In centipedes, each segment with one pair of walking legs; terrestrial; predatory, poison jaws
	Hexapoda: insects such as beetles, butterflies, flies, fleas, grasshoppers, ants, bees, wasps, termites and springtails (>1 million)	Body with head, thorax, and abdomen; mouthparts modified for biting, chewing, sucking, or lapping; usually with two pairs of wings and three pairs of legs; mostly terrestrial, some freshwater; herbivorous, parasitic, or predatory
	Crustacea: crabs, lobsters, shrimp (45,000)	Body of two to three parts; three or more pairs of legs; chewing mouthparts; usually marine

perfectly on its first attempt, indicating that web spinning is an innate (instinctual) behavior (look ahead to Chapter 42).

Scorpions (order Scorpionida) are generally tropical or subtropical animals that feed primarily on insects, though they may eat spiders and other arthropods as well as smaller reptiles and mice. Their pedipalps are modified into large claws, and their abdomen tapers into a stinger, which is used to inject venom. Although the venom of most North American species is generally not fatal to humans, that of the *Centruroides* genus from deserts in the U.S. Southwest and Mexico can be deadly. Fatal species are also found in India, Africa, and other countries. Unlike spiders, which lay eggs, scorpions bear live young that the mother then carries around on her back until they have their first molt (**Figure 25.27b**).

In mites and ticks (order Acari), the two main body segments (cephalothorax and abdomen) are fused and appear as one large segment. Many mite species are free-living scavengers that feed on dead plant or animal material. Other mites are serious pests on crops, and some, like chiggers (*Trombicula alfreddugesi*), are parasites of humans that can spread diseases such as typhus (**Figure 25.27c**). Chiggers are parasites only in their larval stage.

(a) Black widow spider

(b) Scorpion with young

(c) Chigger mite

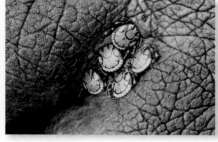

(d) Bont ticks

Figure 25.27 Common arachnids. (a) Female black widow spider (*Latradectus mactans*). **(b)** The Emperor scorpion (*Pandinus imperator*), from Northern Africa, carries its white young on its back. **(c)** SEM of a chigger mite (*Trombicula alfreddugesi*) that can cause irritation to human skin and spread disease. **(d)** These South African bont ticks (*Amblyomma hebraeum*) are feeding on a white rhinoceros.

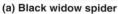

✓ **Concept Check:** *What is one of the main characteristics distinguishing arachnids from insects?*

Chiggers do not bore into the skin; their bite and salivary secretions cause skin irritation. *Demodex brevis* is a hair-follicle mite that is common in animals and humans. The mite is estimated to be present in over 90% of adult humans. Although the mite causes no irritation in most humans, *Demodex canis* causes the skin disease known as mange in domestic animals, particularly dogs.

Ticks are larger organisms than mites, and all are ectoparasitic, feeding on the body surface, on vertebrates. Their life cycle includes attachment to a host, sucking blood until they are replete, and dropping off the host to molt (**Figure 25.27d**). Ticks can carry a huge variety of viral and bacterial diseases, including Lyme disease, a pan-global bacterial disease so named because it was first found in the town of Lyme, Connecticut, in the 1970s. Infection rates in the U.S. are highest in the Northeast, mid Atlantic, and upper Midwest regions.

Subphylum Myriapoda: The Millipedes and Centipedes

Myriapods have one pair of antennae on the head and three pairs of appendages that are modified as mouth parts, including mandibles that act like jaws. The millipedes and centipedes, both wormlike arthropods with legs, are among the earliest terrestrial animal phyla known. Millipedes (class Diplopoda) have two pairs of legs per segment, as their class name denotes (from the Latin *diplo*, meaning two, and *podos*, meaning feet), not 1,000 legs, as their common name suggests (**Figure 25.28a**). They are slow-moving herbivorous creatures that eat decaying leaves and other plant material. When threatened, the millipede's response is to roll up into a protective coil. Many millipede species also have glands on their underside that can eject a variety of toxic, repellent secretions.

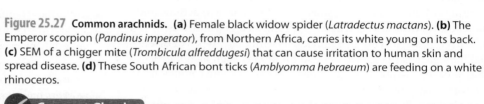

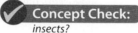

(a) Two millipedes

(b) A centipede

Figure 25.28 Millipedes and centipedes. (a) Millipedes have two pairs of legs per segment. **(b)** The venom of the giant centipede (*Scolopendra heros*) is known to produce significant swelling and pain in humans.

Some millipedes are brightly colored, warning potential predators that they can protect themselves.

Class Chilopoda (from the Latin *chilo*, meaning lip, and *podos*, meaning feet), or centipedes, are fast-moving carnivores that have one pair of walking legs per segment (**Figure 25.28b**). The head of centipedes have powerful claws connected to poison glands. The toxin from venom of some of the larger species, such as *Scolopendra heros*, is powerful enough to cause pain in humans. Most species do not have a waxy waterproofing layer on their cuticle and so are restricted to moist environments under leaf litter or in decaying logs, usually coming out at night to actively hunt their prey.

Subphylum Hexapoda: Insects and Relatives

Hexapods are six-legged arthropods. Most are insects, but there are a few earlier-diverging noninsect hexapods, including soil-dwelling groups such as collembolans, that molecular studies have shown represent a separate but related lineage. Insects are in a class by themselves (Insecta), literally and figuratively. There are more species of insects than all other species of animal life combined. One million species of insects have been described, and, according to best estimates, 2–5 million more species await description. At least 90,000 species of insects have been identified in the U.S. and Canada alone.

Insects are the subject of an entire field of scientific study, **entomology.** Insects live in all terrestrial habitats, and virtually all species of plants are fed upon by many insect species. Because approximately one-quarter of the world's crops are lost annually to insects, scientists are constantly trying to find ways to reduce pest densities. Insect pest reduction often involves chemical control (the use of pesticides) or biological control (the use of living organisms). Many species of insects are also important pests or parasites of humans and livestock, both by their own actions and as vectors of diseases such as malaria and sleeping sickness.

In contrast, insects also provide us with many types of essential biological services. We depend on insects such as honeybees and butterflies to pollinate our crops. Bees also produce honey, and silkworms are the source of silk fiber. Despite the revulsion they provoke in us, fly larvae (maggots) are important in the decomposition process of both dead plants and animals. In addition, we use insects in the biological control of insect pests of crops.

The Insect Body Plan   Of paramount importance to the success of insects was the evolution of wings, a feature possessed by no other arthropod and indeed no other living animal except birds and bats. Unlike vertebrate wings, however, insect wings are actually outgrowths of the body wall cuticle and are not true segmental appendages. This means that insects still have all their walking legs. In contrast, birds and bats have one pair of appendages (arms) modified for flight, which leaves them considerably less agile on the ground.

Insects in different orders have also evolved a variety of mouthparts in which the constituent parts are modified for different functions.

- Grasshoppers, beetles, dragonflies, and many others have mouthparts adapted for chewing.
- Mosquitoes and many plant pests have mouthparts adapted for piercing and sucking.
- Butterflies and moths have a coiled tongue (proboscis) that can be uncoiled, enabling them to drink nectar from flowers.
- Some flies have lapping, spongelike mouthparts that sop up liquid food.

Their varied mouthparts are adaptations that allow insects to specialize their feeding on virtually anything: plant matter, decaying organic matter, and other living animals. The biological diversity of insects is therefore related to environmental diversity, in this case, the variety of foods that insects eat.

Insect Diversity   The great diversity of insects is illustrated by the fact that there are 35 different orders, some of which have over 100,000 species. The most common of the orders are discussed in **Table 25.5.** Although all insects have six legs, different orders have slightly different wing structures, and many of the orders are based on wing type (their names often include the root pter-, from the Greek *pteron*, meaning wing).

- In beetles (Coleoptera), only the back pair of wings is functional, as the front wings have been hardened into protective shell-like coverings under which the back pair folds when not in use.
- Wasps and bees (Hymenoptera) have two pairs of wings hooked together that move as one wing.
- Flies (Diptera) possess only one pair of wings (the front pair); the back pair has been modified into a small pair of balancing organs, called halteres, that act like miniature gyroscopes.
- Butterflies (Lepidoptera) have wings that are covered in scales (from the Greek *lepido*, meaning scale); other insects generally have clear, membranous wings.
- In ant and termite colonies, the queen and the drones (males) retain their wings, whereas female individuals called workers have lost theirs. Other species, such as fleas and lice, are completely wingless.

Insect Reproduction and Development   All insects have separate sexes, and fertilization is internal. During development, the majority (approximately 85%) of insects undergo a change in body form known as **complete metamorphosis** (from the Greek *meta*, meaning change, and *morph*, meaning form) (Figure 25.29a). Animals that undergo complete metamorphosis have four types of stages: egg, larva, pupa, and adult. The dramatic body transformation from larva to adult occurs in the pupa stage. The larval stage is often spent in an entirely different habitat from that of the adult, and larval and adult forms use different food sources. Metamorphosis permits existence of a feeding stage, often a sac-like caterpillar or larva, and a dispersive stage, usually a winged adult.

The remaining insects undergo **incomplete metamorphosis,** in which change is more gradual (Figure 25.29b). Incomplete metamorphosis has only three types of stages: egg, nymph, and adult. Young insects, called nymphs, look like miniature adults when they hatch from their eggs, but usually don't have wings. As they grow and feed, they shed their exoskeleton and replace it with a larger one several times, each time entering a new stage of growth. When the insects reach their adult size, they have also grown wings.

Some insects, such as bees, wasps, ants, and termites, have developed complex social behavior and live cooperatively in underground or aboveground nests. Such colonies exhibit a division of labor, in that some individuals forage for food and care for the brood (workers), others protect the nest (soldiers), and some only reproduce (the queen and drones).

Subphylum Crustacea: Crabs, Lobsters, Barnacles, and Shrimp   The crustaceans are common inhabitants of marine environments, although some species live in fresh water and a few are terrestrial.

Table 25.5	Main Orders and Characteristics of Insects

Order and examples (est. # of species)		Order characteristics
Coleoptera: beetles, weevils (500,000)		Two pairs of wings (front pair thick and leathery, acting as wing cases, back pair membranous); armored exoskeleton; biting and chewing mouthparts; complete metamorphosis; largest order of insects
Hymenoptera: ants, bees, wasps (190,000)		Two pairs of membranous wings; chewing or sucking mouthparts; many have posterior stinging organ on females; complete metamorphosis; many species social; important pollinators
Diptera: flies, mosquitoes (190,000)		One pair of wings with hind wings modified into halteres (balancing organs); sucking, piercing, or lapping mouthparts; complete metamorphosis; larvae are grublike maggots in various food sources; some adults are disease vectors
Lepidoptera: butterflies, moths (180,000)		Two pairs of colorful wings covered with tiny scales; long tubelike tongue for sucking; complete metamorphosis; larvae are plant-feeding caterpillars; adults are important pollinators
Hemiptera: true bugs; bedbug, chinch bug, cicada (100,000)		Two pairs of membranous wings; piercing or sucking mouthparts; incomplete metamorphosis; many plant feeders; some predatory or blood feeders; vectors of plant diseases
Orthoptera: crickets, grasshoppers (30,000)		Two pairs of wings (front pair leathery, back pair membranous); chewing mouthparts; mostly herbivorous; incomplete metamorphosis; powerful hind legs for jumping
Odonata: damselflies, dragonflies (6,500)		Two pairs of long, membranous wings; chewing mouthparts; large eyes; predatory on other insects; incomplete metamorphosis; nymphs aquatic; considered early-diverging insects
Siphonaptera: fleas (2,600)		Wingless, laterally flattened; piercing and sucking mouthparts; adults are bloodsuckers on birds and mammals; jumping legs; complete metamorphosis; vectors of plague
Phthiraptera: sucking lice (2,400)		Wingless ectoparasites; sucking mouthparts; flattened body; reduced eyes; legs with claws for clinging to skin; incomplete metamorphosis; very host-specific; vectors of typhus
Isoptera: termites (2,000)		Two pairs of membranous wings when present; some stages wingless; chewing mouthparts; social species; incomplete metamorphosis

Many species, including crabs, lobsters, crayfish, and shrimp, are economically important food items for humans; smaller species are important food sources for other predators.

The Crustacean Body Plan   The crustaceans are unique among the arthropods in that they possess two pairs of antennae at the anterior end of the body—the antennule (first pair) and antenna (second pair) (**Figure 25.30**). In addition, they have multiple sensory and feeding appendages that are modified mouthparts.

These are followed by walking legs and, often, additional abdominal appendages, called swimmerets, and a powerful tail. In some orders, the first pair of walking legs, or chelipeds, is modified to form powerful claws. The head and thorax are often fused together, forming the cephalothorax. In many species, such as crabs, the cuticle covering the head extends over most of the cephalothorax, forming a hard protective fold called the **carapace.** For growth to occur, a crustacean must molt, or shed the entire exoskeleton.

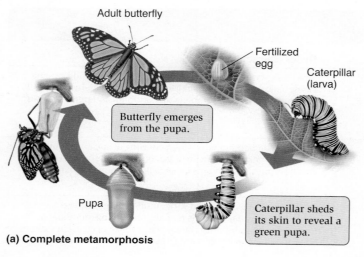

(a) Complete metamorphosis

- Adult butterfly
- Butterfly emerges from the pupa.
- Fertilized egg
- Caterpillar (larva)
- Caterpillar sheds its skin to reveal a green pupa.
- Pupa

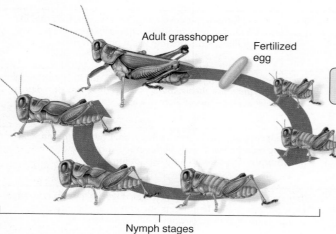

(b) Incomplete metamorphosis

- Adult grasshopper
- Fertilized egg
- Nymphs looks like miniature adults.

Nymph stages

Figure 25.29 Metamorphosis. (a) Complete metamorphosis, as illustrated by the life cycle of a monarch butterfly. The adult butterfly has a completely different appearance than the larval caterpillar. **(b)** Incomplete metamorphosis, as illustrated by the life cycle of a grasshopper. The eggs hatch into nymphs, essentially miniature versions of the adult.

✓ Concept Check: *Name two key insect innovations.*

Many crustaceans are predators, but others are scavengers, and some, such as barnacles, are filter feeders. Gas exchange typically occurs via gills, and crustaceans, like other arthropods, have an open circulatory system. Reproduction usually involves separate sexes, and fertilization is internal.

Crustacean Diversity There are many crustacean clades, but most are small and obscure, although many smaller orders contain important prey items for other marine organisms. For example, copepods are tiny and abundant planktonic crustaceans, which are a food source for filter-feeding organisms and small fish.

The order Euphausiacea are shrimplike krill that grow to about 3 cm and provide a large part of the diet of many whales,

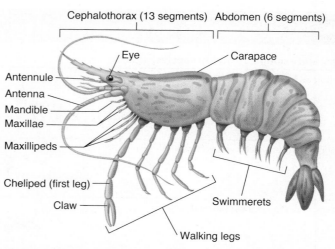

- Cephalothorax (13 segments)
- Abdomen (6 segments)
- Eye
- Carapace
- Antennule
- Antenna
- Mandible
- Maxillae
- Maxillipeds
- Cheliped (first leg)
- Claw
- Swimmerets
- Walking legs

Figure 25.30 Body plan of a crustacean, as represented by a shrimp.

BioConnections: *Look forward to Figure 33.8. Where are a crustacean's organs of balance located?*

seals, penguins, fish, and squid (**Figure 25.31a**). The order Isopoda contains many small species that are parasitic on marine fishes. There are also terrestrial isopods, better known as pill bugs, or wood lice, that retain a strong connection to water and need to live in moist environments such as leaf litter or decaying logs (**Figure 25.31b**). When threatened, they curl up into a tight ball, making it difficult for predators to get a grip on them.

The most famous crustacean order is the Decapoda, which includes the crabs and lobsters, the largest crustacean species (**Figure 25.31c**). As their name suggests, these decapods have 10 walking legs (five pairs), although the chelipeds are invariably modified to support large claws. Most decapods are marine, but there are many freshwater species, such as crayfish, and in hot, moist tropical areas, even some terrestrial species called land crabs.

25.6 Reviewing the Concepts

- The ecdysozoans are so named for their ability to shed their cuticle, a nonliving cover providing support and protection. The two most common ecdysozoan phyla are the nematodes and the arthropods.
- Nematodes, which exist in nearly all habitats, have a cuticle made of collagen, a structural protein. Many nematodes are parasitic in humans (Figures 25.24, 25.25).
- Arthropods are perhaps the most successful phylum on Earth. The arthropod body is covered by a cuticle made of layers of chitin and protein, and it is segmented, with segments fused into functional units called tagmata (Figure 25.26).
- The five main subphyla of arthropods are Trilobita (trilobites; now extinct), Chelicerata (spiders, scorpions, and relatives), Myriapoda (millipedes and centipedes), Hexapoda (insects), and Crustacea (crabs and relatives) (Table 25.4, Figures 25.27, 25.28).

(a) Antarctic Krill—order Euphausiacea

(b) Pill bug—order Isopoda

(c) Coral crab—order Decapoda

Figure 25.31 Common crustaceans. (a) Antarctic krill (*Euphausia superba*) feeding on algae-covered ice. **(b)** Pill bug, or wood louse (*Armadillidium vulgare*). **(c)** Coral crab (*Carpilius maculatus*).

25.6 Testing Your Knowledge

1. Nematodes are distinguished from members of the Lophotrochozoa in that they possess
   a. tracheae.   d. incomplete metamorphosis.
   b. a cuticle.   e. stylets.
   c. a coelom.

2. Which is *not* a feature of the arthropod body plan?
   a. an exoskeleton   d. a closed circulatory system
   b. segmentation   e. metamorphosis
   c. tagmata

3. Characteristics of the class Arachnida include
   a. two tagmata.   d. a lobed body.
   b. six walking legs.   e. both b and d.
   c. an aquatic lifestyle.

25.7 Deuterostomia: The Echinoderms and Chordates

Learning Outcomes:

1. Identify the distinguishing characteristics of echinoderms.
2. List the four critical innovations in the body plan of chordates.
3. Describe the two invertebrate subphyla of the phylum Chordata and their relationship to the vertebrates.

As we mentioned at the beginning of the chapter, the deuterostomes are grouped together because they share similarities in patterns of development (see Figure 25.6). Molecular evidence also supports a deuterostome clade. All animals in the phylum Chordata (from the Greek *chorde*, meaning string, referring to the spinal cord), which includes the vertebrates, are deuterostomes. Interestingly, there is one invertebrate deuterostome group, the

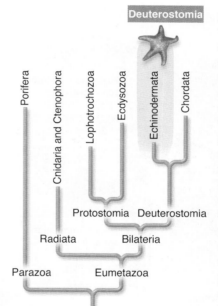

phylum Echinodermata, which includes the sea stars, sea urchins, and sea cucumbers. Although there are far fewer phyla and species of deuterostomes than protostomes, the deuterostomes are generally much more familiar to us. After all, humans are deuterostomes. We will conclude our discussion of invertebrate biology by turning our attention to the invertebrate deuterostomes. In this section, we will explore the phylum Echinodermata and then introduce the phylum Chordata, looking in particular at its distinguishing characteristics and at its two invertebrate subphyla: the cephalochordates, commonly referred to as the lancelets, and the urochordates, also known as the tunicates. We will discuss the subphylum Vertebrata in Chapter 26.

The Phylum Echinodermata Includes Sea Stars and Sea Urchins—Species with a Water Vascular System

The phylum Echinodermata (from the Greek *echinos*, meaning spiny, and *derma*, meaning skin) consists of a unique grouping of deuterostomes. A striking feature of all echinoderms is their modified radial symmetry (see Figure 25.4b). The body of most species can be divided into five parts pointing out from the center. As a consequence, cephalization is absent in most classes. There is no brain and only a simple nervous system consisting of a central nerve ring from which arise radial branches to each limb. The radial symmetry of echinoderms is secondary, present only in adults. The free-swimming larvae have bilateral symmetry and metamorphose into the radially symmetric adult form.

The Echinoderm Body Plan

Most echinoderms have an **endoskeleton,** an internal hard skeleton composed of calcareous plates overlaid by a thin skin (**Figure 25.32**).

Echinoderms possess a true coelom, and a portion of the coelom has been adapted to serve as a unique **water vascular system,** a network of canals that branch into tiny **tube feet** that function in movement, gas exchange, feeding, and excretion (see inset to Figure 25.32). The water vascular system uses hydraulic power (water pressure generated by the contraction of muscles), which enables the tube feet to extend and contract, allowing echinoderms to move only very slowly.

Water enters the water vascular system through the **madreporite,** a sievelike plate on the animal's surface. From there it flows into a **ring canal** in the central disc, into five radial canals, and into the tube feet. At the base of each tube foot is a muscular sac called an **ampulla,** which stores water. Contractions of the ampullae force water into the tube feet, causing them to straighten and extend. When the foot contacts a solid surface, muscles in the foot contract, forcing water back into the ampullae. Sea stars also use their tube feet in feeding, where they can exert a constant and strong pressure on their preferred prey, bivalves, whose adductor muscles open and close the shell. The adductor muscles eventually tire, allowing the shell to open slightly. At this stage, the sea star everts its stomach and inserts it into the shell's opening. It then digests its prey, using juices secreted from extensive digestive glands. Sea stars also feed on sea urchins, brittle stars, and sand dollars, prey that cannot easily escape them.

Most echinoderms exhibit **autotomy,** the ability to intentionally detach a body part, such as a limb, that will later regenerate. In some species, a broken limb can even regenerate into a whole animal. Most echinoderms reproduce sexually and have separate sexes. Fertilization is usually external, with gametes shed into the water. Fertilized eggs develop into free-swimming larvae, which become sedentary adults.

The Major Echinoderm Classes Although over 20 classes of echinoderms have been described from the fossil record, only 5 main classes of echinoderms exist today: the Asteroidea (sea stars), Ophiuroidea (brittle stars), Echinoidea (sea urchins and sand dollars), Crinoidea (sea lilies and feather stars), and Holothuroidea (sea cucumbers). The key features of the echinoderm classes are listed in **Table 25.6.**

The Phylum Chordata Includes All the Vertebrates and Some Invertebrates

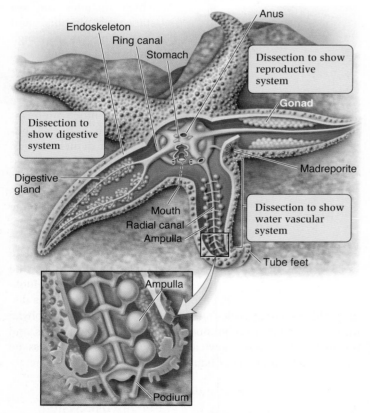

Figure 25.32 **Body plan of an echinoderm, as represented by a sea star.** The arms of this sea star have been dissected to different degrees to show the echinoderm's various organs. The inset shows a close-up view of the tube feet, part of the water vascular system characteristic of echinoderms.

✓ **Concept Check:** *Echinoderms and chordates are both deuterostomes. What are three defining features of deuterostomes?*

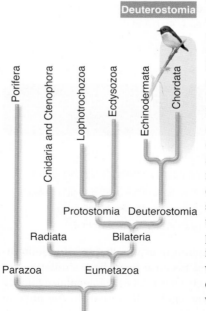

The deuterostomes consist of two major phyla: the echinoderms and the chordates. As deuterostomes, both phyla share similar developmental traits (see Figure 25.6). In addition, both have an endoskeleton, consisting in the echinoderms of calcareous plates and in chordates, for the most part, of bone. However, the echinoderm endoskeleton functions in much the same way as the arthropod exoskeleton, in that an important function is providing protection. The chordate endoskeleton serves a very different purpose. In early-divergent chordates, the endoskeleton is composed of a single flexible rod situated dorsally, deep inside the body. Muscles move this rod, and their

Table 25.6	Main Classes and Characteristics of Echinoderms	
	Class and examples (est. # of species)	**Class characteristics**
	Asteroidea: sea stars (1,600)	Five arms; tube feet; predatory on bivalves and other echinoderms; eversible stomach
	Ophiuroidea: brittle stars (2,000)	Five long, slender arms; tube feet not used for locomotion; browse on sea bottom or filter feed
	Echinoidea: sea urchins, sand dollars (1,900)	Spherical (sea urchins) or disc-shaped (sand dollars); no arms; tube feet and movable spines; many feed on seaweeds
	Crinoidea: sea lilies and feather stars (700)	Cup-shaped; often attached to substrate via stalk; arms feathery and used in filter feeding; very abundant in fossil record
	Holothuroidea: sea cucumbers (1,200)	Cucumber-shaped; no arms; spines absent; endoskeleton reduced; tube feet; browse on sea bottom

contractions cause the back and tail end to move from side to side, permitting a swimming motion in water. The endoskeleton becomes more complex in different lineages that develop limbs, as we will see in Chapter 26, but it is always internal, with muscles attached. This arrangement permits the possibility of complex movements, including the ability to move on land.

Let's take a look at the four critical innovations in the body plan of chordates that distinguish them from all other animal life (**Figure 25.33**):

1. **Notochord**. Chordates are named for the **notochord,** a single flexible rod that lies between the digestive tract and the nerve cord. In most chordates, such as vertebrates, a more complex jointed backbone usually replaces the notochord; its remnants exist only as the soft material within the discs between each vertebra.

2. **Dorsal hollow nerve cord**. Many animals have a long nerve cord, but in nonchordate invertebrates, it is a solid tube that lies ventral to the alimentary canal. In contrast, the nerve cord in chordates is a hollow tube that develops dorsal to the alimentary canal. In vertebrates, the **dorsal hollow nerve cord** develops into the brain and spinal cord.

3. **Pharyngeal slits**. Chordates, like many animals, have a complete gut, with two openings—a mouth and anus. However, in chordates, slits develop in the pharyngeal region, close to the mouth, that open to the outside. This permits water to enter through the mouth and exit via the slits, without having to go through the digestive tract. In early-divergent chordates, **pharyngeal slits** function as a filter-feeding device, whereas in later-divergent chordates, they develop into gills for gas exchange. In terrestrial chordates, the slits do not fully form, and they become modified for other purposes.

4. **Postanal tail**. In most nonchordate phyla, the anus is at the end of the body. Chordates possess a **postanal tail** of variable length that extends posterior to the anal opening. In aquatic chordates such as fishes, the tail is used in locomotion. In terrestrial chordates, the tail may be used in a variety of functions or only present during an early developmental stage.

Although few chordates apart from fishes possess all of these characteristics in their adult life, they all exhibit them at some time during development. For example, in adult humans, the notochord becomes the spinal column, and the dorsal hollow nerve cord becomes the central nervous system. However, humans exhibit pharyngeal slits and a postanal tail only during early embryonic development. All the pharyngeal slits, except one, which forms the auditory (Eustachian) tube in the ear, are eventually lost, and the postanal tail regresses to form the tailbone (the coccyx).

The phylum Chordata consists of the invertebrate chordates—the subphylum Cephalochordata (lancelets) and the subphylum Urochordata (tunicates)—along with the subphylum Vertebrata (vertebrates). Although the Vertebrata is by far the largest of these subphyla, biologists have focused on the cephalochordates and urochordates for clues as to how the chordate phylum may have evolved.

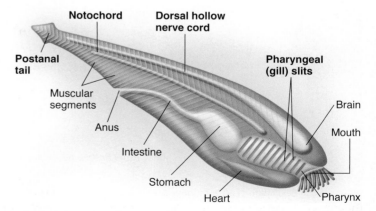

Figure 25.33 Chordate characteristics. The generalized chordate body plan has four main features: notochord, dorsal hollow nerve cord, pharyngeal slits, and postanal tail.

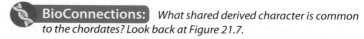

BioConnections: *What shared derived character is common to the chordates? Look back at Figure 21.7.*

Subphylum Cephalochordata: The Lancelets The cephalochordates (from the Greek *kephalo*, meaning head) are commonly referred to as lancelets, in reference to their bladelike shape and size, about 5–7 cm in length (Figure 25.34a). Lancelets are a small subphylum of 26 species, all marine filter feeders, with 4 species occurring in North American waters.

The lancelets live mostly buried in sand, with only the anterior end protruding into the water. Lancelets have the four distinguishing chordate characteristics: a clearly discernible notochord (extending well into the head), dorsal hollow nerve cord, pharyngeal slits, and postanal tail (Figure 25.34b). They are filter feeders, drawing water through the mouth and into the pharynx, where it is filtered through the pharyngeal slits. A mucous net across the pharyngeal slits traps food particles, and ciliary action takes the food into the intestine, while water exits via the opening to the exterior called the atriopore. Gas exchange generally takes place across the body surface. Although the lancelet is usually sessile, it can leave its sandy burrow and swim to a new spot, using a sequence of serially arranged muscles that appear like chevrons (<<<<) along its sides. These muscles reflect the segmented nature of the lancelet body and permit a fishlike swimming motion.

(a) Lancelet in the sand

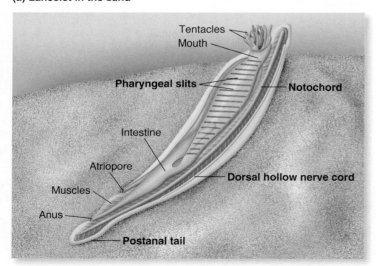

(b) Body plan of the lancelet

Figure 25.34 Lancelets. (a) A bladelike lancelet. **(b)** The body plan of the lancelet clearly displays the four characteristic chordate features.

Subphylum Urochordata: The Tunicates The urochordates (from the Greek *oura*, meaning tail) are a group of 3,000 marine species also known as tunicates. Looking at an adult tunicate, you might never guess that it is a relative of modern vertebrates. The only one of the four distinguishing chordate characteristics that it possesses is pharyngeal slits (Figure 25.35a). The larval tunicate, in contrast, looks like a tadpole and exhibits all four chordate hallmarks (Figure 25.35b). The larval tadpole swims for only a few days, usually without feeding. Larval tunicates settle on and attach to a rock surface, where they metamorphose into adults and in the process lose most of their chordate characteristics.

Adult tunicates are marine animals, some colonial and others solitary, that superficially resemble sponges or cnidarians. Tunicates are filter feeders that draw water through the mouth through an **incurrent siphon,** using a ciliated pharynx, and filter it through extensive pharyngeal slits. The food is trapped on a mucous sheet; passes via ciliary action to the stomach, intestine, and anus; and exits through the excurrent siphon. The whole animal is enclosed in a nonliving **tunic** made of a protein and a cellulose-like material called tunicin. Tunicates are also known as sea squirts for their ability to squirt out water from the **excurrent siphon** when disturbed. They have a rudimentary circulatory system with a heart and a simple nervous system of relatively few nerves connected to sensory tentacles around the incurrent siphon. The animals are mostly hermaphroditic.

25.7 Reviewing the Concepts

- The Deuterostomia includes the phyla Echinodermata and Chordata. A striking feature of the echinoderms is their radial symmetry, which is present only in adults; the free-swimming larvae are bilaterally symmetric. Echinoderms possess a unique water vascular system (Figure 25.32).
- Five main classes of echinoderms exist today: the Asteroidea (sea stars), Ophiuroidea (brittle stars), Echinoidea (sea urchins and sand dollars), Crinoidea (sea lilies and feather stars), and Holothuroidea (sea cucumbers) (Table 25.6).
- The phylum Chordata is distinguished by four critical innovations: the notochord, dorsal hollow nerve chord, pharyngeal slits, and postanal tail (Figure 25.33).
- The subphylum Cephalochordata (lancelets) and subphylum Urochordata (tunicates) are invertebrate chordates. Genetic studies have shown that tunicates are the closest invertebrate relatives of the vertebrate chordates (subphylum Vertebrata) (Figures 25.34, 25.35).

25.7 Testing Your Knowledge

1. Echinodermata are a member of which clade?
   a. protostomia
   b. radiata
   c. eumetazoa
   d. lophotrochozoa
   e. ecdysozoa

Biology Principle

The Genetic Material Provides a Blueprint for Sustaining Life

Genetic similarities between the tunicates and the vertebrates suggest they are indeed our closest invertebrate relatives.

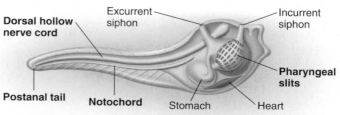

(b) The larval form of the tunicate

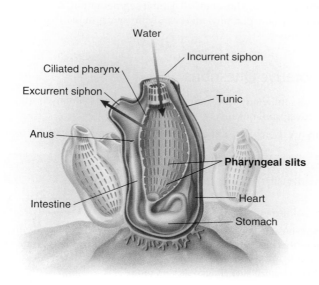

(a) Adult tunicate

(c) Typical tunicate

Figure 25.35 Tunicates. **(a)** Body plan of the sessile, filter-feeding adult tunicate. **(b)** The larval form of the tunicate, which shows the four characteristic chordate features. **(c)** The blue tunicate, *Rhopalaea crassa*.

---

2. Chordates are typified by possession of
   a. a notochord.
   b. a dorsal hollow nerve cord.
   c. pharyngeal slits.
   d. a postanal tail.
   e. all of the above.

3. Which invertebrate phylum is most closely related to the vertebrates?
   a. cephalopoda
   b. cephalochordata
   c. urochordata
   d. radiata
   e. both b and c are equally related to the vertebrates

Assess and Discuss

Test Yourself

1. Which is the correct hierarchy of divisions in the animal kingdom, from most inclusive to least inclusive?
   a. Eumetazoa, Metazoa, Protostomia, Ecdysozoa
   b. Parazoa, Radiata, Lophotrochozoa, Deuterostomia
   c. Metazoa, Eumetazoa, Bilateria, Protostomia
   d. Radiata, Eumetazoa, Deuterostomia, Ecdysozoa
   e. none of the above

2. Bilateral symmetry is strongly correlated with
   a. the ability to move through the environment.
   b. cephalization.
   c. the ability to detect prey.
   d. a and b.
   e. a, b, and c.

3. Protostomes and deuterostomes can be classified based on
   a. cleavage pattern.
   b. destiny of the blastopore.
   c. whether the fate of the embryonic cells is fixed early during development.
   d. all of the above.

4. Indeterminate cleavage is found in
   a. annelids.
   b. mollusks.
   c. nematodes.
   d. vertebrates.
   e. all of the above.

5. Naturally occurring identical twins are possible only in animals that
   a. have spiral cleavage.
   b. have determinate cleavage.
   c. are protostomes.
   d. have indeterminate cleavage.
   e. a, b, and c

6. Which of the following organisms can produce female offspring through parthenogenesis?
   a. cnidarians   c. choanocytes   e. annelids
   b. flukes   d. rotifers

7. What organisms can survive without a mouth, digestive system, or anus?
   a. cnidarians   c. echinoderms   e. nematodes
   b. rotifers   d. cestodes

8. Which phylum does not have at least some members with a closed circulatory system?
   a. Lophotrochozoa
   b. Arthopoda
   c. Annelida
   d. Mollusca
   e. All of the above phyla have some members with a closed circulatory system.

9. A defining feature of the Ecdysozoa is
   a. a segmented body.   d. a complete gut.
   b. a closed circulatory system. e. a lophophore.
   c. a cuticle.

10. Incomplete metamorphosis
    a. is characterized by distinct larval and adult stages that do not compete for resources.
    b. is typically seen in arachnids.
    c. involves gradual changes in life stages where young resemble the adult stage.
    d. is characteristic of the majority of insects.
    e. always includes a pupal stage.

Conceptual Questions

1. Early morphological phylogenies were based on what three features of animal body plans?

2. Compare and contrast the five main feeding types discussed in the chapter.

3. **PRINCIPLES**   A principle of biology is that *all species (past and present) are related by an evolutionary history*. Annelids, arthropods, and chordates all exhibit segmentation. Are these monophyletic, paraphyletic, or polyphyletic groups? Explain your answer.

Collaborative Questions

1. Discuss the many ways that animals can affect humans, both positively and negatively.

2. Why are there more species of insects than any other taxa?

Online Resource

www.brookerprinciples.com

Stay a step ahead in your studies with animations that bring concepts to life and practice tests to assess your understanding. Your instructor may also recommend the interactive eBook, individualized learning tools, and more.

Animal Diversity: The Vertebrates

26

Labordi's chameleon (*Furcifer labordi*). This species has the shortest life cycle of any known land vertebrate, with individuals living 4–5 months at most.

Chapter Outline

26.1 Vertebrates: Chordates with a Backbone

26.2 Gnathostomes: Jawed Vertebrates

26.3 Tetrapods: Gnathostomes with Four Limbs

26.4 Amniotes: Tetrapods with a Desiccation-Resistant Egg

26.5 Mammals: Milk-Producing Amniotes

Assess and Discuss

Most terrestrial vertebrates, such as amphibians, reptiles, birds, and mammals, typically live between 2 to 10 years, with some having much longer or much shorter lives. Humans and turtles may live to 100 years, while some lizards die after a year. Labordi's chameleon (*Furcifer labordi*), discovered only this century in Madagascar, lives only 1 year. Even more unusual is that the chameleon spends two thirds of that time as an egg. After hatching, the chameleons live only about 4 months, growing 2–3 mm each day. They reach sexual maturity and reproduce, after which the entire adult population dies off, leaving only the developing eggs. When the next generation of hatchlings emerges, adult chameleons are not present. With such a precarious life cycle, one bad year in which the eggs fail to hatch would severely affect the species' survival. Scientists are studying *F. labordi*'s unusual life cycle in the hope that it may prove valuable in discovering genes and other factors that affect aging and longevity.

F. labordi is a **vertebrate** (from the Latin *vertebratus*, meaning joint of the spine), an animal with a backbone. Vertebrates range in size from tiny fishes weighing 0.1 g to huge whales of over 100,000 kg. They occupy nearly all of Earth's habitats, from the deepest depths of the oceans to mountaintops and the sky beyond. Throughout history, humans have depended on many vertebrate species for their welfare, domesticating species such as horses, cattle, pigs, sheep, and chickens; using skin and fur for clothes, and keeping countless species, including cats and dogs, as pets. Many vertebrate species are the subjects of conservation efforts, as we will see in Chapter 47.

In Chapter 25, we discussed two chordate subphyla: the cephalochordates (lancelets) and urochordates (tunicates). The third subphylum of chordates, the vertebrata, with about 53,000 species, is by far the largest and most dominant group of chordates. In this chapter, we will explore the characteristics of vertebrates and the evolutionary development of the major vertebrate classes, including fishes, amphibians, reptiles, and mammals.

26.1 Vertebrates: Chordates with a Backbone

Learning Outcomes:

1. List the main distinguishing characteristics of vertebrates.
2. Identify the two classes of existing jawless vertebrates.

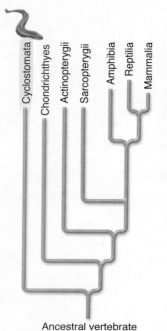

Ancestral vertebrate

Our current understanding of the relationships between vertebrate groups is shown in **Figure 26.1**. Nested within the vertebrates are various clades based on morphological characteristics. The vertebrates retain all chordate characteristics we outlined in Chapter 25, as well as possessing several additional traits, including the following:

1. **Vertebral column.** In vertebrates, the notochord is replaced by a bony or cartilaginous column of interlocking **vertebrae** that provides support and also protects the nerve cord, which lies within its tubelike structure.

2. **Cranium.** The anterior end of the nerve cord is expanded to form a more developed brain that is encased in a protective bony or cartilaginous housing called the **cranium.**

3. **Endoskeleton of cartilage or bone.** The cranium and vertebral column are parts of the endoskeleton, the living skeleton of vertebrates that forms within the animal's body. The endoskeleton contains living cells that secrete the skeleton, which grows with the animal, unlike the nonliving exoskeleton of arthropods.

Although these are the main distinguishing characteristics of vertebrates, there are others. For example, vertebrates have multiple clusters of *Hox* genes, compared with the single cluster of *Hox* genes in tunicates and lancelets. These additional gene clusters are believed to have permitted increasingly complex morphologies beyond those possessed by invertebrate chordates. Vertebrates possess a great diversity of internal organs, including a liver, kidneys, endocrine glands, and a heart with at least two chambers. The liver is unique to vertebrates, and the vertebrate kidneys, endocrine system, and heart are more complex than are analogous structures in invertebrate taxa.

Although these features are exhibited in all vertebrate classes, some classes evolved critical innovations that helped them succeed in specific environments such as on land or in the air. For example, birds developed feathers and wings, structures that enable most species to fly. In fact, each of the vertebrate classes is distinctly different from one another, as outlined in **Table 26.1**. One of the earliest innovations was the development of jaws. All vertebrates except some early-diverging fishes possessed jaws. Today, the only jawless vertebrates are hagfish and lampreys, together known as the Cyclostomata or cyclostomes (circle mouths), eel-like animals that do not possess jaws. Sequencing of RNA libraries in 2010, together with genomic surveys, yields strong support that the Cyclostomata is monophyletic.

The Hagfish Are the Simplest Living Cyclostomes

The hagfish are entirely marine cyclostomes that lack eyes, jaws, and fins and even vertebrae (**Figure 26.2**). The hagfish skeleton consists largely of a notochord and a cartilaginous skull that encloses the brain. The lack of a vertebral column leads to extensive flexibility. How, then, can hagfish be vertebrates without a vertebral column? Strong molecular support for a cyclostome clade suggests hagfish possessed the trait but that it was secondarily lost during evolution. Only the cranium and diversity of organs provide evidence of the organism's vertebrate ancestry.

Hagfish live in the cold waters of northern oceans, close to the muddy bottom, feeding on marine worms and other invertebrates. Essentially blind, hagfish have a very keen sense of smell and are attracted to dead and dying fish, which they attach themselves to via toothed plates on the mouth. The powerful tongue then rasps off pieces of tissue. Though the hagfish cannot see approaching predators, they have special glands that produce copious amounts of slime. When provoked, the hagfish's slime production increases dramatically, enough to potentially distract predators or coat their gills and interfere with breathing. Hagfish can sneeze to clear their nostrils of their own slime.

Figure 26.2 The hagfish.

Figure 26.1 The major clades of vertebrates. Critical innovations of each group are shown. The nested labels across the top of the figure refer to groupings within the vertebrates.

Concept Check: *What seven features do vertebrates typically possess that invertebrates do not?*

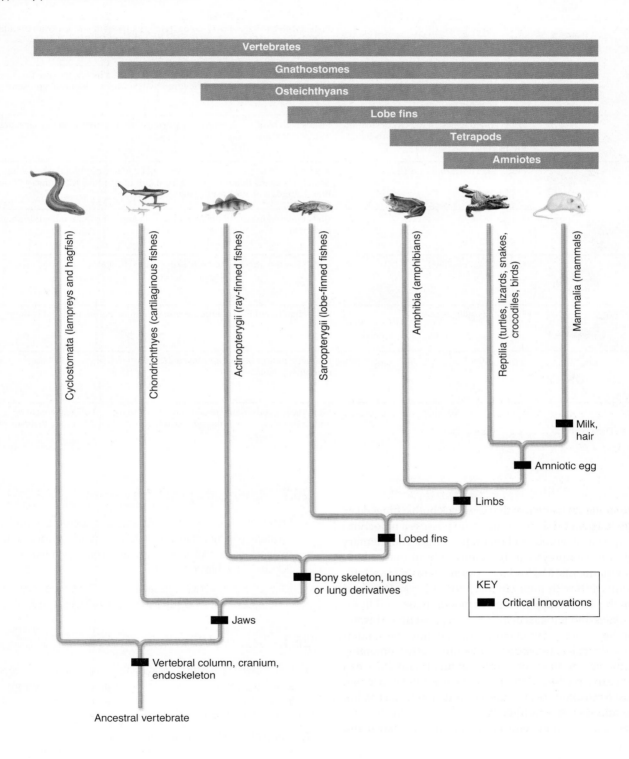

Table 26.1	The Main Clades and Characteristics of Living Vertebrates	
Clade	**Examples (approx. # of species)**	**Main characteristics**
Cyclostomata	Lampreys and hagfish (100)	Jawless fishes; no appendages
Chondrichthyes	Sharks, skates, rays (970)	Fishes with cartilaginous skeleton; teeth not fused to jaw; no swim bladder; well-developed fins; internal fertilization; single blood circulation
Actinopterygii	Ray-finned fishes, most bony fish (27,000)	Fishes with ossified skeleton; gill opening covered by operculum; fins supported by rays, fin muscles within body; swim bladder often present; mucous glands in skin
Sarcopterygii	Lobe-finned fishes, of which coelacanths (2) and lungfishes (6) are the only living members	Fishes with ossified skeleton; bony extensions, together with muscles, project into pectoral and pelvic fins
Amphibia	Frogs, toads, salamanders (6,300)	Adults able to live on land; fresh water needed for reproduction; development usually involving metamorphosis from tadpoles; adults with lungs and double blood circulation; moist skin; shell-less eggs
Testudines	Turtles (310)	Body encased in hard shell; no teeth; head and neck retractable into shell; eggs laid on land
Squamata	Lizards, snakes (7,900)	Lower jaw not attached to skull; skin covered in scales
Crocodilia	Crocodiles, alligators (23)	Four-chambered heart; large aquatic predators; parental care of young
Aves	Birds (10,000)	Feathers; hollow bones; air sacs; reduced internal organs; endothermic; four-chambered heart
Mammalia	Mammals (5,500)	Mammary glands; hair; specialized teeth; enlarged skull; external ears; endothermic; four-chambered heart; highly developed brains; diversity of body forms

The Lampreys Are Eel-like Animals That Lack Jaws

Lampreys are similar to hagfish in that they lack both a hinged jaw and true appendages. However, lampreys do possess a notochord surrounded by a cartilaginous rod that represents a rudimentary vertebral column. Lampreys can be found in both marine and freshwater environments. Marine lampreys are parasitic as adults. They grasp other fish with their circular mouth (**Figure 26.3a**) and rasp a hole in the fish's side, sucking out blood, tissue, and fluids (**Figure 26.3b**). Males and females of all species spawn in freshwater streams, and the resultant larval lampreys bury into the sand or mud, much like lancelets (refer back to Figure 25.34a), emerging to feed on small invertebrates or detritus at night. This stage can last for 3 to 7 years, at which time the larvae metamorphose into adults. In most freshwater species, the adults do not feed at all but quickly mate and die. Marine species migrate from fresh water back to the ocean, until they return to fresh water to spawn and then die.

26.1 Reviewing the Concepts

- Vertebrates have several characteristic features, including a vertebral column, cranium, endoskeleton of cartilage or bone, multiple clusters of *Hox* genes, and complex internal organs (Figure 26.1, Table 26.1).
- Early-diverging vertebrates lacked jaws. Today the only jawless vertebrates are the hagfish and lampreys (Figures 26.2, 26.3).

26.1 Testing Your Knowledge

1. Which of the following is *not* a defining characteristic of vertebrates?
   - **a.** great diversity of organs
   - **b.** hinged jaw
   - **c.** multiple clusters of *Hox* genes
   - **d.** vertebral column
   - **e.** endoskeleton

2. Which of the following taxa are considered cyclostomes?
   - **a.** tunicates
   - **b.** hagfish
   - **c.** lampreys
   - **d.** a and b
   - **e.** b and c

(a) Jawless mouth of a sea lamprey

(b) A sea lamprey feeding

Figure 26.3 **The lamprey, a modern jawless fish.** **(a)** The sea lamprey (*Petromyzon marinus*) has a circular jawless mouth. **(b)** A sea lamprey feeding on a fish.

26.2 Gnathostomes: Jawed Vertebrates

Learning Outcomes:

1. Describe how jaws evolved.
2. Discuss the distinguishing features of sharks.
3. List the three features that distinguish bony fishes from cartilaginous fishes.
4. Outline the differences between the ray-finned fishes and the lobe-finned fishes.

All vertebrate species that possess jaws are called **gnathostomes** (from the Greek, meaning "jaw mouth") (see Figure 26.1). Gnathostomes are a diverse clade of vertebrates that include fishes, amphibians, reptiles, and mammals. The earliest-diverging gnathostomes were fishes. Biologists have identified about 25,000 species of living fishes, more than all other species of vertebrates combined. Most are aquatic, gill-breathing species that usually possess fins and a scaly skin. The three separate clades of jawed fishes—the Chondrichthyes (cartilaginous

fishes), Actinopterygii (ray-finned fishes), and Sarcopterygii (lobe-finned fishes)—each have distinguishing characteristics (see Table 26.1).

The jawed mouth was a significant evolutionary development. It enabled an animal to grip its prey more firmly, which may have increased its rate of capture, and to attack larger prey species, thus increasing its potential food supply. Accompanying the jawed mouth was the development of more sophisticated head and body structures, including two pairs of appendages called fins. Gnathostomes also possess two additional *Hox* gene clusters beyond those in the cyclostomes (bringing their total to four), which likely led to increased morphological complexity.

The hinged jaw developed from the gill arches, cartilaginous or bony rods that help to support gills. Similarities between cells that make up jaws and gill arches support this view. Primitive jawless fishes had nine gill arches surrounding the eight gill slits (Figure 26.4a). During the late Silurian period (about 417 mya), some of these gill arches became modified. The first and second gill arches were lost, and the third and fourth pairs evolved to form the jaws (Figure 26.4b, c). This is how evolution typically works; body features do not appear de novo, but instead, existing features become modified to serve other functions.

Chondrichthyans Are Fishes with Cartilaginous Skeletons

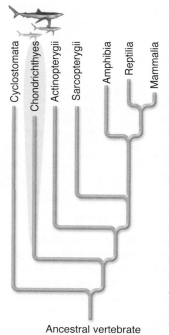

Ancestral vertebrate

Members of the clade Chondrichthyes (the **chondrichthyans**)—sharks, skates, and rays—are called cartilaginous fishes because their skeleton is composed of flexible cartilage rather than bone. The cartilaginous skeleton is considered a derived character, meaning that the ancestors of the chondrichthyans had bony skeletons, but that members of this class subsequently lost this feature. This hypothesis is reinforced by the observation that during development, the skeleton of most vertebrates is cartilaginous and then it becomes bony (ossified) as a hard calcium-phosphate matrix replaces the softer cartilage. A change in the developmental sequence of the cartilaginous fishes is believed to prevent the ossification process.

The Chondrichthyan Body Plan All chondrichthyans are denser than water, which theoretically means that they would sink if they stopped swimming. Many sharks never stop swimming and maintain buoyancy via the use of their fins and a large oil-filled liver. Perhaps the most important fin for propulsion in sharks is the large and powerful caudal fin, or tail fin, which, when swept from side to side, thrusts the fish forward at great speed

Biology Principle

Structure Determines Function

The development of a jaw increased the predatory capabilities of gnathostomes.

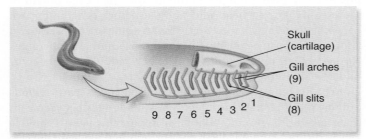

(a) Primitive jawless fishes

Skull (cartilage)

Gill arches (9)

Gill slits (8)

9 8 7 6 5 4 3 2 1

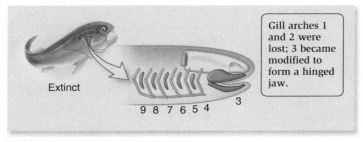

Extinct

Gill arches 1 and 2 were lost; 3 became modified to form a hinged jaw.

9 8 7 6 5 4   3

(b) Early jawed fishes (placoderms)

Living forms

Gill arch 4 also became modified to form a heavier, more efficient jaw.

9 8 7 6 5   4   3

(c) Modern jawed fishes (cartilaginous and bony fishes)

Figure 26.4 The evolution of the vertebrate jaw. (a) Primitive fishes and extant jawless fishes, such as lampreys, have nine cartilaginous gill arches that support eight gill slits. **(b)** In early jawed fishes such as the placoderms, the first two pairs of gill arches were lost, and the third pair became modified to form a hinged jaw. This left six gill arches (4–9) to support the remaining five gill slits, which were still used in breathing. **(c)** In modern jawed fishes, the fourth gill arch also contributes to jaw support, allowing stronger, more powerful bites to be delivered.

(Figure 26.5a). The paired pelvic fins (at the back) and pectoral fins (at the front) act like flaps on airplane wings, allowing the shark to dive deeper or rise to the surface. They also aid in steering. In addition, the dorsal fin (on the shark's back) acts as a stabilizer to prevent the shark from rolling in the water as the tail fin pushes

it forward. Skates and rays are essentially flattened sharks that cruise along the ocean floor by using hugely expanded pectoral fins (Figure 26.5b).

During swimming, water continually enters the shark's mouth and is forced over the gills, allowing the shark to extract oxygen and breathe. How then do skates and rays breathe when they rest on the ocean floor? These species, and a few sharks such as the nurse shark, use a muscular pharynx and jaw muscles to pump water over the gills. In these and indeed all species of fishes, the heart consists of two chambers, an atrium and a ventricle, that contract in sequence. They employ what is known as a single circulation, in which blood is pumped from the heart to capillaries in the gills to collect oxygen, and then it flows through arteries to the tissues of the body before returning to the heart (look ahead to Figure 36.2a).

Sharks were among the earliest fishes to develop teeth, which evolved from rough scales on the skin. Although shark's teeth are very sharp and hard, they are not set into the jaw, as are human teeth, so they break off easily and are continually replaced, row by row (Figure 26.5c). Sharks have a powerful sense of smell, facilitated by sense organs in the nostrils (sharks and other fishes do not use nostrils for breathing). They can see well but cannot distinguish colors. All jawed fishes have a row of microscopic organs in the skin, arranged in a line that runs laterally down each side of the body, which can sense movements in the surrounding water. This system of sense organs, known as the **lateral line,** senses pressure waves and sends nervous signals to the brain (look head to Figure 33.10).

The Chondrichthyan Life Cycle Fertilization is internal in chondrichthyans, with the male transferring sperm to the female via a pair of claspers, modifications of the pelvic fins. Some shark species exhibit **oviparity;** that is, they lay eggs, often inside a protective pouch called a mermaid's purse (Figure 26.5d). In species with **ovoviparity** the eggs are retained within the female's body, but there is no placenta to nourish the young. A few species exhibit **viviparity;** that is, the eggs develop within the uterus, receiving nourishment from the mother via a placenta. Both ovoviparous and viviparous sharks give birth to live young.

Osteichthyans Are Fishes with Bony Skeletons

Unlike the cartilaginous fishes, all other gnathostomes have a bony skeleton and belong to the clade known as Osteichthyes. This term means "bony fish" and was originally proposed for just that group. With the advent of modern phylogenetic systematics, however, the term **osteichthyans** has expanded to include all vertebrates with a bony skeleton, including tetrapods (refer back to Figure 26.1).

Bony Fish Body Plan Bony fishes are the most numerous of all types of fishes, with more species (about 27,000) than any other. The skin of bony fishes, unlike the rough skin of sharks, is covered by a thin epidermal layer containing glands that produce mucus, an adaptation that reduces drag during swimming. Just as in the cartilaginous fishes, water is drawn over the gills for breathing, but in bony fishes, a protective flap called an **operculum** covers the

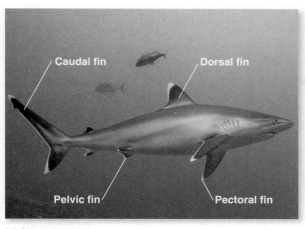

Caudal fin   Dorsal fin

Pelvic fin   Pectoral fin

(a) Silvertip shark

(b) Stingray

(c) Rows of shark teeth

(d) Shark egg pouch

Figure 26.5 **Cartilaginous fishes. (a)** The silvertip shark (*Carcharhinus albimarginatus*) is one of the ocean's most powerful predators. **(b)** Stingrays are essentially flattened sharks with very large pectoral fins. **(c)** Close-up of the mouth of a sand tiger shark (*Carcharias taurus*), showing rows of teeth. **(d)** This mermaid's purse (egg pouch) of a dogfish shark (*Scyliorhinus canicula*) is entwined in vegetation to keep it stationary.

BioConnections: *Look forward to Figure 31.5. What types of cells are responsible for forming cartilage?*

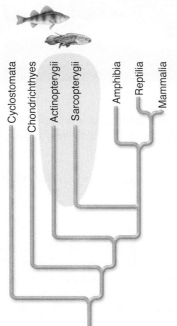

Cyclostomata

Chondrichthyes

Actinopterygii

Sarcopterygii

Amphibia

Reptilia

Mammalia

Ancestral vertebrate

gills (look ahead to Figure 37.4). Muscle contractions around the gills and operculum draw water across the gills so that bony fishes do not need to swim continuously in order to breathe.

Some early bony fishes lived in shallow, oxygen-poor waters and developed lungs as an embryological offshoot of the pharynx. These fish could rise to the water surface and gulp air. As we will see, modern lungfishes operate in much the same fashion. Many other fishes, known as bimodal breathers, can breathe through their gills and by gulping air, absorbing oxygen through their digestive tracts. For example, Siamese fighting fish (*Betta splendens*, known as betta), a popular freshwater aquarium fish, is a bimodal breather that is relatively easy to care for, since it can survive without an air pump in its aquarium. In most bony fishes, the lungs evolved into a **swim bladder,** a gas-filled, balloon-like structure that helps the fish remain buoyant in the water even when it is completely stationary. These three features—bony skeleton, operculum, and swim bladder—distinguish bony fishes from cartilaginous fishes.

Bony Fish Reproduction and Diversity   Reproductive strategies of bony fishes vary tremendously, but most species reproduce via external fertilization, with the female shedding her eggs and the male depositing sperm on top of them. Although adult bony fishes can maintain their buoyancy, their eggs tend to sink. This helps explain why many species spawn in shallow, more oxygen- and food-rich waters and why coastal areas are important fish nurseries.

Bony fishes have colonized nearly all aquatic habitats. Following the cooling of the newly formed planet Earth, water condensed into rain and over a vast period of time filled what are now the oceans. Later, as water evaporated from the oceans and sodium, potassium, and calcium were added via runoff from the land, the oceans became salty. Therefore, most fishes probably evolved in freshwater habitats and secondarily became adapted to marine environments. This, of course, required the development of physiological adaptations to the different osmotic problems seawater presents compared with fresh water (look ahead to Figure 38.3).

Most authorities now recognize two living clades of bony fishes: the Actinopterygii (ray-finned fishes), and the Sarcopterygii, or lobe-finned fishes.

Actinopterygii, the Ray-Finned Fish   The most species-rich clade of bony fishes is the Actinopterygii, or **ray-finned fishes.** In Actinopterygii, the fins are supported by thin, bony, flexible rays and are moved by muscles on the interior of the body. The class has a diversity of forms, from large predatory moray eels to delicate sea dragons (**Figure 26.6**). Whole fisheries are built around the harvest of such ray-finned species as cod, anchovies, and salmon.

Figure 26.6 **An Actinopterygian fish (ray-finned fish).** Black tip grouper (*Epinephelus fasciatus*), Maldives, Indian Ocean.

✓ **Concept Check:** *What features distinguish ray-finned fishes from sharks?*

Sarcopterygii, the Lobe-Finned Fish   In the Sarcopterygii, or **lobe-finned fishes,** the fins are supported by skeletal extensions of the pectoral and pelvic areas that are moved by muscles within the fins. The Actinistia (coelacanths) and Dipnoid (lung fishes) are both considered Sarcopterygii. The name Sarcopterygii used to refer solely to the lobe-finned fishes, but since it has become clear that terrestrial vertebrates (tetrapods) evolved from such fishes, the definition of the group has been expanded to include both lobe-finned fishes and tetrapods (see Figure 26.1).

The Actinistia, or coelacanths, were a very successful group in the Devonian period, but all fishes of the group were believed to have died off at the end of the Mesozoic era (some 65 mya). You can therefore imagine the scientific excitement when in 1938, a modern coelacanth was discovered as part of the catch of a boat fishing off the coast of South Africa (Figure 26.7a). Another species was found more recently in Indonesian waters.

The Dipnoi, or **lungfishes,** like the coelacanths, are also not currently a very species-rich group, having just three genera and six species (Figure 26.7b). Lungfishes live in oxygen-poor freshwater swamps and ponds. They have both gills and lungs, the latter of which enable them to come to the surface and gulp air. In fact, lungfish will drown if they are unable to breathe air. Because they also have muscular lobe fins, they are often able to successfully traverse long distances across land if their ponds dry out.

The morphological features of coelacanths, lungfishes, and primitive terrestrial vertebrates, together with the similarity of their nuclear genes, suggest to many scientists that lobe-finned ancestors gave rise to three lineages: the coelacanths, the lungfishes, and the tetrapods. In the next section we will examine the biology of tetrapods in more detail.

(a)

(b)

Figure 26.7 **The Sarcopterygii (lobe-finned fish). (a)** An actinisian, the coelacanth (*Latimeria chalumnae*). **(b)** A Dipnoi, the Australian lungfish (*Neoceratodus forsteri*).

✓ **Concept Check:** *How are lungfishes similar to coelacanths?*

26.2 Reviewing the Concepts

- A critical innovation in vertebrate evolution is the hinged jaw, which first developed in fishes. Gnathostomes are vertebrate species that possess a hinged jaw (Figure 26.4).
- The chondrichthyans (sharks, skates, and rays) have a skeleton composed of flexible cartilage and powerful appendages called fins. They are active predators with acute senses and were among the earliest fishes to develop teeth (Figure 26.5).
- Bony fishes consist of the Actinopterygii (ray-finned fishes, the most species-rich clade), and the lobe-finned fishes, which includes the Actinistia (coelacanths) and the Dipnoi (lungfishes).

In Actinopterygii, the fins are supported by thin, flexible rays and moved by muscles inside the body (Figure 26.6).

- The lobe fins comprise the lobe-finned fishes (Actinistia and Dipnoi) and the tetrapods. In the lobe-finned fishes, the fins are supported by extensions of the pectoral and pelvic areas and are moved by their own muscles (Figure 26.7).

26.2 Testing Your Knowledge

1. In modern jawed fishes, which gill arches have been modified to form the jaws?
   - **a.** 1 and 2
   - **b.** 2 and 3
   - **c.** 3 and 4
   - **d.** 4 and 5
   - **e.** 1 and 9

2. What is *not* a morphological feature of sharks?
   - **a.** paired pelvic fins
   - **b.** paired pectoral fins
   - **c.** cartilaginous skeleton
   - **d.** swim bladder
   - **e.** multiple rows of teeth

3. Which type of fish is a lobe fin?
   - **a.** moray eel
   - **b.** sea dragon
   - **c.** lamprey
   - **d.** stingray
   - **e.** lungfish

26.3 Tetrapods: Gnathostomes with Four Limbs

Learning Outcomes:

1. List adaptations that the transition to life on land required.
2. Describe the different amphibian orders and what differentiates them.

During the Devonian period (from about 417 to 354 mya, refer back to Figure 18.8), a diversity of plants and animals colonized the land. The presence of plants served as both a source of oxygen and a potential food source for animals that ventured out of the aquatic environment. Terrestrial arthropods appeared during the Devonian, as did the first terrestrial vertebrates.

The transition to life on land involved a large number of adaptations. Paramount among these were adaptations that prevented desiccation, or drying out, and made locomotion and reproduction on land possible. We have seen that some fish evolved the ability to breathe air. In this section, we begin by outlining the development of early **tetrapods,** vertebrate animals having four legs or leglike appendages, and the characteristics of their immediate descendants, the amphibians.

The Origin of Tetrapods Involved the Development of Four Limbs

Over the Devonian period, the fossil records demonstrate the evolution of sturdy lobe-finned fishes to fishes with four limbs. The abundance of light and nutrients in shallow waters encouraged a profusion of plant life and the invertebrates that fed on them. The development of lungs enabled lungfishes to colonize these productive yet often oxygen-poor waters. Here, the ability to move in shallow water clogged with plants and debris was more vital than the ability to swim swiftly through open water and may have favored the progressive development of sturdy limbs. As an animal's weight began to be borne more by the limbs, the adaptations of a strengthened vertebral column and hip bones and shoulder bones that were braced against the backbone for added support were favored. Such modifications are the result of changes in the expression of genes, especially *Hox* genes (see the Feature Investigation).

By the middle of the Carboniferous period (about 320 mya), species similar to modern amphibians had become common in the terrestrial environment. Breathing was accomplished more by lungs than by skin; and species possessed **pentadactyl limbs** (limbs ending in five digits). With a bonanza of terrestrial arthropods to feast on, the amphibians became numerous and species-rich, and often large in body size. The mid-Permian period (some 260 mya) is sometimes known as the Age of Amphibians. However, most of the large amphibians became extinct at the end of the Permian period. This was the largest known mass extinction in Earth's history, with the extinction of 90–95% of marine species and a large proportion of terrestrial species. Most surviving amphibians were smaller organisms resembling modern species.

Amphibian Lungs and Limbs Are Adaptations to a Semiterrestrial Lifestyle

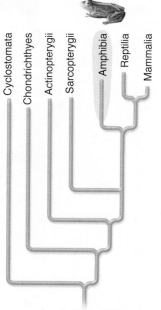

Cyclostomata · Chondrichthyes · Actinopterygii · Sarcopterygii · Amphibia · Reptilia · Mammalia

Ancestral vertebrate

Amphibians (from the Greek, *amphibios* meaning "both ways of life") live in two worlds: They have successfully invaded the land, but most must return to the water to reproduce. One of the first challenges terrestrial animals had to overcome was breathing air when on land. Amphibians breathe in several different ways. They can use the same technique as lungfishes, opening their mouths to let in air. Alternatively, they may take in air through their nostrils. They then close their nostrils and close and raise the floor of the mouth, creating a positive pressure that pumps air into the lungs. This method of breathing is called **buccal pumping** (look ahead to Figure 37.5). In addition, the skin of amphibians is much thinner than that of fishes, and amphibians absorb oxygen from the air directly through their outer moist skin or through the skin lining of the inside of the mouth.

FEATURE INVESTIGATION

Davis and Colleagues Provide a Genetic-Developmental Explanation for Limb Length in Tetrapods

The development of limbs in tetrapods was a vital step that allowed animals to colonize land. The diversity of vertebrate limb types is amazing, from fins in fish and marine mammals, to different wing types in bats and birds, to legs and arms in primates. Early in vertebrate evolution, an ancestral gene complex was duplicated twice to give rise to four groups of genes, called *Hox A, B, C,* and *D,* which control limb development. In 1995, Allen Davis, Mario Capecchi, and colleagues analyzed the effects of mutations in specific *Hox* genes that are responsible for determining limb formation in mice. The vertebrate forelimb is divided into three zones: humerus (upper arm); radius and ulna (forearm); and carpals, metacarpals, and phalanges (digits). The authors had no specific hypothesis in mind; their goal was to understand the role of *Hox* genes in limb formation. As described in **Figure 26.8**, they began with strains of mice carrying loss-of-function mutations in *HoxA-11* or *HoxD-11* that, on their own, did not cause dramatic

Figure 26.8 Relatively simple changes in *Hox* genes control limb formation in tetrapods.

GOAL To determine the role of *Hox* genes in limb development in mice.

KEY MATERIALS Mice with individual mutations in *HoxA-11* and *HoxD-11* genes.

	Experimental level	Conceptual level
1 Breed mice with individual mutations in *HoxA-11* and *HoxD-11* genes. (The *A* and *D* refer to wild-type alleles; *a* and *d* are mutant alleles.)	*AaDd* mice The mice bred were heterozygous for both genes (*AaDd*).	Based on previous studies, researchers expect mutant mice to produce viable offspring, perhaps with altered limb morphologies.

2 Using molecular techniques described in Chapter 16, obtain DNA from the tail and determine the genotypes of offspring.

The resulting genotypes occur in Mendelian ratios, generating mice with different combinations of wild-type and mutant alleles.

	AD	Ad	aD	ad
AD	AADD	AADd	AaDD	AaDd
Ad	AADd	AAdd	AaDd	Aadd
aD	AaDD	AaDd	aaDD	aaDd
ad	AaDd	Aadd	aaDd	aadd ← Double mutant

3 Stain the skeletons and compare the limb characteristics of the wild-type mice (*AADD*) to those of strains carrying mutant alleles in one or both genes.

Mutant mice may have altered bone morphologies.

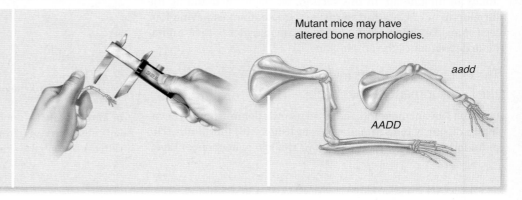

aadd

AADD

4 THE DATA

Genotype	Carpal bone fusions (% of mice showing the fusion)			
	Normal (none fused)	NL fused to T	T fused to P	NL fused to T and P
AADD	100	0	0	0
AaDD	100	0	0	0
aaDD	33	17	50	0
AADd	100	0	0	0
AAdd	0	17	17	67
AaDd	17	17	33	33

5 CONCLUSION Relatively simple mutations involving two genes can cause large changes in limb development.

6 SOURCE Davis, A.P. et al. 1995. Absence of radius and ulna in mice lacking *HoxA-11* and *HoxD-11*. *Nature* 375:791–795.

---

changes in limb formation. They bred the mice and obtained off-spring carrying one, two, three, or four loss-of-function mutations. Double mutants (*aadd*) exhibited dramatically different phenotypes not seen in mice homozygous for the individual mutations. The radius and ulna were almost entirely eliminated.

As seen in the data, the mutations affected the formation of limbs. For example, the wrist contains seven bones: three proximal carpals—called navicular lunate (NL), triangular (T), and pisiform (P)—and four distal carpals (d1–d4). In mice with the genotypes *aaDD* and *AAdd*, the proximal carpal bones are usually fused together. Individuals having one heterozygous recessive allele (*AADd* and *AaDD*) do not show this defect, but individuals heterozygous for two recessive alleles (*AaDd*) often do. Therefore, any two mutant alleles (either from both *HoxA-11* and *HoxD-11* or one from each locus) cause carpal fusions.

Deformities became even more severe with three mutant alleles (*Aadd* or *aaDd*) or four mutant alleles (*aadd*) (data not shown in the figure). Thus, scientists have shown that relatively simple mutations can control relatively large changes in limb development.

Experimental Questions

1. What was the purpose of the study conducted by Davis and colleagues?

2. How were the researchers able to study the effects of individual genes?

3. Explain the results of the experiment and how this relates to limb development in vertebrates.

Because the skin of amphibians is so thin, the animals face the problem of desiccation on land. As a consequence, even amphibian adults are more abundant in damp habitats, such as swamps or rain forests, than in dry areas. Also, most amphibians cannot venture too far from water because their larval stages are still aquatic. In frogs and toads, fertilization is generally external, with males shedding sperm over the gelatinous egg masses laid by the females in water (Figure 26.9a). The fertilized eggs lack a shell and would quickly dry out if exposed to the air for long. They soon hatch into tadpoles (Figure 26.9b), small fishlike animals that lack limbs and breathe through gills. As the tadpole nears the adult stage, the tail and gills are resorbed, and limbs and lungs appear (Figure 26.9c). Such a dramatic change from a juvenile to an adult body form is known as **metamorphosis.** A few species of

amphibians do not require water to reproduce. These species are ovoviviparous or viviparous—retaining the eggs in the reproductive tract and giving birth to live young.

Modern Amphibians Include a Variety of Frogs, Toads, Salamanders, and Caecilians

Approximately 6,300 living amphibian species are known, and the vast majority of these, some 5,600 species, are frogs and toads of the order Anura (from the Greek, meaning tail-less ones) (Figure 26.10a). The other two orders are the Apoda (from the Greek, meaning legless ones), the wormlike caecilians; and the Urodela (from the Latin, meaning tailed ones), the salamanders.

Adult anurans are carnivores, eating a variety of invertebrates by catching them on a long, sticky tongue. In contrast, their

(a) Gelatinous mass of amphibian eggs   **(b)** Tadpole   **(c)** Tadpole undergoing metamorphosis

Figure 26.9 Amphibian development in the European common frog (*Rana temporaria*). **(a)** Amphibian eggs are laid in gelatinous masses in water. **(b)** The eggs develop into tadpoles, aquatic herbivores with a fishlike tail that breathe through gills. **(c)** During metamorphosis, the tadpole loses its gills and tail and develops limbs and lungs.

 Concept Check: *What were some advantages to animals of moving on to land?*

(a) Tree frog

(b) A caecilian

(c) Mud salamander

Figure 26.10 Amphibians. **(a)** Most amphibians are frogs and toads of the order Anura, including this red-eyed tree frog (*Agalychnis callidryas*). **(b)** The order Apoda includes wormlike caecilians such as this species from Colombia, *Caecilia nigricans*. **(c)** The order Urodela includes species such as this mud salamander (*Pseudotriton montanus*).

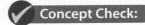 **Concept Check:** *Do all amphibians produce tadpoles?*

aquatic larvae (tadpoles) are primarily herbivores. In addition to secreting mucus, which keeps their skin moist, some frogs can also secrete poisonous chemicals that deter would-be predators. Some amphibians advertise the poisonous nature of their skin with warning coloration (look ahead to Figure 44.12b). Global warming is currently threatening many anurans with extinction (see chapter opener for Chapter 43).

Caecilians are a small order of about 170 species of legless, nearly blind amphibians (**Figure 26.10b**). Most are tropical and burrow in forest soils, but a few live in ponds and streams.

The more than 550 species of salamanders possess legs and a long tail and have a more elongate body than anurans (**Figure 26.10c**). Like frogs, salamanders often have colorful skin patterns that advertise their distastefulness to predators. A few species, such Cope's giant salamander (*Dicamptodon copei*), retain the gills and tail fins characteristic of the larval stage into adulthood, and mature sexually in the larval stage, a phenomenon known as paedomorphosis.

26.3 Reviewing the Concepts

- Fossils record the evolution of lobe-finned fishes to fishes with four limbs. Recent research has shown that relatively simple mutations can control large changes in limb development (Figure 26.8).
- Amphibians live on land but return to the water to reproduce. In frogs and toads, the larval stage undergoes metamorphosis, losing gills and tail and gaining lungs and limbs (Figure 26.9).
- The majority of amphibians belong to the order Anura (frogs and toads). Other orders are the Apoda (caecilians) and Urodela (salamanders) (Figure 26.10).

26.3 Testing Your Knowledge

1. The transition of tetrapods from water to life on land required
   a. prevention of desiccation.
   b. internal fertilization.
   c. the ability to breathe air.
   d. a and c.
   e. a, b, and c.
2. Which of the following amphibian orders have legs?
   a. salamanders
   b. frogs and toads
   c. caecilians
   d. a and b
   e. all amphibian orders have legs

26.4 Amniotes: Tetrapods with a Desiccation-Resistant Egg

Learning Outcomes:

1. Diagram the structure of the amniotic egg.
2. Identify the critical innovations of the amniotes.
3. Describe the distinguishing features of the major amniote clades.
4. List the features that enable birds to fly.

Although amphibians live successfully in a terrestrial environment, they must lay their eggs in water or in a very moist place so their shell-less eggs do not dry out on exposure to air. Thus, a critical innovation in animal evolution was the development of a shelled egg that sheltered the embryo from desiccation on land. A shelled egg containing fluids was like a personal enclosed pond for each developing individual. Such an egg evolved in the common ancestor of turtles, lizards, snakes, crocodiles, birds, and mammals—a group of tetrapods collectively known as the **amniotes.** The amniotic egg permitted animals to lay their eggs in a dry place, so that reproduction was no longer tied to water. It was truly a critical innovation, untethering animals from water in much the same way as the development of seeds liberated plants from water (see Chapter 23).

Over time, the amniotes became very diverse in species and morphology. Mammals are considered amniotes, too, because even though most of them do not lay eggs, they retain other features of amniotic reproduction. In this section, we begin by

discussing in detail the morphology of the amniotic egg and other adaptations that permitted animal species to become fully terrestrial. We then discuss the biology of the reptiles, the first group of vertebrates to fully exploit land.

The Amniotic Egg and Other Innovations Permitted Life on Land

The **amniotic egg** (Figure 26.11) contains the developing embryo and the four separate extraembryonic membranes that it produces:

1. The innermost membrane is the **amnion,** which protects the developing embryo in a fluid-filled sac called the amniotic cavity.
2. The **yolk sac** encloses a stockpile of nutrients, in the form of yolk, for the developing embryo.
3. The **allantois** functions as a disposal sac for metabolic wastes.
4. The **chorion,** along with the allantois, provides gas exchange between the embryo and the surrounding air.

Surrounding the chorion is the albumin, or egg white, which also stores nutrients. The **shell** provides a tough, protective covering that is not very permeable to water and prevents the embryo from drying out. However, the shell remains permeable to oxygen and carbon dioxide, so the embryo can breathe. In birds, this shell is hard and calcareous, whereas in reptiles and early-diverging mammals such as the platypus and echidna, it is soft and leathery. In most mammals, however, the embryos embed into the wall of the uterus and receive their nutrients directly from the mother.

Along with the amniotic egg, other critical innovations that enabled the conquest of land include the following:

- **Desiccation-resistant skin.** Whereas the skin of amphibians is moist and aids in respiration, the skin of amniotes is thicker and water-resistant and contains keratin, a tough protein. As a result, most gas exchange takes place through the lungs.

- **Thoracic breathing.** Amphibians use buccal pumping to breathe, contracting the mouth to force air into the lungs. In contrast, amniotes use **thoracic breathing,** in which coordinated contractions of muscles expand the rib cage, creating a negative pressure to suck air in and then forcing it out later. This results in a greater volume of air being displaced with each breath than with buccal pumping.

- **Water-conserving kidneys.** The ability to concentrate waste prior to elimination and thus conserve water is an important role of the amniotic kidneys.

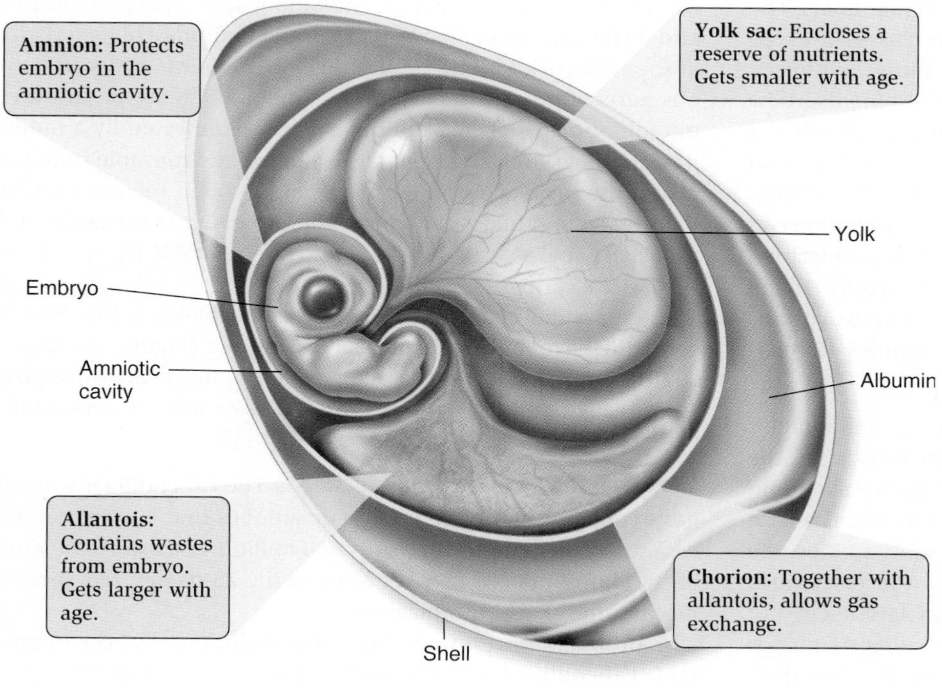

Amnion: Protects embryo in the amniotic cavity.

Yolk sac: Encloses a reserve of nutrients. Gets smaller with age.

Embryo

Amniotic cavity

Yolk

Albumin

Allantois: Contains wastes from embryo. Gets larger with age.

Chorion: Together with allantois, allows gas exchange.

Shell

Figure 26.11 The amniotic egg.

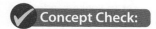

Concept Check: *What are the other critical innovations of amniotes?*

(a) Green turtle

(b) Common collared lizard

(c) Green tree python

Figure 26.12 **A variety of reptiles. (a)** A green turtle (*Chelonia mydas*) laying eggs in the sand in Malaysia. **(b)** Common collard lizard (*Crotaphytus collarus*). **(c)** Juvenile tree python (*Morelia viridis*).

Concept Check: *If snakes are limbless, how can they be considered tetrapods?*

- **Internal fertilization.** Because sperm cannot penetrate a shelled egg, fertilization occurs internally, within the female's body before the shell is secreted. In this process, the male of the species often uses a copulatory organ (penis) to transfer sperm into the female reproductive tract.

Reptiles Include Turtles, Lizards, Snakes, Crocodilians, and Birds

Early amniote ancestors gave rise to all modern amniotes we know today, from lizards and snakes to birds and mammals. The traditional view of amniotes involved three living classes: the reptiles (turtles, lizards, snakes, and crocodilians), birds, and mammals. As we will see later in this chapter, modern systematists now consider that birds are part of the reptilian lineage. This is the classification scheme that we will follow in this chapter. The fossil record includes other reptilian clades, all of which are extinct, including two groups of dinosaurs (ornithischian and saurischian dinosaurs), flying reptiles (pterosaurs), and two groups of ancient aquatic reptiles (icthyosaurs and plesiosaurs).

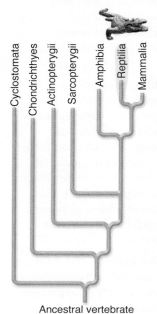

Cyclostomata
Chondrichthyes
Actinopterygii
Sarcopterygii
Amphibia
Reptilia
Mammalia

Ancestral vertebrate

Testudines: The Turtles The major distinguishing characteristic of the turtles is a hard protective shell into which the animal can withdraw its head and limbs. In most species, the vertebrae and ribs are fused to form this shell. All turtles lack teeth but have sharp beaks for biting. All turtles, even the aquatic species, lay their eggs on land, usually in soft sand. The gender of hatchlings is dependent on the temperature of the nest, with high temperatures producing more females. Marine species often make long migrations to sandy beaches to lay their eggs (**Figure 26.12a**). Even though turtles are very long-lived species, often surviving for 120 years or more, they do not appear to show reproductive senescence or aging, and reproduce continually throughout their lifetime. Most organs, such as the liver, lungs, and kidneys, of a centenarian turtle function as effectively as do organs in young individuals, prompting genetic researchers to examine the turtle genome for longevity genes.

Squamata: Lizards and Snakes The clade Squamata is the largest within the traditional reptiles, with about 4,900 species of lizards and 3,000 species of snakes. One of the defining characteristics of the clade is a **kinetic skull,** in which the joints between various parts of the skull are extremely mobile. The lower jaw does not join directly to the skull but rather is connected by a multijointed hinge, and the upper jaw is hinged and movable from the rest of the head. This allows their jaws to open relatively wider than those of other vertebrates, with the result that lizards, and especially snakes, can swallow large prey (**Figure 26.13**). Nearly all species are carnivores.

A main difference between lizards and snakes is that lizards generally have limbs, whereas snakes do not (Figures 26.12b,c). Leglessness is a derived character, meaning snake ancestors possessed legs but later lost them. Also, snakes may be venomous, whereas lizards usually are not.

Crocodilia: The Crocodiles and Alligators The Crocodilia is a small group of large, carnivorous, aquatic animals that have remained essentially unchanged for nearly 200 million years since the time of the dinosaurs (**Figure 26.14**). Most of the 23 recognized species live in tropical or subtropical regions.

Although the group is small, it is evolutionarily very important. Crocodiles have a four-chambered heart, a feature they share with birds and mammals (look ahead to Figure 36.2c). In this regard, crocodiles are more closely related to birds than to any other living reptiles. Their teeth are set in sockets, a feature typical of the earliest birds. Similarly, crocodiles care for their

Figure 26.13 The kinetic skull. In snakes and lizards, both the top and bottom of the jaw are hinged on the skull, thereby allowing them to swallow large prey. African egg-eating snake (*Dasypeltis scabra*) eating an egg.

young, another trait they have in common with birds. These and other features suggest that crocodiles and birds are closely related. As with turtles, the gender of the offspring is dependent on nest temperature.

Aves: The Birds   The defining characteristics of birds are that they have feathers and that nearly all species can fly. Flight has shaped nearly every feature of the bird body. The other vertebrates that have evolved the ability to fly—the bats and the now-extinct pterosaurs—used skin stretched tightly over elongated limbs and digits to form wings. Such a surface can be irreparably damaged, however, though some holes may heal remarkably quickly. In contrast, birds use feathers, epidermal outgrowths that can be replaced if damaged. Recent research shows that feathers evolved in dinosaurs before the appearance of birds.

One of the first known fossils exhibiting the faint impression of feathers was *Archaeopteryx lithographica* (from the Greek, meaning ancient wings and stone picture), found in a limestone quarry in Germany in 1861. The fossil was dated at 150 million years old, which places it during the Jurassic period. Except for the presence of feathers, *Archaeopteryx* appears to have had features similar to those of many other dinosaurs (**Figure 26.15**).

Birds Have Feathers, a Lightweight Skeleton, Air Sacs, and Reduced Organs

Modern birds possess many characteristics, including scales on their feet and legs and shelled eggs, that reveal their reptilian ancestry. In addition, however, among living animals birds have four unique features, all of which are associated with flight.

1. **Feathers.** Feathers are modified scales that keep birds warm and enable flight. Soft, downy feathers, which are close to the body, maintain heat, whereas stiffer contour feathers, supported on a modified forelimb, give the wing the airfoil shape it needs to generate lift.

Australian saltwater crocodile

Figure 26.14 Crocodilians. The Crocodilia is an ancient class that has existed unchanged for millions of years. The Australian saltwater crocodile (*Crocodylus porous*), at up to 6.2 m (20 ft), is the largest species of all.

BioConnections: *Look ahead to Figure 32.2c. In what ways are crocodilians similar to birds and mammals?*

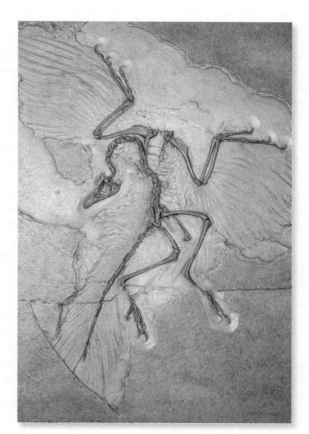

Figure 26.15 *Archaeopteryx lithographica* was a Jurassic animal with dinosaur-like features as well as wings and feathers. This supports the idea that birds and dinosaurs are closely related.

Concept Check: *What adaptations in birds help reduce their body weight to enable flight?*

2. **Air sacs.** Flight requires a great deal of energy generated from an active metabolism that requires abundant oxygen. Birds have nine air sacs—large, hollow sacs that may extend into the bones—that expand and contract when a bird inhales and exhales, while the lungs remain stationary. Air is therefore being constantly moved across the lungs during inhalation and exhalation. Although making bird breathing very efficient, this process also makes birds especially susceptible to airborne toxins (hence, the utility of the canary in the coal mine; the bird's death signaled the presence of harmful carbon dioxide or methane gas that was otherwise unnoticed by miners).

3. **Reduction of organs.** Some organs are reduced in size or are lacking altogether in birds, which reduces the total mass that the bird carries. For example, birds have only one ovary and can carry relatively few eggs. As a result, they lay fewer eggs than most reptile species. In fact, the gonads of both males and females are reduced, except during the breeding season, when they increase in size. Most birds also lack a urinary bladder. In addition, their lack of teeth has reduced weight at the head end.

4. **Lightweight bones.** Most bird bones are thin and hollow and are crisscrossed internally by tiny pieces of bone to give them a strong but lightweight honeycomb structure.

Because birds need a rapid metabolism and the quick production of adenosine triphosphate (ATP) to fuel flight, body temperatures are generally 40–42°C, considerably warmer than the human body's average of 37°C. Birds also have a double circulation and a four-chambered heart that ensures rapid blood circulation. Flight requires good vision, and bird vision is the best in the vertebrate world. Birds generally have high energy needs, and most birds are carnivores, eating insects or other invertebrates. However, some birds, such as parrots, eat nutrient-rich fruits and seeds. Bird eggs also need to be kept warm for successful development, which entails sitting on the nest until the eggs have hatched, a process called brooding. Often, the males and females take turns brooding so that one parent can feed and maintain its strength. Picking successful partners is therefore an important breeding task, and birds often engage in complex courtship rituals (look ahead to Figure 42.17).

With about 10,000 species, birds are the most species-rich group of terrestrial vertebrates. Despite this diversity, birds lack the variety of body shapes that exists in the other class of vertebrates, the mammals, some of which can swim, some of which can fly, others walk on four legs, and yet others walk only on two legs. Most birds fly, and therefore, most have the same general body shape. However, birds feed in many different ways, which is reflected in the variety of their beak shapes (**Figure 26.16**).

26.4 Reviewing the Concepts

- The amniotic egg permitted animals to become fully terrestrial. Other critical innovations included desiccation-resistant skin, thoracic breathing, water-conserving kidneys, and internal fertilization (Figure 26.11).

Biology Principle

Structure Determines Function
Each of these beak shapes permits a different method of feeding.

(a) Cracking beak

(d) Probing beak

(b) Scooping beak

(e) Nectar-feeding beak

(c) Tearing beak

Figure 26.16 A variety of bird beaks. Birds have evolved a variety of beak shapes used in different types of food gathering. **(a)** Hyacinth macaw (*Anodorhynchus hyacinthinus*)—cracking. **(b)** White pelican (*Pelecanus onocrotalus*)—scooping. **(c)** Verreaux's eagle (*Aquila verreauxii*)—tearing. **(d)** American avocet (*Recurvirostra americana*)—probing. **(e)** Lucifer hummingbird (*Calothorax lucifer*)—nectar feeding. **(f)** Roseate spoonbill (*Ajaia ajaja*)—sieving.

(f) Sieving beak

- Living reptilian clades include the Testudines (turtles), Squamata (lizards and snakes), Crocodilia (crocodiles), and Aves (birds) (Figures 26.12–26.14).
- The fossil bird *Archaeopteryx lithographica* helps trace a lineage from dinosaurs to birds (Figure 26.15).
- The four key characteristics of birds are feathers, air sacs, reduced organs, and a lightweight skeleton. Birds are the most species-rich clade of terrestrial vertebrates. The diversity of bird beaks reflects the varied methods they use for feeding (Figure 26.16).

26.4   Testing Your Knowledge

1. The membrane of the amniotic egg that serves as a site for waste storage is the
   a. amnion.
   b. yolk sac.
   c. allantois.
   d. chorion.

2. Which is a critical innovation of amniotes?
   a. buccal pumping
   b. moist skin that aids in respiration
   c. external fertilization
   d. water-conserving kidneys
   e. bony skeleton

3. Possession of a four-chambered heart suggests crocodiles are most closely related to which other living vertebrates?
   a. lizards
   b. turtles
   c. birds
   d. dinosaurs
   e. mammals

4. Which of the following features is associated with the ability of birds to fly?
   a. scaly legs
   b. feathers
   c. air sacs
   d. double circulation
   e. b and c

26.5   Mammals: Milk-Producing Amniotes

Learning Outcomes:

1. Identify the four features that separate mammals from other vertebrate clades.
2. List the defining characteristics of primates.
3. Describe the evolutionary pathway that led to modern humans, *Homo sapiens*.

Mammals evolved from amniote ancestors earlier than birds. About 225 mya, the first mammals appeared in the mid-Triassic period (refer back to Figure 18.8). The extinction of the dinosaurs in the Cretaceous period, some 65 mya, paved the way for

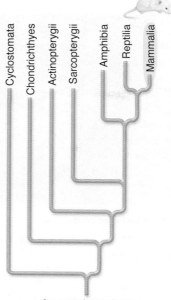

Cyclostomata
Chondrichthyes
Actinopterygii
Sarcopterygii
Amphibia
Reptilia
Mammalia

Ancestral vertebrate

mammals to increase in diversity of size and species. Today, biologists have identified about 5,500 species of mammals, from fishlike dolphins to bird-like bats, and from small insectivores such as shrews to large herbivores such as giraffes and elephants. The range of sizes and body forms of mammals is unmatched by any other living vertebrate group, and mammals are prime illustrations of the concept that organismal diversity is related to environmental diversity. In this section, we will outline the features that distinguish mammals from other taxa. We will also examine the diversity of mammals that exists on Earth and will end by turning our attention to the evolution of primates and in particular humans.

Mammals Have Mammary Glands, Hair, Specialized Teeth, and an Enlarged Skull

Four characteristics distinguish mammals: the possession of mammary glands, hair, specialized teeth, and an enlarged skull.

- **Mammary glands.** Mammals, or the clade Mammalia (from the Latin *mamma*, meaning breast), are named after the female's distinctive **mammary glands,** which secrete milk. Newborn mammals suckle this fluid, which helps promote rapid growth.

- **Hair.** All mammals have hair, although some have more than others. Whales have hair in utero, but adults are hairless or retain only a few hairs on their snout. Mammals are endothermic, and their fur is an efficient insulator. Hair can also take on functions other than insulation. Many mammals, including cats, dogs, walruses, and whales, have sensory hairs called vibrissae (**Figure 26.17a**). Hair can be of many colors, to allow the mammals to blend into their background (**Figure 26.17b**). In some cases, as in porcupines and hedgehogs, the hairs become long, stiffened, and sharp (quills) and serve as a defense mechanism (**Figure 26.17c**).

- **Specialized teeth.** Mammals are the only vertebrates with highly differentiated teeth—incisors, canines, premolars, and molars—that are adapted for different types of diets (**Figure 26.18**).

- **Enlarged skull.** The mammalian skull differs from other amniote skulls in several ways. First, the brain is enlarged and is contained within a relatively large skull. Second, mammals have a single lower jawbone, unlike reptiles, whose lower jaw is composed of multiple bones. Third, mammals have three bones in the middle ear, as opposed to reptiles, which have one bone in the middle ear.

(a) Sensory hairs

(b) Camouflaged coat

(c) Defensive quills

Figure 26.17 Mammalian hair. (a) The sensory hairs (vibrissae) of the walrus (*Odobenus rosmarus*). **(b)** The camouflaged coat of a bobcat (*Lynx rufus*). **(c)** The defensive quills of the crested porcupine (*Hystrix africaeaustralis*).

(a) Biting teeth

(b) Grinding teeth

(c) Gnawing teeth

(d) Tusks

(e) Grasping teeth

Figure 26.18 Mammalian teeth. Mammals have different types of teeth, according to their diet. **(a)** The wolf has long canine teeth that bite and tear its prey. **(b)** The deer has a long row of molars that grind plant material. **(c)** The beaver, a rodent, has long, continually growing incisors used to gnaw wood. **(d)** The elephant's incisors are modified into tusks for defense and combat. **(e)** Dolphins and other fishes or plankton feeders have numerous small teeth used to grasp prey.

Mammals Are the Most Diverse Group of Vertebrates Living on Earth

Modern mammals are incredibly diverse in size and lifestyles (**Table 26.2**). They vary in size from tiny insect-eating bats, weighing in at only 2 g, to leviathans such as the blue whale, the largest animal ever known, which tips the scales at 100 tonnes (over 200,000 lb). Mammalian orders are divided into two distinct subclasses. The subclass Prototheria contains only the order Monotremata, or **monotremes,** which are found in Australia and New Guinea. There are only five species of monotremes: the

duck-billed platypus (**Figure 26.19a**) and four species of echidna, a spiny animal resembling a hedgehog. Monotremes are early-diverging mammals that lay eggs rather than bear live young, lack a placenta, and have mammary glands with poorly developed nipples. The mothers incubate the eggs, and upon hatching, the young simply lap up the milk as it oozes onto the fur.

The subclass Theria, which contains all remaining mammals, is divided into two clades, the Metatheria and the Eutheria. The clade Metatheria, or the **marsupials,** is a group of seven orders, with about 280 species, including the rock wallaby pictured in **Figure 26.19b**. Once widespread, members of this order are now

Table 26.2		The Main Orders of Mammals, in Order of Species Richness	
Order		**Examples (approx. # of species)**	**Main characteristics**
Rodentia		Mice, rats, squirrels, beavers, porcupines (2,277)	Plant eaters; gnawing habit, with two pairs of continually growing incisor teeth
Chiroptera		Bats (1,116)	Insect or fruit eaters; small; have ability to fly; navigate by sonar; nocturnal
Eulipotyphla		Shrews, moles, hedgehogs (452)	Insect eaters; primitive placental mammals
Primates		Monkeys, apes, humans (404)	Opposable thumb; binocular vision; large brains
Carnivora		Cats, dogs, weasels, bears, seals, sea lions (286)	Flesh-eating mammals; canine teeth
Artiodactyla		Deer, antelopes, cattle, sheep, goats, camels, pigs (240)	Herbivorous hoofed mammals, usually with two toes, hippopotamus and others with four toes; many with horns or antlers
Diprotodontia		Kangaroos, koalas, opossums, wombats (143)	Marsupials mainly found in Australia
Lagomorpha		Rabbits, hares (92)	Powerful hind legs; rodent-like teeth
Cetacea		Whales, dolphins (84)	Marine fishes or plankton feeders; front limbs modified into flippers; no hind limbs; little hair except on snout
Perissodactyla		Horses, zebras, tapirs, rhinoceroses (18)	Hoofed herbivorous mammals with odd-numbered toes, one (horses) or three (rhinoceroses)
Monotremata		Duck-billed platypuses, echidna (5)	Egg-laying mammals found only in Australia and New Guinea
Proboscidea		Elephants (3)	Long trunk; large, upper incisors modified as tusks

largely confined to Australia, although some marsupials exist in South America, and one species—the opossum—is found in North America. Fertilization is internal, and reproduction is viviparous in marsupials. Marsupials have a relatively simple, short-lived placenta that nourishes the embryo. Unlike other mammals, however, marsupials are extremely small when they are born (often only 1–2 cm) and make their way to a ventral pouch called a marsupium for further development.

All the other mammalian orders are members of the clade Eutheria and are considered **eutherians,** or placental mammals, such as the orangutans shown in Figure 26.19c. Eutherians have a long-lived and complex placenta, compared with that of marsupials. In eutherians, fertilization is internal, and reproduction is viviparous, but the developmental period, or gestation, of the fetus is prolonged.

Primates Are Mammals with Opposable Thumbs and a Large Brain

The primates, and specifically humans, have had a huge influence on the world. Primates are primarily tree-dwelling (arboreal) species that are believed to have evolved from a group of small, arboreal insect-eating mammals about 85 mya, before dinosaurs went extinct. Primates have several defining characteristics, mostly relating to their arboreal ancestry:

- **Opposable thumb.** Most primate species possess an **opposable thumb,** a thumb that can be placed opposite the fingers of the same hand, which gives them a precision grip and enables primates to manipulate small objects. All primates except humans also have an opposable big toe.

Figure 26.19 **Diversity among mammals.**
(a) Prototherians, such as this duck-billed platypus (*Ornithorhynchus anatinus*), lay eggs, lack a placenta, and possess mammary glands with poorly developed nipples. **(b)** Metatherians, or marsupials, such as this rock wallaby (*Petrogale assimilis*), feed and carry their developing young, or "joeys," in a ventral pouch. **(c)** Gestation lasts longer in eutherians, and their young are more developed at birth, as illustrated by this young orangutan (*Pongo pygmaeus*).

BioConnections: *Look ahead to Figure 40.11. The placenta serves as the provisional lungs, intestine, and kidneys of the developing fetus. How much mixing is there of maternal and fetal blood?*

(a) Prototherian (duck-billed platypus)

(c) Eutherian (orangutan)

(b) Metatherian (rock wallaby)

- **Large brain.** Acute vision, enhancing the ability to move quickly through the trees, requires the efficient processing of large amounts of information. As a result, the primate brain is large and well developed. In turn, this has facilitated complex social behaviors.

- **At least some digits with flat nails instead of claws.** This feature is believed to aid in the manipulation of objects.

- **Binocular vision.** Jumping from branch to branch requires accurate judgment of distances. This is facilitated by binocular vision in which the field of vision for both eyes overlaps, producing a single image.

- **Complex social behavior and well-developed parental care.** Primates have a tendency toward complex social behavior and increased parental care.

Some of these characteristics are possessed by other animals. For example, binocular vision occurs in owls and some other birds, grasping hands are found in raccoons, and relatively large brains occur in marine mammals. Primates are defined by possessing the whole suite of these characteristics.

Primates may be classified in several ways. Taxonomists often divide them into two groups: the strepsirrhini and the haplorrhini (**Figure 26.20**). The **strepsirrhini** contain the smaller species such as bush babies, lemurs, and pottos. These are generally nocturnal and smaller-brained primates with eyes positioned a little more toward the side of their heads (**Figure 26.21a**). The strepsirrhini are named for their wet noses with no fur at the tip. The **haplorrhini** have dry noses with a fully furred nose tip and fully forward-facing eyes. This group consists of the larger-brained and diurnal (active during the day) **anthropoidea:** the monkeys (**Figure 26.21b**) and the **hominoidea** (gibbons, orangutans, gorillas, chimpanzees, and humans) (**Figure 26.21c**).

What differentiates monkeys from hominoids? Most monkeys have tails, but hominoids do not. In addition, apes have more mobile shoulder joints, broader rib cages, and a shorter spine. These features aid in brachiation, the swinging movement that

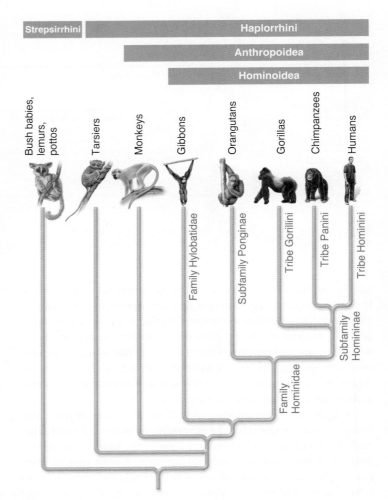

Figure 26.20 **Evolutionary tree of the primates.**

(a) Strepsirrhini (lesser bush baby)   **(b) Anthropoidea (Capuchin monkey)**   **(c) Hominoidea (white-handed gibbon)**

Figure 26.21 Primate classification. Many authorities divide the primates into two groups: **(a)** the strepsirrhini (smaller, nocturnal species such as this lesser bush baby, *Galago senegalensis*), and the haplorrhini (larger diurnal species). Haplorrhini comprise **(b)** the monkeys, such as this Capuchin monkey (*Cebus capucinus*), and **(c)** the hominoids, species such as this white-handed gibbon (*Hylobates lar*).

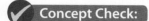 **Concept Check:**   *What are the defining features of primates?*

(a) Gorilla (*Gorilla gorilla*)   **(b) Chimpanzee (*Pan troglodytes*)**   **(c) Human (*Homo sapiens*)**

Figure 26.22 Members of the family Hominidae. **(a)** Gorillas, the largest of the living primates, are ground-dwelling herbivores that inhabit the forests of Africa. **(b)** Chimpanzees are smaller, omnivorous primates that also live in Africa. The chimpanzees are closely related living relatives of modern humans. **(c)** Humans are also members of the family Hominidae. The orangutan is also a member of this group.

allows them to move in trees. Apes also possess relatively long limbs and short legs and, with the exception of gibbons, are much larger than monkeys. The 20 species of hominoids are split into two groups: the lesser apes (family Hylobatidae), or the gibbons; and the greater apes (family Hominidae): the orangutans, gorillas, chimpanzees, and humans (**Figure 26.22**). The lesser apes are strictly arboreal, whereas the greater apes often descend to the ground to feed.

Although humans are closely related to gorillas and chimpanzees, they did not evolve directly from them. Rather, all

hominoid species shared a common ancestor. Recent molecular studies show that gorillas, chimpanzees, and humans are more closely related to one another than they are to orangutans, so scientists have split the family Hominidae into two groups: the subfamily Ponginae (orangutans) and the subfamily Homininae (gorillas, chimpanzees, and humans and their ancestors). In turn, the Homininae are split into three tribes: the Gorillini (gorillas), the Panini (chimpanzees), and the Hominini (humans and their ancestors).

EVOLUTIONARY CONNECTIONS

Comparing the Human and Chimpanzee Genetic Codes

In 2005, the Chimpanzee Sequencing and Analysis Consortium published an initial sequence of the chimpanzee genome that allowed scientists to make detailed comparisons with the human genome. In particular, they generated a catalogue of the genetic differences that have accumulated since humans and chimpanzees diverged from a common ancestor. A male chimp called Clint who lived at a primate research center in Atlanta provided the DNA used to sequence the chimp genome. These comparisons revealed that the sequence of base pairs making up both species' genomes differs by only 1.23%, 10 times less than the difference between the mouse and rat genomes.

Many of the genetic differences between chimps and humans result from chromosome inversions and duplications. Geneticists have found over 1,500 inversions between the chimp and human genomes. Although many inversions occur in the noncoding regions of the genome, the DNA in these regions may regulate the expression of the genes in the coding regions. Duplications and deletions are also common. For example, one gene that codes for a subunit of a protein found in areas of the brain occurs in multiple copies in a wide range of primates, but humans have the most copies. Interestingly, humans appear to have loss-of-function mutations in a gene that in other primates may protect against Alzheimer's disease.

Some interesting genetic differences were apparent between chimps and humans even before their entire genomes were sequenced. In 1998, Indian physician-geneticist Ajit Varki and colleagues investigated a molecule called sialic acid that occurs on cell surfaces and acts as a locking site for pathogens such as malaria and influenza. They found an altered form of the molecule in humans, coded for by a single damaged gene, which may explain why humans are more susceptible to these diseases than are chimpanzees.

In 2002, Swedish molecular geneticist Svante Pääbo discovered differences between humans and chimps in a gene called *FOXP2*, which plays a role in speech development. Proteins coded for by this gene differ in just two amino acids of a 715-amino-acid sequence. Researchers propose that the mutations in this gene have been crucial for the development of human speech.

More recently, a team led by American geneticist David Reich in 2006 discovered that the human X chromosome diverged from the chimpanzee X chromosome about 1.2 million years more recently than the other chromosomes. This indicated to the researchers that the human and chimp lineages split apart, and then began interbreeding before diverging again. This would explain why many fossils appear to exhibit traits of both humans and chimps, because they may actually have been human-chimpanzee hybrids.

Humans Evolved from Ancestral Primates

About 6 mya in Africa, a lineage that led to humans began to separate from other primate lineages. The evolution of humans should not be viewed, however, as a neat, stepwise progression from one species to another. Rather, human evolution, like the evolution of most species, can be visualized like a tree, with one or two **hominin** species—members of the Hominini tribe—likely coexisting at the same point in time, with some eventually going extinct and some giving rise to other species (**Figure 26.23**).

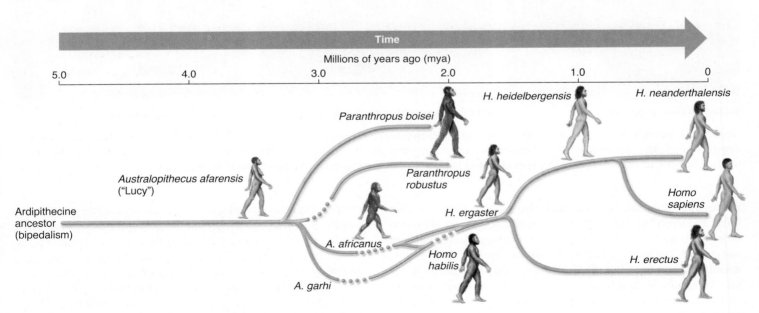

Figure 26.23 A possible scenario for human evolution. In this human family tree (based on the ongoing work of Donald Johanson), several hominin species lived contemporaneously with one another, but only one lineage gave rise to modern humans (*Homo sapiens*).

The key characteristic differentiating hominins from other apes is that hominins walk on two feet; that is, they are **bipedal.** At about the time when hominins diverged from other ape lineages, the Earth's climate had cooled, and the forests of Africa had given way to savannas, which are tropical grasslands. A bipedal method of locomotion and upright stance may have been advantageous in allowing hominins to peer over the tall grass of the savanna to see predators or even prey.

Bipedalism is correlated with many anatomical changes in hominins. First, the opening of the skull where the spinal cord enters shifted forward, allowing the spine to be more directly underneath the head. Second, the hominin pelvis became broader to support the additional weight. And third, the lower limbs, used for walking, became relatively larger than those in other apes. These are the types of anatomical changes paleontologists look for in the fossil record to help determine whether fossil remains are hominin. An early group of hominins includes several species of a small-brained genus, *Australopithecus*, which first emerged in Africa about 4 mya. *Australopithecus afarensis* is generally regarded as the common ancestor of most of these species. From there, the evolution of different species becomes less clear. It is generally agreed that two genera evolved from *Australopithecus*: the robust *Paranthropus* and the more slender *Homo*.

Australopithecines   Since 1924, when the first fossil australopithecine (from the Latin *austral*, meaning southern, and the Greek *pithecus*, meaning ape) was found in South Africa, hundreds of fossils of this group have been unearthed all over southern and eastern Africa, the areas where fossil deposits are best exposed to paleontologists. This was a widespread group, with at least six species. In 1974, American paleontologist Donald Johanson unearthed the skeleton of a female *A. afarensis* in the Afar region of Ethiopia and dubbed her Lucy. (The Beatles' song "Lucy in the Sky with Diamonds" was playing in the camp the night when Johanson was sorting the unearthed bones.) Over 40% of the skeleton had been preserved, enough to provide a good idea of the physical appearance of australopithecines. Compared with modern humans, all were relatively small, about 1–1.5 m in height and around 18 kg in weight. Examination of the bones revealed that *A. afarensis* walked on two legs. They possessed a facial structure and brain size (about 500 cm³) similar to those of a chimp.

The Genus Homo and Modern Humans   In the 1960s, British paleontologist Louis Leakey found hominin fossils estimated to be about 2 million years old in Olduvai Gorge, a site in Tanzania. Two particularly interesting observations stand out about these fossils. First, reconstruction of the skull showed a brain size of about 680 cm³, larger than that of *Australopithecus*. Second, the fossils were found with a wealth of stone tools. As a result, Leakey assigned the fossils to a new species, *Homo habilis*, from the Latin meaning handy man. The discovery of several more *Homo* fossils followed, but there have been no extensive finds, as there were with Lucy. This makes it difficult to determine which *Australopithecus* lineage gave rise to the *Homo* lineage (see Figure 26.23), and scientists remain divided on this point.

Although we are not clear exactly how, researchers believe that *H. habilis* probably gave rise to *Homo ergaster*, one of the most important species of *Homo*. *Homo ergaster* was a hominin that evolved in Africa; it had a human-looking face and skull, with downward-facing nostrils. *Homo ergaster* was also a tool user, and the tools, such as hand axes, were larger and more sophisticated than those found with *H. habilis*. *Homo ergaster* evolved in a period of global cooling and drying that reduced tropical forests even more and promoted savanna conditions. Hairlessness and the regulation of body temperature through sweating may also have evolved at this time as adaptations to a sunnier environment. A leaner body shape was evident. A dark skin probably protected *H. ergaster* from ultraviolet radiation from the sun's rays. The pelvis had narrowed, promoting efficiencies in walking upright, and the size of the brain and hence the skull increased. Researchers have inferred that the shape of the birth canal of the female of the species had narrowed. Females had to push increasingly large-brained infants through a narrowed pelvis, and researchers think that as a result, the human gestation period was shortened. Earlier birth leads to prolonged care of human infants compared with that in other apes. Prolonged childcare required well-nourished mothers, who would have benefited from the support of their male partner and other members of a social group. Some anthropologists have suggested this was the beginning of the family.

Homo ergaster probably was the first type of human to leave Africa, as similar bones have been found in the Eurasian country of Georgia. *Homo ergaster* is believed to be a direct ancestor of later hominin species: *H. erectus*, *H. heidelbergensis*, and eventually *H. sapiens*. *Homo erectus* was a large hominin, as large as a modern human but with heavier bones and a smaller brain capacity of between 750 and 1,225 cm³ (modern brain size is about 1,350 cm³). Fossil evidence shows that *H. erectus* was a social species that used tools, hunted animals, and cooked over fires. The meat-eating habit may have sparked the migration of *H. erectus*, because carnivores had larger ranges than similar-sized herbivores, their prey being scarcer per unit area. *Homo erectus* spread out of Africa soon after the species appeared, over a million years ago, and fossils have been found as far away as China and Indonesia.

Homo heidelbergensis is believed to be a common ancestor of two species: *H. neanderthalensis* and *H. sapiens*. *Homo neanderthalensis* was named for the Neander Valley of Germany, where the first fossils of its type were found. In the Pleistocene epoch, glaciers were locked in a cycle of advance and retreat, and the European landscape was often covered with snow. The more slender body form of *H. heidelbergensis* evolved into a shorter, stockier build that was better equipped to conserve heat; we now call this type of human Neanderthal. Neanderthals also possessed a more massive skull and larger brain size than modern humans, about 1,450 cm³, perhaps associated with their bulk. Males were about 168 cm (5 ft 6 in.) in height and would have been very strong by modern standards. They had a large face with a prominent bridge over the eyebrows, a large nose, and no chin. They lived predominantly in Europe, with a range extending to the Middle East. About 30,000 years ago, this species disappeared,

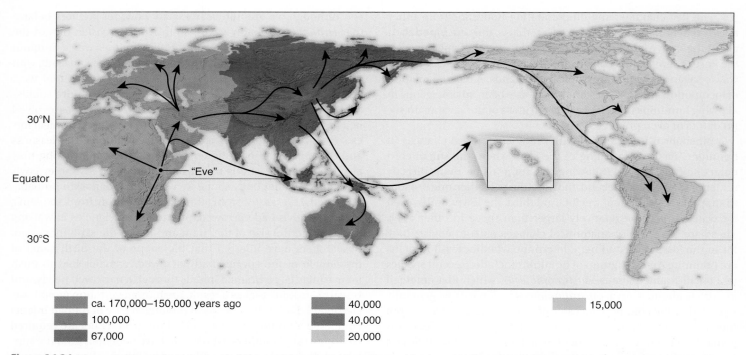

ca. 170,000–150,000 years ago	40,000	15,000
100,000	40,000	
67,000	20,000	

Figure 26.24 **The probable origin and spread of *Homo sapiens* throughout the world.** This map, based on differences of mtDNA throughout current members of the world's population, suggests *Homo sapiens* originated from "mitochondrial Eve" in east Africa. About 100,000 years ago, the species spread into the Middle East and from there to Europe, Asia, Australia, and the Americas.

BioConnections: *Refer back to Figure 14.21. Why is mitochondrial DNA especially useful in determining a "mitochondrial Eve"?*

replaced by another hominin species, *H. sapiens* (from the Latin, meaning wise man), our own species. *Homo sapiens* was a taller, lighter-weight species with a slightly smaller brain capacity than that of the Neanderthals. Researchers posit a variety of reasons for why *H. sapiens* thrived while the Neanderthals died out, including possessing a more efficient body type with lower energy needs, increased longevity, and differences in social structure and cultural adaptations.

Studies of human mitochondrial DNA (mtDNA), which occurs only in the cellular organelles called mitochondria, and which is passed from mother to offspring, show that all modern humans share a common ancestor, dubbed "mitochondrial Eve," dating to about 170,000 years ago. The mtDNA data suggest a migration of *H. sapiens* from eastern Africa to other parts of the globe beginning 170,000–150,000 years ago (**Figure 26.24**). Modern humans spread first into the Middle East and Asia, then later into Europe and Australia, finally crossing the Bering Strait to the Americas.

26.5 Reviewing the Concepts

- The distinguishing characteristics of mammals are mammary glands, hair, specialized teeth, and an enlarged skull (Figures 26.17, 26.18).
- Two subclasses of mammals exist: the Prototheria (monotremes) and the Theria (the live-bearing mammals). The live-bearing mammals consist of the Metatheria (marsupials) and Eutheria (placental mammals) (Table 26.2, Figure 26.19).

- Many defining characteristics of primates relate to their tree-dwelling nature and include opposable thumbs, large brain, flat nails instead of claws, and binocular vision (Figures 26.20–26.22).
- About 6 mya in Africa, a lineage that led to humans began to separate from other primate lineages. A key characteristic of hominins (extinct and modern humans) is bipedalism. Human evolution can be visualized like a tree, with a few hominin species coexisting at the same point in time, some eventually going extinct, and some giving rise to other species (Figure 26.23).

26.5 Testing Your Knowledge

1. What is *not* a derived character of primates?
   - **a.** opposable thumb
   - **b.** grasping hands
   - **c.** grasping tail
   - **d.** flat nails
   - **e.** large brain

2. Mammals can be distinguished from other vertebrate classes because of the possession of
   - **a.** amniotic eggs.
   - **b.** mammary glands.
   - **c.** warm bloodedness.
   - **d.** reduction of organs.
   - **e.** thoracic breathing.

3. An important ancestor of modern humans, *Homo sapiens*, is
   - **a.** *Homo neanderthalensis.*
   - **b.** *Homo erectus.*
   - **c.** *Homo ergaster.*
   - **d.** *Paranthropus boisei.*
   - **e.** *Pongo pygmaeus.*

Assess and Discuss

Test Yourself

1. To which of the following clades does a jawed fish belong?
   a. gnathostomes
   b. lobe fins
   c. tetrapods
   d. amniotes
   e. cyclostomes

2. The presence of a bony skeleton, an operculum, and a swim bladder are all defining characteristics of
   a. class Myxini.
   b. lampreys.
   c. class Chondrichthyes.
   d. bony fishes.
   e. amphibians.

3. Organisms that lay eggs are said to be
   a. oviparous.
   b. ovoviparous.
   c. viviparous.
   d. placental.
   e. none of the above.

4. Which clade does *not* include frogs?
   a. vertebrates
   b. gnathostomes
   c. tetrapods
   d. amniotes
   e. lobe fins

5. Pentadactyl limbs first appeared in
   a. coelacanths.
   b. lungfish.
   c. amphibians.
   d. reptiles.
   e. mammals.

6. The outermost membrane of the amniotic egg is the
   a. amnion.
   b. yolk sac.
   c. allantois.
   d. chorion.
   e. albumin.

7. Which characteristic qualifies lizards as gnathostomes?
   a. a cranium
   b. a skeleton of bone or cartilage
   c. a hinged jaw
   d. the possession of limbs
   e. amniotic eggs

8. Which of the following is *not* a distinguishing characteristic of birds?
   a. amniotic egg
   b. feathers
   c. air sacs
   d. lack of certain organs
   e. lightweight skeletons

9. The mammalian subclass Prototheria contains which order(s)?
   a. Diprodantia
   b. Perissodactyla
   c. Monotremata
   d. a and b
   e. b and c

10. Despite their small size and nocturnal habits, small primates called tarsiers are classed with much larger monkeys and apes as Haplorrhini. The clade Haplorrhini is differentiated from the Strepsirrhini based on which of the following characteristics?
    a. dry, fully furred noses
    b. forward-facing eyes
    c. DNA similarities
    d. a and b
    e. a, b, and c

Conceptual Questions

1. How is vertebrate movement similar to arthropod movement, and how is it different?

2. Why aren't all reptiles endothermic if both birds and mammals are?

3. **PRINCIPLES**   A principle of biology is that *all species (past and present) are related by an evolutionary history.* Are birds living dinosaurs?

Collaborative Questions

1. By what means can vertebrates move?

2. Why are amphibians considered good indicator species, which are species whose status provides information on the overall health of an ecosystem?

Online Resource

www.brookerprinciples.com

Stay a step ahead in your studies with animations that bring concepts to life and practice tests to assess your understanding. Your instructor may also recommend the interactive eBook, individualized learning tools, and more.

UNIT VIII
ECOLOGY

Ecology is the study of interactions among organisms and between organisms and their environments. Interactions among organisms and the living environment are called **biotic** interactions, and those between organisms and the nonliving environment are termed **abiotic** interactions. These interactions, in turn, govern the numbers of species in an area and their population densities. Ecology ranges in scale from the study of the behavior of individual organisms to the study of the physical environment and its effects on the distribution and abundance of organisms to the study of populations, communities, and ecosystems.

In this unit, we introduce each of the broad areas of behavior, organisms and their physical environment, population ecology, community ecology, and ecosystem ecology, and illustrate how knowledge of these ecological disciplines facilitates conservation of life on Earth. Chapter 42 discusses animal behavior and how behavior contributes to the survival and reproductive success of organisms. In Chapter 43, we discuss the effects of physical variables such as temperature and moisture on organisms. At the largest scales, variation in temperature and moisture create distinct large-scale habitats, called biomes. Chapter 44 examines population growth and the constraints on growth provided by competitors and natural enemies. We introduce the demographic tools needed to study population growth, provide simple mathematical models of growth, and examine the special case of human population growth. Chapters 45 and 46 focus on communities and ecosystems. In Chapter 45, we consider the factors that influence the number of species in a community and examine different measures of diversity. Chapter 46 addresses the flow of energy and nutrients through the living and nonliving components of the environment. Last, in Chapter 47 we turn our attention to the conservation of life on Earth and the various strategies biologists use to protect genetic, species, and ecosystem diversity. Throughout Unit VIII, we'll examine the effects of human activities on the environment, including pollution, global warming, and the introduction of exotic species of plants and animals.

Ecological studies have important implications in the real world, as will be amply illustrated by examples discussed throughout the unit. However, there is a distinction between ecology and **environmental science**—the application of ecology to real-world problems. To use an analogy, ecology is to environmental science as physics is to engineering. Both physics and ecology provide the theoretical framework on which to pursue more applied studies. Engineers rely on the principles of physics to build bridges. Similarly, environmental scientists rely on the principles of ecology to solve environmental problems.

The following biology principles will be emphasized in this unit:

- ***Living organisms use energy.*** *In Chapter 46 we discuss the cycle of nutrients and energy flow in ecosystems.*

- ***Living organisms interact with their environment.*** *Chapter 43 provides examples of the influence of temperature, water, pH, salt concentration, and light on the distribution and abundance of organisms.*

- ***Biology is an experimental science.*** *Throughout the unit we provide numerous examples of experiments that ecologists have used to investigate how ecological systems function.*

- ***Biology affects our society.*** *In Chapter 47, the last chapter of the unit, we discuss some of the conservation efforts currently underway to save and secure life on Earth.*

42

Animal Behavior

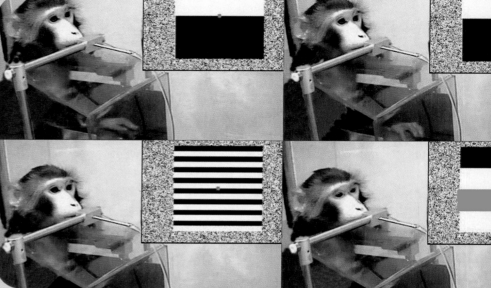

Monkey "working" in Barry Richmond's lab.

Chapter Outline

In 2004, American neuroscientist Barry Richmond and colleagues trained four monkeys to release a lever at the exact moment a spot on a computer screen changed color from red to green. The monkeys had to complete this task three times, but only on the third trial did they receive a food reward, regardless of how they performed on the first two trials. As a result, the monkeys made fewer errors in the third trial than in the first two trials.

Next, the team injected a short strand of DNA into the rhinal cortex that decreased the binding of a receptor known to be involved in processing reward signals. The effects were only temporary, 10–12 weeks, but during that time the monkeys were unable to determine how many trials were left before the reward was given. As a result, the monkeys worked vigilantly to receive the reward on every trial, making few errors even on trials one and two. The researchers believe that this research may eventually provide insight into how human motivation works and how it might be disrupted in behavioral disorders.

Behavior is the observable response of organisms to external or internal stimuli. In the early 20th century, scientific studies of animal behavior, termed **ethology** (from the Greek *ethos*, meaning habit or manner),

focused on the specific genetic and physiological mechanisms of behavior. For example, we could hypothesize that male deer rut or fight with other males in the fall because a change in day length stimulates the eyes, brain, and pituitary gland and triggers hormonal changes in their bodies. These factors are called **proximate causes.** However, we could also hypothesize that male deer fight to determine which deer get to mate with the most female deer and pass on their genes. This hypothesis leads to a different answer from the one that is concerned with changes in day length. This answer focuses on the adaptive significance of fighting to the deer, that is, on the effect of a particular behavior on reproductive success. These factors are called **ultimate causes** of behavior.

In this chapter, we will explore the role of both proximate and ultimate causes of behavior. We begin the chapter by investigating how behavior is achieved, examining the roles of both genetics and the environment. We consider how different behaviors are involved in movement, communication, and group living. Last, we investigate whether an organism can truly behave in a way that benefits others at a cost to itself, and how behavior shapes different mating systems.

42.1 The Influence of Genetics and Learning on Behavior

Learning Outcomes:

1. Outline the differences among innate behavior, classical conditioning, and operant conditioning.
2. Describe how memory is used in local movement.

As we saw in the chapter-opening paragraph, genetics greatly influences animal behavior, but as we will see, behavior is controlled by both genetics and the environment, and in this section, we will discuss the influence of both. Genetics allow the evolutionary responses of ancestors to selection to be incorporated into current behavior while responses to the environment permit animals the opportunity to change their behavior over the short term.

Innate Behavior Patterns Are Genetically Programmed

Behaviors that appear to be genetically programmed are referred to as **innate** (also called instinctual). For example, a spider will spin a specific web without ever seeing a member of its own species build one. A classic example of innate behavior is the egg-rolling response in geese (**Figure 42.1**). If an incubating goose notices an egg out of the nest, she will extend her neck toward the egg, get up, and then roll the egg back to the nest using her beak. Such behavior functions to improve the survival of offspring. Eggs that roll out of the nest can get cold and fail to hatch. Geese that fail to exhibit the egg-rolling response would pass on fewer of their genes to future generations. Interestingly, any round object, from a wooden egg to a volleyball, can elicit or trigger the egg-rolling response. Such objects are called **releasers.**

Learning Occurs When Animals Modify Their Behavior on Past Experience

Although many of the behavioral patterns exhibited by animals are innate, animals can make modifications to their behavior based on previous experience, a process that involves learning. Perhaps the simplest form of learning is **habituation,** in which an organism learns to ignore a repeated stimulus. For example, animals in African safari parks become habituated to the presence of vehicles containing tourists. Habituation can be a problem at airports, where birds eventually ignore the alarm calls designed to scare them away from the runways.

Habituation is a form of nonassociative learning, without a positive or negative reinforcement. A positive or negative association between a stimulus and a response is termed **associative learning.** The two main types of associative learning are termed classical conditioning and operant conditioning.

In **classical conditioning,** an involuntary response comes to be associated with a stimulus that did not originally elicit the response. This type of learning is generally associated with the Russian psychologist Ivan Pavlov. In his original experiments in the 1920s, Pavlov restrained a hungry dog in a harness and presented small portions of food at regular intervals (refer back to Figure 31.15). The dog would salivate whenever it smelled the food. Pavlov then began to sound a metronome when presenting the food. Eventually the dog would salivate at the sound of the metronome whether or not the food was present. Classical conditioning is widely observed in animals. For example, many insects quickly learn to associate certain flower odors with nectar rewards. In some humans, the sound of a dentist's drill is enough to produce a feeling of uneasiness, tension, and sweaty palms.

In **operant conditioning,** an animal's behavior is reinforced by a consequence, either a reward, as noted in the chapter opener, or a punishment. Operant conditioning, also called trial-and-error learning, is common in animals. Often it is associated with negative rather than positive reinforcement. For example, toads eventually refuse to strike at insects that sting, such as wasps and bees, and birds will learn to avoid bad-tasting butterflies (**Figure 42.2**).

In spatial learning specific landmarks are learned to construct cognitive maps, mental representations of the spatial relationships of objects, to aid in local movements. For example, in the fall, some birds known as nutcrackers (genus *Nucifraga*) store thousands of seeds distributed in underground caches, over a 35 km² area. The birds relocate many of these caches in the winter but leave alone the caches of other nutcrackers. As long ago as the 1930s, Dutch-born ethologist Niko Tinbergen showed how the female digger wasp uses landmarks to relocate her nests, as described next.

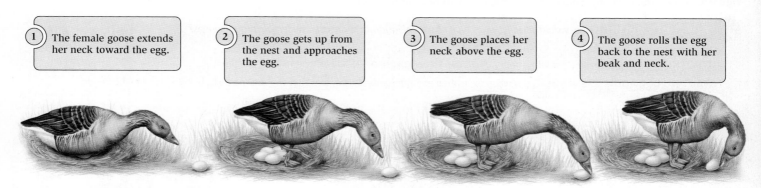

1. The female goose extends her neck toward the egg.

2. The goose gets up from the nest and approaches the egg.

3. The goose places her neck above the egg.

4. The goose rolls the egg back to the nest with her beak and neck.

Figure 42.1 Innate behavior. Female geese retrieve eggs that have rolled outside the nest through a set sequence of movements. The goose completes the entire sequence even if a researcher takes the egg away before the goose has rolled it back to the nest.

(a) Blue jay eating monarch   **(b) Vomiting reaction**

Figure 42.2 **Operant conditioning, also known as trial-and-error learning.** **(a)** A young blue jay will eat a monarch butterfly, not knowing that it is noxious. **(b)** After the first experience of eating a monarch and vomiting, a blue jay will avoid the insects in the future.

Concept Check: *What's the difference between operant conditioning and classical conditioning?*

BioConnections: *Look forward to Figure 44.12. How might operant conditioning relate to the similar appearance of king snakes and coral snakes?*

FEATURE INVESTIGATION

Tinbergen's Experiments Show That Digger Wasps Learn the Positions of Landmarks to Find Their Nests

In the sandy, dry soils of Europe, the solitary female digger wasp (*Philanthus triangulum*) digs four to five nests in which to lay her eggs. Each nest stretches obliquely down into the ground for 40–80 cm. After digging the nesting holes, the wasp performs a sequence of apparently genetically programmed events. She catches and stings a honeybee, which paralyzes it; returns to the nest; drags the bee into the nest; and lays an egg on it. The egg hatches into a larva, which then feeds on the paralyzed bee. However, the larva needs to ingest five to six bees before it is fully developed. This means the wasp must catch and sting four to five more bees for each larva. She can carry only one bee at a time. After each visit, the wasp must seal the nest with soil, to prevent the bee from being stolen, find another bee, relocate the nest, open it, and add the new bee. How does the wasp relocate the nest after spending considerable time away? Niko Tinbergen observed the wasps hover and fly around the nest each time they took off. He hypothesized that they were learning the nest position by creating a cognitive map of the landmarks in the area.

To test his hypothesis, Tinbergen experimentally adjusted the landmarks around the burrow that the wasps might be using as cues (**Figure 42.3**). First, he put a ring of pinecones around the nest entrance to train the wasp to associate the pinecones with the nest. Then, when the wasp was out hunting, he moved the circle of pinecones a distance from the real nest and constructed a sham nest, making a slight depression in the sand and mimicking the covered entrance of the burrow. On returning, the wasp flew straight to the sham nest and tried to locate the entrance. Tinbergen chased it away. When it returned, it again flew to the sham nest. Tinbergen repeated this nine times, and every time the wasp chose the sham nest. Tinbergen got the same result with 16 other wasps, and not once did any of them choose the real nest.

Next Tinbergen experimented with the type of stimulus that might be eliciting the learning. He hypothesized that the wasps could be responding to the distinctive scent of the pinecones rather than their appearance. He trained the wasps by placing a circle of pinecones that had no scent and two small pieces of cardboard coated in pine oil around the real nest. He then moved the cones to surround a sham nest and left the scented cardboard around the real nest. The returning wasps again ignored the real nest with the scented cardboard and flew to the sham nest. He concluded that for the wasps, sight was apparently more important than smell in determining landmarks.

Figure 42.3 **How Niko Tinbergen discovered the digger wasp's nest-locating behavior.**

Concept Check: *How would you test what type of spatial landmarks are used by female digger wasps?*

HYPOTHESIS Digger wasps (*Philanthus triangulum*) use visual landmarks to locate their nests.

STARTING LOCATION The female digger wasp excavates an underground nest, to which she returns daily, bringing food to the larvae located inside.

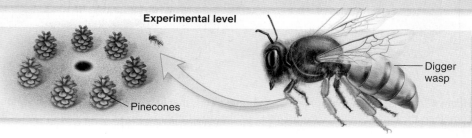

1 Place a ring of pinecones around the nest to train the wasp to associate pinecones with the nest.

Experimental level

Pinecones

Digger wasp

2 After the wasp leaves the nest to hunt, move the pinecones 30 cm from the real nest. The wasp returns and flies to the center of the pinecone circle instead of the real nest. Repeated experiments yield similar results (see data), indicating that the wasp uses landmarks as visual cues.

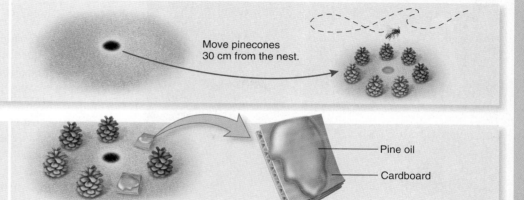

Move pinecones 30 cm from the nest.

3 To test whether it is the shape or the smell of the pinecones that elicits the response, perform the same experiment as above, except use pinecones with no scent and add 2 small pieces of cardboard coated with pine oil.

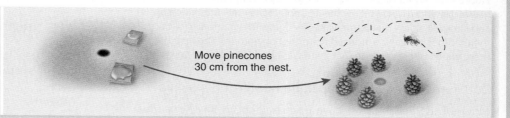

Pine oil

Cardboard

4 After the wasp leaves the nest, move the pinecones 30 cm from the nest, but leave the scented cardboard at the nest. The wasps again fly to the pinecone nest (see data), indicating that it is the arrangement of cones, not their smell, that elicits the learning.

Move pinecones 30 cm from the nest.

5 **THE DATA***

Results from steps 1 and 2:

Wasp #	Number of return visits per wasp to real nest without pinecones	Number of return visits per wasp to sham nest with pinecones
1–17	0	~9

Results from steps 3 and 4:

Wasp #	Number of return visits per wasp to real nest with scented cardboard	Number of return visits per wasp to sham nest with pinecones
18–22	0	~6

*Seventeen wasps, numbered 1–17, were studied as described in steps 1 and 2. Five wasps, numbered 18–22, were studied as described in steps 3 and 4.

6 **CONCLUSION** Digger wasps remember the positions of visual landmarks and use them as aids in local movements.

7 **SOURCE** Tinbergen, N. 1951. The study of instinct. Clarendon Press, Oxford.

Experimental Questions

1. What observations were important for the development of Niko Tinbergen's hypothesis explaining how digger wasps located their nests?

2. How did Tinbergen test the hypothesis that the wasps were using landmarks to relocate the nest? What were the results?

3. Did the Tinbergen experiment rule out any other cue the wasps may have been using besides the sight of pinecones?

Figure 42.4 **Konrad Lorenz being followed by his imprinted geese.** Newborn geese follow the first object they see after hatching and later will follow that particular object only. They normally follow their mother but can be induced to imprint on humans. The first thing these young geese saw after hatching was ethologist Konrad Lorenz.

Both Genetics and Learning Influence Most Behaviors

Much of the behavior we have discussed so far has been presented as either innate (genetic) or learned, but the behavior we observe in nature is usually a mixture of both. Bird songs present a good example. Many birds learn their songs as juveniles, when they hear their parents sing. For example, if juvenile white-crowned sparrows are raised in isolation, their adult songs do not resemble the typical species-specific song. If they hear only the song of a different species, such as the song sparrow, they again sing a poorly developed adult song. However, if they hear the song of the white-crowned sparrow, they will learn to sing a fully developed white-crowned sparrow song. The birds are genetically programmed to learn, but they will sing the correct song only if the appropriate instructive program is in place to guide learning.

Another example of how innate behavior interacts with learning can occur during a limited time period of development, called a **critical period.** At this time, many animals develop irreversible species-specific behavior patterns. This process is called **imprinting.** One of the best examples of imprinting was demonstrated by the Austrian ethologist Konrad Lorenz in the 1930s. Lorenz noted that young birds of some species imprint on their mother during a critical period that is usually within a few hours after hatching. This behavior serves them well, because in many species of ducks and geese, it would be hard for the mother to keep track of all her offspring as they walk or swim. After imprinting takes place, the offspring keep track of the mother.

The survival of the young ducks requires that they quickly learn to follow their mother's movements. Lorenz raised greylag geese from eggs, and soon after they hatched, he used himself as the model for imprinting. As a result, the young goslings imprinted on Lorenz and followed him around (**Figure 42.4**). For the rest of their life, they preferred the company of Lorenz and other humans to geese. Studies have shown that even an object as foreign as a black box, watering can, or flashing light can be imprinted on if it is the first moving object the chick sees during the critical period.

42.1 Reviewing the Concepts

- Behavior is usually due to the interaction of an organism's genes and the environment.
- Genetically programmed behaviors are termed innate and often involve a releaser that initiates the behavior (Figure 42.1).
- Organisms can often make modifications to their behavior based on previous experience, a process called learning. Some forms of learning include habituation, classical conditioning, and operant conditioning (Figure 42.2).
- Much behavior is a mixture of innate and learned behaviors. A good example of this occurs in a process called imprinting, in which animals develop a strong attachment that influences subsequent behavior (Figure 42.4).

42.1 Testing Your Knowledge

1. Birds can come to ignore the presence of a scarecrow in a field of crops. This behavior is
   - **a.** learned.
   - **b.** habituation.
   - **c.** operant conditioning.
   - **d.** classical conditioning.
   - **e.** innate.

2. After their young hatch, black-headed gulls will remove the old egg shells, which, unlike the camouflaged outsides, are white inside and may attract predators. This behavior is likely
   - **a.** learned.
   - **b.** habituation.
   - **c.** operant conditioning.
   - **d.** classical conditioning.
   - **e.** innate.

3. Green sea turtles feed off the coast of Brazil yet swim east for 2,300 km (1,429 miles) to lay their eggs on Ascension Island, an 8-km-wide island in the center of the Atlantic Ocean between Brazil and Africa. What could be the ultimate reason turtles return to this tiny island to lay their eggs?
   - **a.** They use chemical cues.
   - **b.** They use magnetic cues.
   - **c.** Fewer predators exist here than on other beaches.
   - **d.** They use navigation.
   - **e.** They learn underwater landmarks.

42.2 Communication

Learning Outcome:

1. Give examples of how animals use chemical, auditory, visual, and tactile communication.

Much animal behavior is directed at individuals of the same species, for example, in courtship, fighting over mates, or defending territories or food sources. **Communication** is the use of specially designed signals or displays to modify the behavior of others. The use of different forms of communication between organisms depends on the environment in which they live. For example, while animals use a variety of gestures and displays to communicate with each other, visual communication plays little role in the signals of nocturnal animals. Similarly, for animals in dense forests, sounds are of prime importance. Sound, however, is a temporary signal. Scent can last longer and is often used to mark the large territories of some mammals. Many animals use tactile communication, or touch, to communicate with others of their same species. In this section, we outline the various types of communication—chemical, auditory, visual, and tactile—that occur among animals.

Chemical Communication Is Often Used to Mark Territories or Attract Mates

The chemical marking of territories is common among animals, especially among members of the canine and feline families, which urinate on prominent markers at the boundaries of their territories. Scent trails are often used by social insects to recruit workers to help bring prey to the nest. Fire ants (genus *Solenopsis*) attack large, living prey, and many ants are needed to drag the prey back to the nest. The scout that finds the prey lays down a scent trail from the prey back to the nest. The scent excites other workers, which follow the trail to the prey. The scent marker evaporates easily, and the trail effectively disappears in a few minutes to avoid confusion over old trails.

Animals also use chemicals to attract mates. Female moths attract males by powerful chemical attractants called **pheromones.** Male moths have receptors that can detect as little as a single molecule. Among social organisms, some individuals use pheromones to manipulate the behavior of others. For example, a queen bee releases pheromones that suppress the reproductive system of workers, which ensures that she is the only reproductive female in the hive.

Auditory Communication Is Often Used to Attract Mates and to Deter Competitors

Many organisms communicate by making sound. Because the ground can absorb sound waves, sound travels farther in the air, which is why many birds and insects perch on branches or leaves when singing. Air is on average 14 times less turbulent at dawn and dusk than during the rest of the day, so sound carries farther then, which helps explain the preference of most animals for calling at these times. Some insects utilize the very plants on which they feed as a medium of song transmission. Many male leafhopper and planthopper insects vibrate their abdomens on leaves and create species-specific courtship songs that are transmitted by adjacent vegetation and are picked up by nearby females of the same species.

Although many males use auditory communication to attract females, some females use calls to attract the attention of males. Female elephant seals scream loudly when approached by a nondominant male. This attracts the attention of the dominant male, which drives the nondominant male away. In this way, the female is guaranteed a mating with the strongest male. Sound production can attract predators as well as mates. Some bats listen for the mating calls of male frogs to find their prey. Parasitic flies detect and locate chirping male crickets and then deposit larvae on or near them. Sound may also be used by males during competition over females. In many animals, lower-pitched sounds come from larger males, so by calling to one another, males can gauge the size of their opponents and decide whether it is worth fighting.

Visual Communication Is Often Used in Courtship and Aggressive Displays

In courtship, animals use a vast number of visual signals to identify and select potential mates. Competition among males for the most impressive displays to attract females has led to elaborate coloration and extensive ornamentation in some species. For example, peacocks and males of many bird species have developed elaborate plumage to attract females. Male fireflies have developed light flashes that are species specific with regard to number and duration of flashes (**Figure 42.5**). Females respond with a flash of their own.

Visual signals are also used to resolve disputes over territories or mates. Deer and antelope have antlers or horns that they use to display and spar over territory and females. Most of these matches never develop into outright fights, because the males assess their opponent's strength by the size of these ornaments and concede to a stronger rival so as to avoid injury.

Tactile Communication Strengthens Social Bonds and Conveys Information About Food

Animals often use tactile communication to establish bonds between group members. Primates frequently groom one another, and canines and felines may nuzzle and lick each other. Many insects use tactile communication to convey information on the whereabouts of food.

Perhaps the most fascinating example of tactile communication among animals is the dance of the honeybee, elegantly studied by German ethologist Karl von Frisch in the 1940s. Bees commonly live in large hives; in the case of the European honeybee (*Apis mellifera*), the hive consists of 30,000–40,000 individuals. The flowering plants on which the bees forage can be located miles from the hive and store more nectar and pollen than an individual bee can carry back to the nest. The scout bee that locates the plants returns to the hive and recruits more workers to join her (**Figure 42.6a**). The scout dances on the vertical side of a honeycomb, and the dance is monitored by other bees, which follow and touch her to interpret the message. If the food is relatively close to the hive, less than 50 m away, the scout performs a round dance, rapidly moving in a circle, first in one direction and then the other (**Figure 42.6b**). If the food is more than 50 m away, the scout will perform a different type of dance, called a "waggle dance." In this dance, the scout traces a figure 8, in the middle of which she waggles her abdomen and produces bursts of sound. Again, the other bees maintain contact with her. The amazing part of the waggle dance is that the angle at which the central part of the figure 8 deviates from the vertical direction of the comb represents the same angle at which the food source deviates from the point at which the Sun hits the horizon (**Figure 42.6c**). The direction is always up-to-date, because the bee adjusts the dance as the Sun moves across the sky.

Biology Principle

Structure Determines Function

In fireflies, a morphological feature influences animal behavior.

(a) Firefly flashing

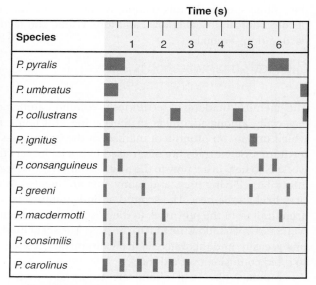

(b) Male flash patterns

Figure 42.5 **Visual communication in fireflies.** **(a)** Communication between fireflies is conducted by species-specific light flashes emitted by organs located on the underside of the abdomen. **(b)** Different species have different flash frequencies and durations. For example, *Photinus pyralis* and *P. umbratus* make relatively long flashes with long intervals between them, whereas *P. consimilis* and *P. carolinus* flashes are short but rapid.

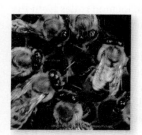

(a) Bees clustering around a recently returned scout, shown on the right

(b) Round dance

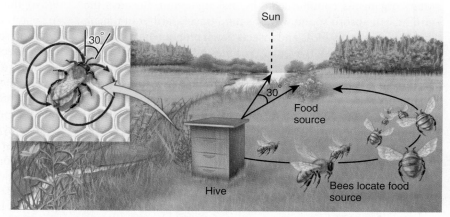

(c) Waggle dance: The angle of the waggle to the vertical orientation of the honeycomb corresponds to the angle of the food source from the Sun.

Figure 42.6 **Tactile communication among honeybees regarding food sources.** **(a)** Bees gather around a newly returned scout to receive information about nearby food sources. **(b)** If the food is less than 50 m away, the scout performs a round dance. **(c)** If the food is more than 50 m away, the scout performs a waggle dance, which conveys information about its location. If the dance is performed at a 30° angle to the right of the hive's vertical plane, then the food source is located at a 30° angle to the right of the Sun.

42.2   Reviewing the Concepts

- Communication is a form of behavior. The use of different forms of communication between organisms depends on the environment in which they live.
- Chemical communication often involves marking territories; auditory and visual forms of communication are often used to attract or defend mates; and tactile communication is used to establish bonds between group members (Figures 42.5, 42.6).

42.2   Testing Your Knowledge

1. Most terrestrial mammals are nocturnal. This means they are likely to communicate primarily via what means?
   - **a.** visual
   - **c.** chemical
   - **e.** b and c
   - **b.** auditory
   - **d.** a and b

42.3   Living in Groups and Optimality Theory

Learning Outcomes:

1. Detail the costs and benefits of living in groups.
2. Outline the costs and benefits of defending a territory.
3. Describe how game theory is used to determine winners between contestants.

Some of the more complex animal behavior occurs when individuals live together in groups such as flocks or herds. When is it best to live alone and when does it benefit an individual to live in a group? One way to approach this question is to assess the costs and benefits involved. Although group living increases competition for food and the spread of disease, it also has benefits that compensate for the costs involved. Many of these benefits relate to group defense against predators and locating and securing food sources. Group living can reduce predator success in at least two ways: through increased vigilance and through protection in numbers.

Living in Large Groups May Reduce the Risk of Predation Because of Increased Vigilance

For many predators, success depends on the element of surprise. If an individual is alerted to an attack, the predator's chance of success is lowered. A woodpigeon (*Columba palumbus*) in a flock takes to the air when it spots a goshawk (*Accipiter gentilis*). Once one pigeon takes flight, the other members of the flock are alerted and follow suit. If each individual in a group occasionally scans the environment for predators, the larger the group, the less time an individual forager needs to devote to vigilance and the more time it can spend feeding. This is referred to as the **many-eyes hypothesis** (Figure 42.7). Of course, cheating is a possibility, because some birds might never look up, relying on others to keep watch while they keep feeding. However, the individual

Figure 42.7   Living in groups and the many-eyes hypothesis. The larger the number of woodpigeons, the less likely an attack will be successful.

Concept Check: *What other advantages are there to large groups of individuals when being attacked by a predator?*

that happens to be scanning when a predator approaches is most likely to escape, a fact that tends to discourage cheating.

Living in Groups Offers Protection by the Selfish Herd

Group living also provides protection in sheer numbers. Typically, predators take one prey animal per attack. In any given attack, an individual antelope in a herd of 100 has a 1 in 100 chance of being selected, whereas a single individual has a 1 in 1 chance. Large herds may be attacked more frequently than a solitary individual, but a herd is unlikely to attract 100 times more attacks than an individual, often because of the territorial nature of predators. Furthermore, large numbers of prey are able to defend themselves better than single individuals, which usually choose to flee. For example, groups of nesting black-headed gulls mob a crow, thereby reducing the crow's ability to steal the gulls' eggs.

Research has shown that within a group, each individual can minimize the danger to itself by choosing the location that is as close to the center of the group as possible. This was the subject of a famous paper, "The Geometry of the Selfish Herd," by the British evolutionary biologist W. D. Hamilton. The explanation of this type of defense is that predators are likely to attack prey on the periphery because they are easier to isolate visually. Many animals in herds tend to bunch close together when they are under attack, making it physically difficult for the predator to get to the center of the herd.

Predator Success May Be Increased in Groups

Group living may allow predators such as lions and wolves the opportunity to locate and take down prey of a disproportionately large size, which a single predator would be unable to handle. Furthermore, as we saw with honeybees, when animals search for food within a group, each individual may be able to exploit the discovery of others. Interestingly, the actual size of predator groups may be different from the optimal size. Imagine that a solitary killer whale hunting for a seal has a given payoff for its efforts (**Figure 42.8**). Here, payoff is defined as the amount of energy gained by eating the prey minus the amount of energy expended in capturing it. If another killer whale joins in the hunt, the seal is more easily caught, and, despite having to share the prey, payoff for either individual increases. A third killer whale increases the payoff even more. Three whales is the optimal group size, for which the payoff to each individual is maximized. When the group size becomes four or five, then the average payoff to each individual decreases, because the food has to be shared among more individuals. However, living in a group of four or five is still a better option than hunting alone so whales continue to join groups of two, three, or four other whales. When the group size is six or more, a whale would do better on its own than in the group. In this example, the most commonly observed or stable group size is five individuals. Paradoxically, the optimal group size of three, which affords the greatest payoff to each whale, is not equivalent to the stable group size.

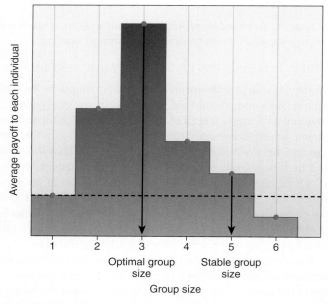

Figure 42.8 **Optimal and stable group size.** The payoff to a group of two or three predators is greater than for a solitary predator. The highest payoff is at a group size of three, which is the optimal size. However, other solitary individuals would benefit from joining the group, and group size increases to five individuals. In a group size of six, any one individual would do better on its own. The stable group size is then five.

Some Animals Defend a Territory

Some animals prefer living a solitary existence to living in a herd. Many of these animals actively defend a **territory,** a fixed area in which an individual excludes other members of its own species, and sometimes other species, by aggressive behavior or territory marking. The primary benefit of a territory is that it provides exclusive access to a particular resource, whether it be food, mates, or sheltered nesting sites. Large territories provide more of a resource but may be costly to defend, whereas small territories that are less costly to defend may not provide enough resources. Size of territory may be predicted by **optimality theory,** which predicts that an animal should behave in a way that maximizes the benefits of a behavior minus its costs. In this case, the benefits are the nutritional or caloric value of the food items within the territory, and the costs are patrolling and defending the territory. When the difference between the energetic benefits of food gathering and the energetic costs of maintaining a territory is maximized, an organism is optimizing its behavior. Optimality theory can also be used in decisions about food gathering and when it may be profitable to remain at a patch to look for food versus when is better to look for a completely new patch.

In studies of the territorial behavior of the golden-winged sunbird (*Nectarinia reichenowi*) in East Africa, American ornithologists Frank Gill and Larry Wolf measured the energy content of nectar as the benefit of maintaining a territory and compared it with the energy costs of activities such as perching, flying, and fighting (**Figure 42.9**). Defending the territory ensured that other sunbirds did not take nectar from available flowers, thus increasing the amount of nectar in each flower. In defending a territory, the sunbird gained 780 Calories (kilocalories) a day in extra nectar content. However, the sunbird also spent 728 Calories kcal in defense of the territory, yielding a net gain of 52 kcal a day and making territorial defense advantageous.

Defending a territory can be dangerous, and biologists have long been interested in determining the outcome of contests between individuals. American mathematician John Nash developed **game theory** to establish the outcome of contests in which an individual's choice of strategy depends on the actions of other individuals. Originally developed to understand human economic behavior, game theory has been used to help understand the behavior of animals in competitive situations.

Figure 42.9 **The golden-winged sunbird of East Africa (*Nectarinia reichenowi*) defends its territory.**

Quantitative Analysis

GAME THEORY ESTABLISHES WHETHER INDIVIDUALS FIGHT OR FLEE

Imagine a game in which individuals of the same species engage in contests over resources. The possible behaviors for any given individual are to display, presenting itself as a contestant; fight to win, attacking until the opponent retreats; and retreating, giving up the resource to the opponent. Some individuals, the "Hawks," always fight to win, risking injury to themselves in the process, whereas others, the "Doves," initially perform displays but always retreat before injury occurs (**Figure 42.10**).

Let's assign the winner of a contest +50 and the loser 0. The cost of injury is −100 because the injured player may not be able to compete again for a long time or may die, and the cost of spending time in a display is −10. It is assumed that Hawks and Doves reproduce in proportion to their scores. What happens when Hawks fight other Hawks or Doves, or when Doves fight Doves? We can analyze such a contest by constructing a two-by-two matrix with the average rewards for four possible types of encounter (**Table 42.1**). In a population of all Hawks, the chance of winning is 50%. Half the population wins and gets a reward of 50, and half the population loses and gets −100. The average is +50 + (−100)/2 = −25. Thus, any individual playing Dove would do better because when a Dove meets a Hawk it gets 0 in every encounter, since it retreats immediately, which is not very good but still better than −25. Therefore, Hawk is not always the best strategy. In a population of all Doves, the chance of winning is 50%. Half of the population wins and gets a reward of 40 (the reward minus the cost of displaying), and half of the population loses and gets −10 (the cost of display); the score, on average is $\frac{1}{2}(50 - 10) + \frac{1}{2}(-10) = +15$. Even though the average score is positive, Dove is not always the best strategy either. In this population, any individual Hawk would do very well, and the Hawk strategy would soon spread because when a Hawk meets a Dove, it gets +50 in every encounter.

Although all individuals in a population will not always adopt a Hawk or Dove strategy, a mixture of Hawk and Dove strategies is more likely. In such a population, a stable equilibrium is reached in which the average reward for a Hawk is equal to the average reward for a Dove. For the rewards we have specified, the stable mixture can be calculated as follows. If h is the proportion of Hawks in the population, the proportion of Doves is $(1 - h)$. The average reward for a Hawk, H, is the reward for each type of fight multiplied by the probability of meeting each type of contestant.

Therefore, the average reward for a Hawk will be:

$$H = -25h + 50(1 - h)$$

For Doves the average reward will be:

$$D = 0h + 15(1 - h)$$

At the stable point, H is equal to D. When H = D, the proportion of Hawks $(h) = 7/12$, and the proportion of Doves $(1 - h) = 5/12$.

This stable point could be achieved in two ways. First, the population could consist of 7/12 of individuals who always played Hawk and 5/12 who always played Dove. Alternatively, the population could consist of individuals who all adopted a mixed strategy, playing Hawk in 7/12 contests and Dove in the other 5/12.

Despite the simplicity of these models, some important conclusions can be drawn from them:

1. Fighting strategy is frequency dependent: It depends on what other animals are doing. A Hawk strategy is good for an individual in a population of Doves but not in one of Hawks. Territory owners may be more likely to behave like Hawks than challengers.
2. The strategies employed by individuals are dependent on the values of rewards. If the rewards are changed, the proportion of individuals playing Hawk and Dove strategies will change.
3. The frequency of Hawk behavior increases as the payoff increases. For males, one of the biggest payoffs is the opportunity to mate with a female because failure to do

Table 42.1	Average Rewards to the Attacker in the Game Between Hawk and Dove	
	Opponent	
Attacker	**Hawk**	**Dove**
Hawk	$\frac{1}{2}(50) + \frac{1}{2}(-100) = -25$	+50
Dove	0	$\frac{1}{2}(50 - 10) + \frac{1}{2}(-10)$ $= +15$

Costs and Rewards: Winner +50   Injury −100

Loser 0   Display −10

Figure 42.10 Hawk and Dove strategies. In these dueling meerkats, the individual on the left is escalating the fight, behaving in a Hawklike manner, and the individual on the right is in a submissive posture, a Dovelike strategy.

so is equivalent to genetic death. Fights over females are therefore commonly severe, sometimes fatal, and Hawk strategies dominate.

In the real world, animals also adjust their strategies according to the vigor of their opponents. It would be pointless to adopt a Hawk strategy against a bigger opponent, even for a territory owner. Players may use a strategy that follows the rule "if larger, behave like a Hawk; if smaller, behave like a Dove; if equally matched, adopt the Hawk strategy if a territory owner."

Crunching the Numbers: What is the average reward to a Hawk in a Hawk-versus-Hawk confrontation, where the reward to the winner is $+30$ and all other rewards are the same as in Table 42.1?

42.3 Reviewing the Concepts

- Many benefits of group living relate to defense against predators, offering protection through sheer numbers. Groups of predators may enjoy greater success hunting in a pack than when alone (Figures 42.7, 42.8).
- Some animals prefer a solitary existence over group living and may maintain exclusive territories. The size of a territory, a fixed area in which an individual or group excludes other members of its own species, tends to be optimized according to the costs and benefits involved (Figure 42.9).
- Game theory can be used to determine the strategies used by animals in contests over territories, food, or mates (Figure 42.10, Table 42.1).

42.3 Testing Your Knowledge

1. In nature, the most commonly observed number of individuals in a group is generally
   a. <100.
   b. >10.
   c. the optimal group size.
   d. the stable group size.
   e. the selfish herd size.

2. What is the main advantage of defending a territory?
   a. exclusive access to mates
   b. exclusive use of resources
   c. reduced conflict with others
   d. reduced transmission of disease
   e. reduced predation pressure

3. In any given population; the most commonly observed fighting strategy is
   a. Hawk.
   b. Dove.
   c. a mixture of Hawks and Doves.
   d. if smaller, behave like a Hawk.
   e. if a territory owner, behave like a Dove.

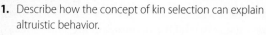
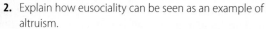

42.4 Altruism

Learning Outcomes:

1. Describe how the concept of kin selection can explain altruistic behavior.
2. Explain how eusociality can be seen as an example of altruism.

Although a primary goal of an organism is to reproduce and pass on its genes, we see many instances in which some individuals that live in groups forgo reproducing altogether, apparently to benefit the group. How do ecologists explain **altruism**—a behavior that appears to benefit others at a cost to oneself?

Kin Selection Is Explained by Hamilton's Rule

We are not surprised if parents forgo food for themselves while passing food on to their offspring because all offspring have copies of their parents' genes; in taking care of their young, parents are actually caring for copies of their own genes. Such behavior is known as **kin selection,** selection for behavior that lowers an individual's own survival and reproductive capabilities but enhances the survival and reproductive success of a relative. As we see later, kin selection can operate via many different relatives, not just parents and their offspring.

The probability that any two individuals will share a copy of a particular gene is a quantity, r, called the **coefficient of relatedness.** During meiosis in a diploid species, any given copy of a gene has a 50% chance of segregating into an egg or sperm. A mother and father are on average related to their children by an amount $r = 0.5$, because half of a child's genes come from its mother and half from its father. By similar reasoning, brothers or sisters are related by an amount $r = 0.5$ (they share half their mother's genes and half their father's); grandchildren and grandparents, by 0.25; and cousins, by 0.125 (**Figure 42.11**). In 1964, ecologist W. D. Hamilton realized the implication of the coefficient of relatedness for the evolution of altruism. An organism can pass on its genes not only through having offspring, but also through ensuring the survival of siblings, nieces, nephews, and cousins. This means an organism has a vested interest in protecting its brothers and sisters, and even the offspring of its parents' siblings.

The term **inclusive fitness** is used to designate the total number of copies of genes passed on through one's relatives, as well as one's own reproductive output. Hamilton proposed that an altruistic gene is favored by natural selection when

$$rB > C$$

where r is the coefficient of relatedness of donor (the altruist) to the recipient, B is the benefit received by the recipient of the altruism, and C is the cost incurred by the donor. This is known as **Hamilton's rule.**

Let's examine a situation involving altruism within a group of animals. Many insect larvae, especially caterpillars, are soft-bodied creatures. They rely on possessing a bad taste or toxin to deter predators and may advertise this condition with bright

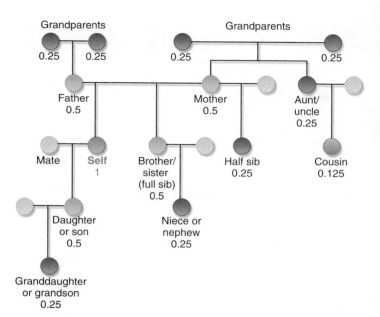

Figure 42.11 **Degree of genetic relatedness to self in a diploid organism.** Pink hatched circles represent completely unrelated individuals.

✔ **Concept Check:** *In theory, should you sacrifice your life to save one sister or nine cousins?*

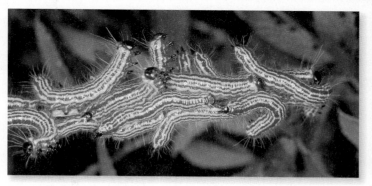

Figure 42.12 **Altruistic behavior.** *Datana ministra* caterpillars exhibit a bright, striped warning pattern to advertise their bad taste to predators.

✔ **Concept Check:** *Why do these caterpillars congregate in clusters?*

Biology Principle

The Genetic Material Provides a Blueprint for Reproduction

The similarities in DNA between kin promote behavior in which some animals act to save the lives of their close relatives.

Figure 42.13 **Alarm calling, an example of kin selection.** This prairie dog sentry is emitting an alarm call to warn other individuals, which are often close kin, of the presence of a predator. It is believed that by doing so, the sentry draws attention away from the others but becomes an easier target itself.

warning colors. For example, noxious *Datana ministra* caterpillars, which feed on oaks and other trees, have bright red and yellow stripes and adopt a specific posture with head and tail ends upturned when threatened (Figure 42.12). Unless it is born with an innate avoidance of this prey type, a predator has to kill and eat one of the caterpillars in order to learn to avoid similar individuals in the future. It is of no personal benefit to a single unlucky caterpillar to be killed. However, animals with warning colors often aggregate in kin groups because they hatch from the same egg mass. In this case, the death of one individual is likely to benefit its siblings, which are less likely to be attacked by the same predator in the future, and thus its genes will be preserved. This explains why the genes for bright color and a warning posture are successfully passed on from generation to generation. In a case where $r = 0.5$, B might be 50, and $C = 1$, the benefit of 25 is greater than 1, so the genes for this behavior are favored by natural selection.

A common example of altruism in social animals occurs when a sentry raises an alarm call in the presence of a predator. This behavior has been observed in Belding's ground squirrels (*Spermophilus beldingi*). The squirrels feed in groups, with certain individuals acting as sentries and watching for predators. As a predator approaches, the sentry typically gives an alarm call, and the group members retreat into their burrows. Similar behavior occurs in prairie dogs (*Cynomys* spp.) (Figure 42.13). In drawing attention to itself, the caller is at a higher risk of being attacked by the predator. However, in many groups, those closest to the sentry are most likely to be offspring or brothers or sisters; thus, the altruistic act of alarm calling is reasoned to be favored by kin selection.

Altruism in Eusocial Animals Arises Partly from Genetics and Partly from Lifestyle

Perhaps the most extreme form of altruism is the evolution of sterile castes in social animals, in which the vast majority of females, known as workers, rarely reproduce themselves but instead help one reproductive female (the queen) to raise offspring, a phenomenon called **eusociality.** In insects, the explanation of eusociality lies partly in the particular genetics of most social insect reproduction. Females develop from fertilized eggs and are diploid, the product of fertilization of an egg by a sperm. Males develop from unfertilized eggs and are haploid. Such a system of sex determination is called the **haplodiploid system** (refer back to Figure 14.16). If they have the same parents, each daughter receives an identical set of genes from her haploid father. The other half of a female's genes comes from her diploid mother, so the coefficient of relatedness (r) of sisters is 0.50 (from father) + 0.25 (from mother) = 0.75. The result is that females are more closely related to their sisters (0.75) than they would be to their own offspring (0.50). This suggests that it is evolutionarily more advantageous for females to stay in the nest or hive and care for other female offspring of the queen, which are their full sisters.

Elegant though these types of explanations are, they do not explain the whole picture. Large eusocial colonies of termites exist, but termites are diploid, not haplodiploid. In this case, how do we account for the existence of eusociality? The particular lifestyle of animals, as well as genetics, promotes eusociality. In the 1970s, a eusocial mammal, the naked mole rat (*Heterocephalus glaber*) was found living in arid areas of Africa in large underground colonies where only one female, the queen, mates with different males and produces offspring (**Figure 42.14**). The large nests or burrows of the mole rat are enclosed, making it difficult for individuals to escape and form their own colony. Many females are forced to live together, making it possible for the queen to suppress reproduction in other females. She does this by producing a pheromone in her urine that is passed around the colony by grooming. In the next section we complete our discussion of behavior by examining the different mating systems that occur in the animal world.

Figure 42.14 **A naked mole rat colony (*Heterocephalus glaber*).** In this mammalian species, most females do not reproduce; only the queen (shown resting on workers) has offspring.

42.4 Reviewing the Concepts

- Altruism is behavior that benefits others at a cost to oneself. Most apparently altruistic acts are often associated with outcomes beneficial to those most closely related to the individual, a concept termed kin selection (Figures 42.11, 42.12, 42.13).
- In eusociality, a phenomenon in which most individuals of a species do not reproduce, altruism may arise partly from the unique genetics of the animals and partly from lifestyle (Figure 42.14).

42.4 Testing Your Knowledge

1. In diploid organisms a mother is related to her daughter by $r =$
   a. 0. **b.** 0.25. **c.** 0.5. **d.** 0.75. **e.** 1.0.
2. The existence of worker ants who do not mate can be explained by
   a. eusociality.
   b. a haplodiploid mating system.
   c. the enclosed nature of their nests.
   d. both a and b.
   e. both b and c.

42.5 Mating Behavior

Learning Outcome:

1. Compare and contrast promiscuous, monogamous, polygynous, and polyandrous mating systems.

In nature, males produce millions of sperm, but females produce far fewer eggs. It would seem that the majority of males are superfluous because one male could easily fertilize all the females in a local area. If one male can mate with many females, why in most species does the sex ratio remain at approximately 1 to 1? The answer lies with natural selection. Let's consider a hypothetical population that contains 10 females to every male; each male mates, on average, with 10 females. A parent whose F_1 offspring were exclusively sons could expect to have 10 times the number of F_2 offspring than a parent with the same number of daughters. Under such conditions, natural selection would favor the spread of genes for male-producing tendencies, and males would become prevalent in the population. If the population were mainly males, females would be at a premium, and natural selection would favor the spread of genes for female-producing tendencies. Such constraints operate on the numbers of both male and female offspring, keeping the sex ratio at about 1:1. This concept was developed in 1930 by the British geneticist Ronald Fisher and has come to be known as Fisher's principle.

Even though the sex ratio is fairly even in most species, that doesn't mean that one female always mates with one male or vice versa. Four different types of mating systems occur in nature (**Figure 42.15**). In some species, mating is promiscuous, with each female and each male mating with many partners within a breeding season. In monogamy, each individual mates exclusively with one partner over at least a single breeding cycle and sometimes for longer. In contrast, polygamy describes a mating pattern in which either males or females mate with more than one partner

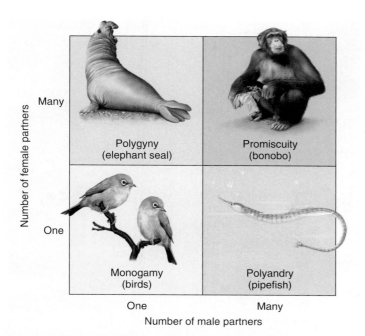

Figure 42.15 The four different animal mating strategies.

in a breeding season. There are two types of polygamy. In polygyny (Greek for many females), one male mates with more than one female, but females mate only with one male. In polyandry (Greek for many males), one female mates with several males, but males mate with only one female.

In Promiscuous Mating Systems, Each Male or Female Mates with Multiple Partners

Chimpanzees and bonobos are somewhat **promiscuous;** each male mates with many females and vice versa. In these species, sex has a social as well as a reproductive function, allowing for the alleviation of conflict within the social group. However, females that maximize the genetic diversity of their offspring are also

more likely to have at least some offspring that will survive in a changing world. Intertidal and terrestrial mollusks are also usually promiscuous. Individuals copulate with several partners and eggs are fertilized with sperm from several different individuals. These mollusks are slow moving and they risk desiccation when searching for a mate. The risk of not finding a mate is believed to promote promiscuous mating.

In Monogamous Mating Systems, Males and Females Are Paired for at Least One Reproductive Season

In **monogamy,** each individual mates exclusively with one partner over at least a single breeding cycle and sometimes for longer. Males and females do not exhibit much **sexual dimorphism—** a pronounced difference in the morphologies of the two sexes within a species—and are generally similar in body size and structure (**Figure 42.16a**). Several hypotheses have been developed to explain the existence of monogamy. The first is the **mate-guarding hypothesis,** which suggests that males stay with a female to protect her from being fertilized by other males. Such a strategy may be advantageous when receptive females are widely scattered and difficult to find.

The **male-assistance hypothesis** maintains that males remain with females to help them rear their offspring. Monogamy is common among birds, where about 70% of the pairings remain intact during at least one breeding season. According to the male-assistance hypothesis, monogamy is prevalent in birds because eggs and chicks take a considerable amount of parental care. Most eggs need to be incubated continuously if they are to hatch, and chicks require almost continual feeding. It is therefore in the male's best interest to help raise his young, because he would have few surviving offspring if he did not.

The **female-enforced monogamy hypothesis** suggests that females stop their male partners from being polygynous. Male and female burying beetles (*Nicrophorus defodiens*) work together to bury small, dead animals, which provide a food resource for their developing offspring. Males release pheromones to attract other

(a) Monogamous species

(b) Polygynous species

(c) Polyandrous species

Figure 42.16 Sexual dimorphism in body size and mating system. **(a)** In monogamous species, such as these Manchurian cranes (*Grus japonensis*), males and females do not exhibit pronounced sexual dimorphism and appear very similar. **(b)** In polygynous species, such as white-tailed deer, (*Odocoileus virginianus*), males are bigger than females and have large horns with which they engage other males in combat over females. **(c)** In polyandrous species, females are usually bigger, as with these golden silk spiders (*Nephila clavipes*).

females to the site. However, although an additional female might increase the male's fitness, the additional developing offspring might compete with the offspring of the first female, decreasing her fitness. As a result, on smelling these pheromones, the first female interferes with the male's attempts at signaling, preserving the monogamous relationship.

In Polygynous Mating Systems, One Male Mates with Many Females

In **polygyny** (Greek, meaning many females), one male mates with more than one female in a single breeding season. Physiological constraints often dictate that female organisms must care for the young. Because of these constraints, at least in many organisms with internal fertilization, such as mammals and some fishes, males are able to mate with and then desert several females. Polygynous systems are therefore associated with uniparental care of young, with males contributing little. Sexual dimorphism is typical in polygynous mating systems, with males developing a larger body size to boost success in competition over mates (Figure 42.16b). Sexual selection is prevalent in polygynous mating systems with females choosing the most attractive males (intersexual selection) or mating with the most competitively superior males (the "winners" of intrasexual selection) (refer back to Figure 19.18). Several types of polygyny are known, including resource-based polygyny, harem mating, and communal courting.

Resource-Based Polygyny   When some critical resource is patchily distributed and in short supply, certain males may dominate the resource and breed with more than one visiting female. The major source of nestling death in the lark bunting (*Calamospiza melanocorys*), which lives in North American grasslands, is overheating from too much exposure to the Sun. Prime territories are therefore those with abundant shade, and some males with shaded territories attract two females, even though the second female can expect no help from the male in the process of rearing young. Males in some exposed territories remain bachelors for the season. From the dominant male's point of view, polygyny is advantageous; from the female's point of view, there may be costs. Although by choosing dominant males, a female may be gaining access to good resources, she will have to share these resources with other females.

Harem Mating   Sometimes males defend a group of females without commanding a resource-based territory. This pattern is more common where females naturally congregate in groups or herds, perhaps to avoid predation, as with horses, zebras, and some deer, and where space is limited, as with southern elephant seals, which mate on beaches. Usually the largest and strongest males command most of the matings, but defending the harem is usually so exhausting that males may only manage to remain the strongest male for a year or two.

Communal Courting   Polygynous mating can occur where neither resources nor groups of females are defended. In some instances, particularly in birds and mammals, males display in designated communal courting areas called **leks** (Figure 42.17). Females come to these areas specifically to find a mate, and they choose a prospective

Figure 42.17   **Male birds at a lek.** Black grouse (*Tetrao tetrix*) congregate at a moorland lek in Scotland in April. Females visit the leks, and males display to them.

mate after the males have performed elaborate displays. Most females seek to mate with males possessing the most desirable traits, so a few of the flashiest males perform the vast majority of the matings. At a lek of the white-bearded manakin (*Manacus manacus*) of South America, one male accounted for 75% of the 438 matings when there were as many as 10 males. A second male mated 56 times (13% of matings), but six others mated a total of only 10 times.

In Polyandrous Mating Systems, One Female Mates with Many Males

Polyandry (Greek, meaning many males), in which one female mates with several males, is rarer than polygyny. Nevertheless, it occurs in some species of birds, fishes, and insects. Sexual dimorphism is present, with the females being the larger of the sexes (see Figure 42.16c). In the Arctic tundra, the summer season is short but very productive, providing a bonanza of insect food for 2 months. The productivity of the breeding grounds of the spotted sandpiper (*Actitis macularia*) is so high that the female becomes rather like an egg factory, laying up to five clutches of four eggs each in 40 days. Her reproductive success is limited not by food but by the number of males she can find to incubate the eggs, and females compete for males, defending territories where the males sit.

Polyandry is also seen in some species where egg predation is high and males are needed to guard the nests. For example, in the pipefish (*Syngnathus typhle*), males have brood pouches that provide eggs with safety and a supply of oxygen- and nutrient-rich water. Females produce enough eggs to fill the brood pouches of two males and may mate with more than one male.

42.5 Reviewing the Concepts

- Four types of mating systems are found among animals: promiscuity, monogamy, polygyny, and polyandry. Relative body size of males and females depends on mating system (Figures 42.15, 42.16).
- Polygynous mating can often occur in situations when males dominate a resource, defend groups of females, or display in common courting areas called leks (Figure 42.17).

42.5 Testing Your Knowledge

1. Fisher's principle suggests the sex ratio of males to females in a population should tend toward
- **a.** 100:1.
- **c.** 1:1.
- **e.** 1:100.
- **b.** 10:1.
- **d.** 1:10.

2. In polyandrous mating systems
- **a.** males are usually bigger than females.
- **b.** females are usually bigger than males.
- **c.** males and females are of roughly equal size.

Assess and Discuss

Test Yourself

1. What is the proximate cause of male deer fighting over females?
   - a. to determine their supremacy over other males
   - b. to injure other males so that these other males cannot mate with females
   - c. to maximize the number of genes they pass on
   - d. because changes in day length stimulate this behavior
   - e. because fighting helps rid the herd of weaker individuals

2. Certain behaviors seem to have very little environmental influence. Such behaviors are the same in all individuals regardless of the environment and are referred to as _____ behaviors.
   - a. genetically programmed
   - d. all of the above
   - b. instinctual
   - e. b and c only
   - c. innate

3. Patrick has decided to teach his puppy a few new tricks. Each time the puppy responds correctly to Patrick's command, the puppy is given a treat. This is an example of
   - a. habituation.
   - d. imprinting.
   - b. classical conditioning.
   - e. orientation.
   - c. operant conditioning.

4. Nutcrackers are able to relocate caches of seeds by means of
   - a. innate behavior.
   - d. operant conditioning.
   - b. imprinting.
   - e. cognitive maps.
   - c. classical conditioning.

5. For group living to evolve, the benefits of living in a group must be greater than the costs associated with it. Which of the following is an example of a benefit of living in a group?
   - a. reduced spread of disease and/or parasites
   - b. increased food availability
   - c. reduced competition for mates
   - d. decreased risk of predation
   - e. all of the above

6. The modification of behavior based on prior experience is called
   - a. habituation.
   - d. adjustment behavior.
   - b. learning.
   - e. innate.
   - c. association.

7. When an individual behaves in a way that reduces its own fitness but increases the fitness of others, the organism is exhibiting
   - a. kin selection.
   - d. selfishness.
   - b. group selection.
   - e. ignorance.
   - c. altruism.

8. In naked mole rats, mothers are related to daughters by $r =$
   - a. 0.
   - b. 0.125.
   - c. 0.25.
   - d. 0.5.
   - e. 0.75.

9. In ants, which employ a haplodiploid mating system, fathers are related to sons by $r =$
   - a. 0.
   - c. 0.25.
   - e. 0.75.
   - b. 0.125.
   - d. 0.5.

10. In a polygynous mating system,
    - a. one male mates with one female.
    - b. one female mates with many different males.
    - c. one male mates with many different females.
    - d. many different females mate with many different males.

Conceptual Questions

1. Some male spiders are eaten by the females after copulation. How can this act be seen to benefit the males?

2. Male parental care occurs in only 7% of fishes and amphibian families with internal fertilization but in 69% of amphibian families with external fertilization. Propose an explanation for why this is so.

3. **PRINCIPLES** A principle of biology is that *new properties emerge from complex interactions.* Male brown bears (*Ursus arctos*) can be infanticidal, killing existing cubs when they move into a new territory. Explain why bear hunting may have severe consequences for bear populations.

Collaborative Questions

1. Whooping cranes (*Grus americana*) are an endangered species that are being bred in captivity to increase their numbers. One problem with this approach is that these cranes are migratory. In the absence of other cranes, can you think of an innovative way human researchers might use crane behavior to ensure their safe passage to overwintering sites?

2. Discuss ways in which organisms communicate with each other, giving examples of each.

Online Resource

43

Ecology and the Physical Environment

Burmese python in the Florida Everglades. Questions for ecologists are how far will these snakes spread and what effects will they have on local wildlife?

Chapter Outline

The Burmese python, *Python molorus*, is an invasive species now well established in an area of south Florida called the Everglades. At up to 7 m (22 feet) long and 90 kg (200 lbs) in weight, the snakes have a large appetite and can eat prey as large as white-tailed deer and alligators. Most likely, a small number of adult snakes, once pets, were released prior to 1985, and since then their numbers have increased dramatically. Concerned citizens want to know how quickly the population will grow and how far will it spread. Should we expect the snake to eventually occur over the entire state of Florida or will it be limited by colder climates further north? Ecologists can provide answers to these types of questions. In January 2012, the U.S. Fish and Wildlife Service banned the importation and interstate transportation of four species of large snakes into the U.S.: the Burmese python, yellow anaconda, and the northern and southern African pythons. They did so based on the work of ecologists who had determined that the snakes had a high risk of spreading to other geographic areas and causing significant damage to native wildlife.

In this chapter of the ecology unit, we will focus on abiotic interactions and examine the effects of factors such as temperature, water, light, pH, and salt concentrations on the distributions of organisms. We also explore the causes of global warming and its effects on species distributions. We conclude with a consideration of climate and its large influence on the major types of habitats where organisms are found.

43.1 | The Environment's Effect on the Distribution of Organisms

Learning Outcomes:

1. Give examples of how extremes of temperature—both low and high—affect the distribution and abundance of life on Earth.
2. Describe how global warming is gradually increasing the Earth's temperature and will likely affect species distributions.
3. Explain how other environmental factors such as wind, availability of water and light, salt concentration, and the pH of soil and water can affect the distributions of organisms.

Table 43.1	Selected Abiotic Factors and Their Effects on Organisms
Factor	**Effect**
Temperature	Low temperatures freeze many plants; high temperatures denature proteins. Some plants require fire for germination.
Wind	Wind amplifies effects of cool temperatures (wind chill) and water loss; creates pounding waves.
Water	Insufficient water limits plant growth and animal abundance; excess water drowns plants and other organisms.
Light	Insufficient light limits plant growth, particularly in aquatic environments.
Salinity	High salinity generally reduces plant growth in terrestrial habitats; affects osmosis in marine and freshwater environments.
pH	Variations in pH affect decomposition and nutrient availability in terrestrial systems; directly influences mortality in both aquatic and terrestrial habitats.

Both the distribution patterns of organisms and their abundance are limited by physical features of the environment such as temperature, wind, availability of water and light, salinity, and pH (**Table 43.1**). In this section, we will examine these features of the environment.

Temperature Has an Important Effect on the Distribution of Plants and Animals

Temperature is perhaps the most important factor in the distribution of organisms because of its effect on biological processes and because of the inability of most organisms to regulate their body temperature precisely. For example, the organisms that form coral reefs secrete a calcium carbonate skeleton. Skeleton formation and coral deposition are accelerated at high temperatures but are suppressed in cold water. Coral reefs are therefore abundant only in warm water, and a close correspondence is observed between the 20°C isotherm for the average daily temperature during the coldest month of the year and the limits of the distribution of coral reefs (**Figure 43.1**). An isotherm is a line on a map connecting points of equal temperature. Coral reefs are located between the two 20°C isotherm lines that are formed above and below the equator.

Low Temperatures   Frost is probably the single most important factor limiting the geographic distribution of tropical and subtropical plants. In plants, cold temperature can be lethal because cells may rupture if the water they contain freezes. The northern boundary of wild madder, *Rubia peregrina*, in Europe corresponds to the 4.5°C January isotherm (**Figure 43.2a**). Although this temperature is well above freezing, the shoots do not grow well at lower

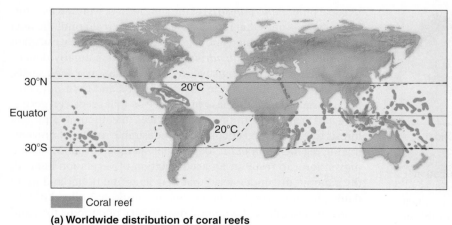

Coral reef

(a) Worldwide distribution of coral reefs

(b) A coral reef

Figure 43.1   Worldwide locations of coral reefs.   (a) Coral reef formation is limited to waters bounded by the 20°C isotherm (dashed line), a line where the average daily temperature is 20°C during the coldest month of the year. **(b)** Coral reef from the Pacific Ocean.

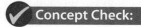 **Concept Check:**   *Why are coral reefs limited to warm water?*

Biology Principle

Living Organisms Interact with Their Environment

The distributional limits of organisms are often set by the physical environment.

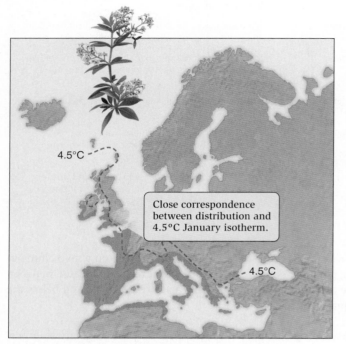

Close correspondence between distribution and 4.5°C January isotherm.

(a) The distribution of wild madder (*Rubia peregrina*) in Europe

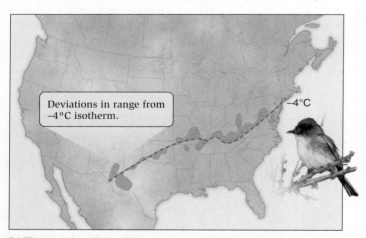

Deviations in range from −4°C isotherm.

(b) The northern limit of the winter range of the Eastern phoebe (*Sayornis phoebe*)

Figure 43.2 Effects of low temperatures on organismal distribution patterns. **(a)** The distribution of wild madder (*Rubia peregrina*) in Europe is limited by cold temperature. Madder distribution (shaded) and the location of the January isotherm for 4.5°C are shown. **(b)** The northern limit of the winter range of the Eastern phoebe (*Sayornis phoebe*) (dashed line) is associated with the −4°C isotherm of minimum January temperatures. The area of deviation between the range boundary and the isotherm is shaded.

temperatures. The geographic range limits of endothermic animals are also affected by temperature. For example, the eastern phoebe (*Sayornis phoebe*), a small bird, has a northern winter range that coincides with an average minimum January temperature of above 4°C (Figure 43.2b). Such limits are probably related to the energy demands associated with cold temperatures. Cold temperatures mean higher metabolic costs, which are, in turn, dependent on high feeding rates. Below 4°C, the eastern phoebe cannot feed fast enough or, more likely, find enough food to keep warm.

Will cold temperatures limit the spread of the Burmese pythons (see chapter-opening figure)? Most people consider these snakes to be inhabitants of the tropical jungle, but in fact their native range includes parts of temperate China and the Himalayas (Figure 43.3). Burmese pythons can live in places with 2 months of mean temperatures as low as 2°C and zero rainfall. Thus, populations could exist not only throughout Florida, but also in much of the South and West, including California.

High Temperatures High temperatures are also limiting for many plants and animals because relatively few species can survive internal temperatures more than a few degrees above their metabolic optimum. We have discussed how corals are sensitive to low water temperatures; however, they are sensitive to high water temperatures as well. When temperatures are too high, the symbiotic algae that live within coral die and are expelled, causing a phenomenon known as coral bleaching. Once bleaching occurs, the coral tissue loses its color and turns white (Figure 43.4). El Niño is a naturally occurring weather phenomenon characterized by a major increase in the water temperature of the equatorial Pacific Ocean. In the winter of 1982–1983, an influx of warm water from the eastern Pacific raised temperatures just 2–3°C for 6 months, which was enough to kill many of the reef-building corals on the coast of Panama. By May 1983, just a few individuals of one species, *Millepora intricata,* were alive.

The ultimate high temperatures that many terrestrial organisms face are the result of fire. However, some species depend on frequent low-intensity fires for their reproductive success. The longleaf pine (*Pinus palustris*) of the southeast U.S. produces serotinous cones—ones that remain sealed by pine resin until the heat of a fire melts them open and releases the seeds. In the west, giant sequoia trees (*Sequoiadendron giganteum*) are similarly dependent on periodic low-intensity fires for germination of their seeds. Such fires both enhance the release of seeds and clear out competing vegetation at the base of the tree so that seeds can germinate and grow. Fire-suppression practices that attempt to protect forests from fires can actually have undesirable results by preventing the regeneration of fire-dependent species. Furthermore, fire prevention can result in an accumulation of vegetation beneath the canopy (the understory) that may later fuel hotter and more damaging fires. The U.S. Forest Service uses controlled human-made fires to mimic the natural disturbance of periodic fires and maintain fire-dependent forest species (Figure 43.5).

The Greenhouse Effect The Earth is warmed by a phenomenon called the **greenhouse effect.** In a greenhouse, sunlight penetrates the glass and raises temperatures, with the glass acting

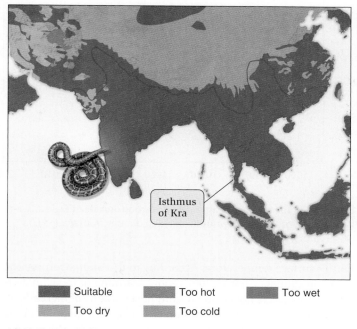

■ Suitable	■ Too hot	■ Too wet
■ Too dry	■ Too cold	

(a) Native range limits

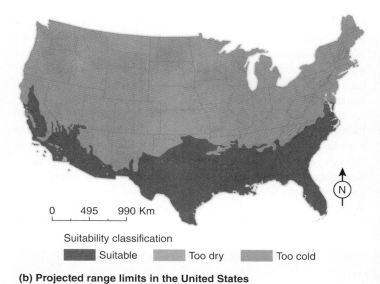

Suitability classification
■ Suitable ■ Too dry ■ Too cold

(b) Projected range limits in the United States

Figure 43.3 **Range limits of the Burmese python.** **(a)** Native range limits. **(b)** Projected range limits in the United States.

to trap the resultant heat inside. Similarly, solar radiation in the form of short-wave energy passes through the atmosphere to heat the surface of the Earth. This energy is radiated from the Earth's warmed surface back into the atmosphere, but in the form of long-wave infrared radiation. Instead of letting it escape back into space, however, atmospheric gases absorb much of this infrared energy and radiate it back to the Earth's surface, causing its temperature to rise further (Figure 43.6). The greenhouse effect is a naturally occurring process that is responsible for keeping the Earth warm enough to sustain life. Without some type of greenhouse

Figure 43.4 **Coral bleaching off the waters of Mantanani Island, Malaysia.** Coral bleaching occurs when stresses such as increased water temperature disrupt the symbiotic relationship between corals and the organisms that live within them.

BioConnections: *Refer back to Section 28.3. What organisms live symbiotically within corals?*

Figure 43.5 **Giant sequoia.** A park ranger uses a drip torch to ignite a fire at Sequoia National Park in California. Periodic, controlled human-made fires mimic the sporadic wildfires that normally burn natural areas. Such fires are vital to the health of giant sequoia populations, because they serve to open the pine cones and release the seeds.

 **Concept Check:** *Why are some fires very destructive to natural systems?*

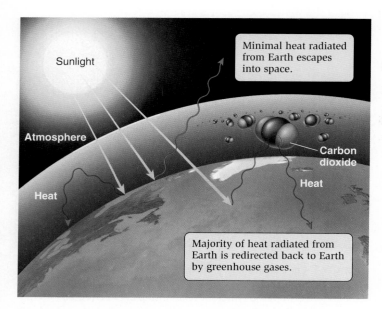

Figure 43.6 **The greenhouse effect.** Solar radiation, in the form of short-wave energy, passes through the atmosphere to heat the Earth's surface. Long-wave infrared energy is radiated back into the atmosphere. Much infrared energy is absorbed by atmospheric gases, including carbon dioxide (CO_2) molecules, and reflected back to Earth, causing global temperatures to rise.

effect, global temperatures would be much lower than they are, perhaps averaging only $-17°C$ compared with the existing average of $+15°C$.

The greenhouse effect is caused by a group of atmospheric gases that together make up less than 1% of the total volume of the atmosphere. These gases—primarily water vapor, carbon dioxide, methane, nitrous oxide, and chlorofluorocarbons—are referred to as greenhouse gases (Table 43.2).

Global Warming Ecologists are concerned that human activities are increasing the greenhouse effect and causing **global warming** (also called global climate change)—a gradual elevation of the

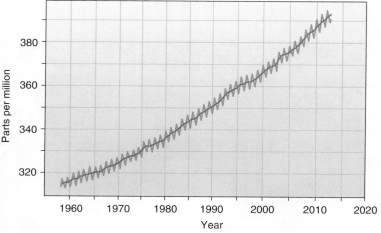

Figure 43.7 **The increase of atmospheric carbon dioxide.** CO_2 levels have shown constant increases in air taken directly from Mauna Loa Observatory, Hawaii, since 1957.

Earth's surface temperature. According to the Intergovernmental Panel on Climate Change 2007 report, warming of the climate is unequivocal, as is now evident from observations of increases in global average air and ocean temperatures, widespread melting of snow and ice, and rising average global sea level. Most greenhouse gases have increased in atmospheric concentration since industrial times. Of those increasing, the most important is carbon dioxide (CO_2). As Table 43.2 shows, although CO_2 has a lower global warming potential per unit of gas (relative absorption) than any of the other major greenhouse gases, its concentration in the atmosphere is much higher. Atmospheric levels of CO_2 have increased by about 25% since 1957, reaching the historic milestone of 400 ppm in May 2013 (Figure 43.7).

To predict the effect of global warming, most scientists focus on a future point, about 2100, when the concentration of atmospheric CO_2 will have doubled—that is, increased to about 700 ppm compared with the late-20th-century level of 350 ppm. Scientists estimate that at that time, should current levels of emissions continue, average global temperatures will be somewhere in the range of 1–6°C (about 2–10°F) warmer than present and will increase an additional 0.5°C each decade. This increase in heat

Table 43.2	Selected Greenhouse Gases and Their Contribution to Global Warming*			
	Carbon dioxide (CO₂)	**Methane (CH₄)**	**Nitrous oxide (N₂O)**	**Chlorofluorocarbons (CFCs)**
Relative absorption in ppm of increase†	1	21	310	10,000
Atmospheric concentration (ppm‡)	400	1.75	0.315	0.0005
Contribution to global warming	73%	7%	19%	1%
Percent from natural sources; type of source	20–30%; volcanoes	70–90%; swamps, gas from termites and ruminants	90–100%; soils	0%
Major human-made sources	Fossil fuel use, deforestation	Rice paddies, landfills, biomass burning, coal and gas exploitation	Cultivated soil, fossil-fuel use, automobiles, industry	Previously manufactured products (for example, aerosol propellants) but now banned in the U.S. and the E.U.

*Water vapor is not included in this table.
†Relative absorption is the warming potential per unit of gas.
‡ppm = parts per million

might not seem like much, but it is comparable to the warming that ended the last Ice Age. Future consequences would include a further contraction of snow cover and a decrease in sea ice extent, heat waves and drought in dry areas, heavier precipitation in moister areas, and an increase in hurricane and tornado intensity.

Assuming this scenario of gradual global warming is accurate, we need to consider what the consequences might be for plant and animal life. Although many species can adapt to slight changes in their environment, the anticipated changes in global climate are expected to occur too rapidly to be compensated for by normal evolutionary processes such as natural selection. Plant species in particular cannot simply disperse and move north or south into the newly created climatic regions that will be suitable for them. Many tree species take hundreds, even thousands, of years for seed dispersal. American paleobotanist Margaret Davis predicted that in the event of a CO_2 doubling, the sugar maple (*Acer saccharum*), which is presently distributed throughout the midwestern and northeastern U.S. and southeastern Canada, would die back in all areas except in northern Maine, northern New Brunswick, and southern Quebec (**Figure 43.8**). Of course, this contraction in the tree's distribution could be offset by the creation of new favorable habitats in central Quebec. However, most scientists believe that the climatic zones would shift toward the poles faster than trees could migrate via seed dispersal; therefore, extinctions would probably occur.

Wind Can Amplify the Effects of Temperature

Wind is created by temperature gradients. As air heats up, it becomes less dense and rises. As hot air rises, cooler air rushes in to take its place. For example, hot air rising in the tropics is replaced by cooler air flowing in from more temperate regions, thereby creating northerly or southerly winds.

Wind affects living organisms in a variety of ways. It increases the rate of heat loss by convection—the transfer of heat by the movement of air next to the body (the wind chill factor). Wind also contributes to water loss in organisms by increasing the rate of evaporation in animals and transpiration in plants. For example, the tree line in alpine areas is often determined by a combination of low temperatures and high winds, an environmental condition in which transpiration exceeds water uptake. Wind is also an important mortality factor in its own right and severe storms can kill trees by blowing them over (**Figure 43.9**). Fifteen million trees in the south of England perished in October 1987 as a result of a severe storm.

The Availability of Water Has Important Effects on the Abundance of Organisms

Water has an important effect on the distribution of organisms. Cytoplasm is 85–90% water, and without moisture, there can be no life. As noted in Chapter 2, water performs crucial functions in all living organisms. It acts as a solvent for chemical reactions, takes part in hydrolysis and dehydration reactions, is the means by which animals eliminate wastes, and is used for support in plants and in some invertebrates as part of a hydrostatic skeleton.

The distribution patterns of many plants are limited by the availability of water. Animals face problems of water balance,

Biology Principle

Biology Affects Our Society
Global warming will change the distributions of many species familiar to us.

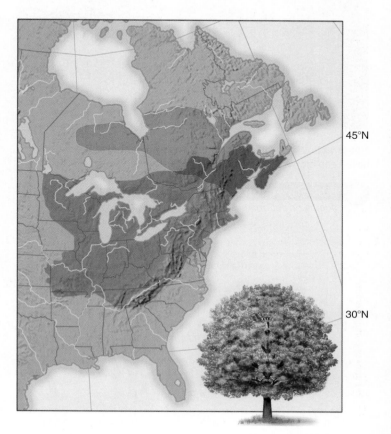

Figure 43.8   **Possible changes in the range of sugar maples due to global warming.** The present geographic range of the sugar maple (blue shading) and its potential range with doubled CO_2 levels (red shading) in North America. Purple shading indicates the region of overlap, which is the only area where the sugar maple would be found before it spread into its new potential range.

✓ **Concept Check:**   *What abiotic factors that influence sugar maple distribution might change in a world with elevated levels of CO_2?*

too, and their distribution and population density can be strongly affected by water availability. Because most animals depend ultimately on plants for food, their distribution is intrinsically linked to those of their food sources. Such a phenomenon regulates the number of buffalo (*Syncerus caffer*) in the Serengeti area of Africa. In this area, grass productivity is related to the amount of rainfall in the previous month. Buffalo density is governed by grass availability, so a significant correlation is found between buffalo density and rainfall (**Figure 43.10**). The only exception occurs in the vicinity of Lake Manyara, where groundwater promotes plant growth.

Figure 43.9 **Winds can directly impact many organisms.** These trees have been blown over and killed by severe winter storms.

BioConnections: *Look back to Section 31.4. In what way does wind chill increase cooling of animals?*

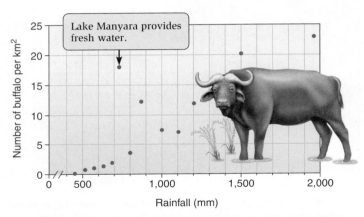

Figure 43.10 **The relationship between the amount of rainfall and the density of buffalo.** In the Serengeti area of Africa, buffalo density is very much dependent on grass availability, which itself depends on annual rainfall. The main exception is where there is permanent water, such as at Lake Manyara. Greater water availability leads to greater grass growth and buffalo densities.

Light Can Be a Limiting Resource for Plants and Algae

Because light is necessary for photosynthesis, it can be a limiting resource for plants. However, what may be sufficient light to support the growth of one plant species may be insufficient for another. Many tropical herbaceous species grow best in the shady conditions of a rainforest canopy.

In aquatic environments, light may be an even more limiting factor because water absorbs light, preventing photosynthesis at depths greater than 100 m. Most aquatic plants and algae are limited to a fairly narrow zone close to the surface and appear green, as they are in terrestrial conditions, because they absorb red and blue light, but not green (**Figure 43.11a**). At greater depths, red light is

(a) Green algae at the ocean's surface

(b) Red algae at a greater depth

Figure 43.11 **Algae growing at different ocean depths. (a)** In the eastern Pacific Ocean, off the coast of California, these green algae floating at the ocean's surface are green, just like terrestrial plants. **(b)** In contrast, at 75-m depth, in the McGrail Bank off of the Gulf of Mexico, most seaweeds are pink and red because the pigments can absorb the blue-green light that reaches such depths.

mostly absorbed by water, leaving predominantly blue-green light. Red algae occur in deeper marine environments because they possess pigments that enable them to utilize blue-green light efficiently, and they reflect red light when they are photographed with a flash underwater or when we see them at the surface (**Figure 43.11b**).

The Concentration of Salt in Water and Soil Can Be Critical

Salt concentrations vary widely in aquatic environments and have a great effect on osmotic balance in animals (refer back to Figure 38.2). Many marine birds and reptiles have salt glands that actively transport sodium chloride from the body to the outside from pores in the nose and around the eyes. In marine fishes, the gills pump out salt into the ocean. Salt in the soil also affects the growth of plants. In arid terrestrial regions, salt accumulates in soil where water settles and then evaporates. This can also be of great significance in agriculture, where continued watering in arid environments, together with the addition of salt-based fertilizers, greatly increases salt concentration in soil and reduces crop yields. A few terrestrial plants are adapted to live in saline soil along seacoasts. Here the vegetation consists largely of **halophytes**—species that can tolerate higher salt concentrations in their cell sap than regular plants. Coastal species such as mangroves and *Spartina*

Figure 43.12 **Plant adaptations for salty conditions.** Special salt glands in the leaves of *Spartina* exude salt (white specks), enabling this grass to exist in saline intertidal conditions.

marsh grasses have salt glands that excrete salt to the surface of the leaves, where it forms tiny white salt crystals (**Figure 43.12**).

The pH of Soil or Water Can Limit the Distribution of Organisms

As discussed in Chapter 2, the pH of water can be acidic, alkaline, or neutral. Variation in pH can have a major effect on the distribution of organisms. Normal rainwater has a pH of about 5.6, which is slightly acidic because the absorption of atmospheric carbon dioxide (CO_2) and sulfur dioxide (SO_2) into rain droplets forms carbonic and sulfuric acids. However, most plants grow best at a soil water pH of about 6.5, a value at which soil nutrients are most readily available to plants. Only a few genera, such as rhododendrons and azaleas (*Rhododendron*), can live in soils with a pH of 4.0 or less. Furthermore, at a pH of 5.2 or less, nitrogen-fixing bacteria do not function properly, which prevents organic matter from decomposing. In general, alkaline soils containing chalk and limestone have a higher pH and sustain a much richer flora (and associated fauna) than do acidic soils (**Figure 43.13**).

Generally, the number of fishes and other species also decreases in acidic waters. The optimal pH for most freshwater fishes and bottom-dwelling invertebrates is between 6.0 and 9.0. Acidity in lakes increases the amount of toxic metals, such as mercury, aluminum, and lead, which can leach into the water from surrounding soil and rock. Both too much mercury and too much aluminum can interfere with gill function, causing fishes to suffocate.

The susceptibility of both aquatic and terrestrial organisms to changes in pH explains why ecologists are so concerned about **acid rain,** precipitation with a pH of less than 5.6. Acid rain results from the burning of fossil fuels such as coal, oil, and natural gas, which releases SO_2 and nitrogen oxide (NO_2) into the atmosphere. These react with oxygen in the air to form sulfuric acid and nitric acid, respectively, which falls to the Earth's surface in rain or snow.

Acid rain is important in terrestrial systems, too. For example, acid rain can directly affect forests by killing leaves or pine needles, as has happened on some of the higher mountaintops in the Great Smoky Mountains. It can also greatly lower soil pH, which can result in a loss of essential nutrients such as calcium and nitrogen. Low soil calcium results in calcium deficiencies in plants, in the snails that consume the plants, and in the birds that eat the snails, ultimately causing weak eggshells that break before hatching.

(a) Rich flora on alkaline soil   **(b) Sparse flora on acidic soil**

Figure 43.13 **Species-rich flora of chalk grassland compared with species-poor flora of acid soils.** **(a)** At Mount Caburn, in the lime-rich chalk hills of Sussex County, England, there is a much greater variety of plant and animal species than at **(b)** a heathland site elsewhere in England. Heathlands are a product of thousands of years of human clearance of natural forest areas and are characterized by acidic, nutrient-poor soils.

✓ **Concept Check:** *Why do acidic soils support fewer species of plants and animals than lime-rich soils?*

Decreased soil pH also kills certain soil microorganisms, preventing decomposition and recycling of nitrogen in the soil. Decreases in soil calcium and nitrogen weaken trees and other plants and may make them more susceptible to insect and fungal attack.

43.1 Reviewing the Concepts

- Abiotic factors such as temperature, wind, water, light, salinity, and pH can have powerful effects on ecological systems (Table 43.1).

- Temperature exerts important effects on the distribution of organisms because of its effect on biological processes and the inability of many organisms to regulate their body temperature (Figures 43.1–43.5).

- The greenhouse effect is the process by which short-wave solar radiation passes through the atmosphere to warm the Earth and is radiated back into the atmosphere as long-wave infrared radiation. Much of this radiation is absorbed by atmospheric gases and radiated back to the Earth's surface, causing its temperature to rise (Figures 43.6, 43.7, Table 43.2).

- An increase in atmospheric gases is increasing the greenhouse effect, causing global warming—a gradual elevation of the Earth's surface temperature. Ecologists predict that global warming will have a large effect on the distribution of the world's organisms (Figure 43.8).

- The availability of water and light, the concentration of salt, and the pH of soil and water can limit the distribution of organisms (Figures 43.10–43.13).

43.1 Testing Your Knowledge

1. Based on data from distribution patterns in its native south Asia, Burmese pythons in Florida are predicted to
   a. be limited to extreme south Florida.
   b. be limited to the "jungle-like" conditions of the Everglades.
   c. spread out of Florida into others areas of the southern U.S.
   d. spread to the Canadian border.
   e. die out fairly quickly over the next 10 years.

2. In the northern hemisphere, what effects should global warming most likely have on the distribution of species?
   a. cause species to spread northward
   b. cause species to spread southward
   c. cause species to spread north and south
   d. cause species to retreat from the north
   e. cause species to spread to the east and west

3. Coastal plants that grow on sand dunes are likely to be limited by
   a. availability of fresh water.   d. pH of sea water.
   b. water salinity.   e. light availability.
   c. high winds.

43.2 Climate and Biomes

Learning Outcomes:

1. Explain how global temperature differentials drive atmospheric circulation.
2. Explain how temperature and rainfall affects the distribution of terrestrial biomes.
3. Describe how the distribution of species on Earth has been affected by continental drift.
4. Explain the concept of biogeographic regions.

Temperature, wind, precipitation, and light are components of **climate,** the long-term prevailing weather pattern in a given region. As we have seen, the distribution and abundance of organisms are influenced by these factors. Therefore, to understand the patterns of abundance of life on Earth, ecologists need to study the global climate. In this section, we examine global climate patterns, focusing on how temperature variation drives atmospheric circulation and how features such as elevation and landmass can alter these patterns. We also note how continental drift and evolution over long time periods have helped shape the distribution patterns of different taxa.

Atmospheric Circulation Is Driven by Global Temperature Differentials

Substantial differences in temperature occur over the Earth, mainly due to latitudinal variations in the incoming solar radiation. In higher latitudes, such as northern Canada and Russia, the Sun's rays hit the Earth obliquely and are spread out over more of the planet's surface than they are in equatorial areas (**Figure 43.14**). More heat is also lost in the atmosphere of higher latitudes

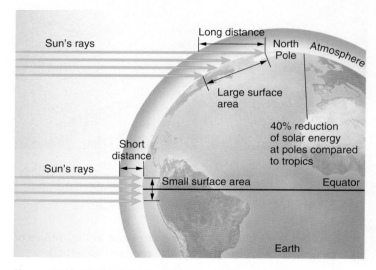

Figure 43.14 The intensity of solar radiation at different latitudes. In polar areas, the Sun's rays strike the Earth at an oblique angle and deliver less energy than at tropical locations. In tropical areas, the energy is concentrated over a smaller surface and travels a shorter distance through the atmosphere.

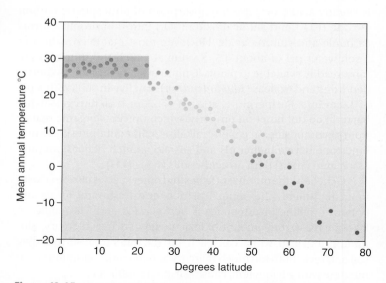

Figure 43.15 Variation of the Earth's temperature. The temperatures shown in this figure were measured at moderately moist continental locations of low elevation.

✓ **Concept Check:** *Why is there a wide band of similar temperatures at the tropics?*

because the Sun's rays travel a greater distance through the atmosphere, allowing more heat to be dissipated by cloud cover. The result is that 40% less solar energy strikes polar latitudes than equatorial areas. Generally, temperatures increase as the amount of solar radiation increases (**Figure 43.15**). However, at the tropics, both cloudiness and rain reduce average temperature, so temperatures do not continue to increase toward the equator.

Global patterns of atmospheric circulation and precipitation are influenced by solar energy. In this model, high temperatures at the equator cause the surface equatorial air to heat up and rise vertically into the atmosphere. The vertical rising of the hot air cools the land by convection. As the warm air rises away from its source of heat, it cools and becomes less buoyant, but the cool air does not sink back to the surface because the warm air behind it blocks the downward flow. The warm air rising near the equator forms towers of cumulus clouds that provide rainfall, which, in turn, maintains the lush vegetation of the equatorial rain forests. As the upper flow in this cell moves toward the poles, it begins to subside, or fall back to Earth, at about 20°–30° north and south of the equator, creating areas of high pressure. The world's tropical deserts are found at these latitudes, because the subsiding air is relatively dry, having released all of its moisture over the equator (**Figure 43.16**).

From the center of this zone, the surface flow splits into two directions, one of which flows toward the poles and the other toward the equator. The equatorial flow from both hemispheres meets near the equator in a region called the intertropical convergence zone (ITCZ). The circulation between 30° and 60° latitude is opposite that of the cell nearest the equator because the net surface flow is poleward. Additional zones of high precipitation occur in this cell, usually between 45° and 55°, dropping rainfall over the wet, temperate forests of the Pacific Northwest and

Western Europe in the Northern Hemisphere and New Zealand and Chile in the Southern Hemisphere. In the final circulation cell at the poles, the air has cooled and descends, but it has little moisture left, explaining why many high-latitude regions are dry and support only short tundra vegetation.

Elevation and Other Features of a Landmass Can Also Affect Climate

Thus far, we have considered how global temperatures and wind patterns affect climate. The geographic features of a landmass can also have an important effect. For example, the elevation of a region greatly influences its temperature range. On mountains, temperatures decrease with increasing elevation. This decrease is a result of a process known as **adiabatic cooling,** in which increasing elevation leads to a decrease in air pressure. When air is blown across the Earth's surface and up over mountains, it expands because of the reduced pressure. As it expands, it cools at a rate of about 10°C for every 1,000 m in elevation, as long as no water vapor or cloud formation occurs. (Adiabatic cooling is also the principle behind the function of a refrigerator, in which refrigerant gas cools as it expands coming out of the compressor.) A vertical ascent of 600 m produces a temperature change roughly equivalent to that brought about by an increase in latitude of

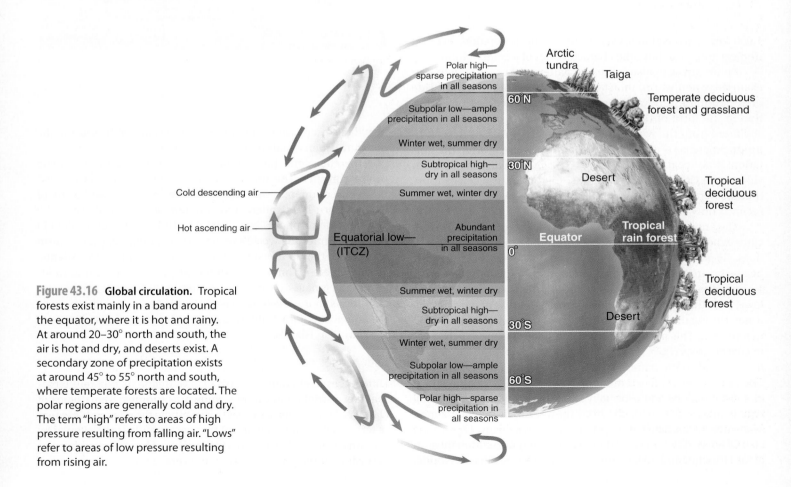

Figure 43.16 Global circulation. Tropical forests exist mainly in a band around the equator, where it is hot and rainy. At around 20–30° north and south, the air is hot and dry, and deserts exist. A secondary zone of precipitation exists at around 45° to 55° north and south, where temperate forests are located. The polar regions are generally cold and dry. The term "high" refers to areas of high pressure resulting from falling air. "Lows" refer to areas of low pressure resulting from rising air.

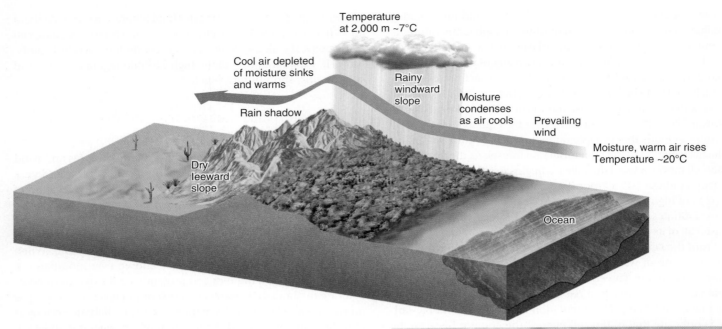

(a) Rain shadow

Figure 43.17 **The influence of elevation and proximity to water on climate.**

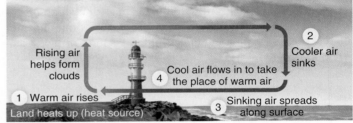

(b) Sea breeze

1,000 km. This explains why mountaintop vegetation, even in tropical areas, can have the characteristics of a colder biome.

Mountains can also influence patterns of precipitation. For example, when warm, moist air encounters the windward side of a mountain, it flows upward and cools, releasing precipitation in the form of rain or snow. On the side of the mountain sheltered from the wind (the leeward side), drier air descends, producing what is called a **rain shadow,** an area where precipitation is noticeably less (Figure 43.17a). In this way, the western side of the Cascade Range in Washington State receives more than 500 cm of annual precipitation, whereas the eastern side receives only 50 cm.

The proximity of a landmass to a large body of water can affect climate because land heats and cools more quickly than the sea does. Recall from Chapter 2 that water has a very high specific heat—the amount of energy required to raise the temperature of 1 gram of a substance by 1°C. The specific heat of the land is much lower than that of the water, allowing the land to warm quicker than water. During the day, the warmed air rises, and cooler air flows in to replace it. This pattern creates the familiar onshore sea breezes in coastal areas (Figure 43.17b). At night, the land cools quicker than the sea, and so the pattern is reversed, creating offshore breezes. The sea, therefore, has a moderating effect on the temperatures of coastal regions and especially islands. The climates of coastal regions may differ markedly from those of their climatic zones. Many never experience frost, and fog is often evident. Thus, along coastal areas, different vegetation patterns may occur from those in areas farther inland. In fact, some areas of the U.S., such as Florida,

would be deserts were it not for the warm water of the sea and the moisture-laden clouds that form above them.

Together with the rotation of the Earth, winds also create ocean currents. The major ocean currents act as "pinwheels" between continents, running clockwise in the ocean basins of the Northern Hemisphere and counterclockwise in those of the Southern Hemisphere (Figure 43.18). The Gulf Stream, equivalent in flow to 50 times the world's major rivers combined, brings warm water from the Caribbean and the U.S. coasts across the Atlantic Ocean, where it combines with the North Atlantic Drift to moderate the climate of Europe. The Humboldt Current brings cool conditions to the western coast of South America and almost to the equator, and the California Current brings a cooler climate to the Hawaiian Islands.

Differences in Climate Define Different Biomes

Differences in climate on Earth help to define its different large-scale terrestrial communities, known as **biomes.** Many types of classification schemes are used for mapping the geographic extent of terrestrial biomes, but one of the most useful was developed by the American ecologist Robert Whittaker, who classified biomes according to the physical factors of average annual precipitation

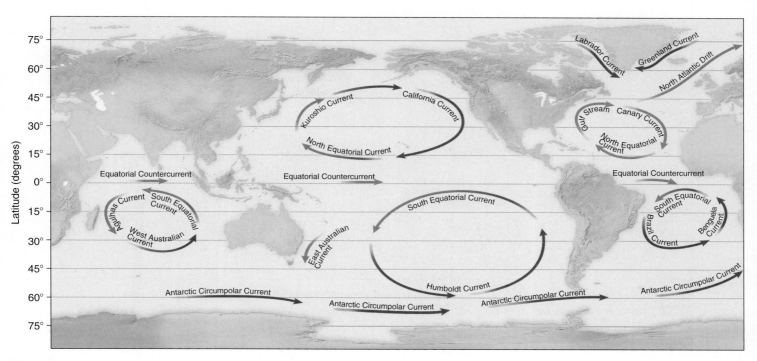

Figure 43.18 Ocean currents of the world. The red arrows represent warm water; the blue arrows, cold water.

and temperature. In this scheme, we recognize 10 terrestrial biomes: tropical rainforest, tropical deciduous forest, tropical grassland (or savannah), hot desert, temperate rainforest, temperate deciduous forest, temperate grassland, cold desert, taiga, and tundra (Figures 43.19, 43.20, 43.21).

Although broad terrestrial biomes are a useful way of defining the main types of communities on Earth, ecologists acknowledge that not all communities fit neatly into 1 of these 10 major biome types. One biome type often grades into another at biome boundaries, as seen on mountain ranges. Soil conditions can also influence biome vegetation. In California, temperate grassland with isolated trees is abundant, except on serpentine soils, which are dry and nutrient-poor, and support only sparse vegetation that is adapted to this extreme environment. In the eastern U.S., most of New Jersey's coastal plain, called the Pine Barrens, consists of sandy, nutrient-poor soil that cannot support the surrounding deciduous forest and instead contains grasses and low shrubs growing among open stands of pygmy pitch pine and oak trees.

Within aquatic environments, several different biome types are also recognized, including marine aquatic biomes (intertidal zone, coral reef, and open ocean) and freshwater habitats (lakes, rivers, and wetlands). These biomes are distinguished primarily by differences in temperature, salinity, oxygen content, depth, current strength, and availability of light (Figure 43.22). Freshwater habitats are traditionally divided into lentic, or standing-water habitats (from the Latin *lenis*, meaning calm), and lotic, or running-water habitats (from the Latin *lotus*, meaning washed).

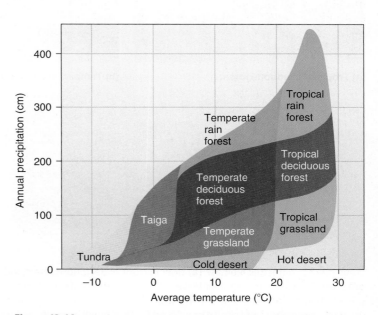

Figure 43.19 The relationship between the world's terrestrial biome types and temperature and precipitation patterns.

✓ **Concept Check:** *What other factors may influence biome types beyond patterns of temperature and precipitation?*

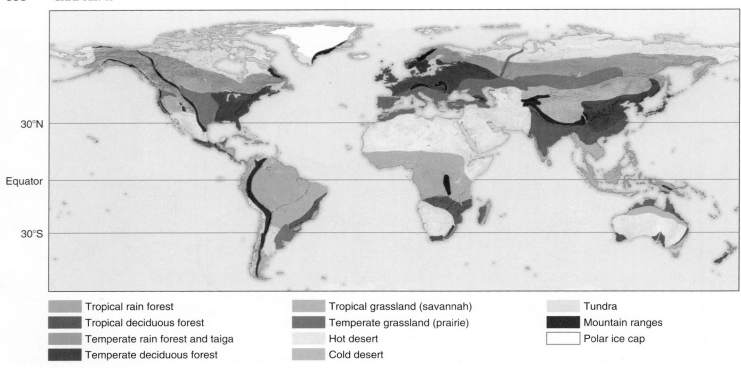

Tropical rain forest
Tropical deciduous forest
Temperate rain forest and taiga
Temperate deciduous forest

Tropical grassland (savannah)
Temperate grassland (prairie)
Hot desert
Cold desert

Tundra
Mountain ranges
Polar ice cap

Figure 43.20 Geographic location of terrestrial biomes. The distribution patterns of taiga and temperate rainforest are combined because of their similarity in tree species and because temperate rainforest is actually limited to a very small area.

(a) Tropical deciduous forest

(b) Temperate coniferous forest, or taiga

(c) Tropical grassland, or savannah

(d) Hot desert

(e) Tundra

Figure 43.21 Terrestrial biomes. (a) Tiger in tropical deciduous forest, India. Tropical deciduous forests have distinct wet and dry seasons. In the dry season trees often shed their leaves. **(b)** Temperate coniferous forest, or taiga, Canada. Taiga consists of coniferous trees with a conical shape to prevent bough breakage under heavy snow. Mammals are often heavily furred. **(c)** Tropical grassland, or savannah, Kenya. Savannah contains the greatest assemblages of large mammals on Earth. Rainfall is insufficient to support large trees but sufficient to support large swaths of grassland with occasional acacias (trees in the background). **(d)** Hot desert, Namibia. Here rainfall is less than 30 cm per year, and temperatures can range from below freezing at night to more than 50°C (112°F) in the day. **(e)** Tundra, Denali National Park, Alaska. Precipitation here is scant, less than 25 cm per year, and the growing season is only 50–60 days long.

✓ **Concept Check:** *In a globally warmed world, what biome might expand into areas currently occupied by tundra?*

(a) Intertidal   **(b) Coral reef**   **(c) Lentic, or lake, habitat**   **(d) Lotic, or river, habitat**

Figure 43.22 Aquatic biomes. (a) Intertidal, Washington State. The intertidal is alternately submerged and exposed by a daily cycle of tides. **(b)** Coral reef, Caribbean Sea. Coral reefs exist in warm water of at least 20°C but less than 30°C. **(c)** Lentic, or lake, habitat, Florida. Lentic habitats consist of still, often deep water. **(d)** Lotic, or river, habitat, Pacific Northwest. Lotic habitats have flowing, often well-oxygenated water and are able to support fish such as trout.

EVOLUTIONARY CONNECTIONS

Continental Drift and Biogeography Help Explain Species Distributions

Knowledge of biomes does not tell us everything about the distribution of plant and animal life on Earth. An understanding of evolution and geological change over large areas and time periods helps explain some of the patterns we see. For example, South America, Africa, and Australia all have similar biomes, ranging from tropical to temperate, yet each continent has distinctive animal life. South America is inhabited by sloths, anteaters, armadillos, and monkeys with prehensile tails. Africa possesses a wide variety of antelopes, zebras, giraffes, lions, baboons, the okapi, and the aardvark. Australia, which has no native placental mammals except bats, is home to a variety of marsupials such as kangaroos, koala bears, Tasmanian devils, and wombats, as well as the egg-laying monotremes, namely, the duck-billed platypus and echidnas. Most continents also have distinct species of plants; for example, eucalyptus trees are native only in Australia. In South American deserts, succulent plants belong to the family Cactaceae, the cacti. In Africa, they belong to the genus Euphorbia, the spurges.

One explanation for these species distributions is that abiotic factors are of paramount importance and that each region supports the fauna best adapted to it. However, the spread of introduced species has proved this explanation incorrect: European rabbits introduced into Australia proliferated rapidly, and eucalyptus from Australia grows well in California. A better explanation is that different flora and fauna are the result of the independent evolution of separate, unconnected populations, which have generated different species in different places. A knowledge of continental drift and evolution is therefore vital to understanding contemporary distributions of species.

The relative location of the landmasses on Earth has changed enormously over time as a result of continental drift, the slow shifting of the Earth's landmasses over time (refer back to Figure 18.9). The current distribution of the essentially flightless bird family, the ratites, in the Southern Hemisphere is the result of continental drift. The common ancestor of these birds occurred in a supercontinent that included what are now South America, Africa, and Australia. As the continent split apart, genera evolved separately so that today we have ostriches in Africa, emus in Australia, and rheas in South America.

Continental drift is not the only mechanism that creates widely separate populations of closely related species. The distributions of many present-day species are relics of once much broader distributions. For example, there are currently four living species of tapir: three in Central and South America and one in Malaysia (**Figure 43.23**). Fossil records reveal a much more widespread distribution over much of Europe, Asia, and North America. The oldest fossils come from Europe, making it likely that this was the center of origin of tapirs. Dispersal resulted in a more widespread distribution. Global cooling resulted in the extinction of tapirs in all areas except the two tropical locations.

Alfred Russel Wallace was one of the earliest scientists to realize that certain plant and animal taxa were restricted to certain geographic areas of the Earth (refer back to Chapter 19). For example, the distribution patterns of guinea pigs, anteaters, and other groups are confined to Central and South America, from central Mexico southward. Based on this and other observations, Wallace divided the world's biota into six major **biogeographic regions:** Nearctic, Palearctic, Neotropical, Ethiopian, Oriental, and Australian (**Figure 43.24**). These regions are still widely accepted today, though debate continues about the exact location of the boundary lines. Biogeographic regions correspond largely to continents but more exactly to areas bounded by major barriers to dispersal, such as oceans, deserts, and mountain ranges.

Biology Principle

All Life Is Related by an Evolutionary History

Knowing that all tapir species share a common European ancestor helps to explain their current distribution pattern.

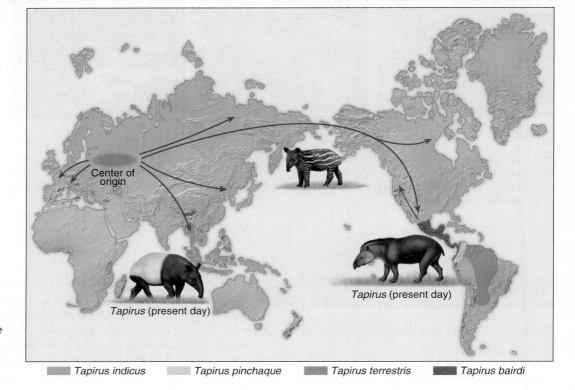

Figure 43.23 **Tapir distribution.** There are four living tapir species: three in Central and South America and one in Malaysia. Fossil evidence suggests a European origin and a more widespread distribution, with tapirs dying out in other regions.

Tapirus indicus   Tapirus pinchaque   Tapirus terrestris   Tapirus bairdi

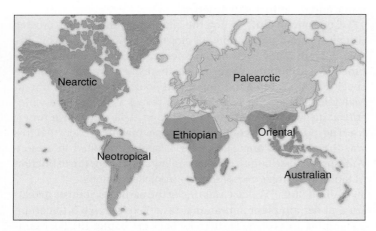

Figure 43.24 **The biogeographic regions proposed by A. R. Wallace.** Note that the borders do not always demarcate continents.

43.2 Reviewing the Concepts

- Global temperature differentials are caused by variations in incoming solar radiation and patterns of atmospheric circulation (Figures 43.14, 43.15, 43.16).
- Elevation and the proximity between a landmass and large bodies of water can similarly affect climate (Figures 43.17, 43.18).
- Climate has a large effect on biomes—major types of habitats characterized by distinctive plant and animal life. Terrestrial biomes are generally named for their climate and vegetation type and include tropical rain forest, tropical deciduous forest, temperate rain forest, temperate deciduous forest, temperate coniferous forest (taiga), tropical grassland (savanna), temperate grassland (prairie), hot and cold deserts, and tundra (Figures 43.19–43.21).
- Within aquatic environments, biomes include marine aquatic biomes (the intertidal zone, coral reef, and open ocean) and freshwater lakes, rivers, and wetlands. These are distinguished by differences in salinity, oxygen content, depth, current strength (lentic versus lotic), and availability of light (Figure 43.22).
- The distribution of living organisms can be explained by continental drift. Six major biogeographic regions—areas of the Earth containing a distinct distribution of flora and fauna—are recognized today: Nearctic, Palearctic, Neotropical, Ethiopian, Oriental, and Australian (Figures 43.23, 43.24).

43.2 Testing Your Knowledge

1. The prevailing winds would likely be southerly if you were standing
   a. at 60°N.   **c.** at 20°N.   **e.** b and c.
   b. at 40°N.   **d.** a and b.

2. The uniquely marsupial fauna of Australia is largely a result of
   a. adiabatic cooling.   **d.** rain shadows.
   b. climate.   **e.** biogeographic regions.
   c. continental drift and evolution.

3. If you were surrounded by zebras, lions, giraffes, and okapis, you would be in which biogeographic region?
   a. Neotropical   **c.** Australian   **e.** Nearctic
   b. African   **d.** Ethiopian

Assess and Discuss

Test Yourself

1. Which of the following is probably the most important factor in the distribution of organisms in the environment?
   a. light   d. water availability
   b. temperature   e. pH
   c. salinity

2. The greenhouse effect is
   a. a new phenomenon resulting from industrialization.
   b. due to the absorption of solar radiation by atmospheric gases.
   c. responsible for the natural warming of the Earth.
   d. all of the above.
   e. b and c only.

3. By what percent have atmospheric levels of carbon dioxide increased since 1957?
   a. 1   d. 20
   b. 5   e. 25
   c. 10

4. Physics is to engineering as ecology is to
   a. biology.   d. mathematics.
   b. environmental science.   e. statistics.
   c. chemistry.

5. What factor helps release seeds from serotinous pine cones?
   a. light   d. fire
   b. freezing temperatures   e. animals
   c. rainfall

6. What is the driving force that determines the circulation of the atmospheric air?
   a. temperature differences of the Earth
   b. winds
   c. ocean currents
   d. mountain ridges
   e. all of the above

7. In this biome, rainfall averages between 25 cm and 125 cm, and temperatures average between −10°C and 20°C. Where are you?
   a. tropical rainforest   d. prairie
   b. tropical deciduous forest   e. temperate deciduous forest
   c. savannah

8. What characteristics are commonly used to identify the biomes of the Earth?
   a. temperature   c. vegetation   e. a and b only
   b. precipitation   d. all of the above

9. What color of light is predominant at greater depths of water?
   a. red   c. blue-green   e. infrared
   b. yellow   d. ultraviolet

10. Which gas contributes most to human-caused global warming?
    a. carbon dioxide   d. methane
    b. nitrous oxide   e. chlorofluorocarbons
    c. sulfur dioxide

Conceptual Questions

1. If mountains are closer to the sun than valleys, why aren't they hotter?

2. Why should cold temperatures limit the distribution of endothermic animals?

3. **PRINCIPLES**   A principle of biology is that *living organisms interact with their environment*. In most locations on Earth, at about 30° latitude, air cools and descends, and hot deserts occur. Florida is situated between 31°N and 24°N. Why does it not support a desert biome?

Collaborative Questions

1. The so-called Telegraph fire, near Yosemite National Park, in 2008, was one of the worst in California that year, burning more than 46 square miles covered by timber that has not burned in over 100 years. What could be done to prevent such a catastrophic fire in the park itself?

2. Based on your knowledge of biomes, identify the biome in which you live. In your discussion, list and describe the organisms that you have observed in your biome. Why might your observations not fit the biome predicted to occur from temperature and precipitation profiles?

Online Resource

www.brookerprinciples.com

Stay a step ahead in your studies with animations that bring concepts to life and practice tests to assess your understanding. Your instructor may also recommend the interactive eBook, individualized learning tools, and more.

44

Population Ecology

A wolf in Yellowstone National Park.

The last wild wolves in Montana, Wyoming, and Idaho were killed in the early 1900s as part of a government-funded wolf extermination project. At the time, it was the policy of the federal government to exterminate wolves everywhere, even in national parks. The last wolves in Yellowstone National Park were killed in 1924, when two pups were killed at Soda Butte Creek in the northeast corner of the park. In the 1960s and 1970s, however, public attitudes changed, and wolves received legal protection under the Endangered Species Act of 1973. Wolves from Canada slowly began to filter into northern Montana in the 1980s. After a long, heated debate, wolf reintroductions were started in the continental United States a decade later. Between 1995 and 1996, 66 wolves were captured near Alberta, Canada, and released in Yellowstone Park, Wyoming, and central Idaho. The combined population of wolves in these states plus Montana showed dramatic growth. In 2011, wolves in Idaho were removed from the endangered species list. Tags for hunting and trapping wolves went on sale May 5th, 2011, in Idaho for the fall hunt. How can a population increase so fast that it is federally endangered only a few years before it is being "managed" by the state?

For sexually reproducing species such as wolves, a **population** can be defined as a group of interbreeding individuals of the same species occupying the same area at the same time.

This chapter explores **population ecology,** the study of the factors that affect population size and how these factors change over space and time. To study populations, we need to employ some of the tools of **demography**—the study of birth rates, death rates, age distributions, and the sizes of populations. We begin our discussion by examining the methods that ecologists use to measure population density. We will explore characteristics of populations and how growth rates are determined by the number of reproductive individuals in the population and their fertility rate. These data are used to construct simple mathematical models that allow us to analyze population growth, such as that of the reintroduced wolves, and predict future growth. We will also look at the factors that limit the growth of populations, such as competition, predation, and parasitism, and conclude the chapter by using these population concepts and models to explore the growth of human populations.

44.1 Measuring Population Size and Density

Learning Outcomes:

1. List the different techniques ecologists use to measure population density.

2. Explain how ecologists use the mark-recapture technique to determine population size.

Within their areas of distribution, organisms occur in varying numbers. We recognize this pattern by saying a plant or animal is "rare" in one place and "common" in another. For more precision, ecologists quantify distribution further and talk in terms of population **density**—the numbers of organisms in a given unit area or volume. Population growth affects population size and population density, and knowledge of both can help us make decisions about the management of species. How long will it take for a population of an endangered species to recover to a healthy level if we protect it from its most serious threats?

The simplest method for measuring population size is to visually count the number of organisms in a given area. We can reasonably do this only if the area is small and the organisms are relatively large. For example, we can readily determine the number of gumbo limbo trees (*Bursera simaruba*) on small islands in the Florida Keys. Normally, however, population ecologists calculate the density of plants or animals in a small area and use these data to estimate the total abundance over a larger area. For plants, algae, or other sessile organisms such as intertidal animals, it is fairly easy to count numbers of individuals per square meter or, for larger organisms such as trees, numbers per hectare (an area of land equivalent to 2.471 acres). However, many plant individuals are clonal; that is, they grow in patches of genetically identical individuals, so that rather than count individuals, we can also use the amount of ground covered by plants as an estimate of vegetation density.

Quadrats and Transects Are Used to Determine the Densities of Plants and Sessile Animals

Plant ecologists use a sampling device called a **quadrat,** a square frame that often measures 50×50 cm and encloses an area of 0.25 m² (**Figure 44.1a**). They then count the numbers of plants of a given species inside the quadrat and repeat this several times to obtain a density estimate per square meter. For example, if you counted densities of 20, 35, 30, and 15 plants in four quadrats, you could reliably say that the average density of this species was 25 individuals per 0.25 m², or $100/$m². For larger plants, such as trees, a quadrat would be ineffective. To count such organisms, many ecologists perform a **line transect,** in which a long piece of string is stretched out and any tree along its length is counted. For example, to count tree species on larger islands in the Florida Keys, we could lay out a 100-m line transect and count all the trees within 1 m on either side of the transect. In effect, this transect is little more than a long, thin quadrat encompassing 200 m². By performing five such transects, we could obtain estimates of tree density per 1,000 m² and then extrapolate that to a number per hectare or per island.

Several different sampling methods exist for quantifying the density of animal populations, which are more mobile than plants. Pitfall traps set into the ground can catch species such as spiders, lizards, or beetles wandering over the surface (**Figure 44.1b**). Sweep nets can be passed over grassland vegetation to dislodge and capture the insects feeding there. Mist nets—very fine netting spread between trees—can entangle flying birds and bats (**Figure 44.1c**). Baited live traps can capture terrestrial animals (**Figure 44.1d**). Population density can thus be estimated as the number of animals caught per trap or per unit area where a given number of traps are set, for example, 10 traps per 100 m² of habitat.

(a) Quadrat   **(b) Pitfall trap**   **(c) Mist net**   **(d) Live mammal trap**

Figure 44.1 Sampling techniques. (a) Quadrats are frequently used to count the number of plants per unit area. **(b)** Pitfall traps set into the ground catch wandering species such as beetles and spiders. **(c)** Mist nets consist of very fine mesh to entangle birds or bats. **(d)** Baited live traps catch terrestrial animals, including Komodo dragons, shown here on Rinca Island, Indonesia.

Quantitative Analysis

MARK-RECAPTURE CAN BE USED TO ESTIMATE POPULATION SIZE

Sometimes population biologists capture animals and then tag and release them (**Figure 44.2**). The rationale behind the **mark-recapture technique** is that after the tagged animals are released, they mix freely with unmarked individuals and within a short time are randomly mixed within the population. The population is then resampled, and the numbers of marked and unmarked individuals are recorded. We assume that the ratio of marked to unmarked individuals in the second sample is the same as the ratio of marked individuals in the first sample to the total population size. Thus,

$$\frac{\text{Number of individuals marked in first catch}}{\text{Total population size, } N} = \frac{\text{Number of marked recaptures in second catch}}{\text{Total number of second catch}}$$

Let's say we catch 50 largemouth bass in a lake and mark them with colored fin tags. A week later, we return to the lake and catch 40 fish and 5 of them were previously tagged fish. If we assume no immigration or emigration has occurred, which is quite likely in a closed system like a lake, and we assume there have been no births or deaths of fish, then the total population size is given by rearranging the equation:

$$\text{Total population size, } N = \frac{\text{Number of marked individuals in first catch} \times \text{Total number of second catch}}{\text{Number of marked recaptures in second catch}}$$

Using our data,

$$N = \frac{50 \times 40}{5} = 400$$

From this equation, we estimate that the lake has a total population size of 400 largemouth bass. This could be useful information for game and fish personnel who wish to know the total size of a fish population in order to set catch limits.

However, the mark-recapture technique can have drawbacks. Some animals that have been marked may learn to avoid the traps. Recapture rates will then be low, resulting in an overestimate of population size. Imagine that instead of 5 tagged fish out of 40 recaptured fish, we get only 2 tagged fish. Now our population size estimate is 2,000/2 = 1,000, a dramatic increase in our population size estimate. On the other hand, some animals can become "trap-happy," particularly if the traps are baited with food. This would result in an underestimate of the population size.

Crunching the Numbers: In a study of rodent populations, you catch 60 mice, mark them with plastic ear tags, and recatch 40, of which 12 are marked. What is the population size? You later realize that half of the ear tags fell off the mice prior to being recaptured. By how much have you misestimated the population size?

Figure 44.2 **The mark-recapture technique for estimating population size.** An ear tag identifies this Rocky Mountain goat (*Oreamnos americanus*) in Olympic National Park, Washington. Recapture of such marked animals permits estimates of population size.

Concept Check: *If we mark 110 Rocky Mountain goats and recapture 100 goats, 20 of which have ear tags, what is the estimate of the total population size?*

Because of the limitations of the mark-recapture technique, ecologists also use other, more novel methods to estimate population size. We can also estimate relative population size by examining catch per unit effort, which is especially valuable in commercial fisheries. We can't easily expect to count the number of fishes in an area of ocean, but we can count the number caught, say, per 100 hours of trawling. For some larger terrestrial or marine species, captured animals can be fitted with radio collars and followed remotely, using an antennal tracking device. Their home ranges can be determined and population estimates developed based on the area of available habitat.

44.1 Reviewing the Concepts

- Population ecology studies how populations grow and what factors promote and limit growth. Ecologists measure population density, the numbers of organisms in a given unit area, in many ways (Figure 44.1). Similarly, a variety of techniques can be used to determine population size including the mark-capture technique (Figure 44.2).

44.1 Testing Your Knowledge

1. What method would you be likely to use to estimate the population density of beetles?
   a. quadrats   c. pitfall traps   e. all of the above
   b. line transects   d. mist nets

44.2 Demography

Learning Outcomes:

1. Describe the difference between information summarized in a life table and in a survivorship curve.

2. Differentiate among type I, II, and III survivorship curves and give examples of organisms that exhibit each of those survivorship curves.

3. Explain how age-specific fertility data can help predict a population's growth.

Population sizes are not always constant, and ecologists are often interested in how populations increase and decrease over time. One way to determine how a population will change is to examine a cohort of individuals from birth to death. For most animals and plants, this involves marking a group of individuals in a population as soon as they are born or germinate and following their fate through their lifetime. For some long-lived organisms, such as tortoises, elephants, or trees, this is impractical, so a snapshot approach is used, in which researchers examine the age structure of a population at one point in time. Recording the presence of juveniles and mature individuals, researchers use this information to construct a **life table**—a table that provides data on the number of individuals alive in each particular age class. Age classes can be created for any time period, but they often represent 1 year. Generally, only females and their female offspring are included in these tables, because only females produce offspring. The resulting numbers are usually similar to those if males and females were counted together. In this section, we will determine how to construct life tables and plot survivorship curves, which show at a glance the general pattern of population survival over time.

Life Tables and Survivorship Curves Summarize Survival Patterns

Let's examine a life table for the North American beaver (*Castor canadensis*). Prized for their pelts, by the mid-19th century, these animals had been hunted and trapped to near extinction. Beavers began to be protected by laws in the 20th century, and populations recovered in many areas, often growing to what some considered to be nuisance status. In Newfoundland, Canada, legislation supported trapping as a management technique. From 1964 to 1971, trappers provided mandibles from which teeth were extracted for age classification. If many mandibles were obtained from, say, 1-year-old beavers, then such animals were probably common in the population. If the number of mandibles from 2-year-old beavers was low, then we know there was high mortality for the 1-year-old age class. From the mandible data, researchers constructed a life table (**Table 44.1**). The number of individuals alive at the start of the time period (in this case, a year) is referred to as n_x, where n is the number, and x refers to the particular age class. By subtracting the value of n_x from the number alive at the start of the previous year, we can calculate the number dying in a given age class or year, d_x. Thus $d_x = n_x - n_{x+1}$. For example, in Table 44.1, 273 beavers were alive at the start of their sixth year (n_5), and only 205 were alive at the start of the seventh year (n_6); thus, 68 died during the sixth year: $d_5 = n_5 - n_6$, or $d_5 = 273 - 205 = 68$.

A simple and informative exercise is to plot numbers of surviving individuals (n_x) at each age, creating a **survivorship curve.**

Table 44.1	Life Table for the Beaver (*Castor canadensis*) in Newfoundland, Canada				
Age (years), x	Number alive at start of year, n_x	Number dying during year, d_x	Age-specific survivorship rate, l_x	Age-specific fertility, m_x	$l_x m_x$
0–1	3,695	1,995	1.000	0.000	0
1–2	1,700	684	0.460	0.315	0.145
2–3	1,016	359	0.275	0.400	0.110
3–4	657	286	0.178	0.895	0.159
4–5	371	98	0.100	1.244	0.124
5–6	273	68	0.074	1.440	0.107
6–7	205	40	0.055	1.282	0.071
7–8	165	38	0.045	1.280	0.058
8–9	127	14	0.034	1.387	0.047
9–10	113	26	0.031	1.080	0.033
10–11	87	37	0.024	1.800	0.043
11–12	50	4	0.014	1.080	0.015
12–13	46	17	0.012	1.440	0.017
13–14	29	7	0.007	0.720	0.005
14+	22	22	0.006	0.720	0.004

Net reproductive rate, $R_0 = \sum l_x m_x = 0.938$

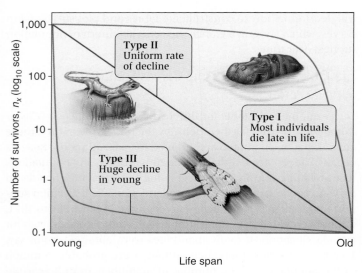

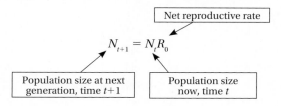

Figure 44.3 **Idealized survivorship curves.**

BioConnections: *Look back at Figure 25.17. Which type of survivorship curve would you expect in trematodes?*

The value of n_x is typically expressed on a logarithmic scale. Survivorship curves generally fall into one of three patterns (Figure 44.3). In a type I curve, the rate of loss for juveniles is relatively low, and most individuals are lost later in life, as they become older and more prone to sickness and predators. Organisms that exhibit type I survivorship have relatively few offspring but invest much time and resources in raising their young. Many large mammals, including humans, exhibit type I curves. At the other end of the scale is a type III curve, in which the rate of loss for juveniles is relatively high, and the survivorship curve flattens out for those organisms that have avoided early death. Many fishes and marine invertebrates fit this pattern. Most of the juveniles die or are eaten, but a few reach a favorable habitat and thrive. For example, once they find a suitable rock face on which to attach themselves, barnacles grow and survive very well. Many insects and plants also fit the type III survivorship curve, because they lay many eggs or release hundreds of seeds, respectively. Type II curves represent a middle ground, with fairly uniform death rates over time. Species with type II survivorship curves include many birds, small mammals, reptiles, and some annual plants.

Age-Specific Fertility Data Are Needed to Predict Population Growth

To calculate how a population grows, we need information on birth rates as well as mortality and survivorship rates. For any given age, we can determine the per female rate of female offspring production or **age-specific fertility rate** (m_x). For example, if 100 females of a given age produce 75 female offspring, $m_x = 0.75$. An examination of the beaver age-specific fertility rates in Table 44.1 illustrates a couple of general points. First, for this beaver population in particular, and for many organisms in general, no babies are born to very young females. As females mature

sexually, age-specific fertility goes up, and it remains fairly high until later in life, when females reach postreproductive age.

With the addition of age-specific fertility data, we can calculate the growth rate of a population. First, we use the survivorship data to find the proportion of individuals alive at the start of any given age class. This **age-specific survivorship rate,** termed l_x, equals n_x/n_0, where n_0 is the number alive at time 0, the start of the study, and n_x is the number alive at the beginning of age class x. Let's examine the beaver life table in Table 44.1. The proportion of the original beaver population still alive at the start of the sixth age class, l_5, equals $n_5/n_0 = 273/3,695$, or 0.074. This means that 7.4% of the original beaver population survived to age 5. Next we multiply the l_x by m_x, the age-specific fertility rate, to give us $l_x m_x$, an average number of female offspring per female in that age class. This column represents the contribution of each age class to the overall population growth rate. In our example, the average number of female offspring per female for beavers aged 5–6 is 0.107.

The number of offspring born to females of any given age class depends on two things: the number of females in that age class and their age-specific fertility rate. Thus, although fertility of young beavers is very low, there are so many females in the age class that $l_x m_x$ for 1-year-olds is quite high. Age-specific fertility for older beavers is much higher, but the fewer females in these age classes cause $l_x m_x$ to be low. Maximum values of $l_x m_x$ occur for females of an intermediate age, 3–4 years old in the case of the beaver. The overall growth rate per generation is the number of offspring born to all females of all ages, where a generation is defined as the mean period between birth of females and birth of their offspring. Therefore, to calculate the generational growth rate, we sum all the values of $l_x m_x$, that is, $\Sigma l_x m_x$, where the Σ symbol means "sum of." This summed value, R_0, is called the **net reproductive rate.**

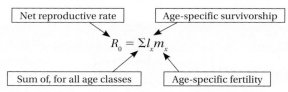

To calculate an estimate of the size of a population in the next generation, N_{t+1}, we multiply the number of individuals in the population at time t by the net reproductive rate, R_0:

To calculate an estimate of the size of a population in the next generation, N_{t+1}, we multiply the number of individuals in the population at time t by the net reproductive rate, R_0:

Let's consider an example in which the number of beavers alive now, N_t, is 1,000, and $R_0 = 1.1$. The size of the population next generation, N_{t+1}, is given by

$$N_{t+1} = N_t R_0$$
$$N_{t+1} = 1,000 \times 1.1$$
$$= 1,100$$

Therefore, the number of beavers in the next generation is 1,100 and the population will have increased. This means the beaver population is reproducing at a rate that is 10% greater than simply replacing itself.

In estimating future population size, much depends on the value of R_0. If $R_0 > 1$, the population is increasing. If $R_0 < 1$, the population is in decline. If $R_0 = 1$, the population size stays the same, and we say it is at **equilibrium.** In the case of the beavers, Table 44.1 reveals that $R_0 = 0.938$, which is less than 1, and therefore the population is declining. This is valuable information, because it tells us that at that time, the beaver population in Newfoundland needed some form of protection (perhaps bans on trapping and hunting) in order to attain a population level at equilibrium.

Because of the effort involved in calculating R_0, ecologists sometimes use a shortcut to predict population growth. Imagine a bird species that breeds annually. To measure population growth, ecologists count the number of birds in the population, N_0. Let's say $N_0 = 100$. The next year, ecologists count 105 birds in the same population, so $N_1 = 105$. The **finite rate of increase,** λ, is the ratio of the population size from one year to the next, calculated as

$$\lambda = N_1/N_0$$

In this case, $\lambda = 1.05$, or 5%. λ is often given as percent annual growth, and t is a number of years. Let's consider a population of birds growing at a rate of 5% per year. To calculate the size of the population after 5 years, we substitute λ for R_0:

$$N_t = 100, \lambda = 1.05, \text{ and } t = 5$$

therefore,

$$N_{t+5} = 100 \, (1.05)^5 = 127.6$$

What's the difference between R_0 and λ? R_0 represents the net reproductive rate per generation. λ represents the finite rate of population change over some time interval, often a year. When species are annual breeders that live 1 year, such as annual plants, $R_0 = \lambda$. For species that breed for multiple years, $R_0 \neq \lambda$. Just as

$$N_t = N_0 R_0^{\,t}, \text{ where } t = \text{a number of generations}$$

so

$$N_t = N_0 \lambda^t, \text{ where } t = \text{a number of time intervals}$$

Populations grow when R_0 or $\lambda > 1$; populations decline when R_0 or $\lambda < 1$; and they are at equilibrium when R_0 or $\lambda = 1$.

44.2 Reviewing the Concepts

- Life tables summarize the survival pattern of a population. Survivorship curves illustrate life tables by plotting the numbers of surviving individuals at different ages (Figure 44.3, Table 44.1).
- Age-specific fertility and survivorship data help estimate the overall growth rate per generation, or the net reproductive rate (R_0). The finite rate of increase, λ, provides information on growth rates over short time periods.

44.2 Testing Your Knowledge

1. In a survivorship curve
   a. l_x is plotted against time.
   b. survivorship is plotted against n_x.
   c. log n_x is plotted against time.
   d. n_x is plotted against log time.
   e. log n_x is plotted against log time.

2. Plot the survivorship curve for American beavers using the data in Table 44.1. What type of curve results?
   a. type I
   b. type II
   c. type III
   d. type IV
   e. none of the above

3. If $\sum l_x m_x = 1.0$, which of the following statements is true?
   a. There are few females of reproductive age.
   b. The population is increasing.
   c. The survivorship of females is low.
   d. Over a 1-year interval $\lambda = 1$.
   e. Population size will be unchanged from one generation to the next.

44.3 How Populations Grow

Learning Outcomes:

1. Explain how the population growth of continuously breeding organisms can be predicted using the per capita growth rate (r).

2. Distinguish between exponential growth and logistic growth.

3. Describe how density-dependent factors can regulate population size.

Life tables can provide estimates about how populations can grow from generation to generation. However, other population growth models can provide valuable insights into how populations grow over time periods shorter than whole generations. The simplest of these assume that populations grow if, for any given time interval, the number of births is greater than the number of deaths. In this section, we will examine two different types of models. The first model assumes resources are not limiting, and it results in prodigious growth. The second, and perhaps more biologically realistic, model assumes resources are limiting, and it results in limits to growth and eventual stable population sizes.

Knowing the per Capita Growth Rate Helps Predict How Populations Will Grow

The change in population size over any time period can be written as the number of births per unit time interval minus the number of deaths per unit time interval.

For example, if in a population of 1,000 rabbits, there were 100 births and 50 deaths over the course of 1 year, then the population would grow in size to 1,050 the next year. We can write this formula mathematically as

$$\frac{\text{Change in numbers}}{\text{Change in time}} = \text{Births} - \text{Deaths}$$

or

$$\frac{\Delta N}{\Delta t} = B - D$$

The Greek letter delta, Δ, indicates change, so that ΔN is the change in number, and Δt is the change in time; B is the number of births per time unit; and D is the number of deaths per time unit.

The numbers of births and deaths can be expressed per individual in the population, so the birth of 100 rabbits to a population of 1,000 would represent a per capita birth rate, b, of 100/1,000, or 0.10. Similarly, the death of 50 rabbits in a population of 1,000 would be a per capita death rate, d, of 50/1,000, or 0.05. Now we can rewrite our equation giving the rate of change in a population.

$$\frac{\Delta N}{\Delta t} = bN - dN$$

For our rabbit example,

$$\frac{\Delta N}{\Delta t} = 0.10 \times 1,000 - 0.05 \times 1,000 = 50$$

so if $\Delta t = 1$ year, the rabbit population would increase by 50 individuals in a year.

Ecologists often simplify this formula by representing $b - d$ as r, the **per capita rate of increase.** Thus, $bN - dN$ can be written as rN. Because ecologists are interested in population growth rates over very short time intervals, so-called instantaneous growth rates, instead of writing

$$\frac{\Delta N}{\Delta t}$$

they write

$$\frac{dN}{dt}$$

which is the notation of differential calculus. The equations essentially mean the same thing, except that dN/dt reflects very short time intervals. Thus,

$$\frac{dN}{dt} = rN = (0.10 - 0.05)N = 50$$

Exponential Growth Occurs When the per Capita Rate of Increase Remains Above Zero

How do populations grow? Clearly, much depends on the value of the per capita rate of increase rate, r. When $r < 0$, the population decreases; when $r = 0$, the population remains constant; and

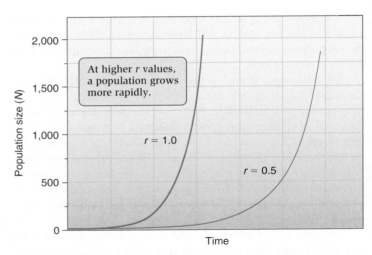

Figure 44.4 Exponential population growth. At higher r values, the slope of the curve gets steeper. In theory, a population with unlimited resources could grow indefinitely.

when $r > 0$, the population increases. When $r = 0$, the population is often referred to as being at equilibrium, where no changes in population size will occur and there is zero population growth.

Even if r is only fractionally above 0, population increase is rapid, and when plotted graphically a J-shaped curve results (Figure 44.4). We refer to this type of population growth as **exponential growth.** How do field data fit this simple model for exponential growth? In a new and expanding population when resources are not limited, exponential growth is often observed. The wolf populations in Montana, Wyoming, and Idaho that we saw at the beginning of the chapter provide a good example. Wolves began dispersing into Montana from Canada in the early 1980s, but the release of wolves in nearby Yellowstone National Park and neighboring Idaho and their subsequent population growth caused an exponential increase in wolf numbers in these areas (Figure 44.5a). As we mentioned in Chapter 43, Burmese pythons, *Python molorus*, native to Southeast Asia, are now well established in south Florida. Researchers fitted an exponential growth curve to python abundance based on capture numbers (Figure 44.5b). From a relatively small number of pythons likely released prior to 1985, population densities in the Everglades National Park were estimated conservatively at 30,000 individuals in 2007 based on similar density estimates of this species in its native India.

Logistic Growth Occurs in Populations in Which Resources Are Limited

Despite its applicability to rapidly growing populations, the exponential growth model is not appropriate in all situations. The model assumes unlimited resources, which is not typically the case in the real world. For most species, resources become limiting as populations grow, and the per capita rate of increase decreases. The maximum population size that can be sustained by an environment is known as the **carrying capacity (K).** A more

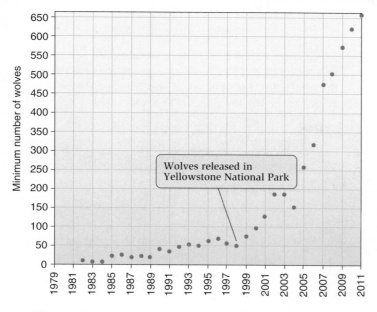

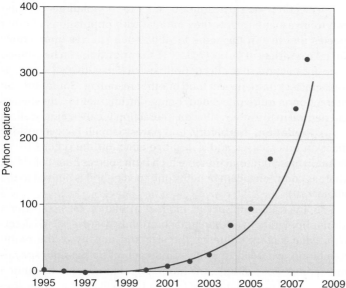

Figure 44.5 **Exponential growth following reintroduction of a species.** **(a)** Wolf population in Montana, 1979–2011. **(b)** Number of Burmese pythons captured in the Florida Everglades, 1995–2007.

realistic equation to explain population growth, one that takes into account the amount of available resources, is

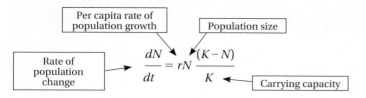

where $(K - N)/K$ represents the proportion of the carrying capacity that is unused by the population. This equation is called the **logistic equation.**

As the population size, N, grows, it moves closer to the carrying capacity, K, with fewer available resources for population growth. If $K = 1,000$, $N = 500$, and $r = 0.1$, then population growth

is 25 individuals per unit of time. At larger values of N, the value of $(K - N)/K$ becomes small, and population growth is smaller. If $K = 1,000$, $N = 900$, and $r = 0.1$, then

$$\frac{dN}{dt} = (0.1)(900) \times \frac{(1,000 - 900)}{1,000}$$

$$\frac{dN}{dt} = 9$$

In this instance, population growth is only 9 individuals per unit of time.

Let's consider how an ecologist would use the logistic equation. First, the value of K would come from intense field and laboratory work from which researchers would determine the amount of resources, such as food, needed by each individual and then determine the amount of available food in the wild. Field censuses determine N, and field censuses of births and deaths per unit time provide r. When this type of population growth is plotted over time, an S-shaped growth curve results (**Figure 44.6**). This pattern, in which the growth of a population slows down as it approaches K, is called **logistic growth.**

Does the logistic growth model provide a better fit to growth patterns of plants and animals in the wild than the exponential model? In some instances, such as laboratory cultures of bacteria and yeasts, the logistic growth model provides a very good fit (**Figure 44.7**). In nature, however, variations in temperature, rainfall, or resources can cause frequent changes in carrying capacity and thus in population size. Therefore, the logistic growth model is rarely an exact fit to population growth in the field. Is the logistic model therefore of little value? Not really. It is a useful starting

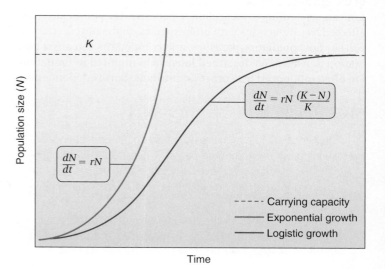

Figure 44.6 **Exponential versus logistic growth.** Exponential (J-shaped) growth occurs in an environment with unlimited resources, whereas logistic (S-shaped) growth occurs in an environment with limited resources.

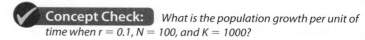

Concept Check: *What is the population growth per unit of time when r = 0.1, N = 100, and K = 1000?*

Biology Principle

Biology Is an Experimental Science

Tests of population growth models are more accurately performed using manipulative experiments than by simple field observations.

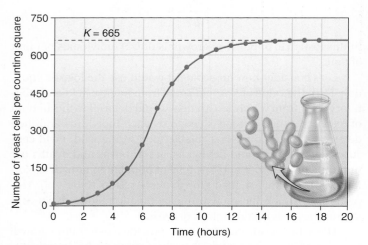

Figure 44.7 Logistic growth of yeast cells in culture. Early tests of the logistic growth curve were validated by growth of yeast cells in laboratory cultures. These populations showed the typical S-shaped growth curve.

point for thinking about how populations grow, and it seems intuitively correct. However, the carrying capacity is a difficult feature of the environment to identify for most species, and it varies with time and according to local climate patterns. Also, populations are affected by interactions with other species. In the next section, we will see how predators, parasites, and competitors can affect population densities. As described later, such population limitations are often influenced by a process known as density dependence.

44.3 Reviewing the Concepts

- The per capita rate of increase (r) helps determine how populations grow over any time period. When r is > 0, exponential (J-shaped) growth occurs. Exponential growth can be observed in an environment where resources are not limited (Figures 44.4, 44.5).
- Logistic (S-shaped) growth takes into account the upper boundary for a population, called carrying capacity, and occurs in an environment where resources are limited (Figures 44.6, 44.7).

44.3 Testing Your Knowledge

1. Under what conditions will a population grow?
   a. $R_0 = 0.5$ **b.** $r = 0.4$ **c.** $\lambda = 0.8$ **d.** a and b   **e.** b and c

2. Suppose you have a pond that is being overgrown by an aggressive weed that doubles in number every day. If unchecked it

would cover the pond in 30 days. Weed growth is very slow, almost negligible, to begin with, and you decide not to remove the weed until the pond is half covered. When will that be?
   a. day 1   **b.** day 10   **c.** day 15   **d.** day 20   **e.** day 29

44.4 Species Interactions

Learning Outcomes:

1. Explain how competition can lead to resource partitioning among species.
2. List and describe strategies plants and animals use to avoid being eaten.
3. Give examples of the effects of natural enemies on prey populations.

In this section, we turn from considering populations on their own to investigating how they interact with populations of other species that live in the same locality. Such species interactions can take a variety of forms (**Table 44.2**). **Competition** can be defined as an interaction that affects both species negatively ($-/-$), as both species compete over food or other resources. Sometimes an interaction is quite one-sided, being detrimental to one species and neutral to the other; such an interaction is called **amensalism** ($-/0$). **Predation, herbivory,** and **parasitism** all have a positive effect on one species and a negative effect on the other ($+/-$). **Mutualism** is an interaction in which both species benefit ($+/+$), whereas **commensalism** benefits one species and is neutral to the other ($+/0$).

To illustrate how species interact in nature, let's consider a rabbit population in a woodland community (**Figure 44.8**). To determine what factors influence the size and density of the rabbit population, we need to understand each of its possible species interactions. For example, the rabbit population could be limited by the quality or availability of food. It is also likely that other species, such as deer, use the same resource and thus compete with the rabbits. The rabbit population could be limited by predation from foxes or by the virus that causes the disease myxomatosis, which is usually spread by fleas and mosquitoes.

Table 44.2	Summary of the Types of Species Interactions	
Nature of interaction	**Species 1***	**Species 2***
Competition	−	−
Amensalism	−	0
Predation, herbivory, parasitism	+	−
Mutualism	+	+
Commensalism	+	0

*+ = Positive effect; − = negative effect; 0 = no effect.

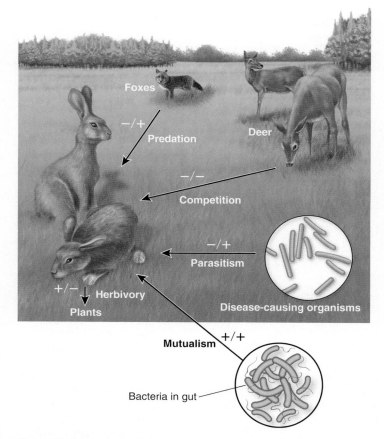

Figure 44.8 **Species interactions.** These rabbits can interact with a variety of species, experiencing predation by foxes, competition with deer for food, and parasitism from various disease-causing organisms. Herbivory occurs when rabbits feed on various plants. The effects of each species on the other are shown by the terms assigned to the arrows, as discussed in the text.

Competition Can Negatively Affect the Population Growth of Competing Species

The influence of competition on population growth was illustrated by the Russian microbiologist Georgyi Gause who, in 1934, studied competition between three protist species, *Paramecium aurelia*, *Paramecium bursaria*, and *Paramecium caudatum*, all of which fed on bacteria and yeast, which in turn fed on an oatmeal medium in a culture tube in the laboratory. More bacteria occurred in the oxygen-rich upper part of the culture tube, and more yeast in the oxygen-poor lower part of the tube. Because each *Paramecium* species was a slightly different size, Gause calculated population growth as a combination of numbers of individuals per milliliter of solution multiplied by their unit volume to give a population volume for each species. When grown separately, population volume of all three *Paramecium* species followed a logistic growth pattern (**Figure 44.9a**). When Gause cultured *P. caudatum* and *P. aurelia* together, *P. caudatum* went extinct (**Figure 44.9b**). Both species utilized bacteria as food, but *P. aurelia* grew at a rate six times faster than *P. caudatum*.

However, when Gause cultured *P. caudatum* and *P. bursaria* together, neither went extinct (**Figure 44.9c**). The population volume of each was much less than when they were grown alone, because

some competition occurred between them. Gause discovered, however, that *P. bursaria* was better able to utilize the yeast in the lower part of the culture tubes. *P. bursaria* have tiny green algae inside them, which produce oxygen and allow *P. bursaria* to thrive in the lower oxygen levels at the bottom of the tubes. From these experiments, Gause concluded that two species with exactly the same requirements cannot live together in the same place and use the same resources, that is, occupy the same **niche.** This became known as the **competitive exclusion principle.** The term **resource partitioning** describes the differentiation of niches, both in space and time, that enables similar species to coexist in a community, just as the two species of *Paramecium* feeding in different parts of the culture tube. We can think of resource partitioning as reflecting the results of past competition, in which competition led the inferior competitor to eventually occupy a different niche.

By reviewing studies that have investigated competition in nature, we can see how frequently it occurs and in what particular circumstances it is most important. In a 1983 review of field studies by American ecologist Joseph Connell, competition was found in 55% of 215 species surveyed, demonstrating that it is indeed frequent in nature. Generally in studies of single pairs of species utilizing the same resource, competition is almost always reported, whereas in studies involving more species, the frequency of competition decreases. Why should this be the case? Imagine a resource such as a series of different-sized grains with four types of species—ants, beetles, mice, and birds—feeding on it (**Figure 44.10a**). The ants feed on the smallest grain, the beetles and mice on the intermediate sizes, and the birds, on the largest. If only adjacent species competed with each other, competition would be expected only between the ant–beetle, beetle–mouse, and mouse–bird. Thus, competition would be found in only three out of the six possible species pairs (50%). Naturally, the percentage would vary according to the number of species on the resource spectrum. If only three species occur along the spectrum, we would expect competition in two of the three pairs (67%). If just two species utilized the resource spectrum, however, we would expect competition in almost 100% of the cases (**Figure 44.10b**).

Some other general patterns were evident from Connell's review. Plants showed a high degree of competition, perhaps because they are rooted in the ground and cannot easily escape or perhaps because they are competing for the same set of limiting nutrients—water, light, and minerals. Marine organisms tended to compete more than terrestrial ones, most likely because many of the species studied lived in the intertidal zone and were attached to the rock face, in a manner similar to the rooting of plants. Because the area of the rock face is limited, competition for space is quite important.

Predators, Herbivores, Parasites, and Parasitoids Can Reduce the Population Growth of Their Prey or Host Species

Predation, herbivory, parasitism, and parasitoidism are interactions that have a positive effect for one species and a negative effect for the other. These categories of species interactions can

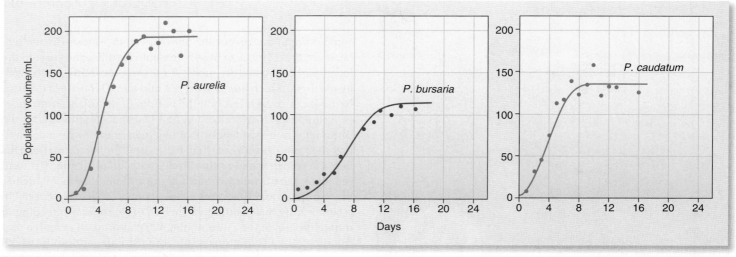

(a) Each *Paramecium* species grown alone

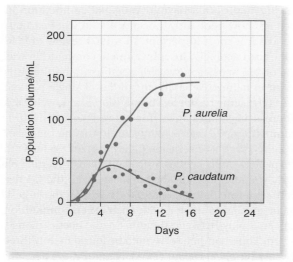

(b) Competition between *P. aurelia* and *P. caudatum*

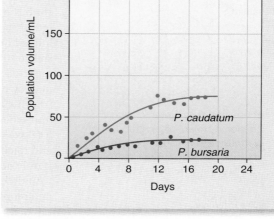

(c) Competition between *P. caudatum* and *P. bursaria*

Figure 44.9 **Competition among *Paramecium* species.** **(a)** When grown alone, each of three species, *Paramecium aurelia, Paramecium bursaria,* and *Paramecium caudatum,* grows according to the logistic model. **(b)** When *P. aurelia* is grown with *P. caudatum,* the density of *P. aurelia* is lower than when grown alone, and *P. caudatum* goes extinct. **(c)** When *P. caudatum* is grown with *P. bursaria,* the population densities of both are lowered, but the species coexist.

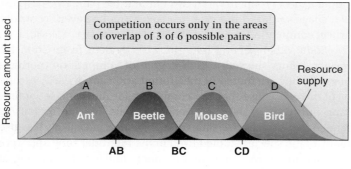

(a) Competition among 4 species for a resource

(b) Competition among 2 species for a resource

Figure 44.10 **The frequency of competition according to the number of species involved.** **(a)** Resource supply and utilization curves of four species, A, B, C, and D, along the spectrum of a hypothetical resource such as grain size. If competition occurs only between species with adjacent resource utilization curves, competition would be expected between three of the six possible pairings: A and B; B and C; and C and D. **(b)** When only two species utilize a resource set, competition would nearly always be expected between them.

Concept Check: *If five species utilized the resource set in part (a), what percent of the interactions would be competitive?*

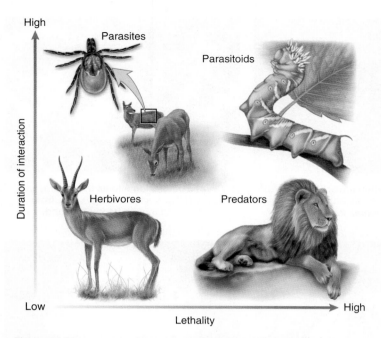

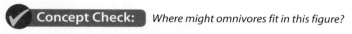

Figure 44.11 **Possible interactions between populations.** Lethality represents the probability that an interaction results in the death of the prey. Duration represents the length of the interaction between the consumer and the prey.

✓ **Concept Check:** *Where might omnivores fit in this figure?*

be classified according to how lethal they are for the prey and the length of association between the consumer and prey (Figure 44.11). Each has particular characteristics that set it apart. Herbivory usually involves nonlethal feeding on plants, whereas predation generally results in the death of the prey. Parasitism, like herbivory, is typically nonlethal and differs from predation in that the adult parasite typically lives and reproduces for long periods in or on the living host (refer back to Figure 25.17). Parasitoids are organisms that lay eggs in a host that the resulting larvae remain with and almost always kill. They thus have features in common with parasites (a long association) and predators (lethality). Parasitoids are common in the insect world and are often utilized in the biological control of pests.

EVOLUTIONARY CONNECTIONS

Organisms Have Evolved Many Defenses Against Natural Enemies

The variety of strategies that organisms have evolved to avoid being eaten suggests that predators, parasites, and parasitoids, also known as natural enemies, are a strong selective force. Common strategies include chemical and mechanical defenses; camouflage and mimicry; displays of intimidation; and armor and weaponry.

Chemical and Mechanical Defenses A great many animal species have evolved chemical defenses against predation. One of the classic examples of a chemical defense involves the bombardier beetle (*Stenaptinus insignis*), which has been studied by entomologist Tom Eisner and coworkers. These beetles possess a reservoir of hydroquinone and hydrogen peroxide in their abdomen. When threatened, they eject the chemicals into an "explosion chamber," where the subsequent release of oxygen causes the whole mixture to be violently ejected as a hot spray (about 88°C, or 190°F) that can be directed at the beetle's attackers (**Figure 44.12a**). Many other arthropods, such as millipedes, also have chemical sprays, and the phenomenon is also found in vertebrates, as anyone who has had a close encounter with a skunk can testify. Often associated with a chemical defense is an **aposematic coloration,** or warning coloration, which advertises an organism's unpalatable taste. For instance, many tropical frogs have bright warning coloration that calls attention to their skin's lethality (**Figure 44.12b**).

An array of unusual and powerful chemicals is present in plants such as nicotine in tobacco, morphine in poppies, cocaine in coca, and caffeine in coffee. Such compounds are not part of the primary metabolic pathway that plants use to obtain energy and are therefore referred to as **secondary metabolites.** Most of these chemicals are bitter tasting or toxic, thereby deterring herbivores from feeding. The staggering variety of secondary metabolites in plants, over 25,000 identified so far, may be testament to the large number of organisms that feed on plants. In an interesting twist, many of these compounds have medicinal properties that have proved to be beneficial to humans. In addition to containing chemical compounds, many plants have an array of mechanical defenses, such as thorns, hairs, and spines.

Camouflage Camouflage is the blending of an organism with the background of its habitat and is a common method of avoiding detection by predators (refer back to Figure 26.17b). For example, many grasshoppers are green and blend in with the foliage on which they feed. Stick insects mimic branches and twigs with their long, slender bodies. In most cases, these animals stay perfectly still when threatened, because movement alerts a predator. Camouflage is prevalent in the vertebrate world, too. Many sea horses adopt a body shape and color pattern similar to the environment in which they are found (**Figure 44.12c**).

Mimicry There are two major types of mimicry. In **Müllerian mimicry,** two or more toxic species converge to look the same, thus reinforcing the basic distasteful design. The viceroy butterfly (*Limenitis archippus*) and the monarch butterfly (*Danaus plexippus*) are examples of Müllerian mimicry. Both species are unpalatable and look similar, but the viceroy can be distinguished from the monarch by a black line that crosses its wings (**Figure 44.12d**).

Batesian mimicry is the mimicry of an unpalatable species (the model) by a palatable one (the mimic). Some of the best examples involve flies, especially hoverflies of the family Syrphidae, which are striped black and yellow and resemble stinging bees and wasps but are themselves harmless. Among vertebrates, the nonvenomous scarlet king snake (*Lampropeltis elapsoides*)

(a) As it is held by a tether attached to its back, this bombardier beetle (*Stenaptinus insignis*) directs its hot, stinging spray at a forceps "attacker."

(b) Aposematic coloration advertises the poisonous nature of this blue poison arrow frog (*Dendrobates azureus*) from South America.

(c) Cryptic coloration allows this Pygmy sea horse (*Hippocampus bargibanti*) from Bali to blend in with its background.

(d) Müllerian mimicry. Viceroy and monarch butterflies are both noxious and have similar color patterns.

(e) In a display of intimidation, this porcupine fish (*Diodon hystrix*) puffs itself up to look threatening to its predators.

(f) In this example of Batesian mimicry, an innocuous scarlet king snake (*Lampropeltis elapsoides*) (left) mimics the venomous eastern coral snake (*Micrurus fulvius*) (right).

(g) Sable antelope have horns that may be used as predator defense.

Figure 44.12 Antipredator adaptations.

 **BioConnections:**   *Look back to Figure 42.2. Do predators learn to avoid bad-tasting prey by habituation, classical conditioning, or operant conditioning?*

mimics the venomous eastern coral snake (*Micrurus fulvius*), thereby gaining protection from would-be predators (**Figure 44.12f**).

Displays of Intimidation   Some animals put on displays of intimidation in an attempt to discourage predators. For example, a cat arches its back, a frilled lizard extends it collar, and a porcupine fish inflates itself when threatened in order to appear larger (**Figure 44.12e**). All of these animals have evolved displays to deceive potential predators about the ease with which they can be eaten.

Armor and Weaponry   The shells of tortoises and turtles are a strong means of defense against most predators, as are the quills of porcupines (refer back to Figure 26.17c). Though many animals developed horns and antlers for sexual selection, these projections can also be used in defense against predators (**Figure 44.12g**). Invertebrate species often have powerful claws, pincers, or, in the case of scorpions, venomous stingers that can be used in defense as well as offense.

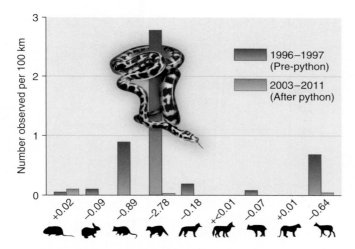
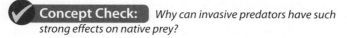

Figure 44.13 **Effects of invasive Burmese pythons.** A huge decline in mammal abundance per 100 km of road surveys in the Everglades National Park, Florida (live and road kills), is seen from 1996–1997, prior to pythons becoming abundant, and 2003–2011, after they had become common.

Concept Check: *Why can invasive predators have such strong effects on native prey?*

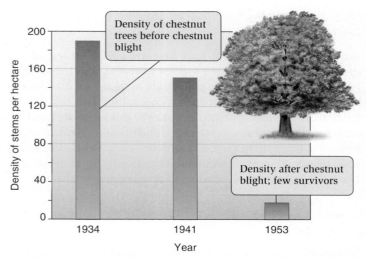

Figure 44.14 **Effects of introduced parasites on American chestnut trees.** The reduction in density of American chestnut trees in North Carolina following the 1904 introduction of chestnut blight disease from Asia shows the severe effect that parasites can have on their hosts. By the 1950s, this once-widespread species was virtually eliminated.

Biology Principle

Biology Affects Our Society

Control of prickly pear by the cactus moth cleared hundreds of thousands of hectares of cacti, allowing sheep to graze the area and farming to thrive.

(a) Before biological control   **(b) After biological control**

Figure 44.15 **Successful biological control of prickly pear cactus.** The prickly pear cactus (*Opuntia stricta*) in Chinchilla, Australia, **(a)** before and **(b)** after control by the cactus moth (*Cactoblastis cactorum*).

Despite this impressive array of defenses, many studies have shown a strong effect of natural enemies on their prey populations. Invasive species provide particularly striking examples of the effects of natural enemies. Three examples will suffice here. The growth of the Burmese python population in the Florida Everglades (see Chapter 43 chapter-opening photo) has caused a precipitous decline in the area's wildlife (**Figure 44.13**). Since the pythons have become common, there has been a 99.3% decline in raccoon observations, a 98.9% decline for possums, a 94.1% decline for white-tailed deer, and an 87.5% decline for bobcats. No rabbits or foxes were even observed in areas where pythons were common.

Chestnut blight (*Cryphonectria parasitica*), a fungus from Asia, was accidentally introduced to New York on imported wood around 1904. At that time, the American chestnut tree (*Castanea dentata*) was one of the most common trees in the eastern United States. It was said that a squirrel could jump from one chestnut to another all the way from Maine to Georgia without touching the ground. By the 1950s, the airborne fungus had significantly reduced the density of American chestnut trees in North Carolina (**Figure 44.14**). Eventually, it eliminated nearly all chestnut trees across North America.

The prickly pear cactus (*Opuntia stricta*) was imported from South America into Australia in the 19th century as a food source for an insect that was used to make a bright red dye for the British. The cactus quickly became invasive and established itself as a major pest of rangeland. The small cactus moth (*Cactoblastis cactorum*), which feeds on *Opuntia* cactus, was introduced from

South America in the 1920s and within a short time had controlled cactus populations. This reuniting of an invasive plant with its natural enemy successfully saved hundreds of thousands of acres of valuable rangeland from being overrun by the cacti (**Figure 44.15**).

Mutualism and Commensalism May Increase the Population Growth of Interacting Species

Not all species interactions have negative effects on one of the species. In mutualism, both species gain from the interaction. For example, in mutualistic pollination systems, such as occurs between plants and insects such as bees, the plant benefits by the transfer of pollen and the bee typically gains a nectar meal. In commensalism, one species benefits, and the other remains unaffected. For example, in some forms of seed dispersal, barbed seeds are transported to new germination sites in the fur of mammals. The seeds benefit, but the mammals are generally unaffected.

Density-Dependent Factors May Regulate Population Sizes

Parasitism, parasitoidism, herbivory, predation, and competition are some of the many factors that may reduce the population densities of living organisms and stabilize them at equilibrium levels. **Density-dependent factors** are those in which the effect of the factors depends on the density of the population. For example, a pathogen that kills more of a population when densities are higher and less of a population when densities are lower is acting in a density-dependent manner. Many predators develop a visual search image for a particular prey. When a prey is rare, predators tend to ignore it and kill relatively few. When a prey is common, predators key in on it and kill relatively more. In England, for example, predatory shrews kill proportionately more moth pupae in leaf litter when the pupae are common than when they are rare. Density-dependent mortality may also occur as population densities increase and competition for scarce resources increases, reducing offspring production or survival. Parasitism may also act in a density-dependent manner. Parasites are able to pass from host to host more easily as the host's densities increase.

Density dependence can be detected by plotting mortality, expressed as a percentage, against population density (Figure 44.16). If a positive slope results and mortality increases with density, the factor tends to have a greater effect on dense populations than on sparse ones and is clearly acting in a density-dependent manner.

A **density-independent factor** is a mortality factor whose influence is not affected by changes in population size or density. When mortality is plotted against density, a flat line results. In general, density-independent factors are physical factors, including weather, drought, freezes, floods, and disturbances such as fire. For example, in hard freezes, the same proportion of organisms such as birds or plants are usually killed, no matter how large the population size.

Finally, a mortality factor that decreases with increasing population size is considered an **inverse density-dependent factor.** In this case, a negative slope results when mortality is plotted against density. For example, if a territorial predator such as a lion always killed the same number of wildebeest prey, regardless of wildebeest density, it is acting in an inverse density-dependent manner, because it is taking a smaller proportion of the population at higher density. Some mammalian predators, being highly territorial, often act in this manner on herbivore density.

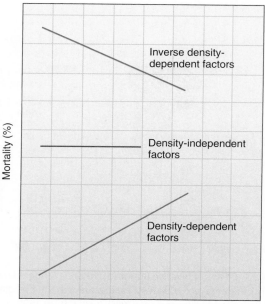

Figure 44.16 **Three ways that factors affect mortality in response to changes in population density.** For a density-dependent factor, mortality increases with population density; for a density-independent factor, mortality remains unchanged. For an inverse density-dependent factor, mortality decreases as a population increases in size.

✔ **Concept Check:** *Which types of factors tend to stabilize populations at equilibrium levels?*

Determining which factors act in a density-dependent or density-independent fashion has large practical implications. Foresters, game managers, and conservation biologists alike are interested in learning how to maintain populations. For example, if a specific disease were to act in a density-dependent manner on elk, there wouldn't be much point in game managers attempting to kill off predators such as wolves to increase herd sizes for hunters, because proportionately more elk would be killed by disease.

44.4 Reviewing the Concepts

- Species interactions can take a variety of forms that differ based on their effect on the species involved from competition, predation, herbivory, parasitism, and parasitoidism to mutualism and commensalism (Figure 44.8, Table 44.2).
- Surveys have shown competition occurs frequently in nature. Research has shown that two species with the same resource requirements cannot occupy the same niche. Resource partitioning between species allows them to coexist in a community (Figures 44.9, 44.10).
- Natural enemies include predators, herbivores, parasites, and parasitoids. The most common defenses against natural enemies are chemical defense and aposematic coloration, camouflage, mimicry, and physical defenses such as spines or armor (Figures 44.11, 44.12).
- Density-dependent factors are mortality factors whose influence varies with population density. Density-independent factors are those whose influence does not vary with density (Figure 44.16).

44.4 Testing Your Knowledge

1. A species interaction in which one species benefits but the other species is unaffected is called
   a. mutualism.   c. parasitism.   e. mimicry.
   b. amensalism.   d. commensalism.

2. According to the competitive exclusion hypothesis,
   a. two species that use the exact same resource show very little competition.
   b. two species with the same niche cannot coexist.
   c. one species that competes with several different species for resources will be excluded from the community.
   d. all competition between species results in the extinction of at least one of the species.
   e. none of the above is correct.

3. Tapeworms have
   a. low lethality and low duration of interaction.
   b. low lethality and high duration of interaction.
   c. high lethality and low duration of interaction.
   d. high lethality and high duration of interaction.
   e. none of the above.

44.5 Human Population Growth

Learning Outcomes:

1. Describe how differences in age structure and human fertility across different countries affect human population growth.
2. Explain the concept of an ecological footprint.

In 2011, the world's population was estimated to be increasing at the rate of 145 people every minute: 2 per minute in developed nations and 143 in less-developed nations. In this section, we examine human population growth trends in more detail and discuss how knowledge of the human population's age structure and fertility levels can help predict its future growth. We then investigate the carrying capacity of the Earth for humans and explore how the concept of an ecological footprint, which measures human resource use, can help us determine this carrying capacity.

Human Populations Show Extreme Recent Growth

Until the beginning of agriculture and the domestication of animals, about 10,000 B.C.E., the average rate of human population growth was very low. With the establishment of agriculture, the world's population grew to about 300 million by 1 C.E. and to 800 million by the year 1750. Between 1750 and 1998, a relatively short period of human history, the world's human population surged from 800 million to 6 billion (**Figure 44.17**). In 2012, the number of humans was estimated at 7 billion. Scientists are very interested in determining when and at what size the human population will level off.

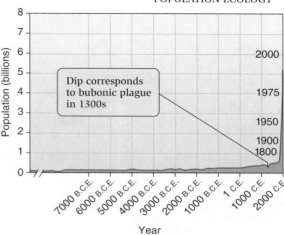

Figure 44.17 **The growth pattern of the human population through history.**

Knowledge of a Population's Age Structure Can Help Predict Its Future Growth

The age structure of a population can help to predict future population growth. In all populations, **age structure** refers to the relative numbers of individuals of each defined age group. This information is commonly displayed as a population pyramid. In West Africa, for example, children younger than age 15 make up nearly half of the population, creating a pyramid with a wide base and narrow top (**Figure 44.18a**). Even if fertility rates decline, there will still be a huge increase in the population as these young people move into childbearing age. The age structure of Western Europe is much more uniform (**Figure 44.18b**). Even if the fertility rate of young women in Western Europe increases to a level higher than that of their mothers, the annual numbers of births would still be relatively low because of the low number of women of childbearing age.

Human Population Fertility Rates Vary Widely Around the World

Global population growth can be examined by looking at the **total fertility rate (TFR)**, the average number of live births a woman has during her lifetime (**Figure 44.19**). The total fertility rate differs considerably from one geographic area to another. In Africa, the total fertility rate of 4.6 in 2010 has declined substantially since the 1970s, when it was around 6.7 children per woman. In Latin America and Southeast Asia, the rates have declined even more from the 1970s and are now at around 2.3. Canada and most countries in Europe have a TFR of less than 2.0 (the TFR is slightly above 2.0 in the U.S.); in Russia, fertility rates have dropped to 1.34. In China, although the TFR is only 1.7, the population there will still continue to increase until at least 2025 because of the large number of women of reproductive age. Although the global TFR has declined from 4.47 in the 1970s to 2.52 in 2010, this is still greater than the average of 2.3 needed for zero population growth. The replacement rate is slightly higher than 2.0, to replace mother and father, due to natural mortality prior to reproduction. The replacement rate varies globally, from 2.1 in developed countries to between 2.5 and 3.3 in developing countries.

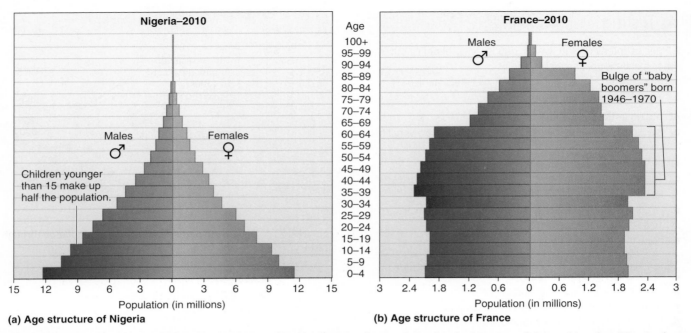

(a) Age structure of Nigeria

(b) Age structure of France

Figure 44.18 **The age structure of human populations in Nigeria and France, as of 2010.** **(a)** In developing areas of the world such as Nigeria, there are far more children than any other age group. Population growth is rapid. **(b)** In the developed countries of Western Europe, the age structure is more evenly distributed. The bulge represents those born in the post–World War II "baby boom," when birth rates climbed due to stabilization of political and economic conditions. Population growth is close to zero.

✔ **Concept Check:** *If the population pyramid in (a) was inverted, what would you conclude about the age structure of the population?*

The wide variation in fertility rates makes it difficult to predict future population growth. The 2010 United Nations report shows world population projections to the year 2100 for three different growth scenarios: low, medium, and high (**Figure 44.20**). The three scenarios are based on three different assumptions about fertility rate. Using a low fertility rate estimate of only 1.5 children per woman, the population would reach a maximum of about

Biology Principle

Biology Affects Our Society

How TFR is calculated has a great influence on assumptions about how human global population size will change over the next 90 years.

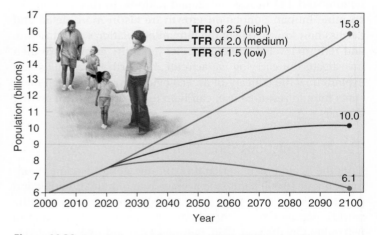

Figure 44.20 **Population predictions for 2000–2100, using three different total fertility rates (TFRs).**

Figure 44.19 **Total fertility rates (TFRs) among major regions of the world.** Data refer to the average number of children born to a woman during her lifetime.

8 billion people by 2050. A more realistic assumption may be to use the fertility rate estimate of 2.0 or even 2.5, in which case the population would continue to rise to 10 or 16 billion, respectively.

The Concept of an Ecological Footprint Helps Estimate Carrying Capacity

Recall that carrying capacity refers to the maximum population size that can be sustained by an environment. What is the Earth's carrying capacity for the human population, and when will it be reached? Estimates vary widely. Much of the speculation on the upper boundary of the world's population size centers on lifestyle. To use a simplistic example, if everyone on the planet ate meat extensively and drove large cars, then the carrying capacity would be a lot less than if people were vegetarians and used bicycles as their main means of transportation.

In the 1990s, Swiss researcher Mathis Wackernagel and his coworkers calculated how much land is needed for the support of each person on Earth. Everybody has an effect on the Earth, because we consume the land's resources, including crops, wood, fossil fuels, minerals, and so on. Thus, each person has an **ecological footprint**—the aggregate total of productive land needed for survival in a sustainable world. The average footprint size for

everyone on the planet is about 3 hectares (1 ha = 10,000 m²), but a wide variation is found around the globe (**Figure 44.21**). The ecological footprint of the average Canadian is 7.5 hectares versus about 10 hectares for the average American.

In most developed countries, the largest component of land is for energy, followed by food and then forestry. Much of the land needed for energy serves to absorb the CO_2 emitted by the use of fossil fuels. If everyone required 10 hectares, as the average American does, we would need three Earths to provide us with the needed resources. Many people in less-developed countries use far fewer resources. However, globally we are already beyond the Earth's carrying capacity for humans if we were to live in a sustainable manner. This has happened because many people currently live in an unsustainable manner, using more resources than can be regenerated in any given year.

What's your personal ecological footprint? Several different calculations are available on the Internet that you can use to find out. A rapidly growing human population combined with an increasingly large per capita ecological footprint makes it increasingly difficult to preserve other species on the planet, a subject we will examine further in our discussion of conservation biology (Chapter 47).

44.5 Reviewing the Concepts

- Human population growth has skyrocketed over the last 250 years (Figure 44.17).
- Differences in the age structure of a population, the numbers of individuals in each age group, can influence future patterns of population growth (Figure 44.18).
- Although they have been declining worldwide, total fertility rates (TFRs) differ markedly between less-developed and more-developed countries. Predicting the growth of the human population depends on the total fertility rate that is projected (Figures 44.19, 44.20).
- The ecological footprint refers to the amount of productive land needed to support each person on Earth. Because people in many countries live in a nonsustainable manner, globally we are already in an ecological deficit (Figure 44.21).

44.5 Testing Your Knowledge

1. The average total fertility rate needed for zero population change across the world is
   - **a.** 1.7.
   - **b.** 1.9.
   - **c.** 2.0.
   - **d.** 2.3.
   - **e.** 2.5.

2. The total fertility rate is highest in
   - **a.** Latin America.
   - **b.** Southeast Asia.
   - **c.** Europe.
   - **d.** Africa.
   - **e.** North America.

Figure 44.21 Ecological footprints of different countries. The term ecological footprint refers to the amount of productive land needed to support the average individual of that country.

 **Concept Check:** *What is your ecological footprint?*

Assess and Discuss

Test Yourself

1. A student decides to conduct a mark-recapture experiment to estimate the population size of mosquitofish, a species of freshwater fish, in a small pond near his home. In the first catch, he marked 45 individuals. Two weeks later, he captured 62 individuals, of which 8 were marked. What is the estimated size of the population based on these data?
   a. 134   c. 558   e. 22,320
   b. 349   d. 1,016

Questions 2–4 refer to the following table:

Age	n_x	d_x	l_x	m_x	$l_x m_x$
0	100	35	1.00	0	0
1	65	?	0.65	0	0
2	45	15	?	3	1.35
3	30	20	0.30	1	?
4	10	10	0.10	1	0.10
5	0	0	0.00	1	0.0

2. How many individuals die between their first and second birthday?
   a. 65   c. 35   e. 20
   b. 45   d. 25

3. What proportion of newborns survives to age 2?
   a. 0.55   c. 0.35   e. 0.15
   b. 0.45   d. 0.20

4. What is the net reproductive rate?
   a. 5   c. 1.75   e. 0.80
   b. 2.5   d. 1.45

5. _____ survivorship curves are usually associated with organisms that have high mortality rates in the early stages of life.
   a. Type I   c. Type III   e. Types II and III
   b. Type II   d. Types I and II

6. If the net reproductive rate (R_0) is equal to 0.5, what assumptions can we make about the population?
   a. This population is essentially not changing in numbers.
   b. This population is in decline.
   c. This population is growing.
   d. This population is in equilibrium.
   e. None of the above is true.

7. The maximum number of individuals a certain area can sustain is known as
   a. the intrinsic rate of growth.   d. the logistic equation.
   b. the resource limit.   e. the equilibrium size.
   c. the carrying capacity.

Questions 8 and 9 refer to the following generalized growth patterns as plotted on arithmetic scales. Match the following descriptions with the patterns indicated below.

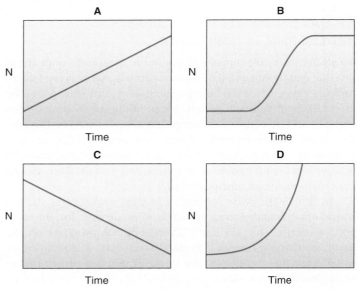

Each pattern may be used once, more than once, or not at all.

8. Which pattern is found when a population exhibits a constant per capita rate of increase?
   a. A   d. D
   b. B   e. none of the above
   c. C

9. Which pattern is found when a population is heading toward extinction?
   a. A   d. D
   b. B   e. none of the above
   c. C

10. The amount of land necessary for survival for each person in a sustainable world is known as
   a. the sustainability level.   d. survival needs.
   b. an ecological impact.   e. all of the above.
   c. an ecological footprint.

Conceptual Questions

1. As a researcher, you are using the mark-recapture procedure (see Figure 44.2) with mice. Say you recapture twice as many mice with ear tags as you should, because they are enticed to come to traps baited with peanut butter. How does this influence your estimate of population size? Does it increase or decrease, and by how much?

2. Using the logistic equation, calculate population growth when $K = 1,000$, $N = 500$, and $r = 0.1$ and when $K = 1,000$, $N = 100$, and $r = 0.1$. Compare the results with those shown in Section 44.3, where $K = 1,000$, $N = 900$, and $r = 0.1$. At which time is population growth highest as a percentage of the population?

3. **PRINCIPLES**   A principle of biology is that *biology affects our society*. In one family, parents, who were born in 1900, have twins at age 20, but then have no more children. Their children, grandchildren, and so on behave in the same way. In another family, parents, who were also born in 1900, delay reproduction until age 33 but have triplets. Their children and grandchildren behave in the same way. Which family has the most descendants by 2000? What can you conclude?

Collaborative Questions

1. Discuss what might limit human population growth in the future.

2. Describe what are the most significant changes you can make to your lifestyle to reduce your ecological footprint.

Online Resource

www.brookerprinciples.com

Stay a step ahead in your studies with animations that bring concepts to life and practice tests to assess your understanding. Your instructor may also recommend the interactive eBook, individualized learning tools, and more.

45

Community Ecology

Mount St. Helens erupting in 1980. Ecologists have been monitoring gradual changes in the species composition of the area since the disturbance.

Chapter Outline

45.1 Patterns of Species Richness and Species Diversity

45.2 Species Diversity and Community Stability

45.3 Succession: Community Change

45.4 Island Biogeography

Assess and Discuss

At 8:32 A.M. on May 18, 1980, Mount St. Helens, in the Washington Cascades, erupted. The blast felled trees over a 600-km² area, and the landslide that followed destroyed everything in its path, killing nearly 60 people. More than 30 years later, much of the area has experienced a relatively rapid recovery of plant and animal communities. First, millions of spiders ballooned in on silken threads. Plant seeds blown in by the wind germinated. Lupines, plants that can fix their own nitrogen, were the first plants to grow. Stands of red alder, willow, and cottonwood grew up around the area lakes. Elk returned to browse, bringing new plant species by defecating seeds. Pocket gopher tunnels helped mix the soil, and their mounds provided habitat for additional plants to grow. Their tunnels also provided refuges for returning frogs, newts, and salamanders. Ecologists were keen to study not only the recovery of each of these species, but also the interactions between them and how the arrival of some species facilitated the arrival of others.

In Chapter 44 we examined the growth of populations. Most populations, however, exist not on their own, but together with populations of many other species. This assemblage of many populations that live in the same place at the same time is known as a **community.** For example, a tropical forest community consists of not only tree species and other vegetation, but also the insects that pollinate them, the herbivores that feed upon the plants, and the predators and parasites of the herbivores.

Community ecology explores the factors that influence the number and abundance of species in a community. In this chapter, we begin with describing patterns of species richness and diversity. We explore why, on a global scale, the number of species is usually greatest in the tropics and declines toward the poles. Ecologists recognize that communities may change, for example, following a disturbance such as a fire or a volcanic eruption. We will discuss why this recovery tends to occur in a predictable sequence of changes, which ecologists have termed succession, and, in particular, we will examine why in certain situations the structure of the community tends toward an equilibrium determined by the balance between the rates of immigration and extinction.

45.1 Patterns of Species Richness and Species Diversity

Learning Outcomes:

1. Identify the latitudinal gradient of species richness.
2. List and describe three hypotheses for observed patterns of species richness.
3. Define species diversity and describe how it is calculated.

Community ecology addresses which factors influence the number of different species in a community, or **species richness.** Globally, the number of species of most taxa varies along a latitudinal gradient, generally increasing from polar to temperate areas and reaching a maximum in the tropics. For example, the species richness of North American birds increases from Arctic Canada to Panama (**Figure 45.1**). A similar pattern exists for mammals, amphibians, reptiles, and plants. Although the latitudinal gradient of species richness is an important pattern, species richness is also influenced by topographical variation. More mountains mean more hilltops, valleys, and differing habitats; thus, the number of birds is greater in the U.S. mountainous west. Species richness is also reduced by the peninsular effect, in which the number of species decreases as a function of distance from the main body of land.

Many hypotheses for the latitudinal gradient in species richness have been advanced. We will consider several hypotheses for patterns of species richness. Although they are treated separately here, these hypotheses are not mutually exclusive. All can potentially contribute to patterns of species richness.

The Species-Time Hypothesis Suggests Communities Diversify with Age

Many ecologists argue that communities diversify, or gain species, with time. Tropical communities are usually older than temperate communities, because the species in temperate regions are periodically wiped out by glaciers. The **species-time hypothesis** proposes that temperate regions have less rich communities than tropical ones because they are younger. According to this idea, ice ages have driven many species away from temperate regions and it takes time for such species to return to those regions after the glaciers have retreated.

In support of the species-time hypothesis, British ecologist H. John Birks found a significant correlation between the numbers of species of insects on various British trees and the evolutionary ages of these tree species in Britain (**Figure 45.2a**). Many of the tree species in Britain are relatively recent colonists, having appeared following the departure of the glaciers that covered most of the islands. Birks used radiocarbon dating of pollen collected from deep lake sediments to estimate the length of time a tree species had been present in Britain. No tree species had been present in Britain for longer than 13,000 years. He then gathered information on numbers of insect species present on trees from lists provided by other experts who had been examining the insect fauna of trees in Britain for many years. The significant relationship

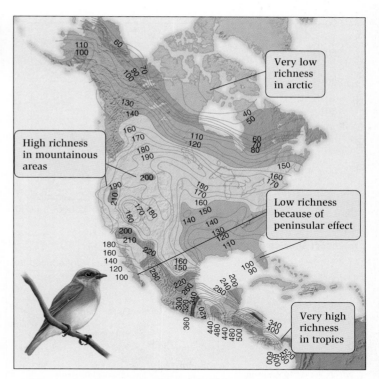

Figure 45.1 **Species richness of birds in North America.** The values indicate the numbers of different species in a given area. Contour lines show equal numbers of bird species, with colors indicating incremental changes. Note the pronounced latitudinal gradient toward the tropics and the high diversity in California and northern Mexico, regions of considerable topographical variation and habitat diversity.

between pollen age and the total number of insects indicated that older tree species support more insect species.

However, ecologists recognize drawbacks to the species-time hypothesis. For example, this hypothesis may help explain variations in the species richness of terrestrial organisms, but it has limited applicability to marine organisms. Although we might not expect terrestrial species, particularly plants, to redistribute themselves quickly following a glaciation—especially if there is a physical barrier like the English Channel to overcome—there seems to be no reason that marine organisms couldn't relatively easily shift their distribution patterns during glaciations, yet the latitudinal gradient of species richness still exists in marine habitats.

The Species-Area Hypothesis Suggests That Large Areas Support More Species

The **species-area hypothesis** proposes that larger areas contain more species than smaller areas because they can support larger populations and a greater range of habitats. Much evidence supports the area hypothesis. For example, in 1974, American ecologist Donald Strong showed that insect species richness on tree species in Britain was better correlated with the area over which a tree species could be found than with time of habitation since the last Ice Age (**Figure 45.2b**). The points cluster more tightly around the line of best fit. Even relatively newly introduced species, such as apple trees, supported a large number of insect herbivores

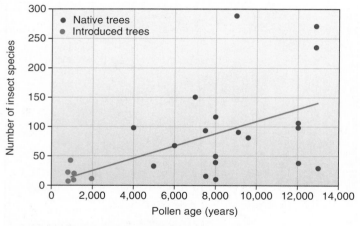

(a) Insect species on older tree species

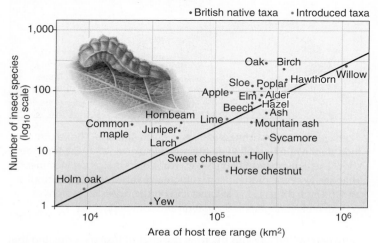

(b) Insect species increase on more widely occurring tree species

Figure 45.2 **Relationship between species richness on British host trees and both evolutionary time and area.** **(a)** Insect species richness is greater on evolutionary older tree species, which supports the species-time hypothesis. **(b)** A positive correlation is found between insect species richness and the area of the host tree's range, in square kilometers (km²), which supports the species-area hypothesis. Note the log scale in part **(b)**.

if they were planted over a wide area. The observation that the number of species tends to increase with increasing area is called the **species-area effect.**

The large, climatically similar area of the tropics has been proposed as a reason why the tropics have high species richness. However, the area hypothesis seems unable to explain why, if increased richness is linked to increased area, more species are not found in certain regions such as the vast contiguous landmass of Asia. Furthermore, although tundra may be the world's largest biome in terms of land mass, it has low species richness. Finally, the largest marine system, the open ocean, which has the greatest volume of any habitat, has fewer species than tropical nearshore waters, which have a relatively small volume.

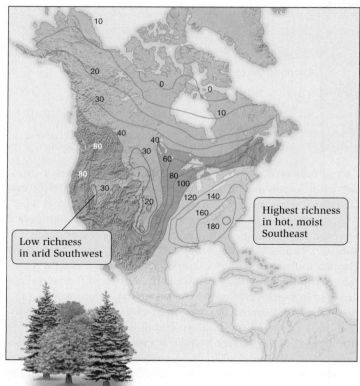

Figure 45.3 **Tree species richness in North America.** Contour lines show equal numbers of tree species, with colors indicating incremental changes. Tree species richness and evapotranspiration rates are highest in the southeast.

Concept Check: *Why doesn't the species richness of trees increase in mountainous areas of the West, as it does for birds?*

The Species-Productivity Hypothesis Suggests That Greater Productivity Results in More Species

The **species-productivity hypothesis** proposes that greater production by plants results in greater overall species richness. An increase in plant productivity, the total weight of plant material produced over time, leads to an increase in the number of herbivores and hence an increase in the number of predator, parasite, and scavenger species. Productivity itself is influenced by factors such as temperature and rainfall, because many plants grow better where it is warm and wet. For example, in 1987, Canadian biologist David Currie and colleagues showed that the species richness of trees in North America is best predicted by the **evapotranspiration rate,** the rate at which water moves into the atmosphere through the processes of evaporation from the soil and transpiration of plants, both of which are influenced by the amount of solar energy (**Figure 45.3**).

Once again, however, exceptions are observed. In 1993, American researchers Robert Latham and Robert Ricklefs showed that although patterns of tree richness in North America support the productivity hypothesis, the pattern does not hold for broad comparisons between continents. For example, the temperate forests of eastern Asia support substantially higher numbers of tree species (729) than do climatically similar areas of North America (253) or Europe (124). These three areas have different evolutionary histories and different neighboring areas from which species might have invaded. In summary, although there is no one simple cause of the polar-to-tropical species richness gradients, the factors of evolutionary time, area, and productivity each influence species richness to some degree.

Quantitative Analysis

CALCULATING SPECIES DIVERSITY

So far, we have discussed communities in terms of variations in species richness. However, ecologists need to take into account not only the number of species in a community but also their frequency of occurrence, or **relative abundance.** For example, consider two hypothetical communities, A and B, both with two species and 100 total individuals.

	Number of individuals of species 1	Number of individuals of species 2
Community A	99	1
Community B	50	50

The species richness of community B equals that of community A, because they both contain two species. However, community B is considered more diverse than A because the distribution of individuals between species is more even. One would be much more likely to encounter both species in community B than in community A, where one species dominates. **Species diversity** is a measure of the diversity of an ecological community that incorporates both species number and relative abundance.

To measure the species diversity of a community, ecologists calculate what is known as a diversity index. Although many different indices are available, the most widely used is the **Shannon diversity index (H_s),** which is calculated as

$$H_s = -\sum p_i \ln p_i$$

where p_i is the proportion of individuals belonging to species i in a community, ln is the natural logarithm, and $\sum$ indicates summation. For example, for a species in which there are 50 individuals out of a total of 100 in the community, p_i is 50/100, or 0.5. The natural log of 0.5 is -0.693. For this species, $p_i \ln p_i$ is then $0.5 \times -0.693 = -0.347$. For a hypothetical community with 5 species and 100 total individuals, the Shannon diversity index is calculated as follows:

Species	Abundance	p_i	$\ln p_i$	$p_i \ln p_i$
1	50	0.5	-0.693	-0.347
2	30	0.3	-1.204	-0.361
3	10	0.1	-2.302	-0.230
4	9	0.09	-2.408	-0.217
5	1	0.01	-4.605	-0.046
Total	5	100	1.00	$\sum p_i \ln p_i = -1.201$

Remember that in the equation, the negative sign in front of the summation changes the summed value to positive, so the index actually becomes 1.201, not -1.201.

Values of the Shannon diversity index for real communities often fall between 1.5 and 3.5, with the higher the value, the greater the diversity. Table 45.1 calculates the diversity of two bird communities in Indonesia with similar species richness but differing species abundance. The bird communities were surveyed in a pristine unlogged forest or in a selectively logged lowland forest. To document diversity, British biologist Stuart Marsden established census stations in the two forests and recorded the type and number of all bird species for a number of 10-minute periods. Although a greater number of individual birds was seen in the logged areas (2,345) than in the unlogged ones (1,824), a high proportion of the individuals in the logged areas (0.386) belonged to just one species, *Nectarinia jugularis.* Although only one more bird species was found in the unlogged area than in the logged area, calculation of the Shannon diversity index showed a higher diversity of birds in the unlogged area, 2.284 versus 2.037, which is a considerable difference, considering the logarithmic nature of the index.

A problem with diversity indices is that the results are not easy to compare. For example, imagine our hypothetical community has 5 species each with 20 individuals ($n = 100$). The Shannon diversity index is 1.609, which is 34% greater than the value of 1.201 from the hypothetical community. A better comparison would be to calculate the **effective number of species,** which converts values from species diversity indices into equivalent numbers of species. For the Shannon diversity index, we take the exponential of 1.609, $e^{1.609}$, so that our value of 1.609 becomes 5.0, which is the same as the actual number of species. For our value of 1.201, the effective number of species is 3.323, which means that this community is 50.5% less diverse than the community with an effective number of species of 5.0.

Crunching the Numbers: (a) Community A has 2 species each with 50 individuals. Community B has 3 species, one with 80 individuals and the other two with 10 individuals each. Calculate the Shannon diversity index for both communities. What can you conclude? **(b)** Calculate the effective number of species for the bird communities in the logged and unlogged areas of the Indonesian forests mentioned above. What is the percentage difference in the effective number of species?

Table 45.1	Shannon Diversity Index of Bird Species on Logged and Unlogged Sites in Indonesia					
		Unlogged			Logged	
Species	N	p_i	$p_i \ln p_i$	N	p_i	$p_i \ln p_i$
Nectarinia jugularis, olive-backed sunbird	410	0.225	−0.336	910	0.386	−0.367
Ducula bicolor, pied imperial pigeon	230	0.126	−0.261	220	0.093	−0.221
Philemon subcorniculatus, grey-necked friarbird	210	0.115	−0.249	240	0.102	−0.233
Nectarinia aspasia, black sunbird	190	0.104	−0.235	120	0.051	−0.152
Dicaeum vulneratum, ashy flowerpecker	185	0.101	−0.232	280	0.119	−0.253
Ducula perspicillata, white-eyed imperial pigeon	170	0.093	−0.221	180	0.076	−0.196
Phylloscopus borealis, arctic warbler	160	0.088	−0.214	140	0.059	−0.167
Eos bornea, red lory	88	0.048	−0.146	73	0.031	−0.108
Ixos affinis, golden bulbul	76	0.042	−0.133	31	0.013	−0.056
Geoffroyus geoffroyi, red-cheeked parrot	44	0.024	−0.089	54	0.023	−0.087
Rhyticeros plicatus, Papuan hornbill	24	0.013	−0.056	27	0.011	−0.050
Cacatua moluccensis, Moluccan cockatoo	12	0.007	−0.035	1	0.001	−0.007
Tanygnathus megalorynchos, great-billed parrot	9	0.005	−0.026	11	0.005	−0.026
Eclectus roratus, electus parrot	7	0.004	−0.022	0	0	0
Macropygia amboinensis, brown cuckoo-dove	6	0.003	−0.017	7	0.003	−0.017
Cacomantis sepulcralis, ruby-breasted cuckoo	3	0.002	−0.012	0	0	0
Trichoglossus haematodus, rainbow lorikeet	0	0	0	64	0.027	−0.097
Total	**1,824**	**1.0**		**2,345**	**1.0**	
Shannon diversity index			**2.284**			**2.037**

45.1 Reviewing the Concepts

- The number of species of most taxa varies according to geographic location, generally increasing from polar areas to tropical areas (Figure 45.1).
- Different hypotheses for the variation in species richness have been advanced, including the species-time hypothesis, the species-area hypothesis, and the species-productivity hypothesis (Figures 45.2, 45.3).
- Species diversity takes into account both species richness and species abundance. The most widely used measure of species diversity is called the Shannon diversity index (Table 45.1), but the most easily interpreted measure is called the effective number of species.

45.1 Testing Your Knowledge

1. In North America, the highest numbers of bird species are generally found
   a. at the tip of peninsulas, such as Florida and Baja California.
   b. in mountainous areas of the U.S. Southwest.
   c. in wet areas of the U.S. Southeast.
   d. in Central America.
   e. in high-productivity areas of the Arctic.

2. Lake Baikal in Siberia is an ancient, unglaciated temperate lake and contains 580 species of bottom-dwelling invertebrates. Great Slave Lake, a comparably sized lake that was once glaciated at the same latitude in northern Canada, contains only four species in the same zone. This supports which of the following hypotheses?
   a. Species-time   c. Species-productivity   e. Both b and c
   b. Species-area   d. Both a and b

Species Diversity and Community Stability

Learning Outcome:

1. Describe the diversity-stability hypothesis and detail the evidence supporting it.

In this section, we consider the relationship between species diversity and community stability. A community is often seen as stable when little to no change can be detected in the number of species and their abundance over a given time period. The community may then be said to be in equilibrium. Community stability is an important consideration to ecologists. A decrease in the stability of a community over time may alert ecologists to a possible problem. For example, an invasive species such as the zebra mussel, *Dreissena polymorpha*, in the Great Lakes can cause changes in the community of other invertebrates living there.

In this section, we explore the question of whether communities with more species diversity are more stable than communities with less diversity, using evidence from a field experiment.

The Diversity-Stability Hypothesis States That Species-Rich Communities Are More Stable Than Those with Fewer Species

The link between species richness and stability was first explicitly proposed by the English ecologist Charles Elton in the 1950s. He suggested that a disturbance in a species-rich community would be cushioned by large numbers of interacting species and would not produce as drastic an effect as it would on a species-poor community. Thus, an introduced predator or parasite could cause extinctions in a species-poor community but probably not in a more diverse community, where its effects would be buffered by interactions with more species. Elton argued that outbreaks of pests are often found on cultivated land or land disturbed by humans, both of which are species-poor communities with few naturally occurring species. His argument became known as the **diversity-stability hypothesis.**

However, some ecologists began to challenge Elton's association of diversity with stability. Ecologists pointed out many examples of introduced species that have assumed pest proportions in species-rich areas, including rabbits in Australia and pigs in North America. They noted that disturbed or cultivated land may suffer from pest outbreaks not because of its simple nature but because individual species, including introduced species, often have no natural enemies in the new environment, in contrast to the long associations between native species and their natural enemies. For example, in Europe, coevolved predators, such as foxes, prevent rabbit populations from increasing to pest proportions. Research was needed to determine if a link existed between diversity and stability.

Field Studies Have Linked Stability to Diversity

In 1996, American ecologist David Tilman reported the relationship between species diversity and stability from an 11-year study of 207 grassland plots in Minnesota that varied in their species

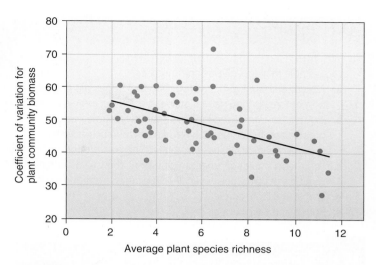

Figure 45.4 **Biomass variation and species richness.** Tilman's 11-year study of grassland plots in Minnesota revealed that year-to-year variability in community biomass was lower in species-rich plots. Each dot represents an individual plot. Only the plots from one field are graphed.

richness. He measured the biomass of every species of plant, in each plot, at the end of every year and obtained the average species biomass. He then calculated how much this biomass varied from year to year through a statistical measure called the coefficient of variation. Less variation in biomass signified community stability. Year-to-year variation in plant community biomass was significantly lower in plots with greater plant species richness (**Figure 45.4**). The results showed that greater diversity enhances community stability.

Tilman suggested that more diverse communities are more likely to contain disturbance-resistant species that, in the event of a disturbance, could grow and compensate for the loss of disturbance-sensitive species. For example, when a change in climate such as drought decreased the abundance of competitively dominant species that thrived in normal conditions, unharmed drought-resistant species increased in mass and replaced them. Such declines in the number of sensitive species and compensatory increases in other species acted to stabilize total community biomass.

Although ecologists recognize a link between species diversity and community stability, they are also aware that, over long periods of time, communities may experience severe disturbances. The change in the composition and structure of communities that follows occurs in a predictable way termed succession, which is described next.

45.2 Reviewing the Concepts

- Community stability is an important concept in ecology. The diversity-stability hypothesis maintains that species-rich communities are more stable than communities with fewer species. Tilman's field studies, which showed that year-to-year variation in plant biomass decreased with increasing species diversity, established a link between diversity and stability (Figure 45.4).

45.2 Testing Your Knowledge

1. Which evidence suggests that more diverse communities are more stable than less diverse communities?
   a. Agricultural land, with fewer species, undergoes less frequent pest outbreaks than natural prairies containing more species.
   b. In Australia, introduced rabbits frequently assume pest proportions. In Europe, coevolved predators such as foxes prevent rabbit populations from reaching pest proportions.
   c. Long-term studies of American grasslands show fields with higher numbers of plant species vary less in biomass from year to year.
   d. Both a and b are correct.
   e. Both b and c are correct.

45.3 Succession: Community Change

Learning Outcomes:

1. Distinguish between primary and secondary succession.
2. Compare and contrast facilitation, inhibition, and tolerance as mechanisms of succession.

Ecologists have developed several terms to describe how change in a community occurs over time. The term **succession** describes the gradual and continuous change in species composition of a community following a disturbance. **Primary succession** refers to succession on a newly exposed site that has no biological legacy in terms of plants, animals, or microbes, such as bare ground caused by a volcanic eruption or the sediment created by the retreat of glaciers. In primary succession on land, the plants must often build up the soil, and thus a long time—even hundreds of years—may be required for the process. Only a tiny proportion of the Earth's surface is currently undergoing primary succession, including the area around Mount St. Helens and on new lava flows around the volcanoes in Hawaii and off the coast of Iceland, and behind retreating glaciers in Alaska and Canada.

Secondary succession refers to succession on a site that has already supported life but has undergone a disturbance such as a fire, tornado, hurricane, or flood. In terrestrial areas, soil is already present. Clearing a natural forest and farming the land for several years is an example of a severe forest disturbance that does not kill all native species. Some plants and many soil bacteria, nematodes, and insects are still present. Secondary succession occurs if farming is ended. The secondary succession in abandoned farmlands (also called old fields) can lead to a pattern of vegetation quite different from one that develops after primary succession following glacial retreat. For example, the plowing and added fertilizers, herbicides, and pesticides may have caused substantial changes in the soil of an old field, allowing species that require a lot of nitrogen to colonize. These species would not be present for many years in newly created glacial soils.

American plant ecologist Frederic Clements is often viewed as the founder of successional theory. His work in the early 20th century emphasized succession as proceeding through several stages to a distinct end point or **climax community.** Although disturbance can return a community from a later stage to an earlier stage, generally

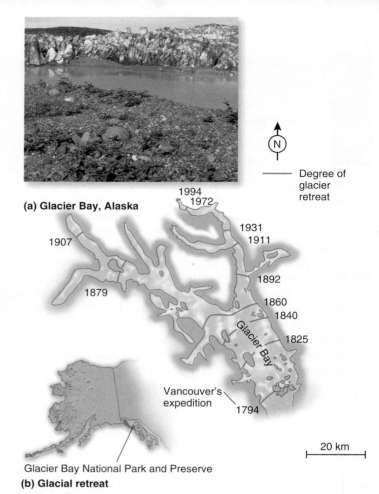

(a) **Glacier Bay, Alaska**

(b) **Glacial retreat**

Figure 45.5   The degree of glacier retreat at Glacier Bay, Alaska, since 1794. (a) Primary succession begins on the bare rock and soil evident at the edges of the retreating glacier. **(b)** The lines reflect the position of the glacier in 1794 and its subsequent retreat northward.

Concept Check: *Why might ecologists think of walking the coastline of Glacier Bay as the equivalent of walking back in time?*

the community progresses in one direction. Clements's depiction of succession focused on a process termed facilitation, but two other mechanisms of succession—inhibition and tolerance—have since been described. Let's examine the evidence for each of them.

Facilitation Assumes Each Invading Species Creates a More Favorable Habitat for Succeeding Species

A key assumption of Clements's view of succession was that each colonizing species makes the environment a little different, such as a little shadier or a little richer in soil nitrogen, so that it becomes more suitable for other species, which then invade and outcompete the earlier residents. This process, known as **facilitation,** continues until the most competitively dominant species have colonized, when the community is at climax. The composition of the climax community for any given region is determined by climate, soil condition, and frequency of disturbance.

Succession following the gradual retreat of Alaskan glaciers is often used as a specific example of facilitation as a mechanism of succession. Over the past 200 years, the glaciers in Glacier Bay have undergone a dramatic retreat of nearly 100 km (**Figure 45.5**).

Succession in Glacier Bay has followed a distinct pattern of vegetation. As glaciers retreat, they leave moraines—deposits of stones, pulverized rock, and debris that serve as soil. In Alaska, the bare soil has a low nitrogen content and scant organic matter. In the pioneer stage, the soil is first colonized by a black crust of cyanobacteria, mosses, lichens, horsetails (*Equisetum variegatum*), and the occasional river beauty (*Epilobium latifolium*) (Figure 45.6a). Because the cyanobacteria are nitrogen fixers (refer back to Figure 37.17), the soil nitrogen increases a little, but soil depth and litterfall (fallen leaves, twigs, and other plant material) are still minimal. At this stage, there may be a few seeds and seedlings of dwarf shrubs of the rose family, commonly called mountain avens (*Dryas drummondii*); alders (*Alnus sinuata*); and spruce; but they are rare. After about 40 years, mountain avens dominates the landscape (Figure 45.6b). Soil nitrogen increases, as does soil depth and litterfall, and alder trees begin to invade.

At about 60 years, alders form dense, close thickets (Figure 45.6c). Alders have nitrogen-fixing bacteria that live mutualistically in their roots and convert nitrogen from the air into a biologically useful form. Soil nitrogen dramatically increases, as does litterfall. Sitka spruce trees (*Picea sitchensis*) begin to invade at about this time. After about 75 to 100 years, the spruce trees begin to overtop the alders, shading them out. The litterfall is still high, and the large volume of needles turns the soil acidic. The shade causes competitive exclusion of many of the original understory species, including alder, and only mosses carpet the ground. At this stage, seedlings of western hemlock (*Tsuga heterophylla*) and mountain hemlock (*Tsuga mertensiana*) may also occur. After 200 years, a mixed spruce-hemlock climax forest results (Figure 45.6d).

What other evidence is there of facilitation? Experimental studies of early primary succession on Mount St. Helens, which show that decomposition of fungi allows mosses and other fungi to colonize the soil, provide evidence of facilitation. Succession on sand dunes also supports the facilitation model, in that pioneer plant species stabilize the sand dunes and facilitate the establishment of subsequent plant species. The foredunes, those nearest the shoreline, are the most frequently disturbed and are maintained in a state of early succession, whereas more stable communities develop farther away from the shoreline.

Succession also occurs in aquatic communities. Although soils do not develop in marine environments, facilitation may still be encountered when one species enhances the quality of settling and establishment sites for another species. When experimental test plates used to measure settling rates of marine organisms were placed in the Delaware Bay, researchers discovered that certain cnidarians enhanced the attachment of tunicates, and both facilitated the attachment of mussels, the dominant species in the community. In this experiment, the smooth surface of the test

Stage	Pioneer	*Dryas*	Alder	Spruce-hemlock
Time (years) since glacial retreat	5	40	60	200
Soil depth (cm)	5.2	7.0	8.8	15.1
Soil N (g/m^2)	3.8	5.3	21.8	53.3
Soil pH	7.2	7.3	6.8	3.6
Litterfall (g/m^2/yr)	1.5	2.8	277	261

Cyanobacteria
Moss
Lichens

Mountain avens
(*Dryas drummondii*)

Alder
(*Alnus sinuata*)

Spruce
(*Picea sitchensis*)
Western hemlock
(*Tsuga heterophylla*)

(a) Pioneer stage   **(b) *Dryas* stage**   **(c) Alder stage**   **(d) Spruce-hemlock stage**

Figure 45.6 **The pattern of primary succession at Glacier Bay, Alaska.** **(a)** The first species to colonize the bare ground following retreat of the glaciers are small species such as cyanobacteria, moss, and lichens. **(b)** Mountain avens (*Dryas drummondii*) is a flower common in the *Dryas* stage. **(c)** Soil nitrogen and litterfall increase rapidly as alder (*Alnus sinuata*) invades. Note also the appearance of a few spruce trees higher up the valley. **(d)** Sitka spruce (*Picea sitchensis*) and hemlock (*Tsuga heterophylla*) trees make up a climax spruce-hemlock forest at Glacier Bay, with moss carpeting the ground. Two hundred years ago, glaciers occupied this spot.

plates prevented many species from colonizing, but once the surface became rougher, because of the presence of the cnidarians, many other species were able to colonize. In a similar fashion, early colonizing bacteria, which create biofilms on rock surfaces, can facilitate succession of other organisms.

Inhibition Implies That Early Colonists Can Prevent Later Arrivals from Replacing Them

Although data on succession in some communities fit the facilitation model, researchers have proposed alternative hypotheses of how succession may operate. In the process known as **inhibition,** early colonists prevent colonization by other species. For example, removing the litter of *Setaria faberi*, an early successional plant species in New Jersey old fields, causes an increase in the biomass of a later species, *Erigeron annuus*. The release of toxic compounds from decomposing *Setaria* litter or physical obstruction by the litter itself blocks the establishment of *Erigeron*. Without the litter present, however, *Erigeron* dominates and reduces the biomass of *Setaria*.

Inhibition has been seen as the primary method of succession in the marine intertidal zone, where space is limited (look back at Figure 43.23a). In this habitat, early successional species are at a great advantage in maintaining possession of valuable space. In 1974, American ecologist Wayne Sousa created an environment for testing how succession works in the intertidal zone by scraping rock faces clean of all algae or putting out fresh boulders or concrete blocks. The first colonists of these areas were the green algae *Ulva*. By removing *Ulva* from the substrate, Sousa showed that the large red alga *Chondracanthus canaliculatus* was able to colonize more quickly (**Figure 45.7**). The results of Sousa's study indicate that early colonists can inhibit rather than facilitate the invasion of subsequent colonists. Succession may eventually occur because early colonizing species, such as *Ulva*, are more susceptible than later successional species, such as *Chondracanthus*, to the rigors of the physical environment and to attacks by herbivores, such as crabs (*Pachygrapsus crassipes*).

Tolerance Suggests That Early Colonists Neither Facilitate nor Inhibit Later Colonists

In 1977, researchers Joseph Connell and Ralph Slatyer proposed a third mechanism of succession, which they termed **tolerance.** In this process, any species can start the succession, but the eventual climax community is reached in a somewhat orderly fashion. The species that establish and remain do not change the environment in ways that either facilitate or inhibit subsequent colonists. Species have differing tolerances to the intensity of competition that results as more species accumulate. Relatively competition-intolerant species are more successful early in succession, when the intensity of competition is low and resources are abundant. Relatively competition-tolerant species appear later in succession and at climax. Connell and Slatyer found the best evidence for the tolerance model in American plant ecologist Frank Egler's earlier work on floral succession. In the 1950s, Egler showed that succession in plant communities is determined largely by species that already exist in the ground as buried seeds or old roots. Whichever species germinates first or regenerates from roots

Biology Principle

Biology Is an Experimental Science
Waiting for a natural ecological disturbance to occur and then studying the resulting succession is unpredictable and time-consuming.

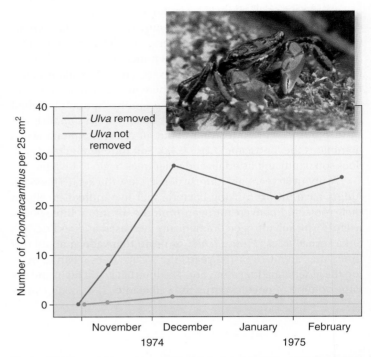

Figure 45.7 Inhibition as a method of succession in the marine intertidal zone. Removing *Ulva* from intertidal rock faces allowed colonization by *Chondracanthus*. The inset shows *Ulva* on a rock face with the striped shore crab *Pachygrapsus crassipes*, a herbivore.

initiates the succession sequence. Germination or root regeneration, in turn, depends on the timing of a disturbance. For example, an early-season tree fall would promote early-germinating species to grow in the subsequent light gap, whereas a late-season tree fall would promote the growth of late-germinating species. As succession proceeds, earlier germinating or regenerating species may be outcompeted by different species.

The key distinction between the three models is in the manner in which succession proceeds. In the facilitation model, species replacement is facilitated by previous colonists; in the inhibition model, it is inhibited by the action of previous colonists; and in the tolerance model, species may be affected by previous colonists, but they do not require them (**Figure 45.8**).

45.3 Reviewing the Concepts

- Succession describes the gradual and continuous change in community structure over time. Primary succession refers to succession on a newly exposed site with no prior biological legacy; secondary succession refers to succession on a site that has supported life but has undergone a disturbance (Figures 45.5, 45.6).

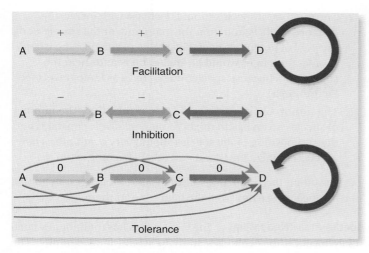

Figure 45.8 Three models of succession. A, B, C, and D represent four stages. D represents the climax community. An arrow indicates "is replaced by," and + = facilitation, − = inhibition, and 0 = no effect. The facilitation model is the classic model of succession. In the inhibition model, early arriving species outcompete later arriving species. The tolerance model depends on which species gets there first. The colored arrows show that succession may bypass some stages in the tolerance model.

✓ **Concept Check:** *Inhibition implies that competition exists between species, with early-arriving species tending to outcompete later arrivals, at least for a while. Does competition or mutualism feature more prominently in facilitation?*

- Three mechanisms have been proposed for succession. In facilitation, each species facilitates or makes the environment more suitable for subsequent species. In inhibition, initial species inhibit later colonists. In tolerance, any species can start the succession, and species replacement is unaffected by previous colonists (Figures 45.7, 45.8).

45.3 Testing Your Knowledge

1. Which of the following are examples of secondary succession?
   a. Plants growing in cracks on the pavement of a quiet street
   b. The recovery of vegetation following the 2004 Indonesian tsunami
   c. The colonization of new sand by beach plants
   d. The recovery of forests following a wild fire
   e. Both b and d

2. In New England salt marshes, *Spartina* grass stabilizes the substrate and reduces water velocity, which enables other seedlings to emerge. This is an example of
   a. primary succession.
   b. facilitation.
   c. tolerance.
   d. inhibition.
   e. a climax community.

45.4 Island Biogeography

Learning Outcomes:

1. Describe the equilibrium model of island biogeography.
2. List the predictions of the model and discuss how well evidence supports them.

In some newly formed habitats such as volcanic islands, succession may be affected not only by facilitation, inhibition, or tolerance, but also by the ability of species to colonize isolated areas. In these cases, species richness is affected by distance of habitats from a source pool of colonists and the size of the areas to be colonized. In the 1960s, two American ecologists, Robert MacArthur and E. O. Wilson, developed a comprehensive model to explain the process of succession on new islands, where a gradual buildup of species proceeds from a sterile beginning. Their model, termed the **equilibrium model of island biogeography,** holds that the number of species on an island tends toward an equilibrium number that is determined by the balance between two factors: immigration rates and extinction rates. Their model has been applied not just to newly formed oceanic islands but also to virtual islands, such as mountains surrounded by deserts, lakes surrounded by dry land, or conservation areas surrounded by agricultural land or urban landscapes. In this section, we explore island biogeography and how well the model's predictions are supported by data.

The Island Biogeography Model Suggests That During Succession, Gains in Immigration Are Balanced by Losses from Extinction

MacArthur and Wilson's model of island biogeography suggests that species repeatedly arrive on an island and either thrive or become extinct. The rate of immigration of new species is highest when no species are present on the island. As the number of species accumulates, the immigration rate decreases, since subsequent immigrants are more likely to represent species already present on the island. The rate of extinction is low at the time of first colonization, because few species are present and many have large populations. With the addition of new species, the populations of some species diminish, so the probability of extinction increases. Over time, the number of species tends toward an equilibrium, $\hat{S}$, in which the rates of immigration and extinction are equal. Species may continue to arrive and go extinct, but the number of species on the island remains approximately the same.

MacArthur and Wilson reasoned that when plotted graphically, both the immigration and extinction lines would be curved, for several reasons (**Figure 45.9a**). First, species arrive on islands at different rates. Some organisms, including plants with seed-dispersal mechanisms and winged animals, are more mobile than others and arrive quickly. Other organisms arrive more slowly. This pattern causes the immigration curve to start off steep but get progressively shallower. On the other hand, extinctions rise at accelerating rates, because as later species arrive, competition increases and more species are likely to go extinct. The strength of

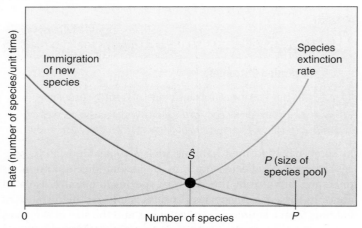

(a) Effects of immigration and extinction on species number

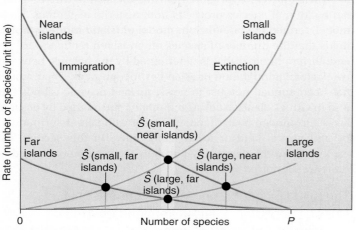

(b) Added effects of island size and proximity to the mainland on species number

Figure 45.9 **MacArthur and Wilson's equilibrium model of island biogeography. (a)** The interaction of immigration rate and extinction rate produces an equilibrium number of species on an island, $\hat{S}$. $\hat{S}$ can vary from 0 species to P species, the total number of species available to colonize. **(b)** $\hat{S}$ varies according to the island's size and distance from the mainland. An increase in distance (near to far) lowers the immigration rate. An increase in island area (small to large) lowers the extinction rate.

Concept Check: *Can you think of a scenario where there would be large numbers of species on a small island?*

BioConnections: *Look forward to Figure 47.10. How might the model of island biogeography be useful in the design of nature reserves?*

the island biogeography model was that it generated several testable predictions:

1. The number of species should increase with increasing island size (area), a concept known as the species-area relationship (see Figure 45.2b). Extinction rates would be lower on larger islands because population sizes would be larger and less susceptible to extinction (Figure 45.9b).

2. The number of species should decrease with increasing distance of the island from the mainland, or the **source pool,** the pool of potential species available to colonize the island. Immigration rates would be greater on islands near the source pool because species do not have as far to travel (see Figure 45.9b).

3. The turnover of species should be considerable. The number of species on an island might remain relatively constant, but the composition of the species should vary over time as new species colonize the island and others become extinct.

Let's examine the predictions of the island biogeography model one by one and see how well the data support them.

Species-Area Relationships   The West Indies has traditionally been a key location for ecologists studying island biogeography. The physical geography and the plant and animal life of the islands are well known. Furthermore, the Lesser Antilles, from Anguilla in the north to Grenada in the south, enjoy a similar climate and are surrounded by deep water (Figure 45.10a). In 1999, Robert Ricklefs and Irby Lovette summarized the available data on the richness of species of four groups of animals—birds, bats, reptiles and amphibians, and butterflies—across 19 islands that varied in area over two orders of magnitude (13–1,510 km²). In each case, a positive correlation occurred between area and species richness (Figure 45.10b).

Species-Distance Relationships   In studies of the numbers of lowland forest bird species in Polynesia, MacArthur and Wilson found that the number of species decreased with the distance from the source pool of New Guinea (Figure 45.11). They expressed the richness of bird species on the islands as a percentage of the number of bird species found on New Guinea. A significant decline in this percentage was observed with increasing distance. More-distant islands contained lower numbers of species than nearer islands. This research substantiated the prediction of species richness declining with increasing distance from the source pool.

Species Turnover   Studies involving species turnover on islands are difficult to perform because detailed and complete species lists are needed over long periods of time, usually many years and often decades. The lists that do exist are often compiled in a casual way and are not usually suitable for comparison with more modern data. In 1980, British researcher Francis Gilbert reviewed 25 investigations carried out to demonstrate turnover and found a lack of this type of rigor in nearly all of them. Furthermore, most of the observed turnover in these studies, usually less than 1% per year, or less than one species per year, appeared to be due to immigrants that never became established rather than to the extinction of well-established species. More recent studies have revealed similar findings, suggesting that the rates of turnover are low rather than high, giving little conclusive support to the third prediction of the equilibrium model of island biogeography. Even the most rigorous study, by E. O. Wilson and his student Dan Simberloff, showed negligible turnover, as described next.

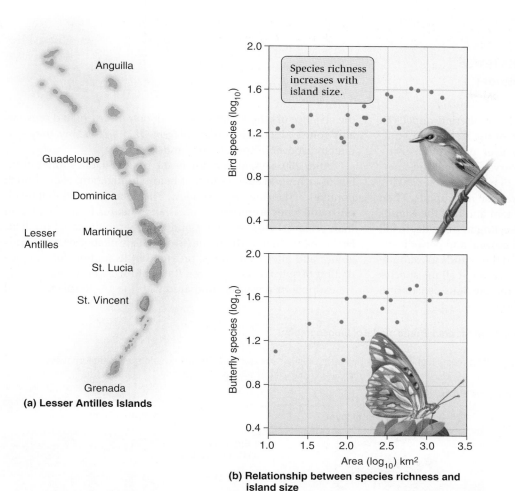

(a) Lesser Antilles Islands

(b) Relationship between species richness and island size

Figure 45.10 **Species richness and island size.** **(a)** The Lesser Antilles extend from Anguilla in the north to Grenada in the south. **(b)** On these islands, the number of bird and butterfly species increases with the area of an island. Note that these relationships are traditionally plotted on a double logarithmic scale, a so-called log-log plot, in which the horizontal axis is the logarithm to the base 10 of the area and the vertical axis is the logarithm to the base 10 of the number of species. A linear plot of the area versus the number of species would be difficult to produce, because of the wide range of area and richness of species involved. Logarithmic scales condense this variation to manageable limits.

✔ **Concept Check:** *Calculate the approximate change in bird species richness across islands in the Lesser Antilles.*

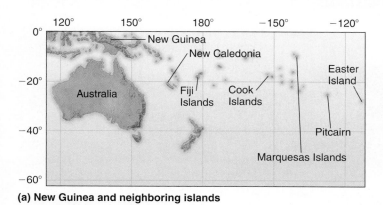

(a) New Guinea and neighboring islands

Figure 45.11 **Species richness and distance from the source pool.** **(a)** Map of Australia, New Guinea, and these Polynesian Islands: New Caledonia, Fiji Islands, Cook Islands, Marquesas Islands, Pitcairn, and Easter Island. **(b)** The number of bird species on the islands decreases with increasing distance from the source pool, New Guinea. The species richness is expressed as the percentage of bird species on New Guinea.

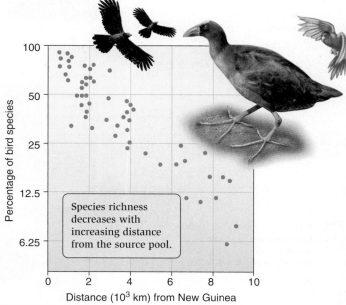

(b) Relationship between species richness and distance from source

FEATURE INVESTIGATION

Simberloff and Wilson's Experiments Tested the Predictions of the Equilibrium Model of Island Biogeography

In the 1960s, American ecologists Daniel Simberloff and E. O. Wilson conducted possibly the most rigorous test of the equilibrium model of island biogeography ever performed, using islands in the Florida Keys. First, they surveyed small red mangrove (*Rhizophora mangle*) islands, 11–25 m in diameter, taking a census of the numbers of all their terrestrial arthropods. Then they enclosed each island with a plastic tent and had the islands fumigated with methyl bromide, a short-acting insecticide, to kill all arthropods on them. The tents were removed, and periodically thereafter Wilson and Simberloff surveyed the islands to examine recolonization rates. At each survey, they counted all the species present, noting any species not there at the previous census and

the absence of others that were previously there but had presumably gone extinct (see the data of **Figure 45.12**). In this way, they estimated turnover of species on islands.

After 250 days, all but one of the islands had a similar number of arthropod species to that before fumigation, even though population densities were still low. The data indicated that recolonization rates were higher on islands nearer to the mainland than on far islands—as the island biogeography model predicts. However, the data, which consisted of lists of species on islands before and after extinctions, provided little support for the prediction of substantial turnover. Rates of turnover were low, only 1.5 extinctions per year, compared with the 15–40 species found

Figure 45.12 Simberloff and Wilson's experiments on the equilibrium model of biogeography.

HYPOTHESIS The island biogeography model predicts higher species richness for islands closer to the mainland and significant turnover of species on islands.

STARTING LOCATION Mangrove islands in the Florida Keys.

Experimental level	Conceptual level

1 Take initial census of all terrestrial arthropods on 4 mangrove islands. Erect a framework over each mangrove island.

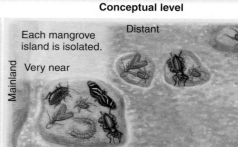

Each mangrove island is isolated.

Distant

Very near

Mainland

2 Cover the framework with tents and fumigate with methyl bromide to kill all arthropod species.

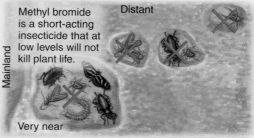

Methyl bromide is a short-acting insecticide that at low levels will not kill plant life.

Distant

Very near

Mainland

3 Remove the tents and conduct censuses every month to monitor recolonization of arthropods and to determine extinction rates.

Mangrove islands are recolonized.

Distant

Very near

Mainland

4 **THE DATA**   Island E2 was closest to the mainland and supported the highest number of species both before and after fumigation. E3 and ST2 were at an intermediate distance from the mainland, and E1 was the most distant.

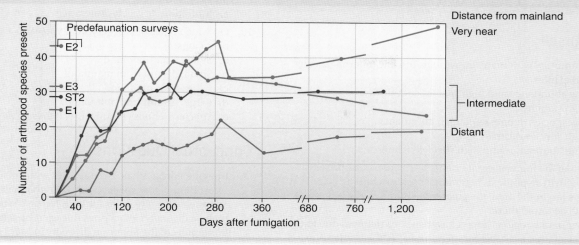

5 **CONCLUSION**   Island distance from the mainland influences species richness on mangrove islands in the Florida Keys. However, species turnover is minimal, and species richness changes little following initial recolonization.

6 **SOURCE**   Simberloff, D. S. 1978. Colonization of islands by insects: immigration, extinction and diversity. pp. 139–153 in L. A. Mound and N. Waloff (eds.). Diversity of insect faunas. *Blackwell Scientific Publications*, Oxford, U.K.

on the islands within a year. Simberloff and Wilson concluded that turnover probably involves only a small subset of transient or less important species, with the more important species remaining permanent after colonization.

Experimental Questions

1. What was the purpose of Simberloff and Wilson's study?

2. Why did the researchers conduct a thorough species survey of arthropods before experimental removal of all the arthropod species?

3. What did the researchers conclude about the relationship between island proximity to the mainland and species richness and turnover?

The equilibrium model of island biogeography has stimulated much research to confirm the strong effects of area and distance on species richness. However, species turnover appears to be low rather than considerable, which suggests that succession on most islands is a fairly orderly process. This means that colonization is not a random process and that the same species seem to colonize first and other species gradually appear in the same order.

It is important to note that the principles of island biogeography have been applied to wildlife preserves, which are essentially islands in a sea of developed land consisting of agricultural fields or urban sprawl. Conservationists have therefore utilized the model of island biogeography in the design of nature preserves, a topic we will return to in Chapter 47.

45.4   Reviewing the Concepts

- In the equilibrium model of island biogeography, the number of species on an island tends toward an equilibrium number determined by the balance between immigration and extinction rates (Figure 45.9).
- The model predicts that the number of species increases with increasing island size; that the number of species decreases with

distance from the source pool; and that turnover is high. Support exists for the first two predictions of the model, but experiments on islands in the Florida Keys refuted the third prediction (Figures 45.10, 45.11, 45.12).

45.4   Testing Your Knowledge

1. Which is part of the original MacArthur-Wilson theory of island biogeography?
   a. S is increased by distance from the source pool.
   b. S is decreased by island size.
   c. S is a balance between immigration and extinction.
   d. Island size influences immigration rates.
   e. Distance from source pool influences extinction rates.

2. Why are the immigration and extinction lines in the MacArthur-Wilson model both curved?
   a. Species arrive at different rates.
   b. Some organisms are more mobile than others.
   c. Competition increases as more species arrive.
   d. Later arriving species tend to be better competitors.
   e. All of the above are true.

Assess and Discuss

Test Yourself

1. A community with many individuals but few different species would exhibit
   a. low abundance and high species complexity.
   b. high stability.
   c. low species richness and high abundance.
   d. high species diversity.
   e. high abundance and high species richness.

2. Which of the following statements best represents the productivity hypothesis regarding species richness?
   a. The larger the area, the greater the number of species that will be found there.
   b. Temperate regions have a lower species richness due to the lack of time available for migration after the last Ice Age.
   c. The number of species in a particular community is directly related to the amount of available energy.
   d. As invertebrate productivity increases, species richness will increase.
   e. Species richness is not related to primary productivity.

3. A community of birds contains 8 individuals of species A, 6 of B, 4 of C and 2 of D. What is the value of the Shannon diversity index?
   a. 4   b. 1   c. 0.30   d. −0.366   e. 1.280

4. Ecologists began to question Elton's link of increased stability to increased diversity because
   a. cultivated land undergoes few outbreaks of pests.
   b. highly disturbed areas have high numbers of species.
   c. pest outbreaks are caused by lack of long associations with natural enemies, not because they occur in simple systems.
   d. all of the above.

5. Extreme fluctuations in species abundance
   a. lead to more diverse communities.
   b. are usually seen in early stages of community development.
   c. may increase the likelihood of extinction.
   d. have very little effect on species richness.
   e. are characteristic of stable communities.

6. The process of primary succession occurs
   a. around a recently erupted volcano.
   b. on a newly plowed field.
   c. on a hillside that has suffered a mudslide.
   d. on a recently flooded riverbank.
   e. on none of the above.

7. The mechanism of succession in which early colonizers exclude subsequent colonists from moving into a community is referred to as
   a. facilitation.   d. inhibition.
   b. competitive exclusion.   e. natural selection.
   c. secondary succession.

8. A tree falls in a forest in spring, and flowers germinate in the light gap. Following a tree fall in autumn, different species of flowers germinate in the light gaps. This illustrates the principle of
   a. facilitation.   d. primary succession.
   b. tolerance.   e. climax communities.
   c. inhibition.

9. In which mechanism of succession do existing species make it harder for new species to colonize?
   a. Inhibition   b. Tolerance   c. Facilitation

10. On which types of islands would you expect species richness to be greatest?
    a. Small, near mainland
    b. Small, distant from mainland
    c. Large, near mainland
    d. Large, distant from mainland
    e. Species richness is equal on all these types of islands.

Conceptual Questions

1. Imagine Forest A has 5 tree species with 100 individuals and forest B has 5 tree species with 10 individuals. What is the Shannon diversity index for both forests? Which forest has the highest diversity? What does this exercise tell you about the limitations of the Shannon diversity index?

2. Distinguish among the species-time, species-area, and species-productivity hypotheses as explanations for the latitudinal gradient in species richness.

3. **PRINCIPLES**   A principle of biology is that *biology is an experimental science*. In the nutrient-poor heathlands of Europe, scotch heather (*Calluna vulgaris*) and cross-leaved heath (*Erica tetralix*) are gradually replaced by variegated purple moor grass (*Molinia caerulea*) and wavy hair grass (*Deschampsia flexuosa*). Adding *Calluna* litter or nitrogen fertilizer speeds up this process. Explain this phenomenon and which mechanism of succession is supported.

Collaborative Questions

1. List some possible ecological disturbances, their likely frequency in natural communities, and the severity of their effects.

2. Calculate the species diversity of the following four communities. Which community has the highest diversity? What is the maximum diversity each community could have?

Community	Relative abundance of species			H_S	Maximum possible diversity
	Species 1	Species 2	Species 3		
1	90	10	—		
2	50	50	—		
3	80	10	10		
4	33.3	33.3	33.3		

Online Resource

www.brookerprinciples.com

Stay a step ahead in your studies with animations that bring concepts to life and practice tests to assess your understanding. Your instructor may also recommend the interactive eBook, individualized learning tools, and more.

Ecosystem Ecology

Chapter Outline

The gypsy moth, *Lymantria dispar*, was introduced into North America around 1868 by E. Leopold Trouvelot, who was experimenting with them for use in the silk industry. Some moths escaped from his laboratory in Massachusetts, and since that time have spread throughout most of the U.S. northeast. Gypsy moth caterpillars are voracious eaters that prefer oak and aspen leaves. About every 10 years there is a serious outbreak, and virtually anything green is eaten. The first outbreak occurred in Massachusetts in 1889. During outbreaks, entire forest canopies can be defoliated. Nitrogen in the foliage is incorporated into caterpillar biomass, caterpillar feces (called frass), and fallen leaves, all of which end up on the forest floor. Some of this nitrogen is leached into streams and rivers, and water nitrate concentrations rise dramatically in areas that previously had low nitrate concentrations. Studies of the effects of gypsy moths underscore the interconnectedness of terrestrial and aquatic systems and how energy flows from one area to another, such as from the forest canopy to streams.

The term **ecosystem** was first used in 1935 by the British plant ecologist A. G. Tansley to describe the system formed by the interaction between a community of organisms and its physical environment.

Ecosystem ecology deals with the flow of energy and cycling of chemical elements within an ecosystem.

In investigating the dynamics of an ecosystem, at least three major constituents can be measured: the flow of energy, the production of biomass, and cycling of elements through ecosystems. We begin the chapter by exploring **energy flow,** the movement of energy through an ecosystem. In examining energy flow, our main task will be to document the complex networks of feeding relationships between species and how these are represented by food webs. Next, we will focus on the measurement of **biomass,** the total mass of living matter in a given area, usually measured in grams or kilograms per square meter. We will examine the amount of biomass produced through photosynthesis, termed primary production, and the amount of biomass produced by the organisms that are the consumers of primary production. In the last section, we will examine **biogeochemical cycles,** the movement of chemicals through ecosystems, and explore the cycling of elements, such as phosphorus, carbon, and nitrogen, and the effects that human activities are having on these ecosystem-wide processes.

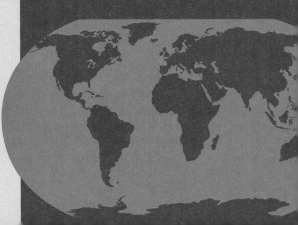

46.1 Food Webs and Energy Flow

Learning Outcomes:

1. Distinguish between autotrophs and heterotrophs and among primary, secondary, and tertiary consumers.
2. List and describe the different types of ecological pyramids.
3. Explain how the process of biomagnification can occur at higher trophic levels.

Simple feeding relationships between organisms can be characterized by an unbranched **food chain**—a linear depiction of energy flow, with each organism feeding on and deriving energy from the preceding organism. In this section, we will consider the unidirectional flow of energy in a food chain and examine a food web, a more complex model of interconnected food chains. We will then explore two of the most important features of food webs—chain length and the pyramid of numbers—and learn how the passage of nutrients through food webs can result in the accumulation of harmful chemicals in the tissues of organisms at higher trophic levels.

The Main Trophic Levels Within Food Chains Consist of Primary Producers, Primary Consumers, and Secondary Consumers

Each level in a food chain is called a **trophic level** (from the Greek *trophos*, meaning feeder), with different species feeding at different levels. In a food-chain diagram, an arrow connects each trophic level with the one above it (**Figure 46.1**). Food chains typically consist of organisms that obtain energy in different ways. Autotrophs harvest light or chemical energy and store that energy in carbon compounds. Most autotrophs, which include plants, algae, and photosynthetic bacteria, use sunlight for this process. These organisms, called **primary producers,** form the base of the food chain. They produce the energy-rich organic molecules upon which nearly all other organisms depend.

Organisms that consume organic molecules from their environment to sustain life and thus receive their nutrition by eating other organisms are termed heterotrophs. Heterotrophs that obtain their food by consuming primary producers are termed **primary consumers** (also called herbivores) and include most protists, most animals, and even some plants such as mistletoe, which is parasitic on other plants. Organisms that eat primary consumers are **secondary consumers** (also called carnivores). Organisms that feed on secondary consumers are **tertiary consumers,** and so on. Thus, energy enters a food chain through primary producers, via photosynthesis, and is passed up the food chain to primary, secondary, and tertiary consumers (see Figure 46.1).

At each trophic level, many organisms die before they are eaten. Most energy from the first trophic level, such as the plants, goes unconsumed by herbivores. Instead, unconsumed plants die and decompose in place. This material, along with dead remains of animals and waste products, is called **detritus.** Consumers that get their energy from detritus, called **detritivores,** or **decomposers,**

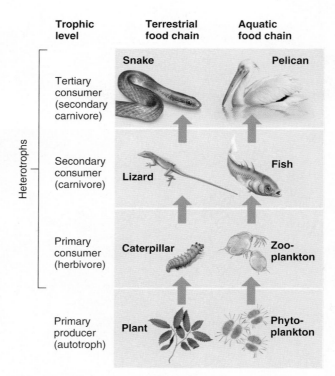

Figure 46.1 Food chains. Two examples of the flow of food energy up the trophic levels: a terrestrial food chain and an aquatic food chain.

BioConnections: *In these two food chains, plants and protists (phytoplankton) are the producers. Look back at Section 22.5. What other organisms are producers and could also support food chains?*

break down dead organisms from all trophic levels. For example, carrion beetles feed on the dead bodies of other animals. In terrestrial systems, detritivores probably consume 80–90% of plant matter, with different groups such as earthworms and fungi working in concert to extract most of the energy. Detritivores may, in turn, support a community of predators that feed on them.

In nature, branching of food chains occurs at all trophic levels. For example, many different herbivore species may feed on the same plant species. Also, each species of herbivore may feed on several different plant species. For instance, on the African savanna, cheetahs, lions, and hyenas all eat a variety of prey, including wildebeest, impala, and Thompson's gazelle. These, in turn, eat a variety of trees and grasses. It is more correct, then, to draw relationships between these plants and animals not as a simple chain but as a **food web,** a complex model of interconnected food chains in which there are multiple links among species (**Figure 46.2**).

In Most Food Webs, Chain Lengths Are Short

Let's examine some of the characteristics of food webs in more detail. The concept of chain length refers to the number of links between the trophic levels involved. For example, if a lion feeds on a zebra, and a zebra feeds on grass, the chain length would be two. In many food webs, chain lengths tend to be short, usually five or fewer because of two main factors. First, many organisms

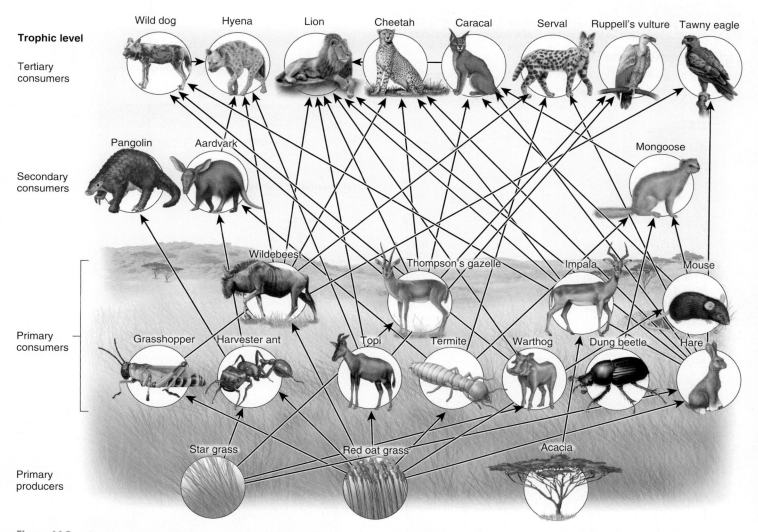

Figure 46.2 **A food web from an African savanna ecosystem.** Each trophic level is occupied by different species. Generally, each species feeds on, or is fed upon by, more than one species.

Concept Check: *At which trophic level do decomposers feed?*

cannot digest all their prey. They take only the easily digestible plant leaves or animal tissue such as muscles and internal organs, leaving the hard wood or energy-rich bones behind. Second, much of the energy assimilated by animals is used in maintenance and is lost from the organism as heat. Both of these factors acting together means that, on average, only about 10% of available energy is transferred from one trophic level to another. Because energy is lost at each link, after a few links, most of the available energy has been expended and relatively little energy is available for higher trophic levels (Figure 46.3).

Ecological Pyramids Describe the Distribution of Numbers, Biomass, or Energy Between Trophic Levels

The abundance of organisms, biomass, or available energy at each trophic level of a food web can be expressed graphically as an ecological pyramid. One of the best-known ecological pyramids, described by British ecologist Charles Elton in 1927, is the **pyramid of numbers,** in which the number of individuals decreases at each trophic level, with a large number of individuals at the base and fewer individuals at the top. For example, in a grassland, there may be hundreds of individual plants per square meter, dozens of insects that feed on the plants, a few spiders feeding on the insects, and birds that feed on the spiders (Figure 46.4a).

Ecologists have, however, discovered some exceptions to this pyramid. One single producer such as an oak tree can support hundreds of herbivorous beetles, caterpillars, and other primary consumers, which, in turn, may support thousands of predators. This is called an inverted pyramid of numbers.

One way to reconcile this apparent exception is to weigh the organisms in each trophic level, creating a **pyramid of biomass.** For example, an oak tree weighs more than all of its herbivores and predators combined. American ecologist Howard Odum

Biology Principle

Living Organisms Use Energy

Within trophic levels, energy is lost to maintenance, and between trophic levels, energy is lost to imperfect efficiency of transfer.

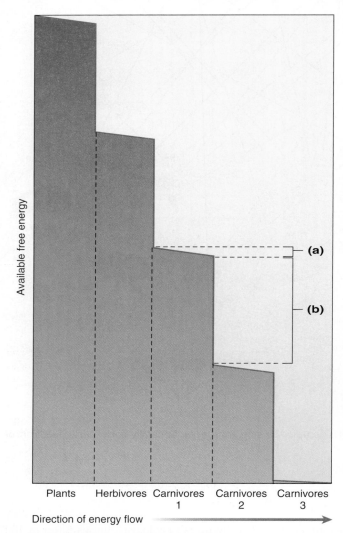

Figure 46.3 **Energy flow through a food web.** In this graph of energy flow through a food web there are five trophic levels and four links between the trophic levels. **(a)** Energy lost as heat in a single trophic level. **(b)** Energy lost in the conversion from one trophic level to another.

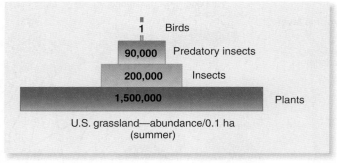

(a) Pyramid of numbers

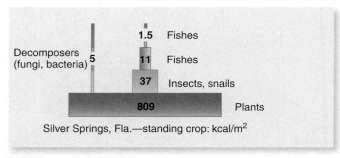

(b) Pyramid of biomass

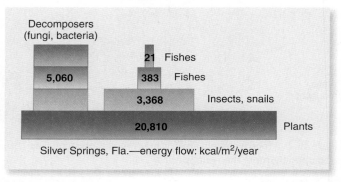

(c) Pyramid of energy

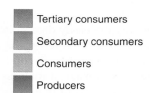

Figure 46.4 **Ecological pyramids in food webs.** **(a)** In this pyramid of numbers, the abundance of species in an American grassland decreases with increasing trophic level. **(b)** In a pyramid of biomass, the amount of biological material is used instead of numbers of individuals. Note the presence of decomposers that decompose material at all trophic levels. **(c)** A pyramid of energy for Silver Springs, Florida. Note the large energy production of decomposers, despite their small biomass.

measured the pyramid of biomass for a freshwater ecosystem, Silver Springs, in Florida (**Figure 46.4b**). Beds of eelgrass (genus *Sagittaria*) and attached algae make up most of the producers. Insects, snails, herbivorous fishes, and turtles eat the producers. Other fishes form the secondary and tertiary consumers. Odum also noted the presence of fungi and bacteria, which were involved in decomposition on all trophic levels.

Another way is to express the pyramid in terms of production rate. The **pyramid of energy** shows the rate of energy production rather than biomass (Figure 46.4c). The laws of thermodynamics ensure that the highest amounts of free energy are found at the lowest trophic levels. The energy pyramid for Silver Springs is also very accurate in that it shows that large amounts of energy pass through decomposers, despite their relatively small biomass.

Biomagnification Can Occur in Higher Trophic Levels

The tendency of certain chemicals to concentrate in higher trophic levels in food chains is called **biomagnification,** and it presents a problem for certain organisms. The passage of dichlorodiphenyl-trichloroethane (DDT), an insecticide used against mosquitoes and agricultural pests, in food chains provides a startling example.

DDT was first synthesized by chemists in 1874. In 1939, its insecticidal properties were recognized by Paul Müller, a Swiss scientist who won the 1948 Nobel Prize in Physiology or Medicine for his discovery and subsequent research on the uses of the chemical. The first important application of DDT was in human health programs during and after World War II, particularly as a means of controlling mosquito-borne malaria; at that time, its use in agriculture also began. The global production of DDT peaked in 1970, when 175 million kilograms of the insecticide was manufactured.

DDT has several chemical and physical properties that profoundly influence the nature of its ecological effect. First, DDT is persistent in the environment. It is not rapidly degraded to other, less toxic chemicals by microorganisms or by physical agents such as light and heat. The typical persistence in soil of DDT is about 10 years, which is two to three times longer than the persistence of many other insecticides. Another important characteristic of DDT is its low solubility in water and its high solubility in fats or lipids. In the environment, most lipids are present in living tissue. Therefore, because of its high lipid solubility, DDT tends to concentrate in biological tissues.

Because biomagnification occurs at each step of the food chain, organisms at higher trophic levels can amass especially high concentrations of DDT in their lipids. A typical pattern of biomagnification is illustrated in Figure 46.5, which shows the relative amounts of DDT found in a Lake Michigan food chain. The highest concentration of the insecticide was found in gulls, tertiary consumers that feed on fishes, which are the secondary consumers that eat small insects. An unanticipated effect of DDT on bird species was its interference with the metabolic process of eggshell formation. The result was thin-shelled eggs that often broke under the weight of incubating birds (Figure 46.6). DDT was responsible for a dramatic decrease in the populations of many birds due to failed reproduction. Relatively high levels of the chemical were also found to be present in some game fishes, which, as a result, became unfit for human consumption.

Because of growing awareness of the adverse effects of DDT, most industrialized countries, including the U.S., banned the use of the chemical by the early 1970s. The good news is that following the outlawing of DDT, populations of the most severely affected bird species have recovered. However, had scientists initially possessed a more thorough knowledge of how DDT accumulated in food chains, some of the damage to the bird populations might have been prevented.

Figure 46.5 **Biomagnification in a Lake Michigan food chain.** The DDT tissue concentration in gulls, a tertiary consumer, was about 240 times that in the small insects sharing the same environment. The biomagnification of DDT in lipids causes its concentration to increase at each successive link in the food chain.

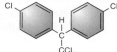

DDT (dichlorodiphenyltrichloroethane)
- Persists in environment
- High solubility in lipids
- Found in high concentrations at higher trophic levels

Figure 46.6 **Thinning of eggshells caused by DDT.** The peregrine falcon egg on the right is light colored, thin-shelled, and easily crushed by the incubating adult. The normal egg on the left is darker in color with a thicker shell.

46.1   Reviewing the Concepts

- Ecosystem ecology concerns the movement of energy and materials through organisms and their communities. Organisms that obtain energy from light or chemicals are primary producers (or autotrophs). Organisms that feed on primary producers are called primary consumers (or herbivores). Organisms that feed on primary consumers are called secondary consumers (or carnivores). Consumers that get their energy from the remains and waste products of organisms are called detritivores, or decomposers (Figures 46.1, 46.2).

- Food webs are a complex model of interconnected food chains in which multiple links occur between species. Food webs tend to have five or fewer links between top and bottom trophic levels. Energy conversions are not 100% efficient, and usable energy is lost within each trophic level and from one trophic level to the next (Figures 46.3, 46.4).

- The increase in the concentration of certain chemicals in living organisms, called biomagnification, can occur at each trophic level of the food web (Figures 46.5, 46.6).

46.1   Testing Your Knowledge

1. As we learned in Chapter 27, some bacteria and archaea are able to use energy from the oxidation of sulfur, iron, or hydrogen. These bacteria can be classified as
   a. heterotrophs.   **c.** producers.   **e.** both b and c.
   b. autotrophs.   **d.** both and b.

2. Detritivores that feed on the dung of herbivores feed at which trophic level?
   a. 1   **b.** 2   **c.** 3   **d.** 4   **e.** 5

46.2   Biomass Production in Ecosystems

Learning Outcomes:

1. Describe the factors that limit primary production in terrestrial and aquatic ecosystems.
2. Determine the fate of most primary production.

In this section, we will take a closer look at biomass production in ecosystems. Because the bulk of the Earth's biosphere, 99.9% by mass, consists of primary producers, when we measure ecosystem biomass production, we are primarily interested in plants, algae, or cyanobacteria. Their production is called **gross primary production (GPP).** Gross primary production is equivalent to the carbon fixed during photosynthesis. **Net primary production (NPP)** is GPP minus the energy used during cellular respiration (R) of photosynthetic organisms.

$$NPP = GPP - R$$

NPP is thus the amount of energy available to primary consumers. Unless otherwise noted, the term **primary production** refers to NPP.

Primary Production Is Influenced in Terrestrial Ecosystems by Water, Temperature, and Nutrient Availability

In terrestrial systems, water is a major determinant of primary production, and primary production shows an almost linear increase with annual precipitation, at least in arid regions (look back at Figure 33.10). Likewise, temperature, which affects production primarily by slowing or accelerating plant metabolic rates, is also important. A lack of **nutrients,** key elements in usable form, particularly nitrogen and phosphorus, can also limit primary production in terrestrial ecosystems, as farmers know only too well. Fertilizers are commonly used to boost the production of annual crops. In 1984, Susan Cargill and Robert Jefferies showed how a lack of both nitrogen and phosphorus limited production in salt marsh sedges and grasses in Hudson Bay, Canada (**Figure 46.7**). Of the two nutrients, nitrogen was the **limiting factor**—the one in the shortest supply for growth; without it, the addition of phosphorus did not increase production. However, once nitrogen was added and was no longer limiting, phosphorus became the limiting factor. The addition of nitrogen and phosphorus together increased production the most. This result supports a principle known as **Liebig's law of the minimum,** named for Justus von Liebig, a 19th-century German chemist, which states that species biomass or abundance is limited by the scarcest factor. This factor can change, as the Hudson Bay experiment showed. When sufficient nitrogen is available, phosphorus becomes the limiting factor. Once phosphorus becomes abundant, then productivity will be limited by another nutrient.

Primary Production in Aquatic Ecosystems Is Limited Mainly by Light and Nutrient Availability

Of the factors limiting primary production in aquatic ecosystems, the most important are the availability of sufficient light and nutrients. Light is particularly likely to be in short supply because water readily absorbs light. At a depth of 1 m, more than half the solar radiation has been absorbed. By 20 m, only 5–10% of the radiation remains. The decrease in light is what limits the depth of algal growth (look back to Figure 43.11).

The most important nutrients affecting primary production in aquatic systems are nitrogen and phosphorus, because they occur in very low concentrations. Whereas soil contains about 0.5% nitrogen, seawater contains only 0.00005% nitrogen. Enrichment of the aquatic environment by the addition of nitrogen and phosphorus occurs naturally in areas of **upwellings**—places where cold, deep, nutrient-rich water containing sediment from the ocean floor is brought to the surface by strong currents, resulting in very productive ecosystems and plentiful fishes. Some of the largest areas of upwelling occur in the Antarctic and along the coasts of Peru and California. However, too much nutrient supply can be harmful to aquatic systems, resulting in large, unchecked growths of algae called algal blooms. When the algae die, they are consumed by bacteria that, as they respire, deplete the surrounding water of oxygen, causing dead zones with little oxygen to support other aquatic life. Such dead zones are prominent along coastal areas where fertilizer-rich rivers

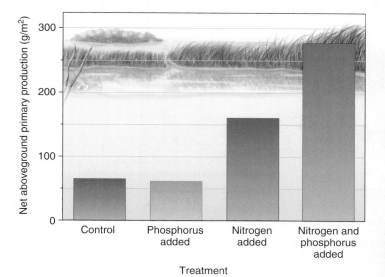

Figure 46.7 **Limitation of primary production by nitrogen and phosphorus.** Net aboveground primary production of a salt marsh sedge (*Carex subspathacea*) in response to nutrient addition. Nitrogen is the limiting factor. After nitrogen is added, phosphorus becomes the limiting factor.

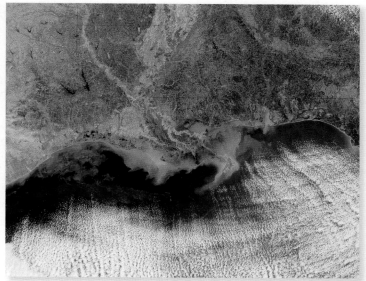

Figure 46.8 **A dead zone in the Gulf of Mexico.** Nutrients from the Mississippi River cause algal blooms, seen here as the blue/green color. When these algae die and decompose, the oxygen levels in the ocean become too low to support much marine life.

discharge into the oceans. The largest of these is the 22,000 km² (8,500 mile²) area in the Gulf of Mexico where the Mississippi River dumps high loads of nutrients (Figure 46.8).

Primary Production Varies Across the Earth's Biomes

Knowing which factors limit primary production helps ecologists understand why the mean net primary production varies across the different biomes on Earth. Modern methods of estimating productivity use orbiting satellites to measure differences in the electromagnetic radiation reflected back from the vegetation of different ecosystems on Earth (Figure 46.9). When we look at the oceans, bright greens, yellows, and reds indicate high chlorophyll concentrations. Some of the highest marine chlorophyll concentrations occur at continental margins, where river nutrients pour into the oceans. Upwellings along coasts also bring nutrient-rich water to the surface. Northern oceans, and to a lesser extent southern oceans, are also very productive, because seasonal storms and temperature changes allow vertical mixing of water, bringing nutrient-rich water to the surface. In the spring, the increased amount of light and nutrients permit rapid phytoplankton growth until the nutrients are all used up. Many other marine areas, including tropical oceans, are highly unproductive.

Over land, the productivity of forests in all parts of the world, from the tropics to northern and southern temperate areas, is high, but production is often higher in temperate than tropical forests. This matches the pattern of productivity observed in the oceans. Although tropical forests enjoy warm temperatures and abundant rainfall, such conditions weather soils rapidly. Tropical soils are low in available forms of most plant nutrients because of loss through leaching. In contrast, temperate soils tend to have much greater concentrations of essential nutrients because of lower rates of nutrient loss and more frequent grinding of fresh minerals by the cycles of continental glaciations over the past

Figure 46.9 **Primary productivity measured by satellite imagery.** Ocean chlorophyll concentrations and the Normalized Difference Vegetation Index (NDVI) on land provide good data on marine and terrestrial productivity, respectively.

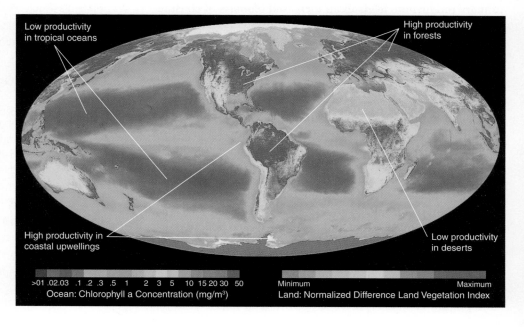

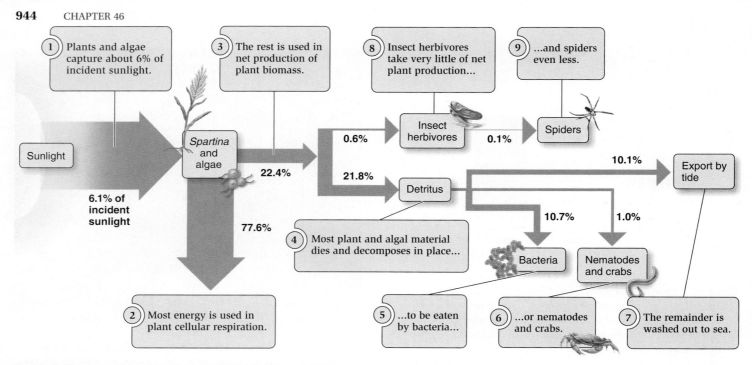

Figure 46.10 Energy-flow diagram for a Georgia salt marsh. Numbers represent the percentage of gross primary production that flows into different trophic levels or is used in plant respiration.

3 million years. Prairies and savannas are also highly productive because their plant biomass usually dies and decomposes each year, returning a portion of the nutrients to the soil, and temperatures and rainfall are not limiting. Deserts and tundra have low productivity because of a lack of water and low temperatures, respectively. Wetlands tend to be extremely productive, primarily because water is not limiting and nutrient levels are high.

Most Primary Production Is Eaten by Detritivores

A strong relationship exists between primary production and secondary production, usually measured as the biomass of herbivores. This means that more plant biomass, and thus more primary production, leads to an increased biomass of consumers. However, it has been shown that in ecosystems as diverse as forests and salt marshes most primary production goes to detritivores, not herbivores.

In 1962, American ecologist John Teal examined energy flow in a Georgia salt marsh (**Figure 46.10**). In salt marshes, most of the energy from the Sun goes to two types of organisms: *Spartina* plants and marine algae. The *Spartina* plants are rooted in the ground, whereas the algae float on the water's surface or live on the mud or on *Spartina* leaves at low tide. These photosynthetic organisms absorb about 6% of the sunlight. Most of the plant energy, 77.6%, is used in plant and algal cellular respiration. Of the energy that is accumulated in plant biomass, 22.4%, most dies in place and rots on the muddy ground, to be consumed by bacteria. Bacteria are the major decomposers in this system, followed distantly by nematodes and crabs, which feed on tiny food particles as they sift through the mud. Some of this dead material is also removed from the system (exported) by the tide. The herbivores take very little of the plant production, around 0.6%, eating only a small proportion of the *Spartina* and none of the algae. A fraction

of herbivore biomass is then consumed by spiders. Overall, if we view the species in ecosystems as transformers of energy, then plants and algae are by far the most important organisms on the planet, bacteria are next, and animals are a distant third.

46.2 Reviewing the Concepts

- Net primary production (NPP) is gross primary production minus the energy released during respiration via photosynthetic organisms. NPP in terrestrial ecosystems is limited primarily by temperature and the availability of water and nutrients. In aquatic ecosystems, it is limited mainly by the availability of light and nutrients (Figures 46.7–46.9).
- Secondary production is limited by available primary production, but most primary production goes to detritivores (Figure 46.10).

46.2 Testing Your Knowledge

1. Net primary production is
   a. the energy that passes from plants on to herbivores.
   b. gross primary production minus the energy used by herbivores.
   c. the energy fixed in photosynthesis.
   d. the energy fixed in photosynthesis minus the energy used in respiration of photosynthetic organisms.
   e. gross primary production minus the energy used by consumers.

2. Primary production in terrestrial systems is often limited by
   a. temperature.   c. nutrients   e. a, b, and c.
   b. water.   d. b and c.

3. Most gross primary production is used in (by)
   a. plant respiration. c. bacteria.   e. c and d.
   b. herbivores.   d. nematodes.

46.3 Biogeochemical Cycles

Learning Outcomes:

1. Describe the phosphorus cycle and the causes of eutrophication.
2. Outline the steps of the carbon cycle and the environmental effects of elevated atmospheric concentrations of CO_2.
3. List the five main steps of the nitrogen cycle and the human influences on it.
4. Describe the processes of the water cycle and how they are affected by humans.

A unit of energy moves through an ecosystem only once, passing through the trophic levels of a food web from producer to consumer and dissipating as heat. In contrast, chemical elements such as carbon or nitrogen cycle, moving from the physical environment to organisms and back to the environment, where the cycle begins again. Although an ecosystem constantly receives energy in the form of light, chemical elements are available in limited amounts. Because the movements of chemicals through ecosystems involve biological, geological, and chemical transport mechanisms, they are termed **biogeochemical cycles.** Biological mechanisms involve the absorption of chemicals by living organisms and their subsequent release back into the environment. Geological mechanisms include weathering and erosion of rocks, and elements transported by surface and subsurface drainage. Chemical transport mechanisms include dissolved matter in rain and snow, atmospheric gases, and dust blown by the wind.

In addition to the basic building blocks of carbon, hydrogen, and oxygen, the elements required in the greatest amounts by living organisms are phosphorus and nitrogen. In this section, we take a detailed look at the cycles of these nutrients. These cycles can be divided into two broad types: (1) local cycles, such as the phosphorus cycle, which involve elements with no atmospheric mechanism for long-distance transfer; and (2) global cycles, which involve an interchange between the atmosphere and the ecosystem. Global cycles, such as the carbon, nitrogen and water cycles, unite the Earth and its living organisms into one giant interconnected ecosystem called the **biosphere.** Most biogeochemical cycles involve assimilation of nutrients from the soil by plants and animals, and decomposition of plants and animals, which releases nutrients back into the soil. A generalized and simplified biogeochemical cycle involves both biotic and abiotic components (**Figure 46.11**). In our discussion of biogeochemical cycles, we will take a particular interest in the alteration of these cycles through human activities, such as the burning of fossil fuels, that increase nutrient inputs.

Biology Principle

Living Organisms Interact with Their Environments

The biomass of organisms is affected by the availability of nutrients in the soil.

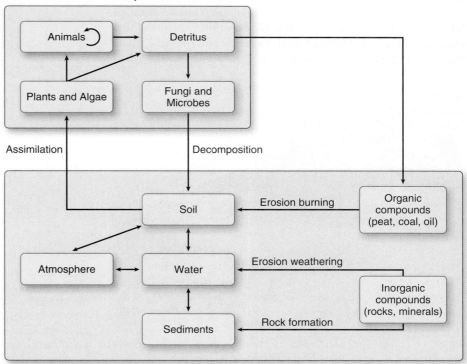

Figure 46.11 A generalized and simplified model of a biogeochemical cycle. Biotic components contain organic material. Abiotic components contain inorganic material in soil and water, which is available to living things as nutrients, fossilized organic material such as peat and coal, which is not available to living things, and minerals in sediments (rocks) which are also unavailable.

Phosphorus Cycles Locally Between Geological and Biological Components of Ecosystems

All living organisms require phosphorus, which becomes incorporated into ATP, DNA, and RNA, and it is also an essential mineral that helps maintain a strong, healthy skeleton.

The phosphorus cycle is relatively simple (Figure 46.12). Phosphorus has no gaseous phase and thus no atmospheric component; that is, it is not moved by wind or rain. As a result, phosphorus cycles only locally. The Earth's crust is the main storehouse for this element. Weathering and erosion of rocks release phosphorus into the soil. Plants have the metabolic means to absorb dissolved ionized forms of phosphorus, the most important of which occurs as phosphate (HPO_4^{2-} or $H_2PO_4^-$). Herbivores obtain their phosphorus only from eating plants, and carnivores obtain it by eating herbivores. When plants and animals excrete wastes or die, the phosphorus becomes available to decomposers, which release it back to the soil.

Leaching and runoff eventually wash much phosphate into aquatic systems, where plants and algae utilize it. Phosphate that is not taken up into the food chain settles to the ocean floor or lake bottom, forming sedimentary rock. Phosphorus can remain locked in sedimentary rock for millions of years, becoming available again through the geological process of uplift.

Human Influences on the Phosphorus Cycle Plants can take up phosphate so rapidly and efficiently that they often reduce soil concentrations of phosphorus to extremely low levels; in which case, phosphorus becomes a limiting factor, as noted previously (see Figure 46.7). The more phosphorus is added to an aquatic ecosystem, the greater the production of algae and aquatic plants. In a pivotal 1974 study, Canadian biologist David Schindler showed that an overabundance of phosphorus caused the rapid growth of algal blooms in an experimental lake in Canada (Figure 46.13). What is the consequence of the rapid growth? When the algae and plants die, they sink to the bottom, where bacteria decompose them and consume the dissolved oxygen in the water. Dissolved oxygen concentrations can drop too low for fishes to breathe, killing them. The process by which elevated nutrient levels lead to an overgrowth of algae and the subsequent depletion of water oxygen concentrations is known as **eutrophication.** Eutrophication is frequently due to the enrichment of water with nutrients derived from human activities, such as fertilizer use and sewage dumping.

Lake Erie became eutrophic in the 1960s due to the runoff of fertilizer rich in phosphorus from farms and to the industrial and domestic pollutants released from the many cities along its shores. Fish species such as white fish and lake trout became severely depleted. Based on research such as Schindler's that showed the dramatic effect of phosphorus on a lake system, the U.S. and Canada teamed together to reduce the levels of discharge by 80%, primarily through eliminating phosphorus in laundry detergents and maintaining strict controls on the phosphorus content of wastewater from sewage treatment plants. Fortunately, lake systems have great potential for recovery after phosphorous inputs are reduced, and Lake Erie has experienced fewer algal blooms, clearer water, and a restoration of fish populations (Figure 46.14).

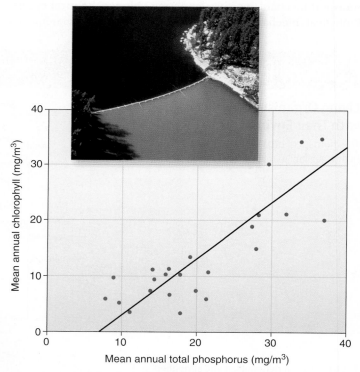

Figure 46.13 The relationship between primary production and total phosphorus concentration. As shown in this graph, primary production (measured by chlorophyll concentration) increases linearly with an increase in phosphorus. Each dot represents a different lake. The aerial photograph shows the contrast in water quality of two basins of an experimental lake in Canada separated by a plastic curtain. Carbon and nitrogen were added to the upper basin, and carbon, nitrogen, and phosphorus were added to the lower basin. The bright green color is from a surface film of algae that resulted from the added phosphorus.

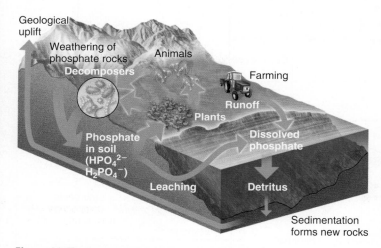

Figure 46.12 The phosphorus cycle. Unlike other major biogeochemical cycles, the phosphorus cycle does not have an atmospheric component and thus cycles only locally. The widths of the lines indicate the relative contribution of each process to the cycle.

(a) Polluted (eutrophication)

(b) Cleared up

Figure 46.14 **Phosphorus pollution in Lake Erie.** The lake **(a)** in the 1960s, when eutrophic and polluted by industrial effluent and fertilizer run-off, and **(b)** in 2007, after eutrophication was reversed by pollution control laws.

Carbon Cycles Among Biological, Geological, and Atmospheric Pools

The movement of carbon from the atmosphere into organisms and back again is known as the carbon cycle (**Figure 46.15**). Carbon dioxide (CO_2) is present in the atmosphere at a level of about 400 parts per million (ppm), or about 0.04%. Autotrophs, primarily plants, algae, and cyanobacteria, acquire CO_2 from the atmosphere and incorporate it into the organic matter of their own biomass via photosynthesis. Each year, plants, algae, and cyanobacteria remove approximately one-seventh of the CO_2 from the atmosphere. At the same time, respiration and the decomposition of plants recycle a similar amount of carbon back into the atmosphere as CO_2. Much material from primary producers is also transformed into deposits of coal, gas, and oil, which are collectively known as **fossil fuels.** Herbivores can return some CO_2 to the atmosphere, eating plants and breathing out CO_2, but the amount flowing through this part of the cycle is minimal. Chemical processes such as diffusion and absorption of CO_2 into and out of oceans also contribute to changes in atmospheric CO_2.

Over time, much carbon is also incorporated into the shells of marine organisms, which eventually form huge limestone deposits on the ocean floor or in terrestrial rocks, where turnover

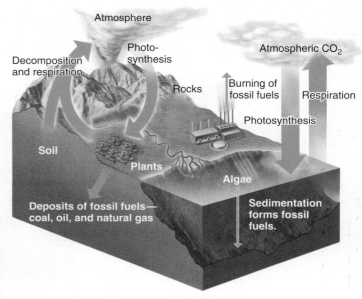

Figure 46.15 **The carbon cycle.** Each year, plants and algae remove about one-seventh of the CO_2 in the atmosphere. Animal respiration is so small it is not represented. The width of the arrows indicates the relative contribution of each process to the cycle.

 Concept Check: *Where are the greatest stores of global carbon?*

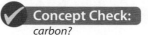 **BioConnections:** *Refer back to Table 2.2. Carbon is one of just four elements that account for the vast majority of atoms in living organisms. What are the other three and, therefore, what biogeochemical cycles might be the most important to us?*

is extremely low. As a result, rocks and fossil fuels contain the largest reserves of carbon. Natural sources of CO_2 such as volcanoes, hot springs, and fires release large amounts of CO_2 into the atmosphere. In addition, human activities, primarily deforestation and the burning of fossil fuels, are increasingly causing large amounts of CO_2 to enter the atmosphere. Direct measurements over the past five decades show a steady rise in atmospheric CO_2 (see Figure 43.9), a pattern that shows no sign of slowing. Elevated levels of atmospheric CO_2 are the primary cause of global warming but also have other dramatic environmental effects, boosting plant growth but lowering the amount of herbivory (see the following Feature Investigation).

FEATURE INVESTIGATION

Stiling and Drake's Experiments with Elevated CO_2 Showed an Increase in Plant Growth but a Decrease in Herbivory

How will forests of the future respond to elevated CO_2? To begin to answer such a question, ecologists ideally would enclose large areas of forests with chambers, increase the CO_2 content within the chambers, and measure the responses. This has proved to be difficult for two reasons. First, it is hard to enclose large trees in chambers, and second, it is expensive to increase CO_2 levels over such a large area. However, in a discovery-based investigation, ecologists Peter Stiling and Bert Drake were able to increase CO_2 levels around patches of forest at the Kennedy Space Center in Cape Canaveral, Florida. In much of Florida's forests, trees are small, only 3–5 m high at maturity, because frequent lightning-initiated fires prevent the growth of larger trees. In the 1990s, Stiling and Drake teamed up with NASA engineers to create 16 circular, open-topped chambers (**Figure 46.16**). In eight of these they increased

atmospheric CO_2 to double their ambient levels, from around 360 ppm to 720 ppm, the latter of which is the atmospheric concentration predicted by the end of the 21st century. The experiments commenced in 1996 and lasted until 2007. Not surprisingly, plants produced more biomass in elevated CO_2, because CO_2 is limiting to plant growth, but the data revealed much more.

Because the chambers were open-topped, insect herbivores could come and go. Insect herbivores cause the largest amount of herbivory in North American forests, because most vertebrate herbivores could not access the high foliage. Censuses were conducted of all damaged leaves, but focused on leaves damaged by leaf miners, the most common type of herbivore at this site. Leaf miners are small moths whose larvae are small enough to burrow between the surfaces of plant leaves, creating brown areas as

Figure 46.16 The effects of elevated atmospheric CO_2 on insect herbivory.

GOAL To determine the effects of elevated CO_2 on a forest ecosystem; effects on herbivory are highlighted here.

STUDY LOCATION Patches of forest at the Kennedy Space Center in Cape Canaveral, Florida.

	Experimental level	Conceptual level

1 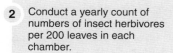 Erect 16 open-top chambers around native vegetation. Increase CO_2 levels from 360 ppm to 720 ppm in half of them.

Expected atmospheric CO_2 level is 720 ppm by end of the 21st century. Open-top chambers allow movement of herbivores in and out of chambers.

2 Conduct a yearly count of numbers of insect herbivores per 200 leaves in each chamber.

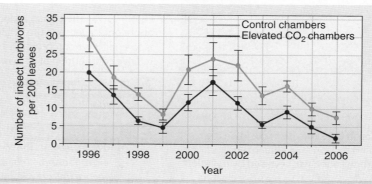

3 Count number of herbivores that died due to nutritional inadequacy. Monitor attack rates on insect herbivores by natural enemies such as predators and parasitoids.

Elevated CO_2 reduces foliar nitrogen, inhibits normal insect development, and prolongs the feeding time of herbivores, allowing natural enemies greater opportunities to attack them.

4 **THE DATA**

Source of mortality*	Elevated CO_2 (% mortality)	Control (% mortality)
Nutritional inadequacy	10.2	5.0
Predators	2.4	2.0
Parasitoids	10.0	3.2

*Data refer only to mortality of larvae within leaves and do not sum to 100%. Mortality of eggs on leaves, pupae in the soil, and flying adults is unknown.

5 **CONCLUSION** Elevated CO_2 decreases insect herbivory in a Florida forest.

6 **SOURCE** Stiling, P., and Cornelissen, T. 2007. How does elevated carbon dioxide (CO_2) affect plant-herbivore interactions? A field experiment and meta-analysis of CO_2-mediated changes on plant chemistry and herbivore performance. *Global Change Biology* 13:1823–1842.

shown in Figure 46.16, part three. The condition of the leaf mine reveals whether the larva survived and emerged, was eaten by predators, or was attacked by parasitoids.

In the chambers with elevated CO_2, although biomass increased, densities of damaged leaves, including those damaged by leaf miners, were lower in every year studied. Part of the reason for the decline was that even though plants increased in mass, the existing soil nitrogen was diluted over a greater volume of plant material, so the nitrogen level in leaves decreased. This resulted in increased insect mortality by two means. First, poorer leaf quality directly increased insect death because leaf nitrogen levels may have been too low to support the normal development of the leaf miners. Second, lower leaf quality increased the amount of time insects needed to feed to gain sufficient nitrogen. Increased feeding times, in turn, led to increased exposure to natural enemies, such as predatory spiders and ants and parasitoids (see Figure 44.11), so mortality from natural enemies also increased (see the Data of Figure 46.15). Thus, in a world of elevated CO_2, plant growth may increase, and herbivory could decrease.

Experimental Questions

1. What was the hypothesis of Stiling and Drake's experiment?
2. What was the purpose of increasing the CO_2 levels in only half of the chambers in the experiment and not all of the chambers?
3. Imagine the percent mortality from parasitoids in the eight elevated CO_2 chambers was 6, 11, 9, 8, 13, 12, 14 and 7, and that in the ambient chambers was 1, 4, 5, 2, 3, 6, 1.6, and 3. Perform a statistical test to see if mortality from parasitoids was different between elevated and ambient CO_2 chambers.

The Nitrogen Cycle Is Strongly Influenced by Biological Processes That Transform Nitrogen into Usable Forms

Nitrogen is an essential component of proteins, nucleic acids, and chlorophyll. Because 78% of the Earth's atmosphere consists of nitrogen gas (N_2), it may seem that nitrogen should not be in short supply for organisms. However, nitrogen is often a limiting factor in ecosystems because N_2 molecules must be broken apart before the individual nitrogen atoms can combine with other elements. Because of its triple bond, N_2 is very stable, and only certain bacteria can break it apart into usable forms such as ammonia (NH_3).

This process, called nitrogen fixation, is a critical component of the five-part nitrogen cycle (**Figure 46.17**):

1. A few species of bacteria can accomplish **nitrogen fixation,** that is, convert atmospheric N_2 to forms usable by other organisms. The bacteria that fix nitrogen are fulfilling their own metabolic needs, but in the process, they release ammonia (NH_3) or ammonium (NH_4^+), which can be used by some plants. Cyanobacteria are important nitrogen fixers in terrestrial and aquatic systems (look back to Figure 29.10).

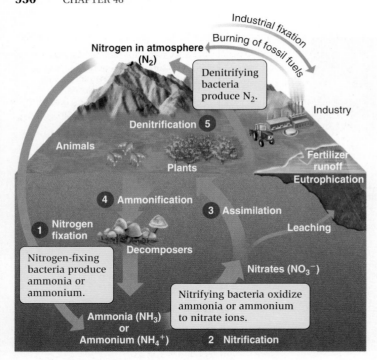

Figure 46.17   The nitrogen cycle. The five main parts of the nitrogen cycle are (1) nitrogen fixation, (2) nitrification, (3) assimilation, (4) ammonification, and (5) denitrification. The recycling of nitrogen from dead plants and animals into the soil and then back into plants is of paramount importance because this is the main pathway for nitrogen to enter the soil. The width of the arrows indicates the relative contribution of each process to the cycle.

2. In the process of **nitrification,** soil bacteria convert NH_3 or NH_4^+ to nitrate (NO_3^-), a form of nitrogen commonly used by plants. The bacteria *Nitrosomonas* and *Nitrococcus* first oxidize the forms of ammonia to nitrite (NO_2^-), after which the bacterium *Nitrobacter* converts NO_2^- to NO_3^-.

3. **Assimilation** is the process by which inorganic substances are incorporated into organic molecules. In the nitrogen cycle, organisms assimilate nitrogen by taking up NH_3, NH_4^+, and NO_3^- formed through nitrogen fixation and nitrification and incorporating them into other molecules. Plant roots take up these forms of nitrogen through their roots, and animals assimilate nitrogen from the plant tissues they ingest.

4. Ammonia can also be formed in the soil through the decomposition of plants and animals and the release of animal waste. **Ammonification** is the conversion of organic nitrogen to NH_3 and NH_4^+. This process is carried out by bacteria and fungi. Most soils are slightly acidic and, because of an excess of H^+, the NH_3 rapidly gains an additional H^+ to form NH_4^+. Because many soils lack nitrifying bacteria, ammonification is the most common pathway for nitrogen to enter the soil.

5. **Denitrification** is the reduction of NO_3^- to N_2. Denitrifying bacteria, which are anaerobic and use NO_3^- in their metabolism instead of O_2, perform the reverse of their nitrogen-fixing counterparts by delivering N_2 to the

atmosphere. This process delivers only a relatively small amount of nitrogen to the atmosphere.

Human Influences on the Nitrogen Cycle   Human alterations of the nitrogen cycle have approximately doubled the rate of nitrogen input to the cycle. Industrial fixation of nitrogen for the production of fertilizer makes a significant contribution to the pool of nitrogen-containing material in the soils and waters of agricultural regions. As with phosphorus, fertilizer runoff can cause eutrophication of rivers and lakes, and, as the resultant algae die, decomposition by bacteria depletes the oxygen level of the water, resulting in fish kills. Excess NO_3^- in surface or groundwater systems used for drinking water is also a health hazard, particularly for infants. In the body, NO_3^- is converted to NO_2^-, which then combines with hemoglobin to form methemoglobin, a type of hemoglobin that does not carry oxygen. In infants, the production of large amounts of NO_2^- can cause methemoglobinemia, a dangerous condition in which the level of O_2 carried through the body decreases. Finally, burning fossil fuels releases not only carbon but also nitrogen in the form of nitrous oxide (N_2O), which contributes to air pollution. N_2O can also react with rainwater to form nitric acid (HNO_3), a component of acid rain, which decreases the pH of lakes and streams and increases fish mortality (see Chapter 43).

The Water Cycle Is Largely a Physical Process of Evaporation and Precipitation

The water cycle, also called the hydrological cycle, differs from the cycles of other nutrients in that very little of the water that cycles through ecosystems is chemically changed by any of the cycle's components (**Figure 46.18**). It is a physical process, fueled by the

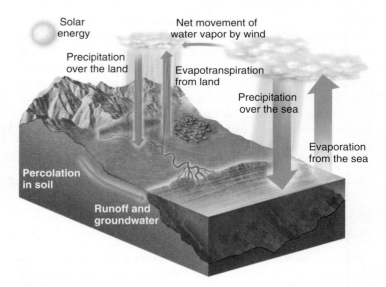

Figure 46.18   The water cycle. This cycle is primarily a physical process, not a chemical one. Solar energy drives the water cycle, causing evaporation of water from the ocean and evapotranspiration from the land. This is followed by condensation of water vapor into clouds and precipitation. The width of the arrows indicates the relative contribution of each step to the cycle.

Biology Principle

Biology Affects Our Society

Interruptions in biogeochemical cycles, such as changes in the water cycle, can have severe repercussions for human societies, such as depletion of fish stocks.

Figure 46.19 **A dam on the Columbia River, Washington State.** Dams can increase water supplies and provide hydroelectric power, but can interfere with migration of fishes, such as salmon and trout.

Sun's energy, rather than a chemical one, because it consists of essentially two phenomena: evaporation and precipitation. Even so, the water cycle has important biological components. Over land, 90% of the water that reaches the atmosphere is moisture that has passed through plants and exited from the leaves via evapotranspiration. Only about 2% of the total volume of Earth's water is found in the bodies of organisms or is held frozen or in the soil. The rest cycles from bodies of water, to the atmosphere, and then to the land and back again.

Human Influences on the Water Cycle   As noted in Chapter 43, water is limiting to the abundance of many organisms, including humans. To increase the amount of available water and also to create hydroelectric power, humans have interrupted the hydrological cycle in many ways, most prominently through the use of dams to create reservoirs. Such dams, such as those on the Columbia River in Washington State (Figure 46.19), can greatly interfere with the migration of fishes such as salmon and affect their ability to reproduce and survive. Other activities, such as tapping into underground water supplies, or **aquifers,** for drinking water removes more water than is put back by rainfall and can cause shallow ponds and lakes to dry up and sinkholes to develop, exacerbating local shortages. On a larger scale, global climate change threatens already dry areas of the world with increased frequency of droughts, while wetter areas may experience higher frequencies of flooding.

46.3 Reviewing the Concepts

- Elements such as phosphorus, carbon, and nitrogen, recycle from the physical environment to organisms and back in what are called biogeochemical cycles (Figure 46.11). The phosphorus cycle lacks an atmospheric component and thus is a local cycle. An overabundance of phosphorus can cause the overgrowth of algae and subsequent depletion of oxygen levels, called eutrophication (Figures 46.12–46.14).

- In the carbon cycle, autotrophs incorporate CO_2 from the atmosphere into their biomass; decomposition of plants and respiration recycle most of this CO_2 back to the atmosphere. Human activities, primarily the burning of fossil fuels, are causing increased amounts of CO_2 to enter the atmosphere (Figure 46.15).

- The nitrogen cycle has five parts: nitrogen fixation, nitrification, assimilation, ammonification, and denitrification. In the nitrogen cycle, atmospheric nitrogen is unavailable for use by most organisms and must be converted to usable forms by certain bacteria. The activities of humans, including fertilizer use, burning of fossil fuels, and deforestation, have dramatically altered the nitrogen cycle (Figure 46.17).

- The water cycle is a physical rather than a chemical process because it consists of essentially two phenomena: evaporation and precipitation. Alteration of the water cycle by dams can greatly disrupt migration of fishes such as salmon and trout (Figures 46.18, 46.19).

46.3 Testing Your Knowledge

1. The largest stores of carbon exist in
   - **a.** the atmosphere.
   - **c.** plants.
   - **e.** animals.
   - **b.** terrestrial rocks.
   - **d.** the ocean.

2. In which part of the nitrogen cycle is NH_3 or NH_4^+ converted to nitrate?
   - **a.** assimilation
   - **c.** nitrogen fixation
   - **e.** ammonification
   - **b.** nitrification
   - **d.** denitrification

3. The water cycle is largely a physical process because
   a. it has no long-distance transfer mechanism.
   b. it is fueled by the Sun's energy.
   c. it is not chemically changed by any of the cycle's components.
   d. it cycles between the atmosphere and the land.
   e. only about 2% of the total volume of the Earth's water is found in the bodies of organisms or found frozen in the soil.

Assess and Discuss

Test Yourself

1. The amount of energy that is fixed during photosynthesis is known as
   a. net primary production.
   b. biomagnification.
   c. the pyramid of energy.
   d. gross primary production.
   e. primary consumption.

2. Autotrophic organisms are
   a. primary consumers.
   b. secondary consumers.
   c. tertiary consumers.
   d. primary producers.
   e. decomposers.

3. When considering the average food chain, which of the following statements is true?
   a. Secondary consumers are the most abundant organisms in an ecosystem.
   b. Most plant biomass is eaten by herbivores.
   c. Biomass decreases as you move up the food chain.
   d. The trophic level with the highest species abundance is usually the primary producers.
   e. All of the above are true.

4. Which organisms are the most important consumers of energy in a Georgia salt marsh?
   a. *Spartina* grass and algae
   b. insects
   c. spiders
   d. crabs
   e. bacteria

5. Primary production in aquatic systems is limited mainly by
   a. temperature and moisture.
   b. temperature and light.
   c. temperature and nutrients.
   d. light and nutrients.
   e. light and moisture.

6. The most highly productive terrestrial ecosystems are
   a. deserts.
   b. prairies.
   c. forests.
   d. savannas.
   e. tundra.

7. Which of the following nutrients do/does not cycle globally?
   a. carbon
   b. nitrogen
   c. phosphorus
   d. a and b
   e. b and c

8. Eutrophication is
   a. caused by an overabundance of nitrogen, which leads to an increase in bacteria populations.
   b. caused by an overabundance of nutrients, which leads to an increase in algal populations.
   c. the normal breakdown of algal plants following a pollution event.
   d. normally seen in dry, hot regions of the world.
   e. none of the above.

9. Terrestrial primary producers acquire the carbon necessary for photosynthesis from
   a. decomposing plant material.
   b. carbon monoxide released from the burning of fossil fuels.
   c. carbon dioxide in the atmosphere.
   d. carbon sources in the soil.
   e. both a and d.

10. Nitrogen fixation is the process
   a. that converts organic nitrogen to NH_3.
   b. by which plants and animals take up NO_3^-.
   c. by which bacteria convert NO_3^- to N_2.
   d. by which N_2 is converted to NH_3 or NH_4^+.
   e. all of the above

Conceptual Questions

1. At what trophic level does a carrion beetle feed?

2. Explain why chain lengths are short in food webs.

3. **PRINCIPLES**   A principle of biology is that *living organisms use energy*. What is a fundamental difference between the passage of energy and the passage of nutrients through ecosystems?

Collaborative Questions

1. What might the atmospheric concentration of CO_2 be in 2100? Discuss what effects this might have on the environment.

2. The Earth's atmosphere consists of 78% nitrogen. Why is nitrogen a limiting nutrient and how can we increase the supply of nitrogen to plants?

Online Resource

www.brookerprinciples.com

Stay a step ahead in your studies with animations that bring concepts to life and practice tests to assess your understanding. Your instructor may also recommend the interactive eBook, individualized learning tools, and more.

Biodiversity and Conservation Biology

Spix's macaw (*Cyanopsitta spixii*). Less than 100 individuals of this species are known to exist in the rainforests of Brazil.

Chapter Outline

47.1 Biodiversity Concerns Genetic, Species, and Ecosystem Diversity

47.2 Biodiversity Is of Great Value to Human Welfare

47.3 The Causes of Extinction and Loss of Biodiversity

47.4 Conservation Strategies

Assess and Discuss

In 2009, Jeff Corwin, an American conservationist and host for programs on *Animal Planet* and other television networks, published a book entitled *100 Heartbeats: The Race to Save the Earth's Most Endangered Species.* The Hundred Heartbeat Club was created earlier by biologist E. O. Wilson to highlight the plight of animal species, such as Spix's macaw (*Cyanopsitta spixii*) in Brazil, the Chinese river dolphin (*Lipotes vexillifer*), and the Philippine eagle (*Pithecophaga jefferyi*), that have 100 or fewer individuals left alive (and hence that number of heartbeats away from extinction). Saving species from extinction is important in its own right, but, as we will see, conservation of biological diversity also has great economic and social value to humankind.

Biological diversity, or **biodiversity**, encompasses the genetic diversity of species, the variety of different species, and the different ecosystems they form. The field of **conservation biology** uses principles and knowledge from molecular biology, genetics, and ecology to protect and sustain biological diversity. Because it draws from nearly all chapters of this textbook, a discussion of conservation biology is a fitting way to conclude our study. In this chapter, we begin by examining

the questions of what biodiversity is and why it should be conserved and explore how much diversity is needed for ecosystems to function properly. We then survey the main threats to the world's biodiversity from habitat loss, overexploitation, and the effects of introduced species, to climate change and pollution. Even if species are not exterminated, many may exist only in very small populations. We will see how these small populations face special problems such as inbreeding, emphasizing the importance of population genetics in conservation biology.

Last, we consider what is being done to help conserve the world's endangered plant and animal life. This includes identifying global areas rich in species and establishing parks and refuges of the appropriate size, number, and connectivity. We also discuss conservation of particularly important types of species and how to restore damaged habitats to a more natural condition. We then examine how captive-breeding programs help to build populations of rare species prior to their release back into the wild. Some programs have also used modern genetic techniques such as cloning to help breed and perhaps eventually increase populations of endangered species.

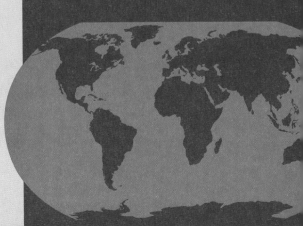

47.1 Biodiversity Concerns Genetic, Species, and Ecosystem Diversity

Learning Outcome:

1. List and describe the three levels of biodiversity.

Biodiversity can be examined on three levels: genetic diversity, species diversity, and ecosystem diversity. Each level of biodiversity provides valuable benefits to humanity.

Genetic diversity consists of the amount of genetic variation occurring within and between populations. Without such variation, populations cannot respond so quickly to changes in environmental conditions, resulting in population decline and even extinction. Maintaining genetic variation in the wild relatives of crops may be vital to the continued success of crop-breeding programs. For example, the café marron (*Ramosmania rodriguesii*), a wild relative of the coffee plant that is native to a tiny island off the coast of Mauritius, was assumed to be extinct until 1979, when one surviving tree was identified. Today, cuttings from the tree are being cultured in London's Kew Gardens (**Figure 47.1**). The plant may contain genes that would allow coffee to be grown in a wider range of soils and elevations.

The second level of biodiversity concerns **species diversity,** the number and relative abundance of species in a community (refer back to Section 45.1). In 1973, the U.S. Endangered Species Act (ESA) was enacted, which was designed to protect both endangered and threatened species. **Endangered species** are those species that are in danger of extinction throughout all or a significant portion of their range. **Threatened species** are those species likely to become endangered in the foreseeable future. Many species are currently threatened. According to the International Union for Conservation of Nature and Natural Resources (IUCN), more than 25% of the fish species that live on coral reefs and 22% of all mammals, 12% of birds, and 31% of amphibians are threatened with

extinction. In 2000, the World Wildlife Foundation placed Atlantic cod, *Gadus morhua*, on the endangered species list as a result of overfishing. Nine of 17 populations of commercially important Chinook salmon, *Oncorhynchus tshawytscha*, in California and Oregon are listed as endangered or threatened.

The last level of biodiversity is ecosystem diversity, the diversity of structure and function within an ecosystem. Conservation has largely focused attention on species-rich ecosystems such as tropical rain forests. Over 120 prescription drugs used to treat malaria, cancer, and other diseases were developed from rain forest plants, yet less than 1% of such plants have been tested for medicinal properties. However, some ecologists have argued that relatively species-poor ecosystems such as prairies are also highly threatened and in equal need of conservation. More than 99% of the original tallgrass prairie in the United States has been converted to agricultural land.

47.1 Reviewing the Concepts

- Biodiversity represents diversity at three levels: genetic diversity, species diversity, and ecosystem diversity. Conservation biology uses knowledge from molecular biology, genetics, and ecology to protect biological diversity (Figure 47.1).

47.1 Testing Your Knowledge

1. In 1977, Rafael Guzman, a Mexican biologist, discovered a previously unknown wild relative of corn that is resistant to many of the viral diseases that infect domestic corn. Agriculturalists believe crossbreeding could improve current corn crops. In this case biodiversity is important at which level?
   a. ecosystem
   b. species
   c. genetic
   d. community
   e. a and b

Figure 47.1 Café marron being cultured in London's Kew Gardens. These plants are derived from just one surviving individual found in Mauritius.

47.2 Biodiversity Is of Great Value to Human Welfare

Learning Outcomes:

1. Outline the benefits of biological diversity to human welfare.
2. Provide graphical representations of possible relationships between biodiversity level and ecosystem function.
3. Describe experimental evidence that shows how species diversity and ecosystem function are linked.

Why should biodiversity be a concern? American biologists Paul Ehrlich and E. O. Wilson have suggested that the loss of biodiversity should be an area of great concern for at least three reasons:

1. Humans depend on plants, animals, and microorganisms for a wide range of food, medicine, and industrial products.

2. Ecosystems provide an array of essential services, such as clean air and water.

3. Humans have an ethical responsibility to protect what are our only known living companions in the universe.

In this section, we examine some of the primary reasons why preserving biodiversity matters and explore the link between biodiversity and ecosystem function.

Society Benefits Economically from Biodiversity

The pharmaceutical industry is heavily dependent on plant and animal products for source material. An estimated 50,000–70,000 plant species are used in traditional and modern medicine. About 25% of the prescription drugs in the U.S. alone are derived from plants, and the 2009 market value of such drugs was estimated to be $300 billion, accounting for a little less than half the global pharmaceutical market. Many medicines come from plants found only in tropical rain forests. These include quinine, a drug from the bark of the Cinchona tree (*Cinchona officinalis*), which is used for treating malaria, and vincristine, a drug derived from rosy periwinkle (*Catharanthus roseus*), which is a treatment for leukemia and Hodgkin disease. Many chemicals of therapeutic importance are likely to be found in the numerous rain forest plant species that have not yet been fully analyzed. The continued destruction of rain forests could thus mean the loss of potential lifesaving medical treatments. Rapamycin was developed from a soil fungus on Easter Island and suppresses immune reactions. It is used to prevent organ rejection in transplants and as a coating on heart stents.

In terms of animals, the blood of the horseshoe crab (*Limulus polyphemus*) clots when exposed to toxins produced by some bacteria. Pharmaceutical industries use the blood enzyme responsible for this clotting to ensure that their products are free of bacterial contamination. The venom of gila monsters, *Heloderma suspectum*, one of only two venomous lizards in the world, is being used to treat people who are resistant to conventional treatment for type 2 diabetes, a disease which may affect 30% of Americans at some point in their life. A protein from the South American pit viper, *Bothrops jacara*, may help control human blood pressure. Tarantula venom may be helpful in treating neurological disorders such as Parkinson disease.

Although humans depend on only about 20 plant species to provide 90% of the world's food, wild relatives of these crops provide a useful reservoir of genetic material for developing pest-resistant varieties or strains that can grow in marginal areas. In the 1970s, infusion of genetic material from wild corn in Mexico was used to protect the U.S. commercial corn from a leaf fungus, which had killed 15% of the crop. The Lake Placid mint, *Dicerandra frutescens*, known only from central Florida, produces a powerful insect-repelling chemical that may have benefits for crop protection. Another endangered species, the buffalo clover, *Trifolium stoloniferum*, has high protein content and is a perennial, making it of high potential value as a forage crop. The guayule, *Parthenium argentartum*, is of great potential value to industry. It has high amounts of natural rubber and grows in the deserts of the southwest U.S., adding economic value to marginal lands. Animals too have great commercial value. Salmon fishing

in the Pacific Northwest supports over 60,000 jobs and injects over $1 billion into the economy. In the United Kingdom, the sea fish catch is worth over $500 million annually.

Natural Ecosystems Provide Essential Services to Humans

Beyond the direct economic gains from biodiversity, humans benefit enormously from the essential services that natural ecosystems provide (**Table 47.1**). For example, forests soak up carbon dioxide, maintain soil fertility, and retain water, helping to prevent or minimize flooding; estuaries provide water filtration and protect rivers and coastal shores from excessive erosion. *Prochlorococcus*, an abundant ocean-dwelling genus of cyanobacteria was discovered only in 1986, yet it is estimated to produce about 20% of the oxygen we breathe. The loss of biodiversity can disrupt an ecosystem's ability to carry out such functions. Other ecosystem functions include the maintenance of populations of natural predators to regulate pest outbreaks and reservoirs of pollinators to pollinate crops and other plants.

In the 1990s, farmers in India began using the anti-inflammatory drug diclofenac to reduce pain and fever in their livestock. They could hardly anticipate that vultures scavenging on dead carcasses would accumulate large doses of the drug and die of renal failure. But the consequences did not stop there. Following a 97% reduction in vulture numbers over a 14-year period, the population of feral dogs exploded, buoyed by the

Table 47.1	Examples of the World's Ecosystem Services
Service	**Example**
Atmospheric gas supply	Regulation of carbon dioxide, ozone, and oxygen levels
Climate regulation	Regulation of carbon dioxide, nitrogen dioxide, and methane levels
Water supply	Irrigation; water for industry
Pollination	Pollination of crops
Biological control	Pest population regulation
Wilderness and refuges	Habitat for wildlife
Food production	Crops; livestock
Raw materials	Fossil fuels; timber
Genetic resources	Medicines; genes for plant resistance to pests and diseases
Recreation	Ecotourism; outdoor recreation
Cultural	Aesthetic and educational value
Disturbance regulation	Storm protection; flood control
Waste treatment	Sewage purification
Soil erosion control	Retention of topsoil; reduction of accumulation of sediments in lakes
Nutrient cycling	Nitrogen, phosphorus, carbon, and sulfur cycles

availability of uneaten carcasses. The incidence of rabies in humans increased, with estimates of an additional 48,000 people dying over the 14-year time span. The loss of the scavenging services of these vultures was estimated to cost India $24 billion.

A 1997 paper in the journal *Nature* by economist Robert Costanza and colleagues made an attempt to calculate the monetary value of ecosystems to various economies. They came to the conclusion that, at the time, the world's ecosystems were worth more than $33 trillion a year, nearly twice the gross national product of the world's economies combined ($19 trillion).

There Are Ethical Reasons for Conserving Biodiversity

Arguments can also be made against the loss of biodiversity on ethical grounds. As only one of many species on Earth, it has been argued that humans have no right to destroy other species and the environment around us. American philosopher Tom Regan suggests that animals should be treated with respect because they have a life of their own and therefore have value apart from anyone else's interests. American law professor Christopher Stone, in an influential 1972 article titled "Should Trees Have Standing?" has argued that entities such as nonhuman natural objects like trees or lakes should be given legal rights just as corporations are treated as individuals for certain purposes. As E. O. Wilson proposed in a 1984 concept known as biophilia, humans have innate attachments with species and natural habitats because of our close association for over millions of years.

Ecologists Have Described Several Relationships Between Ecosystem Function and Biodiversity

Because biodiversity affects the health of ecosystems, ecologists have explored the question of how much diversity is needed for ecosystems to function properly. In doing so, they have described several possible relationships between biodiversity and ecosystem function. In the 1950s, ecologist Charles Elton proposed in the **diversity-stability hypothesis** that species-rich communities are more stable than those with fewer species (refer back to Section 45.2). If we use stability as a measure of ecosystem function, Elton's hypothesis suggests a linear correlation between diversity and ecosystem function; as diversity increases, ecosystem function increases proportionately (Figure 47.2a). Australian ecologist Brian Walker proposed an alternative to this idea, termed the **redundancy hypothesis** (Figure 47.2b). According to this hypothesis, ecosystem function increases rapidly at fairly low levels of diversity so that most additional species are functionally redundant. Two other alternatives relating species richness and ecosystem services have been proposed. The **keystone hypothesis** (Figure 47.2c) proposes ecosystem function dramatically rises as biodiversity approaches its natural levels. Lastly, the **idiosyncratic hypothesis** addresses the possibility that although ecosystem function can change as the number of species increases or decreases, the amount and direction of change is unpredictable (Figure 47.2d).

Determining which model is most correct is very important, as our understanding of the effect of species loss on ecosystem function can greatly affect the way we manage our environment.

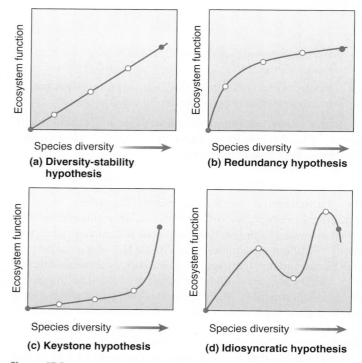

Figure 47.2 **Graphical representations of possible relationships between ecosystem function and biodiversity.** The two solid dots represent the end points of a continuum of species richness. The first dot is at the origin, where there are no species and no community services. The second dot represents natural levels of species diversity. The relationship is strongest in **(a)** and weakest in **(d)**.

Field Experiments Have Been Used to Determine How Much Diversity Is Needed for Normal Ecosystem Function

In the mid-1990s, David Tilman and colleagues performed experiments in the field to determine how much biodiversity was necessary for proper ecosystem functioning. Tilman's previous experiments had suggested that species-rich grasslands were more stable (that is, they were more resistant to the ravages of drought and recovered from drought more quickly) than species-poor grasslands (refer back to Figure 45.4). In the subsequent experiments, Tilman's group sowed multiple plots, each 3 m × 3 m, and on comparable soils, with seeds of 1, 2, 4, 6, 8, 12, or 24 species of prairie plants. Exactly which species were sown into each plot was determined randomly from a pool of 24 native species. The treatments were replicated 21 times, for a total of 147 plots. The results showed that plots with more species (more diverse plots) had increased productivity, expressed as a percentage of plant cover (the amount of ground covered by leaves of plants) than plots with fewer species (less diverse plots). This occurred because of a greater variety of plant growth forms that could utilize light at different levels of the canopy. More diverse plots also used more nutrients, such as nitrate (NO_3^-), than less-diverse plots because a greater variety of plant root lengths could utilize nutrients at different levels of the soil (Figure 47.3a,b). Furthermore, the frequency of invasive plant species (species not originally planted in the plots) decreased with increased plant species richness (Figure 47.3c).

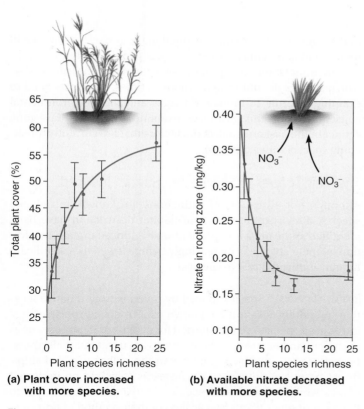

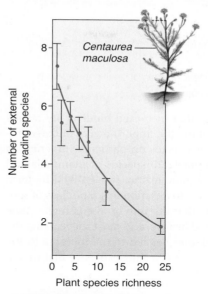

(a) Plant cover increased with more species.

(b) Available nitrate decreased with more species.

(c) Invasive species decreased with more species.

Figure 47.3 The relationship of species richness to ecosystem function.

Although Tilman's experiments show a relationship between species diversity and ecosystem function, they also suggest that most of the advantages of increasing diversity come with the first 5–10 species, beyond which adding more species appears to have little to no effect. This supports the redundancy hypothesis (compare Figure 47.3a with Figure 47.2b). This is also observed on a larger scale. The productivity of temperate forests on different continents is roughly the same, despite different numbers of tree species being present—729 in East Asia, 253 in North America, and 124 in Europe. The presence of more tree species may ensure a supply of "backups" should some of the most-productive species die off from insect attack or disease. This can happen, as was seen in the demise of the American chestnut tree. Diseases devastated this species, and its presence in forests dramatically decreased by the mid-20th century (refer back to Figure 44.14). The forests filled in with other species and continued to function as before in terms of nutrient cycling and gas exchange. However, although the forests continued to function without the American chestnuts, some important changes occurred. For example, the loss of chestnuts deprived bears and other animals of an important source of food and may have affected their reproductive capacity and hence the size of their populations.

47.2 Reviewing the Concepts

- The preservation of biodiversity has been justified because of its economic value, because of the value of ecosystem services, and on ethical grounds (Table 47.1).

- Four models describe the relationship between biodiversity and ecosystem function: the diversity-stability, redundancy, keystone, and idiosyncratic hypotheses (Figure 47.2).

- Field experiments have shown that increased biodiversity results in increased ecosystem function and support the redundancy hypothesis (Figure 47.3).

47.2 Testing Your Knowledge

1. The idea that there is a linear correlation between diversity and ecosystem function is known as the _____ hypothesis.
   a. keystone
   b. diversity-stability
   c. linear
   d. redundancy
   e. idiosyncratic

2. Experimental evidence suggests that
   a. ecosystem function levels off at fairly low levels of diversity.
   b. ecosystem function plummets as soon as biodiversity decreases from natural levels.
   c. there is a linear correlation between diversity and ecosystem function.
   d. there is an unpredictable relationship between diversity and ecosystem function.
   e. there is no relationship between diversity and ecosystem function.

47.3 The Causes of Extinction and Loss of Biodiversity

Learning Outcomes:

1. List and describe the four main human-induced threats to species.
2. Explain how the genetic diversity of small populations is threatened by inbreeding.

In light of research showing that increased biodiversity results in increased ecosystem function, the importance of understanding and preventing species loss takes on particular urgency. In the past 100 years, approximately 20 species of mammals and over 40 species of birds have gone extinct (Figure 47.4). The term **biodiversity crisis** is often used to describe this rapid loss of species. Many scientists believe that the rate of loss is higher now than during most of geological history, and most suggest that the growth in the human population has led to the increase in the number of extinctions. In fact, most scientists believe that we are in the middle of a sixth mass extinction (refer back to Chapter 18 for a discussion of mass extinctions over geological time).

To understand the process of extinction, the process by which species die out in more modern times, ecologists need to examine the role of human activities and their environmental consequences. In this section, we examine why species have gone extinct in the past and look at the factors that are currently threatening species with extinction.

The Main Threats to Species Are Human-Induced

Although not all causes of extinctions are known, introduced species, direct exploitation, and habitat destruction have been identified as the most important human-induced threats. In addition, climate change is increasingly being viewed as a significant human-induced threat to species.

Invasive Species   Species moved by humans from a native location to another location are known as introduced species. Most introduced species are transported for agricultural purposes or as sources of timber, meat, or wool. Others are unintentionally transported, such as marine organisms in the ballast water of ships. Insect pests can enter new countries as eggs laid on imported plants, while the seeds of weeds can arrive via soil attached to the roots of other plants. Regardless of their method of introduction, some introduced species become **invasive species,** spreading and outcompeting native species for space and resources. For example, the burmese python, introduced into the Florida Everglades, has decimated the native wildlife populations (refer back to Figure 44.13). Parasitism and disease carried by introduced organisms have also been important in causing extinctions, as we saw in the case of the American chestnut (see Figure 44.14). Avian malaria in Hawaii, spread by introduced mosquito species, is believed to have contributed to the demise of up to 50% of native Hawaiian birds (Figure 47.5a).

Direct Exploitation   Direct exploitation, particularly the hunting of animals, has been the cause of many extinctions in the past. The passenger pigeon, *Ectopistes migratorius*, was once the most common bird in North America, probably accounting for over 40% of the entire bird population (Figure 47.5b). Their total population size was estimated to be over 3 billion birds. Habitat loss because of deforestation was a contributing factor in their demise, but hunting as a cheap source of meat was the main factor. The flocking behavior of the birds made them relatively easy targets for hunters, who used special firearms to harvest the birds in quantity. In 1876, in Michigan alone, over 1.6 million birds were killed and sent to markets in the eastern U.S. Many whale species were driven to the brink of extinction by direct exploitation prior to the 1988 moratorium on commercial whaling.

Habitat Destruction   Habitat destruction through **deforestation,** the conversion of forested areas to nonforested land, has historically been a prime cause of the extinction of species. The

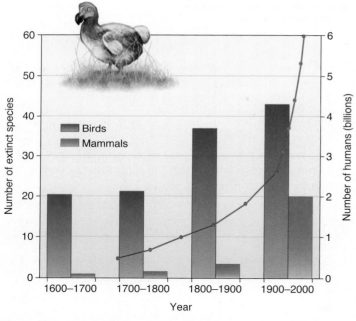

Figure 47.4 Bird and mammal extinctions since the 17th century in relation to human population growth. Increasing numbers of known extinctions in birds and mammals are concurrent with the exponential increase in the global human population (red line). These data suggest that as the human population increases, more and more species will go extinct. The inset depicts a dodo bird from the island of Mauritius, which was hunted to extinction for its meat within 100 years after contact with humans.

✔ Concept Check: *Why might the increasing human population result in an increase in the extinction rate of other species?*

(a) Introduced species

(b) Direct exploitation

(c) Habitat destruction

Figure 47.5 **Causes of extinction. (a)** Many Hawaiian honeycreepers were exterminated by avian malaria from introduced mosquito species. This Apapane (*Himatione sanguinea*) is one of the few remaining honeycreeper species. **(b)** The passenger pigeon (*Ectopistes migratorius*), which was once among the most abundant bird species on Earth, was hunted to extinction for its meat. **(c)** The ivory-billed woodpecker (*Campephilus principalis*), the third-largest woodpecker in the world, was long thought to be extinct in the southeastern U.S. because of habitat destruction, but a possible sighting occurred in 2004. This nestling was photographed in Louisiana in 1938.

ivory-billed woodpecker (*Campephilus principalis*), the largest woodpecker in North America and an inhabitant of wetlands and forests of the southeastern U.S., was widely assumed to have gone extinct in the 1950s due to destruction of its habitat by heavy logging (**Figure 47.5c**). In 2004, the woodpecker was purportedly sighted in the Big Woods area of eastern Arkansas, though this has not been confirmed despite concerted efforts. Deforestation is not the only form of habitat destruction. Prairies are often replaced by agricultural crops. Wetlands have been drained for agricultural purposes, and others have been filled in for urban or industrial development. In the U.S., as much as 90% of the freshwater marshes and 50% of the estuarine marshes have disappeared.

Global Warming   As discussed in Chapter 43, human-induced climate change, or global warming, will affect the distribution of trees as climate zones shift, with such shifts occurring faster than many plants can migrate via seed dispersal (refer back to Figure 43.10). However, climate change has also been implicated in the dramatic decrease in the population sizes of frog species in Central and South America. One effect of global warming is to increase the cloud cover, which reduces daytime temperatures and raises nighttime temperatures. Researchers believe that this combination has created favorable conditions for the spread of a disease-causing fungus, *Batrachochytrium dendrobatidis*, and other diseases, which thrive in cooler daytime temperatures. In 2006, a study led by J. Alan Pounds of the Monteverde Cloud Forest Preserve in Costa Rica reported that fully two-thirds of the 110 species of harlequin frogs in mountainous areas of Central and South America had become extinct over the previous 20 years.

Small Populations Are Threatened by the Loss of Genetic Diversity

Even if habitats are not destroyed, many become fragmented, leading to the development of small, isolated populations. Such populations are more vulnerable to the loss of genetic diversity resulting from inbreeding.

Inbreeding, which is mating among genetically related relatives, is more likely to take place in nature when population size becomes very small and the number of potential mates shrinks drastically (see Section 19.6). In many species, the health and survival of offspring declines as populations become more inbred. This is because inbreeding produces homozygotes, which, because of an increase in recessive genes, are less fit, thereby decreasing the reproductive success of the population (see Figure 19.23).

One of the most striking examples of the effects of inbreeding in conservation biology involves the greater prairie chicken (*Tympanuchus cupido*). The male birds have a spectacular mating display that involves inflating the bright orange air sacs on their throat, stomping their feet, and spreading their tail feathers. The prairies of the Midwest were once home to millions of these birds, but as the prairies were converted to farmland, the population sizes of the bird shrank dramatically. The population of prairie chickens in Illinois decreased from 25,000 in 1933 to less than 50 in 1989. At that point, according to studies by Ronald Westemeier and colleagues, only 10 to 12 males existed. Because of the decreasing numbers of males, inbreeding in the population had increased. This was reflected in the steady reduction in the hatching success of eggs (**Figure 47.6**). In the early 1990s, conservation biologists began trapping prairie chickens in Kansas

Biology Principle

New Properties Emerge from Complex Interactions

The conversion of prairies to farmland reduced the available prairie chicken habitat in Illinois, and populations of the bird decreased dramatically. The consequent increase in inbreeding led to a path toward extinction that was difficult to reverse.

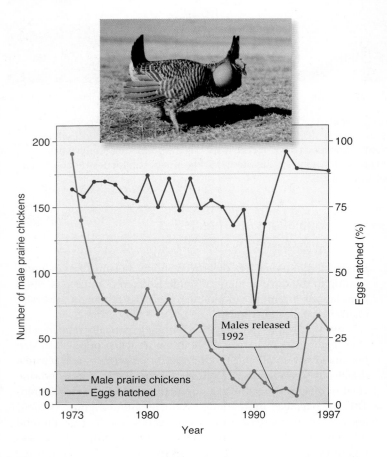

Figure 47.6 **Changes in the abundance and egg-hatching success rate of prairie chickens in Illinois.** As the number of males decreased, inbreeding increased, resulting in a decrease in fertility, as indicated by a reduced egg-hatching rate. An influx of genetically unrelated males in the early 1990s increased the egg-hatching success rate dramatically.

 **Concept Check:**   *Is the fitness of all organisms decreased by inbreeding?*

and Nebraska, where populations remained larger and more genetically diverse, and moved them to Illinois, bringing an infusion of new genetic material into the population. This transfer resulted in a rebounding of the egg-hatching success rate to over 90% by 1993.

Quantitative Analysis

DETERMINING EFFECTIVE POPULATION SIZE

In many populations, the **effective population size,** the number of individuals that contribute genes to future populations, may be smaller than the actual number of individuals in the population, particularly in animals with a mating structure in which only a few dominant males breed. A small effective population size exacerbates the effects of inbreeding. For example, a relatively few male black grouse are preferred as mating partners by the majority of females, so a few males command all the matings (refer back to Figure 42.17).

If a population consists of breeding males and females, the effective population size is given by

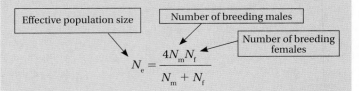

$$N_e = \frac{4N_m N_f}{N_m + N_f}$$

In a population of 500, a 50:50 sex ratio, and all individuals breeding, the effective population size (N_e) = (4 × 250 × 250)/(250 + 250) = 500, or 100% of the actual population size. However, if 10 males breed with 250 females, the effective population size (N_e) = (4 × 10 × 250)/(10 + 250) = 38.5, or 8% of the actual population size.

Knowledge of effective population size is vital to ensuring the success of conservation projects. One notable project in the U.S. involved planning the sizes of preserves designed to protect grizzly bear populations in the contiguous 48 states. The grizzly bear (*Ursus arctos*) has declined in numbers from an estimated 100,000 in 1800 to less than 1,500 at present. The range of the species is now less than 1% of its historical range and is restricted to six separate populations in four states (**Figure 47.7**). Research by American biologist Fred Allendorf has indicated that because not all bears breed, the effective population size of grizzly populations is generally only about 25% of the actual population size. Thus, even fairly large, isolated populations, such as the 200 bears in Yellowstone National Park, are vulnerable to the harmful effects of loss of genetic variation because the effective population size is much smaller. Allendorf and his colleagues proposed that an exchange of grizzly bears between populations or zoo collections would help tremendously in promoting genetic variation. Even an exchange of two bears per generation between populations would greatly reduce the loss of genetic variation.

Crunching the Numbers: If there is 1:1 sex ratio in the 200 bears of Yellowstone National Park but only 25% of the males breed, what is the effective population size and by what percentage is it reduced from the real population size?

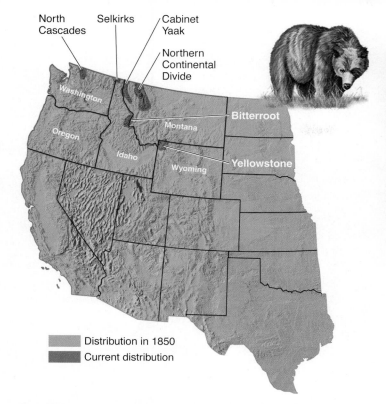

North Cascades   Selkirks   Cabinet Yaak   Northern Continental Divide   Bitterroot   Yellowstone

Washington, Oregon, Idaho, Montana, Wyoming

☐ Distribution in 1850
■ Current distribution

Figure 47.7   Past and current ranges of the grizzly bear. The range of the grizzly bear (*Ursus arctos*) is currently less than 1% of its historical range. The current range in the continental U.S. has contracted to just six populations in four states, as the population size has shrunk from 100,000 before the West was settled to about 1,500 today.

47.3   Reviewing the Concepts

- Extinction has been a natural phenomenon throughout the history of life on Earth. However, the loss of species has increased dramatically in the past 100 years, a phenomenon called the biodiversity crisis (Figure 47.4).
- The main causes of extinctions have been and continue to be introduced species, direct exploitation, and habitat destruction. In addition, climate change is increasingly viewed as a significant threat to species (Figure 47.5).
- Reduced population size can lead to a reduction of genetic diversity through inbreeding—mating among genetically related relatives. A small effective population size exacerbates the effects of inbreeding (Figures 47.6, 47.7).

47.3   Testing Your Knowledge

1. The main causes of extinction are
   a. habitat destruction.   **c.** invasive species.   **e.** all of the above.
   b. climate change.   **d.** direct exploitation.
2. A relatively few male elephant seals dominate mating with nearly all the females. This affects genetic diversity by reducing
   a. inbreeding.   **d.** a and b.
   b. the effective population size.   **e.** b and c.
   c. genetic drift.

47.4   Conservation Strategies

Learning Outcomes:

1. Detail the different criteria that conservation biologists use to target areas for protection.
2. Explain how the principles of the model of island biogeography and landscape ecology are used to create nature preserves.
3. Describe different approaches conservation biologists use to protect individual species.
4. Define restoration ecology and the approaches used to restore degraded ecosystems and populations of species.

In their efforts to maintain the diversity of life on Earth, conservation biologists are currently active on many fronts. How do they decide on which areas or species to focus on and which strategies to employ to protect diversity? We begin this section by discussing how conservation biologists identify the global habitats most in need of conservation. Next, we explore the concept of nature preserves and how they should be constructed. These issues are within the realm of landscape ecology, which studies the spatial arrangement of communities and ecosystems in a geographic area. Next we discuss how conservation efforts often focus on certain species that can have a disproportionate influence on their ecosystem. We will also examine the field of restoration ecology, studying how wildlife habitats can be established from degraded areas and how captive breeding programs have been used to reestablish populations of threatened species in the wild.

Conservation Seeks to Establish Protected Areas

Currently, about 12.85% of the global land area is under some form of environmental protection. More than 147,000 separate areas are protected, with more being added daily. Conservation biologists often must make decisions regarding which habitats should be protected. Many conservation efforts have focused on saving habitats in so-called megadiversity countries, because they often have the greatest number of species. However, more recent strategies have promoted preservation of certain key areas with the highest levels of unique species or the preservation of representative areas of all types of habitat, even relatively species-poor areas.

Megadiversity Countries   One method of targeting areas for conservation is to identify **megadiversity countries,** those countries with the greatest numbers of species. Using the number of plants, vertebrates, and selected groups of insects as criteria, American biologist Russell Mittermeier and colleagues determined that just 17 countries are home to nearly 70% of all known species. Brazil, Indonesia, and Colombia top the list, followed by Australia, Peru, Mexico, Madagascar, China, and nine other countries. The megadiversity country approach suggests that conservation efforts should be focused on the most biologically rich countries. However, although megadiversity areas may contain the most species, they do not necessarily contain the greatest number of unique species.

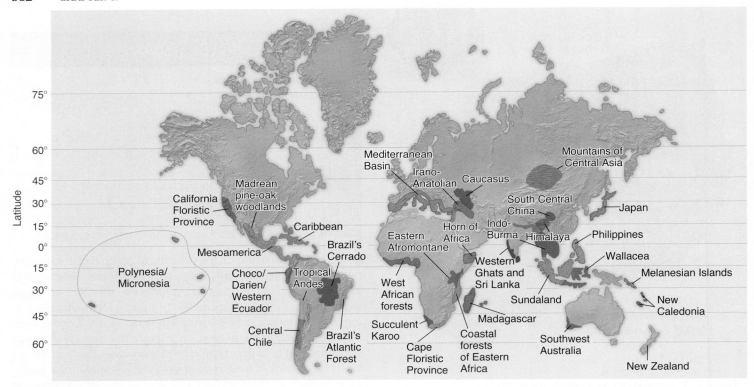

Figure 47.8 **Location of major biodiversity hot spots around the world.** Biodiversity hot spots have high numbers of endemic species. Different colors are used to more clearly demarcate separate regions.

The mammal species list for Peru is 344, and for Ecuador, it is 271; of these, however, 208 species are common to both.

Areas Rich in Endemic Species   Another method of setting conservation priorities—one adopted by the organization Conservation International—takes into account the number of species that are **endemic;** that is, they are found only in a particular place or region and nowhere else. This approach suggests that conservationists focus their efforts on **biodiversity hot spots,** regions that are biologically diverse and under threat of destruction. To qualify as a biodiversity hot spot, a region must meet two criteria: (1) It must contain at least 1,500 species of vascular plants as endemic species and (2) have lost at least 70% of its original habitat. Vascular plants were chosen as the primary group of organisms to determine whether or not an area qualifies as a hot spot, mainly because most other terrestrial organisms depend on them to some extent.

Conservationists Norman Myers, Russell Mittermeier, and colleagues identified 34 hot spots that together occupy a mere 2.3% of the Earth's surface but contain 150,000 endemic plant species, or 50% of the world's total (Figure 47.8). This approach proposes that protecting geographic hot spots will prevent the extinction of a larger number of endemic species than would protecting areas of a similar size elsewhere. The main argument against using hot spots as the criterion for targeting conservation efforts is that the areas richest in endemic species—tropical forests—would receive the majority of attention and funding, perhaps at the expense of protecting other areas.

Representative Habitats   In a third approach to prioritizing areas for conservation, scientists have recently argued that we need to conserve representatives of all major habitats. Prairies are a case in point. An example is the Pampas region of South America, which is arguably the most threatened habitat on the continent because of rapid conversion of its natural grasslands to ranch land and agriculture. The Pampas does not compare well in richness or endemics with the rain forests, but it is a unique area that without preservation could disappear (Figure 47.9). By selecting habitats that are most distinct from those already preserved, many areas that are threatened but not biologically rich may be preserved in addition to the less immediately threatened, but richer, tropical forests.

Ecologists are divided as to which is the best way to identify areas for habitat conservation. Some ecologists feel that the best approach might be one that creates a "portfolio" of areas to conserve, containing some areas of high species richness, others with large numbers of endemic species, and some with various habitat types.

Preserve Design Incorporates Principles of Island Biogeography and Landscape Ecology

After identifying areas to preserve, conservationists must determine the size, arrangement, and management of the protected land. Among the questions conservationists ask is whether one large preserve is preferable to an equivalent area composed of smaller preserves. Ecologists also need to determine whether

Figure 47.9 **The pampas, Argentina.** This habitat is not rich in species but is threatened due to conversion of grassland to ranching and agriculture. The guanaco, shown here in the foreground, is a characteristic grazer of pampas grass.

parks should be close together or far apart and whether or not they should be connected by strips of suitable habitat to allow the movement of plants and animals between them.

The Role of Island Biogeography   In exploring the equilibrium model of island biogeography (refer back to Section 45.4), we noted that nature preserves are, in essence, islands in a sea of human-altered habitat. Seen this way, the principles of the equilibrium model of island biogeography can be applied not only to a body of land surrounded by water, but also to nature preserves. One question for conservationists is how large a protected area

should be (Figure 47.10a). According to island biogeography, the number of species should increase with increasing area (the species-area effect). Thus, a larger area would mean that a larger number of species would be protected. In addition, larger parks have other benefits. For example, they are beneficial for organisms that require large spaces, including migrating species and species with extensive territories, such as lions and tigers.

A related question is whether it is preferable to protect a single, large preserve or several smaller ones (Figure 47.10b). This is called the **SLOSS debate** (for <u>s</u>ingle <u>l</u>arge <u>o</u>r <u>s</u>everal <u>s</u>mall). Proponents of the single, large preserve claim that a larger preserve is better able to protect more and larger populations than an equal area divided into small areas. According to island biogeography, a larger block of habitat should support more species than several smaller blocks.

However, many empirical studies suggest that multiple small sites of equivalent area will contain more species, because a series of small sites is more likely to contain a broader variety of habitats than one large site. Looking at a variety of sites, American researchers Jim Quinn and Susan Harrison concluded that animal life was richer in collections of small parks than in a smaller number of larger parks. In their study, having more habitat types outweighed the effect of area on biodiversity. In addition, another benefit of a series of smaller parks is a reduction of extinction risk by a single event such as a wildfire or the spread of disease.

The Role of Landscape Ecology   Landscape ecology is an area of ecology that examines the spatial arrangement of communities and ecosystems in a geographic area. Landscape ecologists have suggested that small preserves should be linked together by **movement corridors,** thin strips of land that may permit the movement of species between patches (Figure 47.10c). Such corridors ideally facilitate movements of organisms that are vulnerable to predation outside of their natural habitat or that have poor powers of dispersal between habitat patches. In this way, if a population in one small preserve experiences a disaster, immigrants

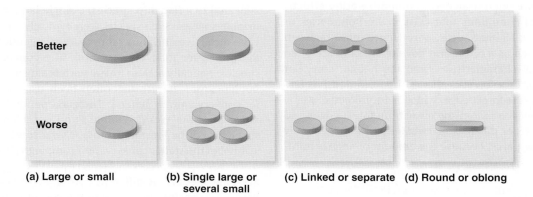

(a) Large or small   (b) Single large or several small   (c) Linked or separate   (d) Round or oblong

Figure 47.10 **The theoretical design of nature preserves.** **(a)** A larger preserve holds more species and has low extinction rates. **(b)** A given area should be fragmented into as few pieces as possible. **(c)** Maintaining or creating corridors between fragments may also enhance dispersal. **(d)** Circular-shaped areas minimize the amount of edge effects. The labels "better" and "worse" refer to theoretical principles generated by the equilibrium model of island biogeography, but empirical data have not supported all the predictions.

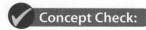 **Concept Check:**   *What are some of the potential risks in connecting areas via movement corridors?*

Figure 47.11   **Movement corridors.**

Concept Check: *How do these European hedgerows act as movement corridors?*

from neighboring populations can more easily recolonize it. This avoids the need for humans to physically move new plants or animals into an area.

Several types of habitat function as movement corridors, including hedgerows in Europe, which facilitate movement and dispersal of species between forest fragments (Figure 47.11). In China, corridors of habitat have been established to link small, adjacent populations of giant pandas. However, disadvantages are associated with movement corridors. Corridors also can facilitate the spread of disease, invasive species, and fire between small preserves.

Finally, parks are often designed to minimize **edge effects,** the special physical conditions that exist at the boundaries or edges of ecosystems. Habitat edges, particularly those between a natural habitat such as a forest and developed land, are often different in physical characteristics from the habitat core. For example, the center of a forest is shaded by trees and has less wind and light than the forest edge, which is unprotected. Many forest-adapted species therefore shy away from forest edges and prefer forest centers. For this reason, circular parks are generally preferable to oblong parks, because the amount of edge is minimized (Figure 47.10d).

The Single-Species Approach Focuses Conservation Efforts on Particular Types of Species

The single-species approach to conservation focuses on saving species that are deemed particularly important. As with habitat conservation, there are different approaches to identifying which species to focus effort on.

Indicator Species   Some conservation biologists have suggested that certain organisms can be used as **indicator species,** those species whose status provides information on the overall health of an ecosystem. For example, corals are good indicators of marine processes such as siltation—the accumulation of sediments transported by water. Because siltation reduces the availability of light, the abundance of many marine organisms decreases in such situations, with corals among the first to display a decline in health. Coral bleaching is also an indicator of climate change (refer back to Figure 43.6). Polar bears (*Ursus maritimus*) are thought to be a mammalian indicator species of global climate change (Figure 47.12a). Most scientists are in agreement that global warming is causing the ice in the Arctic to melt earlier in the spring than in the past. Because polar bears rely on the ice to hunt for seals, the earlier breakup of the ice is leaving the bears less time to feed and build the fat that enables them to sustain themselves and their young. A U.S. Geological Survey study concluded that future reduction of arctic ice could result in a loss of two-thirds of the world's polar bear population within 50 years. In May 2008, the polar bear was listed as a threatened species under the U.S. Endangered Species Act (ESA).

Umbrella Species   **Umbrella species** are those whose habitat requirements are so large that protecting them would protect many other species existing in the same habitat. The Northern spotted owl (*Strix occidentalis*) of the Pacific Northwest is considered to be an important umbrella species (Figure 47.12b). A pair of birds needs at least 800 hectares of old-growth forest for survival and reproduction, so maintaining healthy owl populations is thought to help ensure survival of many other forest-dwelling species. In the southeast area of the U.S., the red-cockaded woodpecker (*Picoides borealis*) is often seen as the equivalent of the spotted owl because it requires large tracts of old-growth long-leaf pine (*Pinus palustris*), including old diseased trees in which it can excavate its nests.

Flagship Species   In the past, conservation resources were often allocated to a **flagship species,** a single large or instantly recognizable species. Such species were typically chosen because they were attractive and thus more readily engendered support from the public for their conservation. The concept of the flagship species, typically a charismatic vertebrate such as the American buffalo (*Bison bison*), has often been used to raise awareness for conservation in general. The giant panda (*Ailuropoda melanoleuca*) is the World Wildlife Fund's emblem for endangered species, and the Florida panther (*Puma concolor*) has become a symbol of the state's conservation campaign (Figure 47.12c).

Keystone Species   A different conservation strategy focuses on **keystone species,** species within a community that have a role out of proportion to their abundance or biomass. The beaver, a relatively small animal, can completely alter the composition of a community by building a dam and flooding an entire river valley (Figure 47.12d). The resultant lake may become a home to fish species, wildfowl, and aquatic vegetation. A decline in the number of

(a) Indicator species: Polar bear

(b) Umbrella species: Northern spotted owl

Figure 47.12 Indicator, umbrella, flagship, and keystone species. **(a)** Polar bears have been called an indicator species of global climate change. **(b)** The Northern spotted owl is considered an umbrella species for the old-growth forest in the Pacific Northwest. **(c)** The Florida panther has become a flagship species for Florida. **(d)** The American beaver, a keystone species, creates large dams across streams, and the resultant lakes provide habitats for a great diversity of species.

(c) Flagship species: Florida panther

(d) Keystone species: American beaver

beavers could have serious ramifications for the remaining community members, promoting fish die-offs, waterfowl loss, and the death of vegetation adapted to waterlogged soil.

American ecologist John Terborgh considers tropical palm nuts and figs to be keystone plant species because they produce fruit during otherwise fruitless times of the year and are thus critical resources for tropical forest fruit-eating animals, including primates, rodents, and many birds. Together, these fruit eaters account for as much as three-quarters of the tropical forest animal biomass. Without the fruit trees, wholesale extinction of these animals could occur.

Restoration Ecology Attempts to Rehabilitate Degraded Ecosystems and Populations

Another approach to conservation is to rehabilitate previously degraded habitat. **Restoration ecology** is the full or partial repair or replacement of biological habitats and/or their populations that have been degraded or destroyed. It can focus on restoring or rehabilitating a habitat, or it can involve returning species to the wild following captive breeding.

Habitat Restoration The three basic approaches to habitat restoration are complete restoration, rehabilitation, and ecosystem replacement. In complete restoration, conservationists attempt to return a habitat to its composition and condition prior to the disturbance. Under the leadership of American ecologist Aldo

Leopold, the University of Wisconsin pioneered the restoration of prairie habitats as early as 1935, converting agricultural land back to species-rich prairies (Figure 47.13a).

The second approach aims to return the habitat to something similar to, but a little less than, full restoration, a goal called rehabilitation. In Florida, phosphate mining involves removing a layer of topsoil or "overburden," mining the phosphate-rich layers, returning the overburden, and replanting the area. Often, exotic species such as cogongrass (*Imperata cylindrica*), an invasive Southeast Asian species, invade these disturbed areas, and the intent of the restoration is merely to revegetate the area (Figure 47.13b).

The third approach, termed replacement, makes no attempt to restore what was originally present but instead replaces the original ecosystem with a different one. Ecosystem replacement is particularly useful for land that has been significantly damaged by past activities. It would be nearly impossible to re-create the original landscape of an area that was mined for stone or gravel. In these situations, however, wetlands or lakes may be created in the open pits (Figure 47.13c).

Reintroductions and Captive Breeding Reintroducing species to areas where they previously existed is a valuable conservation strategy. Reintroductions reestablish populations into areas where they once occurred and may increase genetic diversity and reduce the effects of inbreeding (see Figure 47.6 and Chapter 44

Biology Principle

Biology Affects Our Society

Restoration of human-degraded habitats can lead to recovery of habitat and increased biodiversity.

(a) Complete restoration

(b) Rehabilitation

(c) Ecosystem replacement

Figure 47.13 Habitat restoration. (a) The University of Wisconsin pioneered the practice of complete restoration of agricultural land to native prairies. **(b)** In Florida, complete restoration after phosphate mining is not usually possible. After topsoil is replaced, exotic species such as cogongrass often invade, resulting in habitat rehabilitation rather than complete restoration. **(c)** These old open-pit mines in Middlesex, England, have been converted to valuable freshwater habitats, replacing the wooded ecosystem that was originally present.

opening photograph). Captive breeding, the propagation of animals and plants outside their natural habitat to produce stock for subsequent release into the wild, has proved valuable in reestablishing breeding populations following extinction or near extinction. Zoos, aquariums, and botanical gardens often play a key role in captive breeding, propagating species that are highly threatened in the wild.

Several classic programs illustrate the value of reintroduction and captive breeding. The peregrine falcon (*Falco peregrinus*) became extinct in nearly all of the eastern U.S. by the mid-1940s, a decline that was linked to the effects of DDT (refer back to Figure 46.6). In 1970, American biologist Tom Cade gathered falcons from other parts of the country to start a captive breeding program at Cornell University. Since then, the program has released thousands of birds into the wild, and in 1999, the peregrine falcon was removed from the list of endangered species. A captive breeding program is helping save the California condor (*Gymnogyps californicus*) from extinction. At a cost of $35 million, this is the most expensive species conservation project ever undertaken in the U.S. In the 1980s, there were only 22 known condors, some in captivity and some in the wild. Scientists made the decision to capture the remaining wild birds in order to protect and breed them (**Figure 47.14a**). By 2011, the captive population numbered 203 individuals,

and 181 birds were living in the coastal mountains of California; northern Baja California, Mexico; the Grand Canyon area of Arizona; and Zion National Park, Utah (**Figure 47.14b**). A milestone was reached in 2003, when a pair of captive-reared California condors bred in the wild.

Because the number of individuals in any captive breeding program is initially small, care must be exercised to avoid inbreeding. Matings are usually carefully arranged to maximize resultant genetic variation in offspring. The use of genetic engineering to

(a) A condor chick being fed using a puppet

(b) A released captive-bred condor

Figure 47.14 Captive breeding programs. The California condor (*Gymnogyps californicus*), the largest bird in the U.S., with a wingspan of nearly 3 m, has been bred in captivity in California. **(a)** A researcher at the San Diego Wild Animal Park feeds a chick with a puppet so that the birds will not become habituated to the presence of humans. **(b)** This captive-bred condor soars over the Grand Canyon. Note the tag on the underside of its wing.

clone endangered species is a new area that may eventually help bolster populations of captive-bred species.

Can Cloning Save Endangered Species?

In 1997, geneticist Ian Wilmut and colleagues at Scotland's Roslin Institute announced to the world that they had cloned a now-famous sheep, Dolly, from mammary cells of an adult ewe (refer back to Figure 16.14). Since then, interest has arisen among conservation biologists about whether the same technology might be used to save species on the verge of extinction. Scientists were encouraged that in January 2001, an Iowa farm cow called Bessie gave birth to a cloned Asian gaur (*Bos gaurus*), an endangered species. The gaur, an oxlike animal native to the jungles of India and Burma, was cloned from a single skin cell taken from a dead animal. To clone the gaur, scientists removed the nucleus from a cow's egg and replaced it with a nucleus from the gaur's cell. The treated egg was then placed into the cow's womb. Unfortunately, the gaur died from dysentery 2 days after birth, although scientists believe this was unrelated to the cloning procedure. In 2003, another type of endangered wild cattle, the Javan banteng (*Bos javanicus*), was successfully cloned (**Figure 47.15**). In 2005, clones of the African wildcat (*Felis libyca*) successfully produced wildcat kittens. This is the first time that clones of a wild species have bred. In 2009 a cloned Pyrenean ibex (*Capra pyrenaica*) was born but lived only 7 minutes due to physical defects in the lungs. The last wild Pyrenean ibex had died in Spain in 2000. Other candidates for cloning include the Sumatran tiger (*Panthera tigris*) and the giant panda. Brazil plans to clone eight of its endangered species. Cloning extinct animals such as the woolly mammoth (*Mammuthus primigenius*) or Tasmanian tiger (*Thylacinus cynocephalus*) would be more difficult due to a lack of preserved DNA.

Despite the promise of cloning, a number of issues remain unresolved:

1. Scientists would have to develop an intimate knowledge of different species' reproductive cycles. For sheep and cows, this was routine, based on the vast experience in breeding these species, but eggs of different species, even if they could be harvested, often require different nutritive media in laboratory cultures.

2. Because it is desirable to leave natural mothers available for breeding, scientists will have to identify surrogate females of similar but more common species that can carry the fetus to term.

3. Some argue that cloning does not address the root causes of species loss, such as habitat fragmentation or poaching, and that resources would be better spent elsewhere, for example, in preserving the remaining habitat of endangered species.

4. Cloning might not be able to increase the genetic variability of the population. However, if it were possible to use cells from deceased animals, for example from their skin, these clones could theoretically reintroduce lost genes back into the population.

Many biologists believe that while cloning may have a role in conservation, it is only part of the solution and that we need

Biology Principle

The Genetic Material Provides a Blueprint for Reproduction

Genetic cloning utilizes a somatic cell, which contains the complete DNA or genetic blueprint of the animal that is to be cloned.

Figure 47.15   **Cloning an endangered species.** In 2004, this 8-month-old cloned Javan banteng (*Bos javanicus*) made its public debut at the San Diego Zoo.

BioConnections: *Livestock and even pets have been cloned as well as endangered species (refer back to Figure 16.14 and the chapter-opening photograph of Chapter 16). What are some of the arguments in favor and against genetic cloning of species?*

to address what made the species go extinct before attempting to restore it.

Conservation is clearly a matter of great importance, and a failure to value and protect our natural resources adequately could be a grave mistake. Some authors, most recently the American ecologist and geographer Jared Diamond, have investigated why many societies of the past—including Angkor Wat, Easter Island, and the Mayans—collapsed or vanished, leaving behind monumental ruins. Diamond has concluded that the collapse of these societies occurred partly because people inadvertently destroyed the ecological resources on which their societies depended. Modern nations such as Rwanda face similar issues. The country's population density is the highest in Africa, and it has a limited amount of land that can be used for growing crops. By the late 1980s, the need to feed a growing population led to the wholesale clearing of Rwanda's forests and wetlands, with the result that little additional land was available to farm. Increased population pressure, along with food shortages fueled by environmental scarcity, were likely contributing factors in igniting the genocide of 1994.

As we hope you have seen throughout this textbook, an understanding of biology is vital to comprehending and helping to solve many of society's problems. Biological disciplines have a huge potential for improving people's lives and society at large. These disciplines offer the opportunity to unlock new diagnoses and treatments for diseases, to improve nutrition and food production, and to maintain biological diversity.

47.4 Reviewing the Concepts

- Habitat conservation strategies commonly target megadiversity countries, countries with the largest number of species; biodiversity hot spots, areas with the largest number of endemic species, those unique to the area; and representative habitats, areas that represent the major habitats (Figures 47.8, 47.9).
- Conservation biologists employ many strategies in protecting biodiversity. Principles of the equilibrium model of island biogeography and landscape ecology are used in the theory and practice of park preserve design (Figures 47.10, 47.11).
- The single-species approach focuses conservation efforts on indicator species, umbrella species, flagship species, and keystone species (Figure 47.12).
- Restoration ecology seeks to repair or replace populations and their habitats. Three basic approaches to habitat restoration are complete restoration, rehabilitation, and ecosystem replacement (Figure 47.13).
- Captive breeding is the propagation of animals outside their natural habitat and reintroducing them to the wild. Cloning of endangered species has been accomplished on a very small scale and despite its limitations may have a role in conservation biology (Figures 47.14, 47.15).

47.4 Testing Your Knowledge

1. According to the equilibrium model of island biogeography, which type of park would contain most species?
   a. one large park
   b. several small parks of combined area equal to a large park
   c. several small parks connected by a movement corridor
   d. a circular park
   e. all of the above

2. Over time, dark forms of the peppered moth (*Biston betularia*) became more common in polluted environments because predators were less able to detect them on trees darkened by soot. These moths are regarded by many as
   a. keystone species.
   b. indicator species.
   c. umbrella species.
   d. flagship species.
   e. endangered species.

3. After being used for mining, what was once a deciduous forest is replaced by grassland to be used for public recreation. This process is known as
   a. complete restoration.
   b. rehabilitation.
   c. ecosystem replacement.
   d. bioremediation.
   e. habitat repair.

Assess and Discuss

Test Yourself

1. Which of the following statements best describes an endangered species?
   a. a species that is likely to become extinct in a portion of its range
   b. a species that has disappeared in a particular community but is present in other natural environments
   c. a species that is extinct
   d. a species that is in danger of becoming extinct throughout all or a significant portion of its range
   e. both b and d

2. Biological diversity is important and should be preserved because
   a. food, medicines, and industrial products are all benefits of biodiversity.
   b. ecosystems provide valuable services to us in many ways.
   c. many species can be used as valuable research tools.
   d. we have an ethical responsibility to protect our environment.
   e. all of the above are correct.

3. The research conducted by Tilman and colleagues demonstrated that
   a. as diversity increases, productivity increases.
   b. as diversity decreases, productivity increases.
   c. areas with higher diversity demonstrate less efficient use of nutrients.
   d. species-richness increases lead to an increase in invasive species.
   e. increased diversity results in increased susceptibility to disease.

4. The extinctions and reductions in population size caused by invasive species that were noted in this chapter have been caused by
   a. predation of native species.
   b. parasitism of native species.
   c. competition with native species.
   d. a and b.
   e. b and c.

5. What is the effective population size of an island population of parrots of 30 males and 30 females, in which only 10 of the males breed?
   a. 10   c. 30   e. 47
   b. 20   d. 40

6. Saving endangered habitats, such as the Argentine pampas, focuses on
   a. saving genetic diversity.
   b. saving keystone species.
   c. conservation in a megadiversity country.
   d. preserving an area rich in endemic species.
   e. preservation of a representative habitat.

7. Geographic hotspots are those areas rich in
   a. species.
   b. habitats.
   c. rare species.
   d. biodiversity.
   e. endemic species.

8. A canine distemper pathogen that decimates a population of black-footed ferrets is known as a(n)
   a. keystone species.
   b. endemic species.
   c. indicator species.
   d. umbrella species.
   e. flagship species.

9. Small strips of land that connect and allow organisms to move between small patches of natural habitat are called
   a. biological conduits.
   b. edge effects.
   c. movement corridors.
   d. migration pathways.
   e. landscape breaks.

10. The American buffalo, *Bison bison*, is considered a
    a. keystone species.
    b. flagship species.
    c. umbrella species.
    d. indicator species.
    e. extinct species.

Conceptual Questions

1. Why do managers go to the expense of keeping breed registries (lists of animals of a specific breed whose parents are known) and moving males and females between zoos to produce offspring?

2. Which types of species are most vulnerable to extinction?

3. **PRINCIPLES**   A principle of biology is that *biology affects our society*. What is the value of increased biodiversity for human society?

Collaborative Questions

1. Discuss several causes of species extinction.

2. You are called upon to design a park to maximize biodiversity in a tropical country. What are your recommendations?

Online Resource

www.brookerprinciples.com

Stay a step ahead in your studies with animations that bring concepts to life and practice tests to assess your understanding. Your instructor may also recommend the interactive eBook, individualized learning tools, and more.

APPENDIX A

Periodic Table of the Elements

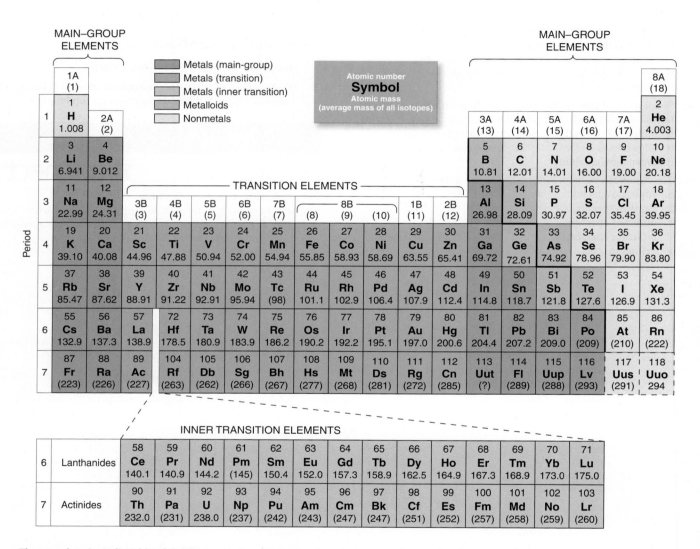

MAIN–GROUP ELEMENTS

MAIN–GROUP ELEMENTS

Metals (main-group)
Metals (transition)
Metals (inner transition)
Metalloids
Nonmetals

Atomic number
Symbol
Atomic mass
(average mass of all isotopes)

Period	1A (1)	2A (2)	3B (3)	4B (4)	5B (5)	6B (6)	7B (7)	8B (8)	8B (9)	8B (10)	1B (11)	2B (12)	3A (13)	4A (14)	5A (15)	6A (16)	7A (17)	8A (18)
1	1 **H** 1.008																	2 **He** 4.003
2	3 **Li** 6.941	4 **Be** 9.012											5 **B** 10.81	6 **C** 12.01	7 **N** 14.01	8 **O** 16.00	9 **F** 19.00	10 **Ne** 20.18
3	11 **Na** 22.99	12 **Mg** 24.31											13 **Al** 26.98	14 **Si** 28.09	15 **P** 30.97	16 **S** 32.07	17 **Cl** 35.45	18 **Ar** 39.95
4	19 **K** 39.10	20 **Ca** 40.08	21 **Sc** 44.96	22 **Ti** 47.88	23 **V** 50.94	24 **Cr** 52.00	25 **Mn** 54.94	26 **Fe** 55.85	27 **Co** 58.93	28 **Ni** 58.69	29 **Cu** 63.55	30 **Zn** 65.41	31 **Ga** 69.72	32 **Ge** 72.61	33 **As** 74.92	34 **Se** 78.96	35 **Br** 79.90	36 **Kr** 83.80
5	37 **Rb** 85.47	38 **Sr** 87.62	39 **Y** 88.91	40 **Zr** 91.22	41 **Nb** 92.91	42 **Mo** 95.94	43 **Tc** (98)	44 **Ru** 101.1	45 **Rh** 102.9	46 **Pd** 106.4	47 **Ag** 107.9	48 **Cd** 112.4	49 **In** 114.8	50 **Sn** 118.7	51 **Sb** 121.8	52 **Te** 127.6	53 **I** 126.9	54 **Xe** 131.3
6	55 **Cs** 132.9	56 **Ba** 137.3	57 **La** 138.9	72 **Hf** 178.5	73 **Ta** 180.9	74 **W** 183.9	75 **Re** 186.2	76 **Os** 190.2	77 **Ir** 192.2	78 **Pt** 195.1	79 **Au** 197.0	80 **Hg** 200.6	81 **Tl** 204.4	82 **Pb** 207.2	83 **Bi** 209.0	84 **Po** (209)	85 **At** (210)	86 **Rn** (222)
7	87 **Fr** (223)	88 **Ra** (226)	89 **Ac** (227)	104 **Rf** (263)	105 **Db** (262)	106 **Sg** (266)	107 **Bh** (267)	108 **Hs** (277)	109 **Mt** (268)	110 **Ds** (281)	111 **Rg** (272)	112 **Cn** (285)	113 **Uut** (?)	114 **Fl** (289)	115 **Uup** (288)	116 **Lv** (293)	117 **Uus** (291)	118 **Uuo** 294

TRANSITION ELEMENTS

INNER TRANSITION ELEMENTS

6	Lanthanides	58 **Ce** 140.1	59 **Pr** 140.9	60 **Nd** 144.2	61 **Pm** (145)	62 **Sm** 150.4	63 **Eu** 152.0	64 **Gd** 157.3	65 **Tb** 158.9	66 **Dy** 162.5	67 **Ho** 164.9	68 **Er** 167.3	69 **Tm** 168.9	70 **Yb** 173.0	71 **Lu** 175.0
7	Actinides	90 **Th** 232.0	91 **Pa** (231)	92 **U** 238.0	93 **Np** (237)	94 **Pu** (242)	95 **Am** (243)	96 **Cm** (247)	97 **Bk** (247)	98 **Cf** (251)	99 **Es** (252)	100 **Fm** (257)	101 **Md** (258)	102 **No** (259)	103 **Lr** (260)

The complete Periodic Table of the Elements. In some cases, the average atomic mass has been rounded to one or two decimal places, and in others only an estimate is given in parentheses due to the short-lived nature or rarity of those elements. The symbols and names of some of the elements between 113–118 are temporary until the chemical characteristics of these elements become better defined. Element 117 is currently not confirmed as a true element, and little is known about element 118.

Answers to In-Chapter and End-of-Chapter Questions

Answers to Collaborative Questions and Crunching the Numbers can be found online.

Chapter 1

Concept Checks

Figure 1.4   It would be at the population level.

Figure 1.5   In monkeys, the tail has been modified to grasp onto things, such as tree branches. In skunks, the tail is modified with a bright stripe; the tail can stick up and act as a warning signal to potential predators. In cattle, the tail has long hairs and is used to swat insects. Many more examples are possible.

Figure 1.6   Natural selection is a process that causes vertical evolution to happen.

Figure 1.8   Taxonomy helps us appreciate the unity and diversity of life. Organisms that are closely related evolutionarily are placed in smaller groups.

Figure 1.9   The pheromone attracts male bees, which aid in pollination.

Figure 1.11   A researcher can compare the results in the experimental group and control group to determine if a single variable is causing a particular outcome in the experimental group.

Figure 1.12   After the *CFTR* gene was identified by discovery-based science, researchers realized that the *CFTR* gene was similar to other genes that encoded proteins that were already known to be transport proteins. This provided an important clue that the *CFTR* gene also encodes a transport protein.

BioConnections

Figure 1.3   This figure is emphasizing that structure determines function.

Figure 1.7   Fungi are more closely related to animals.

Testing Your Knowledge

1.1: 1. c 2. c

1.2: 1. c 2. b

1.3: 1. e 2. e 3. b

Test Yourself

1. d 2. a 3. c 4. c 5. d 6. b 7. d 8. d 9. a 10. b

Conceptual Questions

1. Principles (a) through (f) apply to individuals whereas (g) and (h) apply to populations.

2. The unity among different species occurs because modern species have evolved from a group of related ancestors. Some of the traits in those ancestors are also found in modern species, which thereby unites them. The diversity is due to the variety of environments on the Earth. Each species has evolved to occupy its own unique environment. For every species, many traits are evolutionary adaptations to survival in a specific environment. For this reason, evolution also promotes diversity.

3. The principles are outlined in Figure 1.3. Students can rephrase these principles in their own words.

Chapter 2

Concept Checks

Figure 2.11   The oil would be in the center of the soap micelles.

Figure 2.14   It is 10^{-6} M. Since $[H^+][OH^-]$ always equals 10^{-14} M, if $[H^+] = 10^{-8}$ M (that is, pH 8.0), then $[OH^-]$ must be 10^{-6} M.

BioConnections

Figure 2.14   At a pH of 5.0, the H^+ concentration would be 10^{-5} M, as can be seen from the figure but which can also be calculated by the equation pH = $-\log_{10}[H^+]$. (From this information, you can also determine that the OH^- concentration must be 10^{-9} M, because the product of the H^+ and OH^- concentrations must be equal to 10^{-14} M).

Testing Your Knowledge

2.1: 1. b 2. b

2.2: 1. d 2. c

2.3: 1. a

2.4: 1. b 2. d

2.5.1: 1. b   2. b

Test Yourself

1. b 2. b 3. b 4. d 5. c 6. e 7. b 8. c 9. e 10. b

Conceptual Questions

1. Covalent bonds are bonds in which atoms share electrons. A hydrogen bond is a weak polar covalent bond that forms when a hydrogen atom from one polar molecule becomes electrically attracted to an electronegative atom. A nonpolar covalent bond is one between two atoms of similar electronegativities, such as two carbon atoms. The van der Waal forces are temporary, weak bonds, resulting from random electrical forces generated by the changing distributions of electrons in the outer shells of nearby atoms. The strong attraction between two oppositely charged atoms forms an ionic bond.

2. Within limits, bonds within molecules can rotate and thereby change the shape of a molecule. This is important because it is the shape of a molecule that determines, in part, the ability of that molecule to interact with other molecules. Also, when two molecules do interact through such forces as hydrogen bonds, the shape of one or both molecules may change as a consequence. The change in shape is often part of the mechanism by which signals are sent within and between cells.

3. A good example of emergent properties at the molecular level is that of the formation of sodium chloride (NaCl), a solid white crystalline compound that is very important for living organisms. In their elemental states, sodium is a soft, highly reactive metal and chlorine is a toxic gas. When they combine through ionic bonds, the two elements produce a completely new and harmless substance found in all the world's oceans and soils. Another example described in this chapter is water, a liquid that is vital for all life but which is formed from two gases, hydrogen and oxygen, with very different properties.

Chapter 3

Concept Checks

Figure 3.5   Recall that the reverse of a dehydration reaction is called a hydrolysis reaction, in which a molecule of water is added to the molecule being broken down, resulting in the formation of monomers.

Figure 3.9   The phospholipids would be oriented such that their polar regions dissolved in the water layer and the nonpolar regions dissolved in the oil. Thus, the phospholipids would form a layer at the interface between the water and oil.

Figure 3.12   71; one less than the number of amino acids in the polypeptide.

Figure 3.18   Yes. The opposite strand must be the mirror image of the first strand, because pairs can form only between A and T, and G and C. For instance, if a portion of the first strand is AATGCA, the opposite strand along that region would be TTACGT.

BioConnections

Figure 3.6   Cellulose is believed to be the most abundant organic molecule on earth. In addition to being part of plant cells, it is also found in many other organisms, including many protists.

Feature Investigation Questions

1. Many scientists assumed that protein folding was directed by some cellular factor, meaning some other molecule in the cytoplasm, and therefore, protein folding could not occur spontaneously. Others assumed that protein folding was determined somehow by the ribosome, because this organelle is primarily responsible for synthesizing proteins.

2. Anfinsen was testing the hypothesis that the information necessary for determining the three-dimensional shape of a protein is contained within the protein itself. In other words, the chemical characteristics of the amino acids that make up a protein determines the three-dimensional shape.

3. The urea disrupts hydrogen bonds and ionic interactions that are necessary for protein folding. The mercaptoethanol disrupted the S–S bonds that also form between certain amino acids of the same polypeptide chains. Both substances essentially allow the polypeptide chain to unfold, disrupting the three-dimensional shape. Anfinsen removed the urea and mercaptoethanol from the protein solution by size-exclusion chromatography. After removing the urea and mercaptoethanol, Anfinsen discovered that the protein refolded into its proper three-dimensional shape and became functional again. This was important because the solution contained only the protein and lacked any other cellular material that could possibly assist in protein folding. This demonstrated that the protein could refold into the functional conformation.

Testing Your Knowledge

3.1: 1. b 2. e

3.2: 1. e

3.3: 1. e 2. c

3.4: 1. b 2. a

3.5: 1. b 2. d

3.6: 1. a 2. d

Test Yourself

1. b 2. b 3. e 4. b 5. d 6. b 7. b 8. d 9. b 10. b

Conceptual Questions

1. If the amino acid sequence of a protein is changed, as might occur in a mutation (as you will learn in later chapters), the arrangement of bonds between amino acids may change. This can create local regions of altered tertiary structure, and in some cases can significantly alter the shape of the entire protein.

2. Saturated fatty acids are saturated with hydrogen and have only single (C—C) bonds, whereas unsaturated fatty acids have one or more double (C═C) bonds. The double bonds in unsaturated fatty acids alters their shape, resulting in a kink in the structure. Saturated fatty acids are unkinked and are better able to stack tightly together. Fats containing saturated fatty acids have a higher melting point than those containing mostly unsaturated fatty acids; consequently, saturated fats tend to be solids at room temperatures, and unsaturated fatty acids are usually liquids at room temperature.

3. The structures of macromolecules in all cases determine their function. For example, the structure of a protein determines its three-dimensional shape. This, in turn, allows a protein to interact specifically with certain other molecules. Certain intracellular signaling molecules, for example, have shapes that are determined by the structural arrangement of various protein domains; by themselves, these domains may have no function, but when combined in a precise way they create a functional protein. Likewise, the structure of different lipids determines such functional characteristics as male/female differences, cellular membrane formation, and energy storage. The different structures of polysaccharides determine their usefulness as energy stores, or as components of plant cell walls.

Chapter 4

Concept Checks

Figure 4.1   You would use transmission electron microscopy. The other methods do not have good enough resolution.

Figure 4.3   The primary advantage is that it gives an image of the 3-D surface of a material.

Figure 4.7   Centrioles: Not found in plant cells; their role is not entirely clear, but they are found in the centrosome, which is where microtubules are anchored. Chloroplasts: Not found in animal cells; function in photosynthesis. Cell wall: Not found in animal cells; important in cell shape.

Figure 4.12   Both dynein and microtubules are anchored in place. Using ATP as a source of energy, dynein tugs on microtubules. Because the microtubules are anchored, they bend in response to the force exerted by dynein.

Figure 4.15   The nuclear lamina organizes the nuclear envelope and also helps to organize/anchor the chromosomes. The nuclear matrix is inside the nucleus and helps to organize the chromosomes into chromosome territories.

Figure 4.18   A secreted protein begins its synthesis in the cytosol and then is further synthesized into the ER. It travels via a vesicle to the *cis-*, *medial-*, and *trans-*Golgi and then is secreted when a vesicle fuses with the plasma membrane.

Figure 4.22   It increases the surface area where ATP synthesis takes place, thereby making it possible to increase the amount of ATP synthesis.

Figure 4.25   Bacteria and mitochondria are similar in size; they both have circular chromosomes; they both divide by binary fission; and they both make ATP. Bacterial chromosomes are larger, and they make all of their own cellular proteins. Mitochondria chromosomes are smaller, and they import most of their proteins from the cytosol.

Figure 4.27   The four functions of the ECM in animals are strength, structural support, organization, and cell signaling.

Figure 4.28   The proteins would become more linear, and the fiber would come apart.

Figure 4.29   GAGs are highly negatively charged molecules that tend to attract positively charged ions and water. Their high water content gives GAGs a gel-like character, which makes them difficult to compress.

Figure 4.30   Because the secondary cell wall is usually rigid, it prevents cell growth. If it were made too soon, it might prevent a cell from attaining its proper size.

BioConnections

Figure 4.6   Alternative splicing produces proteins with slightly different structures, because they have certain regions that have different amino acid sequences. The functions of such proteins are often similar, but specialized for the cell type in which they are expressed.

Figure 4.8   The surfaces of cells involved with gas exchange are highly convoluted. This provides a much greater surface area, thereby facilitating the movement of gases across the membrane.

Figure 4.11   The type of movement shown in part (b) occurs during muscle contraction.

Figure 4.13   Cilia carry out a variety of functions, including motility, moving food particles into a feeding groove, and dispersing across moist surfaces.

Figure 4.16   During cell division, the chromosomes condense and form more compact structures.

Figure 4.24   These processes are very similar in that DNA replication occurs and then mitochondria or bacterial cells split in two. They are different in that bacteria have cell walls and septa must form between the two daughter cells, which does not occur when mitochondria divide.

Testing Your Knowledge

4.1: 1. b   2. d

4.2: 1. c   2. d   3. b

4.3: 1. b   2. b   3. e

4:4: 1. a   2. b   3. e

4.5: 1. c   2. d

4.6: 1. d

4.7: 1. e   2. c   3. b

4.8: 1. c   2. b

Test Yourself

1. d   2. d   3. b   4. c   5. e   6. d   7. e   8. e   9. d   10. c

Conceptual Questions

1. There are a lot of possibilities. The interactions between a motor protein (dynein) and cytoskeletal filaments (microtubules) cause a flagellum to bend. Tubulin proteins bind to each other to form microtubules.

2. If the motor is bound to a cargo and the motor can walk along a filament that is fixed in place, this will cause the movement of the cargo when the motor is activated. If the motor is fixed in place and the filament is free to move, this will cause the filament to move when the motor is activated. If both the motor and filament are fixed in place, the activation of the motor will cause the filament to bend.

3. ATP synthesis occurs along the inner mitochondrial membrane. The invaginations of this membrane greatly increase its surface area, thereby allowing for a greater amount of ATP synthesis.

Chapter 5

Concept Checks

Figure 5.3   Probably not. The hydrophobic tails of both leaflets touch each other, so the heavy metal would probably show a single, thick dark line. Osmium tetroxide shows two parallel lines because it labels the polar head groups, which are separated by the hydrophobic interior of the membrane.

Figure 5.4   More double bonds and shorter fatty acyl tails make the membrane more fluid. Changing the cholesterol concentration can also affect fluidity, but that depends on the starting level of cholesterol. If cholesterol was at a level that maximized stability, increasing the cholesterol concentration would probably increase fluidity.

Figure 5.5   The low temperature prevents lateral diffusion of membrane proteins. Therefore, after fusion, all of the mouse proteins would stay on one side of the fused cell, and all of the human proteins would remain on the other.

Figure 5.8   Although both of these molecules penetrate the bilayer fairly quickly, methanol has a polar —OH group and therefore crosses a bilayer more slowly than methane.

Figure 5.11   Water will move from outside to inside, from the hypotonic medium into the hypertonic medium.

Figure 5.13   The purpose of gating is to regulate the function of channels.

Figure 5.21   The function of the protein coat is to promote the formation of a vesicle.

Figure 5.23   Adherens junctions and desmosomes are cell-to-cell junctions, whereas hemidesmosomes and focal adhesions are cell-to-ECM junctions.

Figure 5.25   Tight junctions in your skin prevent harmful things like toxins and viruses from entering your body. They also prevent materials like nutrients from leaking out of your body.

BioConnections

Figure 5.8   Leucine would cross an artificial membrane more easily because it is more hydrophobic than lysine.

Figure 5.9   Gradients of sodium and potassium ions are important for the conduction of action potentials.

Figure 5.20   Plasmodesmata facilitate the movement of nutrients in a cell-to-cell manner. This is called symplastic transport.

Figure 5.25   If tight junctions did not exist, substances in the lumen of your intestine might directly enter your blood. This could be potentially harmful if you consumed something with a toxic molecule in it. Likewise, materials from blood could be lost by diffusing into the lumen of your small intestine.

Feature Investigation Questions

1. Most cells allow movement of water across the cell membrane by passive diffusion. However, it was noted that certain cell types had a much higher rate of water movement, indicating that something different was occurring in these cells.

2. The researchers identified water channels by characterizing proteins that are present in red blood cells and kidney cells but not other types of cells. Red blood cells and kidney cells have a faster rate of water movement across the membrane than other cell types. These cells are more likely to have water channels. By identifying proteins that are found in both of these types of cells but not in other cells, the researchers were identifying possible candidate proteins that function as water channels. In addition, CHIP28 had a structure that resembled other known channel proteins.

3. Agre and his associates experimentally created multiple copies of the gene that produces the CHIP28 protein and then artificially transcribed the genes to produce many mRNAs. The mRNAs were injected into frog oocytes where they could be translated to make the CHIP28 proteins. After altering the frog oocytes by introducing the CHIP28 mRNAs, they compared the rate of water transport in the altered oocytes versus normal frog oocytes. This procedure allowed them to introduce the candidate protein to a cell type that normally does not have the protein present. After artificially introducing the candidate protein into the frog oocytes, the researchers found that the experimental oocytes took up water at a much faster rate in a hypotonic solution as compared to the control oocytes. The results indicated that the presence of the CHIP28 protein did increase water transport into cells.

Testing Your Knowledge

5.1: 1. c   2. c

5.2: 1. c   2. b

5.3: 1. e   2. c

5.4: 1. d   2. b

5.5: 1. c

5.6: 1. c

5.7: 1. e

Test Yourself

1. c   2. c   3. b   4. d   5. c   6. e   7. d   8. e   9. e   10. c

Conceptual Questions

1. See Figure 5.1 for the type of drawing you should have made. The membrane is considered a mosaic of lipid, protein, and carbohydrate molecules. The membrane exhibits properties that resemble a fluid because lipids and proteins can move relative to each other within the membrane.

2. Integral membrane proteins can contain transmembrane segments that cross the membrane, or they may contain lipid anchors. Peripheral

membrane proteins are noncovalently bound to integral membrane proteins or to the polar heads of phospholipids.

3. Lipid bilayers, channels, and transporters cause the plasma membrane to be selectively permeable. This allows a cell to take up needed nutrients from its extracellular environment and to export waste products into the environment.

Chapter 6

Concept Checks

Figure 6.2   The solution of dissolved Na^+ and Cl^- has more entropy. A salt crystal is very ordered, whereas the ions in solution are much more disordered.

Figure 6.4   It speeds up the rate. When the activation energy is lower, it takes less time for reactants to reach a transition state where a chemical reaction can occur. It does not affect the direction of a reaction.

Figure 6.5   The activation energy is lowered during the second step when the substrates undergo induced fit.

Figure 6.6   At a substrate concentration of 0.5 mM, enzyme A would have a higher velocity. Enzyme A would be very near its V_{max}, whereas enzyme B would be well below its V_{max}.

Figure 6.9   The oxidized form is NAD^+.

Figure 6.12   The first phase is named the energy investment phase because some ATP is used up. The second phase is called the cleavage phase because a 6-carbon molecule is broken down into two 3-carbon molecules. The energy liberation phase is so named because NADH and ATP are made.

Figure 6.13   The molecules that donate phosphates are 1,3-bisphosphoglycerate and phosphoenolpyruvate.

Figure 6.16   The net products are 2 CO_2, 3 NADH, 1 $FADH_2$, and 1 ATP.

Figure 6.18   It is called cytochrome oxidase because it removes electrons from (oxidizes) cytochrome *c*. Another possible name would be oxygen reductase because it reduces oxygen.

Figure 6.19   The γ subunit turns clockwise, when viewed from the intermembrane space. The β subunit in the back right is in conformation 3, and the one on the left is in conformation 1.

Figure 6.22   The advantage is that the cell can use the same enzymes to metabolize different kinds of organic molecules. This saves the cell energy because it is costly to make a lot of different enzymes, which are composed of proteins.

BioConnections

Figure 6.12   Glycolytic muscle fibers rely on glycolysis for their ATP needs. Because glycolysis does not require oxygen, such muscle fibers can function without oxygen.

Feature Investigation Questions

1. The researchers attached an actin filament to the γ subunit of ATP synthase. The actin filament was fluorescently labeled so the researchers could determine if the actin filament moved when viewed under the fluorescence microscope.

2. When functioning in the hydrolysis of ATP, the actin filament was seen to rotate. The actin filament was attached to the γ subunit of ATP synthase. The rotational movement of the filament was the result of the rotational movement of the enzyme. In the control experiment, no ATP was added to stimulate enzyme activity. In the absence of ATP, no movement was observed.

3. No, the observation of counterclockwise rotation is the opposite of what would be expected inside the mitochondria. During the experiment, the enzyme was not functioning in ATP synthesis but instead was running backwards and hydrolyzing ATP.

Testing Your Knowledge

6.1: 1. e 2. b

6.2: 1. a 2. a

6.3: 1. e 2. d 3. c

6.4: 1. c 2. d

6.5: 1. a

6.6: 1. e

6.7: 1. e 2. d 3. e

6.8: 1. d

Test Yourself

1. d   2. e   3. b   4. d   5. c   6. a   7. b   8. a   9. d   10. b

Conceptual Questions

1. During feedback inhibition, the product of a metabolic pathway binds to an allosteric site on an enzyme that acts earlier in the pathway. The product inhibits this enzyme, thereby preventing the overaccumulation of the product.

2. The movement of H^+ through the *c* subunits causes the γ subunit to rotate. As it rotates, it sequentially alters the conformation of the subunits, where ATP is made. This causes (1) ADP and P_i to bind with moderate affinity, (2) ADP and P_i to bind very tightly such that ATP is made, and (3) ATP to be released.

3. As discussed in this chapter, the phases of glucose metabolism are regulated in a variety of ways. For example, key enzymes in glycolysis and the citric acid cycle are regulated by the availability of substrates and by feedback inhibition. The electron transport chain is regulated by the ATP/ADP ratio. Such regulation ensures that a cell does not waste energy making ATP when it is in sufficient supply. Also, the production of too much NADH is potentially harmful because at high levels it has the potential to haphazardly donate its electrons to other molecules and promote the formation of free radicals, highly reactive chemicals that damage DNA and cellular proteins.

Chapter 7

Concept Checks

Figure 7.1   Both heterotrophs and autotrophs carry out cellular respiration.

Figure 7.3   The Calvin cycle can occur in the dark as long as there is sufficient CO_2, ATP, and NADPH.

Figure 7.4   Gamma rays have higher energy than radio waves.

Figure 7.5   To drop down to a lower orbital at a lower energy level, an electron could release energy in the form of heat, release energy in the form of light, or transfer energy to another electron by resonance energy transfer.

Figure 7.7   By having different pigment molecules, plants can absorb a wider range of wavelengths of light.

Figure 7.8   ATP and NADPH are made in the stroma. O_2 is made in the thylakoid lumen.

Figure 7.9   Noncyclic electron flow produces equal amounts of ATP and NADPH. However, plants usually need more ATP than NADPH. Cyclic photophosphorylation allows plants to make just ATP, thereby increasing the relative amount of ATP.

Figure 7.11   An electron has its highest amount of energy just after it has been boosted by light in PSI.

Figure 7.12   NADPH reduces organic molecules and makes them more able to form C—C and C—H bonds.

Figure 7.15   The arrangement of cells in C_4 plants makes the level of CO_2 high and the level of O_2 low in the bundle sheath cells.

Figure 7.16   When there is plenty of moisture and it is not too hot, C_3 plants are more efficient. However, under hot and dry conditions, C_4 and

CAM plants have the advantage because they lose less water and avoid photorespiration.

BioConnections

Figure 7.2   Two guard cells make up one stoma.

Figure 7.15   Water is taken up by the roots of plants and moves via the vascular system to the leaves.

Feature Investigation Questions

1. The researchers were attempting to determine the biochemical pathway of the process of carbohydrate synthesis in plants. The researchers wanted to identify different molecules produced in plants over time to determine the steps of the biochemical pathway.

2. The purpose for using ^{14}C was to label the different carbon molecules produced during the biochemical pathway. The researchers could "follow" the carbon molecules from CO_2 that were incorporated into the organic molecules during photosynthesis. The radioactive isotope provided the researchers with a method of labeling the different molecules. The purpose of the experiment was to determine the steps in the biochemical pathway of photosynthesis. By examining samples from different times after the introduction of the labeled carbon source, the researchers would be able to determine which molecules were produced first and, thus, products of the earlier steps of the pathway versus products of later steps of the pathway. The researchers used two-dimensional paper chromatography to separate the different molecules from each other. Afterward, the different molecules were identified by different chemical methods. The text describes the method of comparing two-dimensional paper chromatography results of unknown molecules to known molecules and identifying the unknown with the known molecule it matched.

3. The researchers were able to determine the biochemical process that plants use to incorporate CO_2 into organic molecules. The researchers were able to identify the biochemical steps and the molecules produced at these steps in what is now called the Calvin cycle.

Testing Your Knowledge

7.1: 1. e 2. d 3. e

7.2: 1. b 2. b 3. a

7.3: 1. c 2. d

7.4: 1. b 2. a

7.5: 1. a 2. e

Test Yourself

1. c 2. c 3. c 4. a 5. b 6. b 7. c 8. b 9. e 10. c

Conceptual Questions

1. The two stages of photosynthesis are the light reactions and the Calvin cycle. The key products of the light reactions are ATP, NADPH, and O_2. The key product of the Calvin cycle is carbohydrate. The initial product is G3P, which is used to make sugars and other organic molecules.

2. NADPH is used during the reduction phase of the Calvin cycle. It donates its electrons to 1,3-BPG.

3. At the level of the biosphere, the role of photosynthesis is to incorporate carbon dioxide into organic molecules. These organic molecules can then be broken down, by autotrophs and by heterotrophs, to make ATP. The organic molecules made during photosynthesis are also used as starting materials to synthesize a wide variety of organic molecules and macromolecules that are made by cells.

Chapter 8

Concept Checks

Figure 8.1   It is glucose.

Figure 8.3   Endocrine signals are more likely to exist for a longer period of time. This is necessary because endocrine signals called hormones travel relatively long distances to reach their target cells. Therefore, the hormone must exist long enough to reach its target cells.

Figure 8.4   The effect of a signaling molecule is to cause a cellular response. Most signaling molecules do not enter the cell. Therefore, to exert an effect, they must alter the conformation of a receptor protein, which, in turn, stimulates an intracellular signal transduction pathway that leads to a cellular response.

Figure 8.6   Phosphorylation of a protein via a kinase involves ATP hydrolysis, which is an exergonic reaction. The energy from this reaction usually alters the conformation of the phosphorylated protein, thereby influencing its function. Phosphorylation is used to regulate protein function.

Figure 8.7   The α subunit has to hydrolyze its GTP to GDP and P_i. This changes the conformation of the α subunit so that it can reassociate with the β and γ subunits.

Figure 8.13   The signal transduction pathway begins with the G protein and ends with protein kinase A being activated. The cellular response involves the phosphorylation of target proteins. The phosphorylation of target proteins will change their function in some way, which is how the cell is responding.

Figure 8.14   Depending on the protein involved, phosphorylation can activate or inhibit protein function. Phosphorylation of phosphorylase kinase and glycogen phosphorylase activates their function, whereas it inhibits glycogen synthase.

Figure 8.15   Signal amplification allows a single signaling molecule to affect many proteins within a cell, thereby amplifying a cellular response.

BioConnections

Figure 8.5   Most receptors and enzymes bind their ligands noncovalently and with high specificity. Enzymes, however, convert their ligands (which are reactants) into products, whereas receptors undergo a conformation change after a ligand binds.

Figure 8.10   The GTP-bound form of Ras is active and promotes cell division. To turn the pathway off, Ras hydrolyzes GTP to GDP and P_i. If this cannot occur due to a mutation, the pathway will be continuously on, and uncontrolled cell division will result.

Testing Your Knowledge

8.1: 1. e 2. e 3. b

8.2: 1. c 2. c

8.3: 1. e 2. d

8.4: 1. c

8.5: 1. a 2. d

8.6: 1. b 2. e

Test Yourself

1. d 2. c 3. d 4. e 5. d 6. a 7. a 8. b 9. d 10. e

Conceptual Questions

1. Cells need to respond to a changing environment, and cells need to communicate with each other.

2. In the first stage, a signaling molecule binds to a receptor, causing receptor activation. In the second stage, one type of signal is transduced or converted to a different signal inside the cell. In the third stage, the cell responds in some way to the signal, possibly by altering the activity of enzymes, structural proteins, or transcription factors. When the estrogen receptor is activated, the second stage, signal transduction, is not needed because the estrogen receptor is an intracellular receptor that directly activates the transcription of genes to elicit a cellular response.

3. Cell signaling allows cells to respond to environmental changes. For example, if a yeast cell is exposed to glucose, cell signaling will allow it to adapt to that change and utilize glucose more readily. Likewise, cell signaling allows plants to grow toward light. In addition, cells in a multicellular organism respond to changes in signaling molecules, such as hormones, and thereby coordinate their activities.

Chapter 9

Concept Checks

Figure 9.4   Cytosine is found in both DNA and RNA.

Figure 9.5   A phosphoester bond is a single covalent bond between a phosphorus atom and an oxygen atom. A phosphodiester linkage involves two phosphoester bonds. This linkage occurs along the backbone of DNA and RNA strands.

Figure 9.6   Because it is antiparallel and obeys the AT/GC rule, it would be 3'–CTAAGCAAG–5'.

Figure 9.11   It would be 1/8 half-heavy and 7/8 light.

Figure 9.17   The lagging strand is made discontinuously in the direction opposite to the movement of the replication fork.

Figure 9.21   Proteins hold the bottoms of the loops in place.

Figure 9.22   Proteins that compact the radial loop domains are primarily responsible for the X shape.

BioConnections

Figure 9.1   When a bacterium dies, it may release some of its DNA into the environment. Such DNA can be taken up via transformation by living bacteria, even bacteria of other species. If the DNA that is taken up encodes an antibiotic resistance gene, such a gene may be incorporated into the genome of the living bacterium and make it resistant to an antibiotic.

Figure 9.22   If chromosomes did not become compact, they might get tangled up with others during cell division, which would prevent the even segregation of chromosomes into the two daughter cells.

Feature Investigation Questions

1. Previous studies had indicated that mixing different strains could lead to transformation or the changing of a strain into a different one. Griffith had shown that mixing heat-killed type S with living type R would result in the transformation of the type R to type S. Though mutations could cause the changing of the identity of certain strains, the type R to type S transformation was not due to mutation but was more likely due to the transmission of a biochemical substance between the two strains. Griffith recognized this and referred to the biochemical substance as the "transformation principle." If Avery, MacLeod, and McCarty could determine the biochemical identity of this "transformation principle," they could identify the genetic material of this organism.

2. A DNA extract contains DNA that has been purified from a sample of cells.

3. The researchers could not verify that the DNA extract was completely pure and did not have small amounts of contaminating molecules, such as proteins and RNA. The researchers were able to treat the extract with enzymes to remove proteins (using protease), RNA (using RNase), or DNA (using DNase). Removing the proteins or RNA did not alter the transformation of the type R to type S strains. Only the enzymatic removal of DNA disrupted the transformation, indicating that DNA is the genetic material.

Testing Your Knowledge

9.1: 1. b

9.2: 1. a 2. b 3. c

9.3: 1. c 2. d

9.4: 1. b 2. c

9.5: 1. d 2. c 3. a

9.6: 1. d 2. c

Test Yourself

1. d 2. b 3. d 4. d 5. b 6. c 7. b 8. d 9. d 10. c

Conceptual Questions

1. The genetic material must contain the information necessary to construct an entire organism. The genetic material must be accurately copied and transmitted from parent to offspring and from cell to cell during cell division in multicellular organisms. The genetic material must contain variation that can account for the known variation within each species and among different species. Griffith discovered something called the transformation principle, and his experiments showed the existence of biochemical genetic information. In addition, he showed that this genetic information can move from one individual to another of the same species. In his experiments, Griffith took heat-killed type S bacteria and mixed them with living type R bacteria and injected them into a live mouse, which died after the injection. By themselves, these two strains would not kill the mouse, but when they were put together, the genetic information from the heat-killed type S bacteria was transferred into the living type R bacteria, thus transforming the type R bacteria into type S.

2. In a DNA double helix, the two strands hydrogen-bond with each other according to the AT/GC rule. This provides the basis for DNA replication. In addition, as described in later chapters, hydrogen bonding between complementary bases is the basis for the transcription of RNA, which is needed for gene expression.

3. As discussed in the answer to number 2, the structure of DNA provides a way for it to be replicated. In addition, the sequences of bases within genes store information to make polypeptides with a defined amino acid sequence.

Chapter 10

Concept Checks

Figure 10.1   The usual direction of flow of genetic information is from DNA to RNA to protein, though exceptions occur.

Figure 10.2   If a terminator was removed, transcription would occur beyond the normal stopping point. Eventually, RNA polymerase would encounter a terminator from an adjacent gene, and transcription would end.

Figure 10.6   The ends of structural genes do not have a poly T region that acts as a template for the synthesis of a poly A tail. Instead, the poly A tail is added after the pre-mRNA is made by an enzyme that attaches many adenine nucleotides in a row.

Figure 10.7   A structural gene would still be transcribed into RNA if the start codon was missing. However, it would not be translated properly into a polypeptide.

Figure 10.8   It would bind to a 5'–UGG–3' codon, and it would carry tryptophan.

Figure 10.10   The function of the anticodon in tRNA is to recognize a codon in an mRNA.

Figure 10.13   Each mammal is closely related to the other mammals, and *E. coli* and *Serratia marcescens* are also closely related. The mammals are relatively distantly related to the bacterial species.

Figure 10.14   A region near the 5' end of the mRNA is complementary to a region of rRNA in the small subunit. These complementary regions hydrogen-bond with each other to promote the binding of the mRNA to the small ribosomal subunit.

BioConnections

Figure 10.3   Both DNA and RNA polymerase use DNA strands as a template and connect nucleotides to each other in a 5' to 3' direction based on the complementarity of base pairing. One difference is that DNA polymerase needs a pre-existing strand, such as an RNA primer, to begin DNA replication, whereas RNA polymerase can begin the synthesis of RNA on a bare template strand. Another key difference is that DNA polymerase connects deoxyribonucleotides, whereas RNA polymerase connects ribonucleotides.

Figure 10.11   The attachment of an amino acid to a tRNA is an endergonic reaction. ATP provides the energy to catalyze this reaction.

Feature Investigation Questions

1. A triplet mimics mRNA because it can cause a specific tRNA to bind to the ribosome. This was useful to Nirenberg and Leder because it allowed them to correlate the binding of a tRNA carrying a specific amino acid with a triplet sequence.

2. The researchers were attempting to match codons with appropriate amino acids. By labeling one amino acid in each of the 20 tubes for each codon, the researchers were able to identify the correct relationship by detecting which tube resulted in radioactivity on the filter.

3. The AUG triplet would have shown radioactivity in the methionine test tube. Even though AUG acts as the start codon, it also codes for the amino acid methionine. The other three codons act as stop codons and do not code for an amino acid. In these cases, the researchers would not have found radioactivity trapped on filters.

Testing Your Knowledge

10.1: 1. b 2. d 3. d

10.2: 1. d 2. a

10.3: 1. b 2. d

10.4: 1. d 2. d

10.5: 1. d 2. d 3. c

10.6: 1. d 2. c

Test Yourself

1. b 2. d 3. d 4. b 5. c 6. e 7. d 8. d 9. d 10. b

Conceptual Questions

1. This mutation would not affect transcription. RNA polymerase would still transcribe the gene. However, it would affect translation. A polypeptide would be made that was only 5 amino acids long.

2. Each of these 20 enzymes catalyzes the attachment of a specific amino acid to a specific tRNA molecule.

3. During transcription, a DNA strand is used as a template for the synthesis of RNA. Most genes encode mRNAs, which contain the information to make polypeptides. During translation, an mRNA binds to a ribosome and a polypeptide is made, which becomes a unit within a functional protein.

Chapter 11

Concept Checks

Figure 11.2   Gene regulation causes each cell type to express its own unique set of proteins, which, in turn, are largely responsible for the morphologies and functions of cells.

Figure 11.6   The *lacZ*, *lacY*, and *lacA* genes are under the control of the *lac* promoter.

Figure 11.7   Negative control refers to the action of a repressor protein, which inhibits transcription when it binds to the DNA. Inducible refers to the action of a small effector molecule. When it is present, it promotes transcription.

Figure 11.9   In this case, the repressor keeps the *lac* operon turned off unless lactose is present in the environment. The activator allows the bacterium to choose between glucose and lactose.

Figure 11.10   Both proteins are similar in that they repress transcription. They prevent RNA polymerase from transcribing the operons. They are different with regard to the effects of their small effector molecules. For the lac repressor, the binding of allolactose causes a conformational change that prevents the repressor from binding to its operator site. In contrast, the binding of tryptophan to the trp repressor allows it to bind to its operator site. Another difference is that the lac repressor binds to the DNA sequence found in the *lac* operator site, whereas the trp repressor recognizes a different DNA sequence that is found in the trp operator site.

Figure 11.15   Some histone modifications may alter chromatin structure in a way that promotes transcription, whereas others may inhibit transcription.

Figure 11.18   The advantage of alternative splicing is that it allows a single gene to encode two or more polypeptides. This enables organisms to have smaller genomes, which is more efficient and easier to package into a cell.

Figure 11.20   When iron levels rise in the cell, the iron binds to IRP and removes it from the mRNA that encodes ferritin. This results in the rapid translation of ferritin protein, which can store excess iron. Unfortunately, ferritin storage does have limits, so iron poisoning can occur if too much is ingested.

BioConnections

Figure 11.8   In eukaryotic cells, cAMP acts as a second messenger in signal transduction pathways.

Figure 11.16   A nucleosome is composed of DNA wrapped around an octamer of histone proteins.

Testing Your Knowledge

11.1: 1. d 2. a

11.2: 1. b 2. c

11.3: 1. c 2. e

11.4: 1. d 2. b

11.5: 1. d 2. e 3. a

Test Yourself

1. d 2. b 3. c 4. c 5. c 6. d 7. c 8. c 9. d 10. c

Conceptual Questions

1. In an inducible operon, the presence of a small effector molecule causes transcription to occur. In repressible operons, a small effector molecule inhibits transcription. The effects of these small molecules are mediated through regulatory proteins that bind to the DNA. Repressible operons usually encode anabolic enzymes, and inducible operons encode catabolic enzymes.

2. a. regulatory protein; b. small effector molecule; c. segment of DNA; d. small effector molecule; and e. regulatory protein.

3. Gene regulation offers key advantages such as (1) proteins are made only when they are needed; (2) proteins are made in the correct cell type; and (3) proteins are made at the correct stage of development. These advantages are important for reproduction and sustaining life.

Chapter 12

Concept Checks

Figure 12.1   Only germ-line cells give rise to gametes (sperm or egg cells). A somatic cell cannot give rise to a gamete and therefore cannot be passed to offspring.

Figure 12.2   This is a mutation that occurred in a somatic cell, so it cannot be transmitted to an offspring.

Figure 12.5   A thymine dimer is harmful because it can cause errors in DNA replication.

Figure 12.6   If we divide 44 by 2 million, the rate is 2.2×10^{-5}.

Figure 12.7   UvrC and UvrD are responsible for removing the damaged DNA. UvrC makes cuts on both sides of the damage, and then UvrD removes the damaged region.

Figure 12.9   Growth factors turn on a signaling pathway that ultimately leads to cell division.

Figure 12.12   The type of cancer associated with this fusion is leukemia, which is a cancer of blood cells. The gene fusion produces a chimeric gene that is expressed in blood cells because it has the *bcr* promoter. The abnormal fusion protein promotes cancer in these cells.

Figure 12.13   Checkpoints prevent cell division if a genetic abnormality is detected. This helps to properly maintain the genome, thereby minimizing the possibility that a cell harboring a mutation will divide to produce two daughter cells.

Figure 12.14   Cancer would not occur if both copies of the Rb gene and both copies of the *E2F* gene were rendered inactive due to mutations. An active copy of the *E2F* gene is needed to promote cell division.

BioConnections

Figure 12.9   Drugs that inhibit protein kinases may be used to combat cancer if they target the protein kinases that are overactive in certain forms of cancer.

Feature Investigation Questions

1. Some biologists believed that heritable traits may be altered by physiological events. This suggests that mutations may be stimulated by certain needs of the organism. Others believed that mutations are random. If a mutation had a beneficial effect that improved survival and/or reproductive success, these mutations would be maintained in the population through natural selection.

2. The Lederbergs were testing the hypothesis that mutations are random events. By subjecting the bacteria to some type of environmental stress, the bacteriophage, the researchers would be able to see if the stress induced mutations or if mutations occurred randomly.

3. When looking at the number and location of colonies that were resistant to viral infection, the pattern was consistent among the secondary plates. This indicates that the mutation that allowed the colonies to be resistant to viral infection occurred on the master plate. The secondary plates introduced the selective agent that allowed the resistant bacteria colonies to survive and reproduce while the other colonies were destroyed. Thus, mutations occurred randomly in the absence of any selective agent.

Testing Your Knowledge

12.1: 1. b 2. d

12.2: 1. b 2. d

12.3: 1. e

12.4: 1. d 2. d

Test Yourself

1. c 2. d 3. d 4. e 5. d 6. b 7. a 8. b 9. c 10. d

Conceptual Questions

1. Random mutations are more likely to be harmful than beneficial. The genes within each species have evolved to work properly. They have functional promoters, coding sequences, terminators, and so on, that allow the genes to be expressed. Mutations are more likely to disrupt these sequences. For example, mutations within the coding sequence may produce early stop codons, frameshift mutations, and missense mutations that result in a nonfunctional polypeptide. On rare occasions, however, mutations are beneficial; they may produce a gene that is expressed better than the original gene or produce a polypeptide that functions better.

2. A spontaneous mutation originates within a living cell. It may be due to spontaneous changes in nucleotide structure, errors in DNA replication, or products of normal metabolism that may alter the structure of DNA. The causes of induced mutations originate from outside the cell. They may be physical agents, such as UV light or X-rays, or chemicals that act as mutagens. Both spontaneous and induced mutations may cause a harmful phenotype such as a cancer. In many cases, induced mutations are avoidable if the individual can prevent exposure to the environmental agent that acts as a mutagen.

3. Mutations may alter the expression of a gene and/or alter the function of a protein encoded by a gene. In many cases, such changes are harmful because a gene may not be expressed at the correct level, or the protein may not function as well as the normal (nonmutant) protein.

Chapter 13

Concept Checks

Figure 13.1   Chromosomes are readily seen when they are compacted in a dividing cell. By adding such a drug, you increase the percentage of cells that are actively dividing.

Figure 13.2   Interphase consists of the G_1, S, and G_2 phases of the cell cycle.

Figure 13.4   As shown in the inset, each object is a pair of sister chromatids.

Figure 13.5   The astral microtubules, which extend away from the chromosomes, are important for positioning the spindle apparatus within the cell. The polar microtubules project into the region between the two poles. Polar microtubules that overlap with each other play a role in the separation of the two poles. Kinetochore microtubules are attached to kinetochores at the centromeres and are needed to sort the chromosomes.

Figure 13.7   The mother cell (in G_1 phase) and the daughter cells have the same chromosome composition. They are genetically identical.

Figure 13.8   Cytokinesis in both animal and plant cells separates a mother cell into two daughter cells. In animal cells, cytokinesis involves the formation of a cleavage furrow, which constricts like a drawstring to separate the cells. In plants, the two daughter cells are separated by the formation of a cell plate, which forms a cell wall between the two daughter cells.

Figure 13.11   The mother cell is diploid with two sets of chromosomes, whereas the four resulting cells are haploid with one set of chromosomes.

Figure 13.12   The reason for meiosis in animals is to produce gametes. These gametes combine during fertilization to produce a diploid organism. Following fertilization, the purpose of mitosis is to produce a multicellular organism.

Figure 13.14   Inversions and the translocations shown here do not affect the total amount of genetic material.

BioConnections

Figure 13.3   Checkpoints prevent cancer by checking the integrity of the genome. If abnormalities in DNA structure are detected or if a chromosome is not properly attached to the spindle, the checkpoint will delay cell division until the problem is fixed. If it cannot be fixed, the checkpoint will initiate the process of apoptosis, thereby killing a cell that may harbor mutations. This prevents the proliferation of cells that have the potential to be cancerous.

Testing Your Knowledge

13.1: 1. d 2. b 3. d

13.2: 1. c 2. b 3. d

13.3: 1. a 2. a 3. c

13.4: 1. d 2. e 3. c

Test Yourself

1. b 2. e 3. b 4. e 5. c 6. a 7. c 8. d 9. b 10. c

Conceptual Questions

1. In diploid species, chromosomes are present in pairs, one from each parent, and contain similar gene arrangements. Such chromosomes are homologous. When DNA is replicated, two identical copies are created and are sister chromatids.

2. There are four copies. A karyotype shows homologous chromosomes that come in pairs. Each member of the pair has replicated to form a pair of sister chromatids. Therefore, four copies of each gene are present. See the inset to Figure 13.1.

3. Mitosis is a process that produces two daughter cells with the same genetic material as the original daughter cell. In the case of plants and animals, this allows a fertilized egg to develop into a multicellular organism composed of many genetically identical cells.

Chapter 14

Concept Checks

Figure 14.2 Having blue eyes is a variant (also called a trait). A character is a more general term, which in this case would refer to eye color.

Figure 14.4 In this procedure, stamens are removed from the purple flower to prevent self-fertilization.

Figure 14.5 The reason why offspring of the F_1 generation exhibit only one variant of each character is because one trait is dominant over the other.

Figure 14.6 The ratio of alleles (T to t) is 1:1. The reason why the phenotypic ratio is 3:1 is because T is dominant to t.

Figure 14.7 If the linked hypothesis had been correct, the ratio would have been 3 round, yellow to 1 wrinkled, green.

Figure 14.10 There would be four possible ways of aligning the chromosomes, and eight different types of gametes (*ABC, abc, ABc, abC, Abc, aBC, AbC, aBc*) could be produced.

Figure 14.11 No. If two parents are affected with the disease, they must be homozygous for the mutant allele if it's recessive. Two homozygous parents would have to produce all affected offspring. If they don't, then the inheritance pattern is not recessive.

Figure 14.12 In a dominant pattern of inheritance, all affected offspring have at least one affected parent.

Figure 14.15 No. You need a genetically homogenous population to study the norm of reaction. A wild population of squirrels is not genetically homogenous, so it could not be used.

Figure 14.16 The person would be a female. The presence of the Y chromosome determines maleness in humans.

Figure 14.17 The Barr body is much more compact than the other X chromosome in the cell. This compaction prevents most of the genes on the Barr body from being expressed.

Figure 14.20 Crossing over occurred during oogenesis in the heterozygous female of the F_1 generation to produce the recombinant offspring of the F_2 generation.

Figure 14.22 The gene is located in the chloroplast DNA. In this species, chloroplasts are transmitted from parent to offspring via eggs but not via sperm.

BioConnections

Figure 14.8 Sexual reproduction is the process in which two haploid gametes (for example, sperm and egg) combine with each other to begin the life of a new individual. Each gamete contributes one set of chromosomes. The resulting zygote has chromosomes that occur in pairs (one from each parent). The members of each pair are called homologs of each other; they carry the same types of genes.

Figure 14.9 Alleles segregate from each other during the process of meiosis. Meiosis begins with a diploid mother cell that has pairs of genes, which may be found in different alleles. During meiosis, these pairs of genes separate and end up in different haploid cells. Therefore, each haploid cell has only one copy of each gene. In other words, each haploid cell has only one allele of a given gene.

Figure 14.20 Crossing over occurs during prophase of meiosis I.

Figure 14.21 The evolutionary origin of these organelles is an ancient endosymbiotic relationship. Mitochondria are derived from purple bacteria, and chloroplasts are derived from cyanobacteria.

Feature Investigation Questions

1. Bateson and Punnett were testing the hypothesis that the gene pairs that influence flower color and pollen shape would assort independently of each other. The two traits were expected to show a pattern consistent with Mendel's law of independent assortment.

2. The expected results were a phenotypic ratio of 9:3:3:1. The researchers expected 9/16 of the offspring would have purple flowers and long pollen, 3/16 of the offspring would have purple flowers and round pollen, 3/16 of the offspring would have red flowers and long pollen, and 1/16 of the offspring would have red flowers and round pollen.

3. In this problem, you hypothesize that the genes independently assort, because this allows you to calculate the expected values as shown in the data of Figure 14.19. The calculated chi square value is very high and you would reject the hypothesis that the genes independently assort. As an alternative, you would accept the hypothesis that the genes are linked.

Testing Your Knowledge

14.1: 1. c 2. d

14.2: 1. b 2. b

14.3: 1. b

14.4: 1. b 2. d

14.5: 1. b 2. d

14.6: 1. a 2. c

14.7: 1. c 2. b

14.8: 1. a 2. d

Test Yourself

1. c 2. c. 3. d 4. d 5. d 6. d 7. d 8. c 9. c 10. d

Conceptual Questions

1. Two affected parents having an unaffected offspring would rule out recessive inheritance. If two unaffected parents had an affected offspring, dominant inheritance is ruled out. However, it should be noted that this answer assumes that no new mutations are happening. In rare cases, a new mutation could cause or alter these results. For recessive inheritance, two affected parents could have an unaffected offspring if the offspring had a new mutation that converted the recessive allele to the dominant allele. Similarly for dominant inheritance, two unaffected parents could have an affected offspring if the offspring inherited a new mutation that was dominant. Note: New mutations are expected to be relatively rare.

2. This may happen due to X inactivation. As a matter of bad luck, a female embryo may preferentially inactivate the X chromosome carrying the normal allele in the embryonic cells that will give rise to the eyes. If the X chromosome carrying the allele for color blindness is preferentially expressed, one or both eyes may show color blindness to some degree.

3. The environment is needed so that genes can be expressed. For example, organic molecules and energy are needed for transcription and translation. In addition, environmental factors influence the outcome of traits. For example, sunlight can cause a tanning response, thereby affecting the darkness of the skin.

Chapter 15

Concept Checks

Figure 15.2 Viruses vary with regard to their structure and their genomes. Genome variation is described in Table 15.1.

Figure 15.4 The advantage of the lytic cycle is that the virus can make many copies of itself and proliferate. However, sometimes the growth conditions may not be favorable to make new viruses. The advantage of the lysogenic cycle is that the virus can remain latent until conditions become favorable to make new viruses.

Figure 15.6 There appears to be three nucleoids in the bacterial cell to the far right.

Figure 15.8 The loop domains are held in place by proteins that bind to the DNA at the bases of the loops. The proteins also bind to each other.

Figure 15.9 Bacterial chromosomes and plasmids are similar in that they typically contain circular DNA molecules. However, bacterial chromosomes are usually much longer than plasmids and carry many more genes. Also, bacterial chromosomes tend to be more compacted due to the formation of loop domains and supercoiling.

Figure 15.10   16 hours is the same as 32 doublings. So, 2^{32} = 4,294,967,296. (The actual number would be much less because the cells would deplete the growth media and grow more slowly than the maximal rate.)

Figure 15.13   Yes. The two strains would have mixed together, allowing them to conjugate. Therefore, there would have been colonies on the plates.

Figure 15.14   During conjugation, only one strand of the DNA from an F factor is transferred from the donor to the recipient cell. The single-stranded DNA in both cells is then used as a template to create double-stranded F factor DNA in both cells.

Figure 15.16   Transduction is not a normal part of the phage life cycle. It is a mistake in which a piece of the bacterial chromosome is packaged into a phage coat and is then transferred to another bacterial cell.

BioConnections

Figure 15.3   Viral release occurs as a budding process in which a membrane vesicle is formed that surrounds the capsid. Similarly, exocytosis involves the formation of a membrane vesicle that encloses some type of cargo.

Figure 15.6   A nucleoid is not a membrane-bound organelle. It is simply a region where a bacterial chromosome is found. A cell nucleus in a eukaryotic cell has an envelope with a double membrane.

Figure 15.15   Griffiths was able to show that genetic material was transferred to type R bacteria, which converted them to type S. This occurred via transformation. Later, Avery, MacLeod, and McCarty determined that DNA was the material that was being transferred.

Feature Investigation Questions

1. Lederberg and Tatum were testing the hypothesis that genetic material could be transferred from one bacterial strain to another.

2. The experimental growth medium lacked particular amino acids and biotin. The mutant strains were unable to synthesize these particular amino acids or biotin. Therefore, they were unable to grow due to the lack of the necessary nutrients. The two strains used in the experiment each lacked the ability to make two essential nutrients necessary for growth. The appearance of colonies growing on the experimental growth medium indicated that some bacterial cells had acquired the normal genes for the two mutations they carried. By acquiring these normal genes, the ability to synthesize the essential nutrients was restored.

3. Bernard Davis placed samples of the two bacterial strains in different arms of a U-tube. A filter allowed the free movement of the liquid in which the bacterial cells were suspended, but prevented the actual contact between the bacterial cells. After incubating the strains in this environment, Davis found that genetic transfer did not take place. He concluded that physical contact between cells of the two strains was required for genetic transfer.

Testing Your Knowledge

15.1: 1. d 2. a

15.2: 1. c 2. d 3. e

15.3: 1. b 2. a

Test Yourself

1. c 2. e 3. c 4. b 5. b 6. a 7. d 8. d 9. b 10. c

Conceptual Questions

1. Viruses are similar to living cells in that they contain a genetic material that provides a blueprint to make new viruses. However, viruses are not composed of cells, and by themselves, they do not carry out metabolism, use energy, maintain homeostasis, or even reproduce. A virus or its genetic material must be taken up by a living cell to replicate.

2. Conjugation—The process involves a direct physical contact between two bacterial cells in which a donor cell transfers a strand of DNA to a recipient cell. Transformation—This occurs when a living bacterium takes up genetic information that has been released from a dead bacterium. Transduction—When a virus infects a donor cell, it incorporates a fragment of bacterial chromosomal DNA into a newly made virus particle. The virus then transfers this fragment of DNA to a recipient cell.

3. Horizontal gene transfer is the transfer of genes from another organism without being the offspring of that organism. These acquired genes sometimes increase survival and therefore may have an evolutionary advantage. Such genes may even promote the formation of new species. From a medical perspective, an important example of horizontal gene transfer is when one bacterium acquires antibiotic resistance from another bacterium and then itself becomes resistant to that antibiotic. This phenomenon is making it increasingly difficult to treat a wide variety of bacterial diseases.

Chapter 16

Concept Checks

Figure 16.2   No. A recombinant vector has been made, but it has not been cloned. In other words, many copies of the recombinant vector have not been made yet.

Figure 16.3   The insertion of chromosomal DNA into the vector disrupts the *lacZ* gene, thereby preventing the expression of β-galactosidase. The functionality of *lacZ* can be determined by providing the growth medium with a colorless compound, X-Gal, which is cleaved by β-galactosidase into a blue dye. Bacterial colonies containing recircularized vectors form blue colonies, whereas colonies containing recombinant vectors carrying a segment of chromosomal DNA will be white.

Figure 16.5   The 600-bp piece would be closer to the bottom. Smaller pieces travel faster through the gel.

Figure 16.6   The primers are complementary to sequences at each end of the DNA region to be amplified.

Figure 16.8   If a dideoxynucleotide ddNTP is added to a growing DNA strand, the strand can no longer grow because the 3'—OH group, the site of attachment for the next nucleotide, is missing.

Figure 16.9   A fluorescent spot identifies a cDNA that is complementary to a particular DNA sequence. Because the cDNA was generated from mRNA, this technique identifies a gene that has been transcribed in a particular cell type under a given set of conditions.

Figure 16.10   The reason why the A and B chains are made as fusion proteins is because the A and B chains are rapidly degraded when expressed in bacterial cells by themselves. The fusion proteins, however, are not.

Figure 16.12   Only the T DNA within the Ti plasmid is transferred to a plant cell.

Figure 16.14   Not all of Dolly's DNA came from a mammary cell. Her mitochondrial DNA came from the oocyte donor.

Figure 16.15   Stem cells can divide and they can differentiate into specific cell types.

BioConnections

Figure 16.2   Plasmids are small, circular molecules of DNA that exist independently of the bacterial chromosome. They have their own origin of replication. Many plasmids carry genes that convey some type of selective advantage to the host cell, such as antibiotic resistance.

Figure 16.6   Primers are needed in a PCR experiment because DNA polymerase cannot begin DNA replication on a bare template strand.

Figure 16.16   The RNA is first copied into DNA via reverse transcriptase. The DNA is then integrated into a host-cell chromosome via integrase.

Feature Investigation Questions

1. Gene therapy is the introduction of cloned genes into living cells to correct genetic mutations. The hope is that the cloned genes will correct or restore the normal gene function, thereby eliminating the clinical effects

of the disease. ADA deficiency is a recessive genetic disorder in which an enzyme, adenosine deaminase, is not functional. The absence of this enzyme causes a buildup of deoxyadenosine, which is toxic to lymphocytes. When lymphocytes are destroyed, a person's immune system begins to fail, leading to a severe combined immunodeficiency disease (SCID).

2. The researchers introduced normal copies of the ADA gene into lymphocytes, restoring normal cell metabolism. The researchers isolated lymphocytes from the patient and used a viral vector to introduce the gene into the lymphocytes. These lymphocytes were then reintroduced back into the patient.

3. Following several rounds of treatment with gene therapy, researchers were able to document continued production of the correct enzyme by the lymphocytes over the course of 4 years. However, because the patients were also receiving other forms of treatment, it was not possible to determine if the gene therapy reduced the negative effects of the genetic disease.

Testing Your Knowledge

16.1: 1. d 2. b 3. b
16.2: 1. e 2. c
16.3: 1. c 2. c 3. c 4. d

Test Yourself

1. e 2. d 3. b 4. b 5. b 6. c 7. d 8. c 9. e 10. b

Conceptual Questions

1. The restriction enzyme cuts the plasmid at a specific site, leaving sticky ends. The gene of interest, cut with the same enzyme, has complementary sticky ends that allow hydrogen bonding between the gene of interest and the plasmid. The connections are then made permanent, using DNA ligase that connects the DNA backbones.

2. A ddNTP is missing an oxygen at the 3' position. This prevents the further growth of a DNA strand, thereby causing chain termination.

3. Many people feel that reproductive cloning is morally wrong, particularly when applied to the possibility of cloning humans. Others feel that it has agricultural and research potential and should be pursued. Overall, most people seem to have issues with human cloning, but less issues with the cloning of other animals. Society will have to wrestle with these issues and may need to enact appropriate laws to deal with them.

Chapter 17

Concept Checks

Figure 17.2 One reason is that more complex species tend to have more genes. A second reason is that species vary with regard to the amount of repetitive DNA present in their genome.

Figure 17.7 For DNA transposons, inverted repeats are recognized by transposase, which cleaves the DNA and inserts the transposon into a new location.

Figure 17.8 Retroelements. A single retroelement can be transcribed into multiple copies of RNA, which can be converted to DNA by reverse transcriptase, and inserted into multiple sites in the genome.

Figure 17.9 The two main advantages of having a computer program translate a genetic sequence are that it's faster and probably more accurate.

Figure 17.10 It is possible for orthologs to have exactly the same DNA sequence if neither of them has accumulated any new mutations that would cause their sequences to become different. This is likely only for closely related species that have diverged relatively recently from each other.

BioConnections

Figure 17.4 The family members that are expressed at early stages of development (embryonic and fetal stages) have a higher affinity for oxygen than the adult form. This allows the embryo and fetus to obtain oxygen from its mother's bloodstream.

Feature Investigation Questions

1. The goal of the experiment was to sequence the entire genome of *Haemophilus influenzae*. By conducting this experiment, the researchers would have information about genome size and the types of genes the bacterium has.

2. The shotgun approach of DNA sequencing does not require mapping of the genome prior to sequencing. Instead, many fragments are randomly sequenced. The advantage of the shotgun approach is the speed at which the sequencing can be conducted because the researchers do not have to spend time mapping the genome first. The disadvantage is that because the researchers are sequencing random fragments, some fragments may be sequenced more than necessary.

3. The researchers were successful in sequencing the entire genome of the bacterium. The genome size was determined to be 1,830,137 base pairs, with a predicted 1,743 structural genes. The researchers were also able to predict the function of many of these genes. More importantly, the results were the first complete genomic sequence of a living organism.

Testing Your Knowledge

17.1: 1. e 2. b
17.2: 1. d 2. d
17.3: 1. d 2. c
17.4: 1. b 2. d

Test Yourself

1. a 2. e 3. a 4. c 5. e 6. b 7. b 8. d 9. c 10. c

Conceptual Questions

1. a. yes
   b. No, it's only one chromosome in the nuclear genome.
   c. yes
   d. yes

2. One reason is that more complex eukaryotes usually have more genes in their genome. A second source of variation is that the amount of repetitive sequences can be quite different among various species.

3. The genome contains the information for the production of cellular proteins; it is a blueprint. The production of proteins is largely responsible for determining cellular characteristics, which, in turn, determine an organism's traits and allow it to reproduce.

Chapter 18

Concept Checks

Figure 18.2 Organic molecules form the chemical foundation for the structure and function of living organisms. Modern organisms can synthesize organic molecules. However, to explain how life got started, biologists need to understand how organic molecules were made prior to the existence of living cells.

Figure 18.3 These vents release hot gaseous substances from the interior of the Earth. Organic molecules can form in the temperature gradient between the extremely hot vent water and the cold water that surrounds the vent.

Figure 18.4 A liposome is more similar to real cells, which are surrounded by a membrane that is composed of a phospholipid bilayer.

Figure 18.5 Certain chemicals, such as RNA molecules, have properties that provide advantages and therefore cause them to increase in number relative to other molecules.

Figure 18.6 In a sedimentary rock formation, the layer at the bottom is usually the oldest.

Figure 18.7 For this time frame, you would analyze the relative amounts of the rubidium-87 and strontium-87 isotopes.

Figure 18.13 Most animal species, including fruit flies, fishes, and humans, exhibit bilateral symmetry.

BioConnections

Figure 18.4   Phospholipids are amphipathic molecules; they have a polar end (the head groups) and a nonpolar end (the two fatty acyl tails). Phospholipids form a bilayer such that the heads interact with water, whereas the tails are shielded from the water. This is an energetically favorable structure.

Figure 18.11   First, the process of membrane invagination created the nuclear envelope. Second, endocytosis may have enabled an ancient archaeon to take up a bacterial cell. Over time, bacterial genes were transferred to the nucleus, which gave rise to the eukaryotic nuclear genome. An engulfed bacterial cell eventually became a mitochondrion, and an engulfed cyanobacterial cell became a chloroplast in algae and plants.

Figure 18.16   Two key features are mammary glands and hair. They also have specialized teeth, external ears, and enlarged skulls that harbor highly developed brains. Mammals are typically endothermic.

Testing Your Knowledge

18.1: 1. c 2. c 3. b

18.2: 1. b 2. e

18.3: 1. c 2. a 3. b 4. e

Test Yourself

1. b 2. e 3. b 4. c 5. e 6. a 7. b 8. c 9. b 10. d

Conceptual Questions

1. Nucleotides and amino acids were produced prior to the existence of cells. Nucleotides and amino acids became polymerized to form DNA, RNA, and proteins. Polymers became enclosed in membranes. Polymers enclosed in membranes evolved cellular properties.

2. The relative ages of fossils can be determined by the locations in sedimentary rock formation. Older fossils are found in lower layers. A common way to determine the ages of fossils is via radioisotope dating, which is often conducted using a piece of igneous rock from the vicinity of the fossil. A radioisotope is an unstable isotope of an element that decays spontaneously, releasing radiation at a constant rate. The half-life is the length of time required for a radioisotope to decay to exactly one-half of its initial value. To determine the age of a rock (and that of a nearby fossil), scientists can measure the amount of a given radioisotope as well as the amount of the decay product.

3. Several examples are described in this chapter. In some cases, catastrophic events like volcanic eruptions and glaciers caused mass extinctions, which allowed new species to evolve and flourish. In other cases, changing environmental conditions (for example, changes in temperature and moisture) played key roles. One interesting example is adaptation to terrestrial environments. Plant species evolved seeds that are desiccation resistant, whereas animal species evolved eggs. Mammalian species evolved internal gestation.

Chapter 19

Concept Checks

Figure 19.2   A single organism does not evolve. Populations may evolve from one generation to the next.

Figure 19.5   Due to a changing global climate, the island fox became isolated from the mainland species. Over time, natural selection resulted in adaptations for the population on the island and eventually resulted in a new species with characteristics that are somewhat different from the mainland species.

Figure 19.6   Many answers are possible. One example is the wing of a bird and the wing of a bat.

Figure 19.9   Rhesus and green monkeys = 0, Congo puffer fish and European flounder = 2, and Rhesus monkey and Congo puffer fish = 10. Pairs that are closely related evolutionarily have fewer differences than do pairs that are more distantly related.

Figure 19.11   If C^R is 0.4, then C^W must be 0.6, because the allele frequencies add up to 1.0. The heterozygote ($2pq$) equals 2(0.4)(0.6), which equals 0.48, or 48%.

Figure 19.12   Over the short run, alleles that confer better fitness would be favored and increase in frequency, perhaps enhancing diversity. Over the long run, however, an allele that confers high fitness in the homozygous state may become monomorphic, thereby reducing genetic diversity.

Figure 19.13   Stabilizing selection eliminates alleles that give phenotypes that deviate significantly from the average phenotype. For this reason, it tends to decrease genetic diversity.

Figure 19.15   If malaria was eradicated, there would be no selective advantage for the heterozygote. The H^S allele would eventually be eliminated because the $H^S H^S$ homozygote has a lower fitness. Directional selection would occur.

Figure 19.18   This is likely to be a form of intersexual selection. Such traits are likely to be involved in mate choice.

Figure 19.20   The bottleneck effect decreases genetic diversity. This may eliminate adaptations that promote survival and reproductive success. Therefore, the bottleneck effect makes it more difficult for a population to survive.

Figure 19.22   Migration promotes gene flow, which tends to make the allele frequencies in neighboring populations more similar to each other. It also promotes genetic diversity by introducing new alleles into populations.

BioConnections

Figure 19.2   Both natural selection and chemical selection involve processes in which the relative proportions of something in a population increase compared with something else. In natural selection, it is the relative proportions of individuals with certain traits that increases. In chemical selection, molecules with certain characteristics increase their relative numbers compared with other molecules.

Figure 19.9   When comparing homologous genes or proteins, species that are closely related evolutionarily have more similar sequences than do more distantly related species.

Figure 19.21   There are lots of possibilities. The idea is that you are changing one codon to another codon that specifies the same amino acid. For example, changing a codon from GGA to GGG is likely to be neutral because both codons specify glycine.

Figure 19.23   Inbreeding favors homozygotes. Initially, inbreeding would result in more homozygotes in a population. Over the long run, however, if a homozygote has a lower fitness, inbreeding would accelerate the elimination of the allele from the population.

Feature Investigation Questions

1. The island has a moderate level of isolation but is located near enough to the mainland to have some migrants. The island is an undisturbed habitat, so the researchers would not have to consider the effects of human activity on the study. Finally, the island had an existing population of ground finches that would serve as the study organism over many generations.

2. First, the researchers were able to show that beak depth is a genetic trait that has variation in the population. Second, the depth of the beak is an indicator of the types of seeds the birds can eat. The birds with larger beaks can eat larger and drier seeds; therefore, changes in the types of seeds available could act as a selective force on the bird population. During the study period, annual changes in rainfall occurred, which affected the seed sizes produced by the plants on the island. In the drier year, fewer small seeds were produced, so the birds would have to eat larger, drier seeds.

3. The researchers found that following the drought in 1978, the average beak depth in the finch population increased. This indicated that birds with larger beaks were better able to adapt to the environmental changes due to the drought and produce more offspring. This is direct evidence of the phenomenon of natural selection.

Testing Your Knowledge

19.1: 1. e 2. e
19.2: 1. e 2. b
19.3: 1. e 2. e
19.4: 1. c 2. a 3. a
19.5: 1. b 2. b
19.6: 1. e 2. a

Test Yourself

1. d 2. b 3. b 4. b 5. d 6. d 7. c 8. e 9. b 10. d

Conceptual Questions

1. The process of convergent evolution produces two different species from different lineages that show similar characteristics because they occupy similar environments. An example is the long snout and tongue of both the giant anteater, found in South America, and the echidna, found in Australia. This enables these animals to feed on ants, but the two structures evolved independently. These observations support the idea that evolution results in adaptations to particular environments.

2. The frequency of the disease is a genotype frequency because it represents individuals with the disease. If we let q^2 represent the genotype frequency, then q equals the square root of 0.04, which is 0.2. If $q = 0.2$, then $p = 1 - q$, which is 0.8. The frequency of heterozygous carriers is $2pq$, which is $2(0.8)(0.2) = 0.32$, or 32%.

3. Homologous structures are two or more structures that are similar because they are derived from a common ancestor. An example is the same set of bones that is found in the human arm, turtle arm, bat wing, and whale flipper. The forearms in these species have been modified to perform different functions. This supports the idea that all of these animals evolved from a common ancestor by descent with modification.

Chapter 20

Concept Checks

Figure 20.1   There are a lot of possibilities. Certain grass species look quite similar. Elephant species look very similar. And so on.

Figure 20.3   Temporal isolation is an example of a prezygotic isolating mechanism. Because the species breed at different times of the year, hybrid zygotes are not formed between the two species.

Figure 20.5   Hybrid sterility is a type of postzygotic isolating mechanism. A hybrid forms between the two species, but it is sterile.

Figure 20.10   The insects on different host plants would tend to breed with each other, and natural selection would favor the development of traits that are an advantage for feeding on that host. Over time, the accumulation of genetic changes may lead to reproductive isolation between the populations of insects.

Figure 20.11   If the *Gremlin* gene was underexpressed, less Gremlin protein would be produced. Because Gremlin protein inhibits apoptosis, more cell death would occur, and the result would probably be smaller feet, and maybe they would not be webbed.

Figure 20.12   By comparing the number of *Hox* genes in many different animal species, a general trend is observed that animals with more complex body structures have a greater number of *Hox* genes.

BioConnections

Figure 20.2   Female choice is a prezygotic isolating mechanism.

Figure 20.7   The Hawaiian Islands have many different ecological niches that can be occupied by birds. The first founding bird inhabitants evolved to occupy those niches, thereby evolving into many different species.

Feature Investigation Questions

1. Podos hypothesized that the morphological changes in the beak would also affect the birds' songs. A bird's song is an important component for mate choice. If changes in the beak alter the song of the bird, reproductive ability would be affected. Podos suggested that changes in the beak morphology could thus lead to reproductive isolation among the birds.

2. Podos first caught male birds in the field and collected data on beak size. The birds were banded for identification and released. Later, the banded birds' songs were recorded and analyzed for range of frequencies and trill rates. The results were then compared with similar data from other species of birds to determine if beak size constrained the frequency range and trill rate of the song.

3. The results of the study did indicate that natural selection on beak size due to changes in diet could lead to changes in song. Considering the importance of bird song to mate choice, the changes in the song could also lead to reproductive isolation. The phrase "by-product of adaptation" refers to changes in the phenotype that are not directly acted on by natural selection. In the case of the Galápagos finches, the changes in beak size were directly related to diet; however, as a consequence of that selection, the song pattern was also altered. The change in song pattern was a by-product.

Testing Your Knowledge

20.1: 1. d 2. a
20.2: 1. b 2. b
20.3: 1. a 2. e
20.4: 1. d

Test Yourself

1. b 2. c 3. e 4. d 5. c 6. a 7. b 8. b 9. c 10. b

Conceptual Questions

1. Prezygotic isolating mechanisms prevent the formation of the zygote. An example is mechanical isolation, the incompatibility of genitalia. Postzygotic isolating mechanisms act after the formation of the zygote. An example is inviability of the hybrid that is formed. (Other examples shown in Figure 20.2 would also be correct.) Postzygotic mechanisms are more costly because some energy is spent in the formation of a zygote and its subsequent growth.

2. Allopatric speciation and sympatric speciation are distinguished by the level of geographic isolation. In allopatric species, two groups of the same species become very isolated from each other and then develop into separate species. This typically involves the accumulation of many small genetic changes that leads to adaptations and reproductive isolation. In sympatric speciation, there may not be a physical separation. For example, polyploidy can cause reproductive isolation and result in new species. Also, species may become adapted to local environments and develop into new species.

3. One example involves the *Hox* genes, which control morphological features along the anteroposterior axis in animals. An increase in the number of *Hox* genes during evolution is associated with an increase in body complexity and may have spawned many different animal species.

Chapter 21

Concept Checks

Figure 21.2   A phylum is broader than a family.

Figure 21.3   Yes. They can have many common ancestors, depending on how far back you go in the tree. For example, dogs and cats have a common ancestor that gave rise to mammals, and an older common ancestor that gave rise to vertebrates. The most recent common ancestor is the point at which two species diverged from each other.

Figure 21.4   An order is a smaller taxon that would have a more recent common ancestor.

Figure 21.7   A hinged jaw is the character common to the salmon, lizard, and rabbit, but not to the lamprey.

Figure 21.8   Changing the second G to an A is common to species A, B, and C, but not to species G.

Figure 21.11   Gorillas and humans would be expected to have fewer genetic differences because their common ancestor (named C) is more recent than that of orangutans and gorillas, which is ancestor B.

Figure 21.12   Monophyletic groups are based on the concept that a particular group of species descended from a common ancestor. When horizontal gene transfer occurs, not all of the genes in a species were inherited from the common ancestor, so this muddles the concept of monophyletic groups.

BioConnections

Figure 21.1   The domains Bacteria and Archaea have organisms with prokaryotic cells.

Figure 21.10   There are lots of possibilities. The idea is that you are changing one codon to another codon that specifies the same amino acid. For example, changing a codon from GGA to GGG is likely to be neutral because both codons specify glycine.

Testing Your Knowledge

21.1: 1. c 2. b

21.2: 1. d 2. a 3. b

21.3: 1. b 2. c

21.4: 1. a 2. d

21.5: 1. c

Test Yourself

1. c 2. d 3. e 4. d 5. b 6. d 7. b 8. b 9. c 10. e

Conceptual Questions

1. The scientific name of every species has two parts, which are the genus name and the species epithet. The genus name is always capitalized, but the species name is not. Both names are italicized. An example is *Canis lupus*.

2. If neutral mutations occur at a relatively constant rate, they act as a molecular clock on which to measure evolutionary time. Genetic diversity between species that is due to neutral mutation gives an estimate of the time elapsed since the last common ancestor. A molecular clock can provide a timescale to a phylogenetic tree.

3. Morphological analysis focuses on morphological features of extinct and modern species. Many traits are analyzed to obtain a comprehensive picture of two species' relatedness. Convergent evolution leads to similar traits that arise independently in different species as they adapt to similar environments. Convergent evolution can, therefore, cause errors if a researcher assumes that a particular trait arose only once and that all species having the trait have the same common ancestor.

Chapter 22

Concept Checks

Figure 22.8   SEM images are made using electrons, not visible light.

Figure 22.11   The motion of the stiff filament of a prokaryotic flagellum is more like that of a propeller shaft than the flexible arms of a human swimmer.

Figure 22.13   Endospores allow bacterial cells to survive treatments and environmental conditions that would kill ordinary cells.

Figure 22.24   Gametes of *Plasmodium falciparum* undergo fusion to produce zygotes while in the mosquito host.

Feature Investigation Questions

1. Many bacteria are known to produce organic compounds that function as antibiotics, and are potential food sources for chemoheterotrophic bacteria.

2. Researchers isolated and cultivated bacteria from different types of soils, then grew the cultured bacteria on media that contained one of several common types of antibiotics as the only source of organic food.

3. It was important to know if soil bacteria are a source of antibiotic resistance that can be medically significant.

Testing Your Knowledge

22.1: 1. a 2. e

22.2: 1. d 2. c

22.3: 1. b 2. c

22.4: 1. d 2. a

22.5: 1. a 2. d

22.6: 1. e 2. d

22.7: 1. c 2. a 3. b 4. d

22.8: 1. c 2. a 3. b 4. d

Test Yourself

1. b 2. c 3. d 4. b 5. d

Conceptual Questions

1. Small cell size and simple division processes allow many bacteria to divide much more rapidly than eukaryotes. This helps to explain why food can spoil so quickly and why infections can spread very rapidly within the body. Other factors also influence these rates.

2. Many bacterial cells are capable of motility; bacterial cells that enter a body can be moved via the circulatory systems of animals or the internal transport systems of plants.

3. Endospores that enter the human body or food supplies may germinate, thereby producing progeny that produce toxins.

Chapter 23

Concept Checks

Figure 23.3   Liverworts, mosses, and hornworts grow very close to surfaces such as soil or tree trunks. Raising their sporophytes off the surface helps to disperse spores into air currents.

Figure 23.9   The polyester cutin found in cuticle, sporopollenin on spore walls, and lignin on water-conducting tracheids of vascular tissues are resistant to decay and thus help plants fossilize.

Figure 23.10   During the Carboniferous period (Coal Age), atmospheric oxygen levels reached historic high levels that were able to supply the large needs of giant insects, which obtain oxygen by diffusion.

Figure 23.22   Importantly, ears of modern *Zea mays* do not readily shatter when the fruits are mature, as do those of teosinte. This feature enables human harvesting of the fruits (known as grains).

Testing Your Knowledge

23.1: 1. a 2. c

23.2: 1. d 2. e

23.3: 1. e 2. e

23.4: 1. d 2. b

23.5: 1. d

Feature Investigation Questions

1. The investigators obtained many samples from around the world because they wanted to increase their chances of finding as many species as possible.

2. The researchers grew plants in a greenhouse under consistent environmental conditions because they wanted to reduce the possible effect of environmental variation on the ratio of cannabinoids produced.

3. Although cannabinoids are produced in glandular hairs that cover the plant surface, these compounds are most abundant on leaves near the flowers. Collecting such leaves reduces the chances that compounds might be missed by the analysis.

Test Yourself
1. c 2. e 3. d 4. a 5. c 6. d 7. a 8. d

Conceptual Questions
1. Flowering plants display many co-evolutionary associations with animals; these associations enhance plant pollination and seed dispersal and also benefit the animals. Flowering plants have also taken advantage of wind (and sometimes water) to transport pollen and seeds effectively. These reproductive adaptations have greatly enhanced evolutionary diversification of the flowering plants.

2. Apple, strawberry, and cherry plants coevolved with animals that use the fleshy, sweet portion of the fruits as food and excrete the seeds, thereby dispersing them. Humans have sensory systems similar to those of the target animals and likewise are attracted by the same colors, odors, and tastes.

3. Vascular tissues allow tracheophytes to effectively conduct water from roots to stems and to leaves. Waxy cuticle helps prevent loss of water by evaporation through plant surfaces. Stomata allow plants to achieve gas exchange under moist conditions and help them avoid losing excess water under arid conditions.

Chapter 24

Concept Checks
Figure 24.4 Fungal hyphae growing into a substrate having a much higher solute concentration will tend to lose cell water to the substrate, a process that could inhibit fungal growth. This process explains how salting or drying foods helps to protect them from fungal degradation and thus are common preservation techniques.

Figure 24.6 You might filter the air entering the patient's room and limit the entry of visitors.

Figure 24.13 Modern AM (arbuscular mycorrhizal fungi), also known as Glomeromycota, do not occur separately from photosynthetic hosts, as far as is known.

Figure 24.14 Mycorrhizal fungi provide their plant partners with water and minerals absorbed from a much larger area of soil than plant roots can exploit on their own.

BioConnections
Figure 24.7 The *Saccharomyces cerevisiae* genome is only 12 million base pairs in size, relatively small for a eukaryote.

Figure 24.9 The amanitin toxin, by interfering with the function of RNA polymerase II, inhibits transcription in eukaryotic cells.

Testing Your Knowledge
24.1: 1. d 2. c
24.2: 1. a 2. c
24.3: 1. a 2. b
24.4: 1. e 2. b
24.5: 1. c

Test Yourself
1. c 2. b 3. e 4. a 5. e 6. b 7. a

Conceptual Questions
1. Fungi are like animals in being heterotrophic, having absorptive nutrition, and storing surplus organic compounds in their cells as glycogen. Fungi are like plants in having rigid cell walls and reproducing by means of walled spores that are dispersed by wind, water, or animals.

2. Toxic or hallucinogenic compounds likely help to protect the fungi from organisms that would consume them.

3. Some fungi partner with algae or cyanobacteria to form lichens. Some fungi associate with plant roots to form mycorrhizae. Some fungi grow as endophytes within the bodies of plants. In all cases, the heterotrophic fungi receive photosynthetic products from the autotrophic partner.

Chapter 25

Concept Checks
Figure 25.3 Simple choanoflagellates are single-celled organisms. Only later, when such organisms became colonial and groups of cells acquired specialized functions, as in sponges, can we consider them early animals.

Figure 25.7 The coelom functions as a hydrostatic skeleton, which aids in movement. This feature permitted increased burrowing activity and contributed to the development of a profusion of wormlike body shapes.

Figure 25.9 The main members of the Ecdysozoa are the arthropods (insects, spiders, and crustaceans) and the nematodes.

Figure 25.11 Sponges aren't eaten by other organisms because they produce toxic chemicals and contain needle-like silica spicules that are hard to digest.

Figure 25.12 The dominant life stages are jellyfish: medusa; sea anemone: polyp; Portuguese man-of-war: polyp (in a large floating colony).

Figure 25.15 Having no specialized respiratory or circulatory system, flatworms obtain oxygen by diffusion. A flattened shape ensures no cells are too far from the body surface.

Figure 25.19 (1) A ciliary feeding device, and (2) a respiratory device are the two main functions of the lophophore.

Figure 25.22 Some advantages of segmentation are organ duplication, minimization of body distortion during movement, and specialization of some segments.

Figure 25.24 An annelid is segmented and possesses a true coelom whereas a nematode is unsegmented and has a pseudocoelom. In addition, nematodes molt but annelids do not.

Figure 25.27 All arachnids have a body consisting of two tagmata: a cephalothorax and an abdomen. Insects have three tagmata: a head, thorax, and abdomen.

Figure 25.29 Some key insect adaptations are the development of wings, an exoskeleton that reduced water loss and aided in the colonization of land, and the development of a variety of mouthparts.

Figure 25.32 In embryonic development, deuterostomes have radial cleavage, indeterminate cleavage, and the blastopore becomes the anus. (In protostomes, cleavage is spiral and determinate, and the blastopore becomes the mouth.)

Figure 25.34 Two unique features of an echinoderm are an internal skeleton of calcified plates and a water vascular system.

BioConnections
Figure 25.5 A shared derived character.

Figure 25.21 Mollusks arose in the Cambrian period, 543–490 mya. Three hundred million years later ammonites flourished, yet none are alive today.

Figure 25.30 These organs, called statocysts, are located at the base of the antennules.

Figure 25.33 Notochord

Testing Your Knowledge

25.1: 1. b

25.2: 1. a 2. c 3. c

25.3: 1. d 2. b

25.4: 1. c 2. c

25.5: 1. c 2. c 3. a

25.6: 1. b 2. d 3. a

25.7: 1. c 2. e 3. c

Test Yourself

1. c 2. e 3. d 4. d 5. d 6. d 7. c 8. b 9. c 10. c

Conceptual Questions

1. (1) Absence or existence of different tissue types. (2) Type of body symmetry. (3) Patterns of embryonic development.

2. The five main feeding methods used by animals are (1) suspension feeding, (2) decomposition, (3) herbivory, (4) predation, and (5) parasitism. Suspension feeding is usually used to filter out food particles from the water column. A great many phyla are filter feeders, including sponges, rotifers, lophophorates, some mollusks, and echinoderms and tunicates. Decomposers usually feed on dead material such as animal carcasses or dead leaves. For example, many fly and beetle larvae feed on dead animals, and earthworms consume dead leaves from the surface of the Earth. Earthworms and crabs also sift through soil or mud, eating the substrate and digesting the soil-dwelling bacteria, protists, and dead organic material. Herbivores eat plants or algae and are especially common in the arthropoda. Adult moths and butterflies also consume nectar. Snails are also common plant feeders. Predators feed on other animals, killing their prey, and may be active hunters or sit-and-wait predators. Many scorpions and spiders actively pursue their prey, whereas web-spinning spiders ambush their prey using webs. Parasites also feed on other animals but do not normally kill their hosts. Endoparasites live inside their hosts and include flukes, tapeworms, and nematodes. Ectoparasites live on the outside of their hosts and include ticks and lice.

3. Polyphyletic.

Chapter 26

Concept Checks

Figure 26.1 Vertebrates (but not invertebrates) usually possess a (1) notochord; (2) dorsal hollow nerve cord; (3) pharyngeal slits; (4) postanal tail, exhibited by all chordates; (5) vertebral column; (6) cranium; and (7) endoskeleton of cartilage or bone.

Figure 26.6 Ray-finned fishes (but not sharks) have a (1) bony skeleton; (2) mucus-covered skin; (3) swim bladder; and (4) operculum covering the gills.

Figure 26.7 Both lungfishes and coelocanths are Sarcopterygians, having lobe fins.

Figure 26.9 The advantages to animals that moved onto land included an oxygen-rich environment and a bonanza of food in the form of terrestrial plants and the insects that fed on them.

Figure 26.10 No. Caecilians and some salamanders give birth to live young.

Figure 26.11 Besides the amniotic egg, other critical innovations in amniotes are thoracic breathing; internal fertilization; a thicker, less permeable skin; and more efficient kidneys.

Figure 26.12 Snakes evolved from tetrapod ancestors but subsequently lost their limbs. Some species have tiny vestigial limbs.

Figure 26.15 Adaptations in birds to reduce body weight for flight include a lightweight skull; reduction of organ size; and a reduction of organs outside of breeding season. Also female birds have one ovary and relatively few eggs, and no urinary bladder.

Figure 26.21 Defining features of primates are grasping hands; eyes situated on the front of the head to facilitate binocular vision; a large brain; and digits with flat nails instead of claws.

BioConnections

Figure 26.5 Collagen-secreting cells. Cartilage is not mineralized and is softer and more flexible than bone.

Figure 26.14 Both classes have four-chambered hearts and care for their young.

Figure 26.19 None. The bloodstreams of fetus and mother are brought into close contact in the placenta, but they do not mix.

Figure 26.24 Mitochondrial genes are maternally inherited in humans and most other species.

Feature Investigation Questions

1. The researchers were interested in determining the method in which *Hox* genes controlled limb development.

2. The researchers bred mice that were homozygous for certain mutations in specific *Hox* genes. This allowed the researchers to determine the function of individual genes.

3. The researchers found that homozygous mutants would develop limbs of shorter lengths compared to the wild-type mice. The reduced length was due to the lack of development of particular bones in the limb, specifically, the radius, ulna, and some carpels. These results indicated that simple mutations in a few genes could lead to dramatic changes in limb development.

Testing Your Knowledge

26.1: 1. b 2. e

26.2: 1. c 2. d 3. e

26.3: 1. e 2. d

26.4: 1. c 2. d 3. c 4. e

26.5: 1. c 2. b 3. c

Test Yourself

1. a 2. d 3. a 4. d 5. c 6. d 7. c 8. a 9. c 10. d

Conceptual Questions

1. Both taxa have external limbs that move when the attached muscles contract or relax. The difference is that arthropods have external skeletons with the muscles attached internally, whereas vertebrates have internal skeletons with the muscles attached externally.

2. Endothermy (warm-bloodedness) probably evolved independently in both birds and mammals. If the common ancestor of reptiles and birds were endothermic, the chances are that all reptiles would be endothermic.

3. Possibly. Both birds and reptiles lay amniotic eggs and possess scales, though these only cover the legs in birds. Birds and crocodilians also share a four-chambered heart. Finally, birds share many skeletal similarities with certain dinosaurs.

Chapter 27

Concept Checks

Figure 27.6 As in the case of shoots, the capacity to divide the root into two equal pieces by means of a line drawn from the circular edges through the center would indicate that a root has superficial radial symmetry. In order to determine that an organ has radial symmetry at the cellular level, you would have to compare the microscopic views of randomly chosen, wedge-shaped pieces of cross slices. If the structure of the wedges is similar, the organ has radial symmetry at the microscopic level.

Figure 27.8 Locating stomata on the darker and cooler lower leaf surface helps reduce water loss from the leaf.

Figure 27.12   A twig having five sets of bud scale scars is likely to be approximately 6 years old.

Figure 27.16   Cactus stems are green and photosynthetic, playing the role served by the leaves of most plants.

Figure 27.20   A woody stem builds up a thicker layer of wood than inner bark, in part because older tracheids and vessel element walls are not lost during shedding of bark, which is the case for secondary phloem. In addition, plants typically produce a greater volume of xylem than phloem tissue per year, in part because vessel elements are relatively wide. A large volume of water-conducting tissue helps plants maintain a large amount of internal water.

Figure 27. 23   Lateral roots are produced from internal meristematic tissue because roots do not produce axillary buds like those from which shoot branches develop. Internal production of branch roots helps to prevent them from shearing off as the root tip grows through abrasive soil.

BioConnections

Figure 27.1   The flowering plant life cycle is like that of other plants in that a haploid gametophyte generation alternates with a diploid sporophyte generation, but the size of flowering plant gametophytes is smaller than those of moss and fern.

Figure 27.9   Plant cells often possess a large vacuole, whereas animal cell vacuoles are relatively small.

Figure 27.11   There is no difference in microtubule structure among eukaryotes.

Feature Investigation Questions

1. The advantages of using natural plants include the opportunity to avoid influencing plants with unnatural environmental factors, such as artificial light, and the exposure of all experimental plants to similar growth conditions. In addition, the investigators studied the leaves of some large trees, which would be hard to accommodate in a greenhouse.

2. Pinnately-veined leaves were splinted to prevent their breaking, since they were cut at the single main vein, which has both support and conducting functions.

3. Sack and associates measured leaf water conduction at two or more places on each leaf because the effect of cutting a vein might have affected some portions of leaves more than others.

Testing Your Knowledge

27.1: 1. c 2. a

27.2: 1. a 2. b

27.3: 1. d 2. e

27.4: 1. d 2. c

Test Yourself

1. d 2. b 3. a 4. c 5. a 6. d 7. e 8. b

Conceptual Questions

1. If overall plant architecture were bilaterally symmetrical, plants would be shaped like higher animals, with a distinct front (ventral surface) and back (dorsal surface). By comparison with radially symmetrical organisms, bilaterally symmetrical plants would have reduced ability to deploy branches and leaves in a way that would fill available lighted space and would thus be unable to take optimal photosynthetic advantage of their habitats.

2. If leaves were generally radially symmetrical (shaped like spheres or cylinders), leaves would not have maximal ability to absorb sunlight, and they would not be able to optimally disperse excess heat from their surfaces.

3. Although tall herbaceous plants exist (palms and bamboo are examples), the additional support and water-conducting capacity that are provided by secondary xylem allow woody plants to grow tall.

Chapter 28

Concept Checks

Figure 28.4   Auxin efflux carriers could be located on the upper sides of root cells, thereby allowing auxin to move upward in roots.

Figure 28.6   The triple response of dicot seedlings to internally produced ethylene allows them to protect the delicate apical meristem from damage as the seedling emerges through the soil.

Figure 28.7   The active conformation of phytochrome absorbs far-red light. Such absorption causes the active conformation of phytochrome to change to the inactive conformation and to move out of the nucleus and into the cytosol.

Figure 28.8   The inactive conformation of phytochrome would absorb the red portion of sunlight, thereby converting phytochrome into the active conformation.

Figure 28.9   Exposing plants to brief periods of darkness during the daytime will have no effect on flowering because flowering is determined by night length.

Figure 28.11   Yes, just as shoots exhibit negative gravitropism in upward growth, roots are capable of using negative phototropism to grow downward, because light decreases with depth in the soil.

Figure 28.13   Predators are more likely to be able to find their prey if the latter are concentrated and exposed while feeding on plants. Plants benefit when predation removes herbivores, a process that lessens damage to plants.

Figure 28.15   Similar suites of protective plant hormones, such as jasmonic acid, are used in both types of defenses.

BioConnections

Figure 28.3   The defense hormone/plasma membrane receptor is the plant signaling system most similar to the general diagram shown in Figure 8.4.

Testing Your Knowledge

28.1: 1. a

28.2: 1. d 2. b 3. a 4. c 5. e 6. d

28.3: 1. a 2. c 3. b 4. c

28.4: 1. c

28.5: 1. e

Test Yourself

1. c 2. c 3. a 4. e 5. d 6. c 7. d 8. d

Conceptual Questions

1. Behavior is defined as the responses of living things to a stimulus. Therefore, because plants display many kinds of responses to diverse stimuli, they display behavior.

2. Many kinds of disease-causing bacteria and fungi occur in nature, and these organisms evolve very quickly, producing diverse elicitors. Thus, plants must maintain a stock of resistance genes, each having many alleles.

3. Talking implies a conversation with "listeners" who detect a message and respond to it. Thus, plants that exude volatile compounds that attract enemies of herbivores could be interpreted as "talking" to those enemies. The message is "Hey, you guys, there's food for you over here." In addition, research has revealed that some plants near those under attack respond to volatile compounds by building up defenses. "Talking" to other plants does not enhance the "talker's" fitness. But the ability to "listen" enhances the "listener's" fitness, because it can take preemptive actions to prevent attack.

Chapter 29

Concept Checks

Figure 29.8   Mineral leaching occurs more readily from sandy soils than from clay soils.

Figure 29.10   Soil crusts containing nitrogen-fixing cyanobacteria increase soil fertility, fostering the growth of larger plants that stabilize soils against erosion and provide forage for animals.

Figure 29.16   Your drawing should show that equivalent amounts of water will move into and out of a turgid cell having a water potential of 0, when placed into pure water. When placed in pure water, a plasmolyzed cell having a water potential of -1.0 MPa will gain water. Your drawing should show that more water moves into the cell than out of it. When placed in pure water, a flaccid cell having a water potential of -0.5 MPa will gain water. This is because water moves from a region of higher water potential to a region of lower water potential, and 0 is greater than -0.5. Your drawing should show that more water moves into the flaccid cell than out of it.

Figure 29.22   The evaporation of water has a powerful cooling effect because it disperses heat so effectively. Water has the highest heat of vaporization of any known liquid.

Figure 29.25   In its desert habitat, times of drought and contrasting availability of water sufficient to support the development and photosynthetic function of leaves do not occur at predictable times, as is the case for temperate forests. For this reason, ocotillo leaf abscission is not amenable to the evolution of genetic mechanisms that allow leaf drop to be precisely timed in anticipation of the onset of drought.

BioConnections

Figure 29.19   Tight junctions of intestinal epithelium and Casparian strips of endodermal cells of plant roots both incorporate materials that form a tight seal, preventing movement of materials from one location to another.

Testing Your Knowledge

29.1: 1. e 2. b

29.2: 1. c 2. c

29.3: 1. c 2. d

29.4: 1. d 2. d

29.5: 1. d 2. c 3. d

Test Yourself

1. e 2. a 3. b 4. d 5. a 6. e 7. a 8. c

Conceptual Questions

1. In the case of plant fertilizers, more is not better, because the ion concentration of overfertilized soil may become so high as to draw water from plant cells. In this case, the cells would be bathed in a hypertonic solution and would likely lose water to the solution. If plant cells lose too much water, they will die.

2. Agricultural experts are concerned that adding excess fertilizer to crop fields increases the costs of crop production. Ecologists are concerned that excess fertilizers will wash from crop fields into natural waters and cause harmful overgrowths of cyanobacteria, algae, and aquatic plants. Methods for closely monitoring crop nutrient needs so that only the appropriate amount of fertilizer is applied would help to allay both groups' concerns.

3. When the natural vegetation is removed, transpiration stops, so water is not transported from the ground to the atmosphere, where it may be an important contributor to local rainfall. Extensive removal of plants actually changes local climate in ways that reduce agricultural productivity and human survival.

Chapter 30

Concept Checks

Figure 30.2   Because gametophytes are haploid, they lack the potential for allele variation at each gene locus that is present in diploid sporophytes. Hence, gametophytes are more vulnerable to environmental stresses. By living within the diploid tissues of flowers, flowering plant gametophytes are protected to some extent, and the plant does not lose its gamete-producing life cycle stage.

Figure 30.3   Some flowers lack some of the major flower parts.

Figure 30.4   By clustering its stamens around the pistil, the hibiscus flower increases the chance that a pollinator will both pick up pollen and deliver pollen from another hibiscus flower on the same trip.

Figure 30.6   The absence of showy petals often correlates with wind pollination, because large petals would interfere with the shedding of pollen in the wind.

Figure 30.9   The maximum number of cells in a mature male gametophyte of a flowering plant is three: a tube cell and two sperm cells.

Figure 30.10   Female gametophytes are not photosynthetic and cannot produce their own food. Enclosed within ovules, female gametophytes lack direct access to the outside environment. Carpels contain veins of vascular tissue that bring nutrients from sporophytic tissue to ovules.

Figure 30.13   During their maturation, the cotyledons of eudicot seeds absorb the nutrients originally present in endosperm.

BioConnections

Figure 30.1   The female gametophytes of a flowering plant are produced within ovules that lie within ovaries of flowers. The male gametophytes of flowering plants are produced by pollen grains that originate within the stamen anthers of a flower.

Figure 30.11   The plant pollen tube is analogous in function to a human penis in that both structures accomplish internal fertilization. The plant pollen tube grows long enough to deposit sperm at the micropyle within the body of the female gametophyte, much as an animal penis deposits sperm within the female's body. In both cases, sperm are more likely to survive and accomplish fertilization than if they were deposited outside the female body.

Feature Investigation Questions

1. The large flowers of this lily enabled investigators to more easily mark petals and record the positions of marks over time.

2. Time-lapse video reduced the amount of time investigators would have to spend recording changes in the positions of petal marks.

3. Results obtained by using mathematical models can be compared with actual measurements to assess the accuracy of the models. An accurate mathematical model indicates a relatively full understanding of the physical processes involved. If models are sufficiently accurate, they can be utilized in other situations.

Testing Your Knowledge

30.1: 1. d 2. a

30.2: 1. c

30.3: 1. b

30.4: 1. b

30.5: 1. d

Test Yourself

1. a 2. b 3. d 4. b 5. d 6. e 7. b 8. c 9. c

Conceptual Questions

1. Pollen grains are vulnerable to mechanical damage and microbial attack during the journey through the air from the anthers of a flower to a stigma. Sporopollenin is an extremely tough polymer that helps to

protect pollen cells from these dangers. The function of the beautiful sculptured patterns of sporopollenin on pollen surfaces is unclear.

2. The embryos within seeds are vulnerable to mechanical damage and microbial attack after they are dispersed. Seed coats protect embryos from these dangers and also help to prevent seeds from germinating until conditions are favorable for seedling survival and growth.

3. Flower diversity is an evolutionary response to diverse pollination circumstances. For example, plants such as oak and corn that are wind-pollinated produce flowers having a poorly developed perianth. If such wind-pollinated flowers had large, showy perianths, they would get in the way of pollen dispersal or acquisition. On the other hand, flowers that are pollinated by animals often have diverse shapes and attractive petals of differing colors or fragrances that have coevolved with different types of animal pollinators.

Chapter 31

Concept Checks

Figure 31.6 No. The brain, for example, does not contain muscle tissue (although the blood vessels supplying the brain do contain smooth muscle).

Figure 31.7 Blood, including plasma and blood cells, would leak out of the blood vessel into the interstitial space. The fluid level of the bloodstream would decrease, and that of the interstitial space near the site of the injury would increase. Eventually the blood that entered the interstitial space would be degraded by enzymes, resulting in the characteristic skin appearance of a bruise. If the injury were very severe, the fluid level in the blood could decrease to a point where the various tissues and organs of the body would not receive sufficient nutrients and oxygen to function normally.

Figure 31.8 Surface area is important to any living organism that needs to exchange materials with the environment. A good example of a high surface area/volume ratio is that of most tree leaves. This makes leaves ideally suited for such processes as light absorption (required for photosynthesis) and the exchange of gases and water with the environment.

Figure 31.10 No, not necessarily. Body temperature, for example, is maintained at different set points in birds and mammals. Other vertebrates and most invertebrates do not have temperature set points; their body temperature simply conforms close to that of the environment. As another example, a giraffe has a set point for blood pressure that is higher than that of a human being, because a giraffe's circulatory system must generate enough pressure to pump blood up its long neck to its brain.

Figure 31.12 Humans are endotherms and homeotherms.

BioConnections

Figure 31.6 Note that both the stomach and the intestine depicted in Figures 31.6 and 35.6 contain layers of muscle wrapped around the lumen. Although you will learn later that the stomach and intestine have many different functions, this similarity in anatomy suggests that both of these organs may perform the similar activity of mechanically breaking apart chunks of food, and propelling the contents from one region to another.

Feature Investigation Questions

1. Pavlov studied feedforward regulation of saliva production that occurs in hungry dogs even before they receive food. He hypothesized that the feedforward response could be conditioned to other, nonrelevant stimuli such as sounds, as long as the sounds were presented simultaneously with food.

2. Pavlov remained outside the room where the dog was housed when the conditioning stimulus—a metronome—was started. In addition, the room was carefully sealed to prevent any other stimuli, including smells, sights, and sounds, from interfering with the conditioning response.

3. He measured the amount of saliva secreted by salivary glands in the dog's mouth by collecting the saliva through a tube and funnel, and then recording the number of drops. He discovered that once a dog had become conditioned to hearing the sound of the metronome whenever presented with food, the sound itself was sufficient to stimulate the feedforward response of salivation. This experiment revealed that feedforward processes could be modulated by experience and learning.

Testing Your Knowledge

31.1: 1. b 2. (See following text)

Supports the body and produces locomotion	Musculoskeletal system
Absorbs nutrients into the body	Digestive system
Regulates growth, metabolism, reproduction, mineral balance	Endocrine system
Distributes solutes throughout the body	Circulatory system
Provides a barrier against pathogens entering the body	Integumentary system

31.2: 1. d

31.3: 1. a 2. c

31.4: 1. c 2. e

Test Yourself

1. c 2. c 3. d 4. b 5. c 6. c 7. d 8. b 9. d 10. e

Conceptual Questions

1. Structure and function are related in that the function of a given organ, for example, depends in part on the organ's size, shape, and cellular and tissue arrangement. Clues about a physical structure's function can often be obtained by examining the structure's form. For example, the extensive surface area of a moth's antennae suggests that the antennae are important in detecting the presence of airborne chemicals. Likewise, any structure that contains a large surface area for its volume is likely involved in some aspect of signal detection, cell-to-cell communication, or transport of materials within the animal or between the animal and the environment. Surface area increases by a power of 2, and volume increases by a power of 3 as an object enlarges; this means that in order to greatly increase surface area of a structure such as an antenna, without occupying enormous volumes, specializations must be present (such as folds) to package the structure in a small space.

2. Homeostasis is the ability of animals to maintain a stable internal environment by adjusting physiological processes, despite changes in the external environment. Examples include maintenance of salt and water balance, pH of body fluids, and body temperature. Some animals conform to their external environment to achieve homeostasis, but others regulate their internal environment themselves. Ectotherms depend on the environment to warm themselves, while endotherms generate their own internal heat. Heterotherms have body temperatures that may vary widely; homeotherms maintain a relatively stable body temperature. Body temperature influences most chemical reactions in an animal's body and is therefore closely linked with homeostasis.

3. Maintaining homeostasis requires continual supplies of energy. Animals consume food, and the energy from that food helps sustain activities that maintain variables such as body temperature and pH, and synthesis of complex molecules. Without this energy, it would be difficult or impossible for animals to maintain many important biological processes within a narrow range despite changes in the environment.

Chapter 32

Concept Checks

Figure 32.3 Many reflexes, such as the knee-jerk reflex, cannot be prevented once started. Others, however, can be controlled to an extent. Open your eyes widely and gently touch your eyelashes. A reflex that protects your eye will tend to make you close your eyelid. However, you can overcome this reflex with a bit of difficulty if you need to, for example, when you are putting in contact lenses.

Figure 32.5 Yes, the flow of K^+ down its concentration gradient does create an electrical gradient because K^+ is electrically charged. The net flow of K^+ will stop when the concentration gradient balances the electrical gradient. This occurs at the equilibrium potential.

Figure 32.8 When the K^+ channels open (at 1 msec), the Na^+ channels would still be opened, so the part of the curve that slopes downward would not occur as rapidly, and perhaps the cell would not be able to restore its resting potential.

Figure 32.10   The action potential can move faster down an axon. This is especially important for long axons, such as those that carry signals from the spinal cord to distant muscles.

Figure 32.12   In the absence of such enzymes, neurotransmitters would remain in the synapse for too long, and the postsynaptic cell could become overstimulated. In addition, the ability of the postsynaptic cell to respond to multiple, discrete inputs from the presynaptic cell would be compromised.

Figure 32.20   No, these divisions are present in all vertebrates.

Figure 32.21   The occipital lobe is part of the cerebral cortex, and therefore also part of the cerebrum.

Figure 32.23   Thinking requires energy! Even daydreaming requires energy; imagine how much energy the brain uses when you concentrate for 60 minutes on a difficult exam. In fact, you just expended energy thinking about this question!

BioConnections

Figure 32.6   Water molecules move through membrane channels called aquaporins.

Figure 32.14   Animals are multicellular heterotrophs (cannot make their own food) whose cells lack a cell wall. Most animals have a nervous system, muscles, the ability to move about during at least some phase of their life cycle, and to reproduce sexually.

Feature Investigation Questions

1. Gaser and Schlaug hypothesized that repeated exposure to musical training would increase the size of certain areas of the brain associated with motor, auditory, and visual skills. All three skills are commonly used in reading and performing musical pieces.

2. The researchers used MRI to examine the areas of the brain associated with motor, auditory, and visual skills in three groups of individuals: professional musicians, amateur musicians, and nonmusicians. The researchers found that certain areas of the brain were larger in the professional musicians compared to the other groups, and larger in the amateur musicians compared to the nonmusicians.

3. Schmithorst and Holland found that, when exposed to music, certain regions of the brains of musicians were activated differently compared with the brains of nonmusicians. This study supports the hypothesis that there is a difference in the brains of musicians versus nonmusicians. The experiment conducted by Gaser and Schlaug compared the size of certain regions of the brain among professional musicians, amateur musicians, and nonmusicians. Schmithorst and Holland, however, were also able to detect functional differences between musicians and nonmusicians.

Testing Your Knowledge

32.1: 1. d 2. c

32.2: 1. a 2. e

32.3: 1. d   2. a

32.4: 1. a 2. c

32.5: 1.

nerve net—cnidarian

two ventral nerve cords—*Planaria*

nerve ring and radial nerves—sea star (echinoderm)

segmented brain—*Drosophila*

32.5: 2. c

32.6: 1. c

32.6: 2.

thalamus—filtering incoming sensory information

hypothalamus—controlling body temperature and circadian rhythms

basal nuclei—fine tuning, starting, or inhibiting movement

cerebral cortex—decision making and exercising judgment

pons—controlling breathing/relay between cerebellum and rest of brain

32.7: 1. d 2. b

Test Yourself

1. c 2. d 3. d 4. e 5. b 6. d 7. b 8. a 9. a 10. b

Conceptual Questions

1. In a graded potential, a weak stimulus causes a small change in the membrane potential, whereas a strong stimulus produces a greater change. Graded potentials occur along the dendrites and cell body. If a graded potential reaches the threshold potential at the axon hillock, an action potential results. This is a change in the membrane potential that is of a constant value and is propagated from the axon hillock to the axon terminal.

2. An increase in extracellular Na^+ concentration would slightly depolarize neurons, thereby changing the resting membrane potential. This effect would be minimal, however, because the resting membrane is not very permeable to Na^+. However, the shape of the action potentials in such neurons would be a little steeper, and the peak a little higher, because the electrochemical gradient favoring Na^+ entry into the cell through voltage-gated channels would be greater.

3. The activities of animal nervous systems are replete with examples of new properties emerging from complex interactions. For example, you learned about reflexes in this chapter, which are behaviors that emerge from interactions between individual neurons that form communication circuits between the peripheral and central nervous systems. You also learned about such "higher" properties as conscious thought, which also emerges from the interactions between many individual cells, each of which is in communication with up to hundreds of thousands of other cells. Individually, the cells cannot "think," but networked together in elaborate ways, a person like yourself can think, remember, plan ahead, and interpret your environment.

Chapter 33

Concept Checks

Figure 33.8   This orientation permits animals to detect circular or angular movement of the head in three different planes. The fluid in a canal that is oriented in the same plane as the plane of movement will respond maximally to the movement. For example, the canal that is oriented horizontally would respond greatest to horizontal movements, while the other two canals would not. Overall, by comparing the signals from the three canals, the brain can interpret the motion in three dimensions.

Figure 33.14   Because red-green color blindness is a sex-linked recessive gene, males require only a single defective allele on an X chromosome, whereas females require two defective alleles, one on each X chromosome.

Figure 33.20   The receptor proteins are located in the membranes of microvilli extending from the sensory receptor cells.

BioConnections

Figure 33.1   The term sensory receptor refers to a type of cell that can respond to a particular type of stimulus. The term membrane receptor refers to a protein within a cell membrane that binds a ligand, thereby generating signals that initiate a cellular response.

Figure 33.3   Cilia are cell extensions that contain, in their internal structure, microtubules and motor proteins that cause the cilia to beat, or move, in a coordinated fashion. Stereocilia are membrane projections that are not motile, but instead are deformed by the movements of surrounding fluids.

Figure 33.7   Statoliths are also found in the roots and shoots of plants. They serve as a gravity-detection mechanism that results in roots growing downward, and shoots upward.

Feature Investigation Questions

1. One possibility is that many different types of odor molecules might bind to one or just a few types of receptor proteins, with the brain responding differently depending on the number or distribution of the activated receptors. The second hypothesis is that organisms can make a large number of receptor proteins, each type binding a particular odor molecule or group of odor molecules. According to this hypothesis,

it is the *type* of receptor protein, and not the number or distribution of receptors, that is important for olfactory sensing. The researchers extracted RNA molecules from the olfactory receptor cells of the nasal epithelium. They then used this RNA to identify genes that encoded G-protein-coupled receptor proteins.

2. In their study, they identified at least 100 different genes that encoded different G-protein-coupled receptor proteins that were uniquely expressed in the olfactory sensory cells.

3. The results of the experiment conducted by Buck and Axel support the hypothesis that animals discriminate between different odors based on having a variety of receptor proteins that recognize different odor molecules. Current research suggests that each olfactory receptor cell has a single type of receptor protein that is specific to particular odor molecules. Because most odors are due to multiple chemicals that activate many different types of odor receptor proteins, the brain detects odors based on the combination of the activated receptor proteins. Odor seems to be discriminated by many olfactory receptor proteins, which are in the membrane of separate olfactory receptor cells.

Testing Your Knowledge

33.1: 1. b

33.2: 1. c 2. c

33.3: 1. c

33.4: 1. e 2. c

33.5: 1. c 2. c

33.6: 1. b 2. c

Test Yourself

1. e 2. b 3. a 4. b 5. d 6. b 7. c 8. b 9. d 10. b

Conceptual Questions

1. Sensory transduction—The process by which incoming stimuli are converted into neural signals. An example would be the signals generated in the retina when a photon of light strikes a photoreceptor. Perception—An awareness of the sensations that are experienced. An example would be an awareness of what a particular visual image is.

2. The organ of Corti contains the hair cells and sensory neurons that initiate signaling. The hair cells sit on top of the basilar membrane, and their stereocilia are embedded in the tectorial membrane at the top of the organ of Corti. Pressure waves of different frequencies cause the basilar membrane to vibrate at particular sites. This bends the stereocilia of hair cells back and forth, sending oscillating signals to the sensory neurons. Consequently, the sensory neurons send intermittent action potentials to the CNS via the auditory nerve. Hair cells at the end of the basilar membrane closest to the oval window respond to high-pitched sounds, and lower-pitched sounds trigger hair cell movement farther along the basilar membrane.

3. Of the various senses, the sense of olfaction (smell) is least important for the survival of humans. As diurnal animals, we rely largely on our visual sense. Sounds are a critical way to learn about impending danger, such as a car horn, but also are our major means of communication. Other senses, such as the ability to sense pain, have acutely important functions from time to time. Olfaction, though often a pleasurable sense and at times a protective one (think of the smell of spoiled food), nonetheless provides little survival advantage to us. In fact, many people spend much of their lives with greatly diminished olfactory abilities, whether from chronic allergies or other problems, and are not hindered in any significant way. The story is very different for animals such as nocturnal mammals, which rely very heavily on olfaction to find food, locate mates, and avoid predators.

Chapter 34

Concept Checks

Figure 34.1 In addition to not having a requirement to shed their skeletons periodically, animals with endoskeletons can use their skin as an efficient means of heat transfer (and, to an extent in amphibians, water transfer). In addition, the body surface of such animals is often a highly sensitive sensory organ.

Figure 34.3 If a tendon is torn, its ability to link a muscle to bone is reduced or lost. Therefore, when a muscle such as the one shown in this illustration contracts, it will not be able to move the bone from which the tendon has become dislodged.

Figure 34.11 Na^+ enters the muscle cell because all cells have an electrochemical gradient for Na^+ that favors diffusion of Na^+ from extracellular to intracellular fluid (see Chapter 32). This is because cells have a negative membrane potential and because Na^+ concentrations are higher in the extracellular fluid. The acetylcholine receptor on skeletal muscle cells is also a ligand-gated ion channel; when acetylcholine binds the receptor, it induces a shape change that opens the channel. This allows the entry of Na^+ into the cell.

BioConnections

Figure 34.10 Voltage-gated Ca^{2+} channels exist in the terminals of all axons that communicate by chemical signaling (neurotransmitter release). In those cases, depolarization of the axon terminal opens Ca^{2+} channels, allowing Ca^{2+} to enter the terminal and trigger exocytosis of stored vesicles containing neurotransmitter molecules.

Figure 34.11 Myelin is a lipid-rich membrane sheath that speeds up conduction of action potentials along an axon. Action potentials are regenerated at discrete lengths along the axon wherever the myelin sheath is interrupted by a node of Ranvier. This is known as saltatory conduction.

Testing Your Knowledge

34.1: 1. b 2. b

34.2: 1. e 2. d

34.3: 1. c

34.4: 1. e 2. c

Test Yourself

1. d 2. e 3. d 4. c 5. e 6. d 7. a 8. e 9. c 10. e

Conceptual Questions

1. Exoskeletons are on the outside of an animal's body, and endoskeletons are inside the body. Both function in support and protection, but only exoskeletons protect an animal's outer surface. Exoskeletons must be shed when an animal grows, whereas endoskeletons grow with an animal.

2. a. The cycle begins with the binding of an energized myosin cross-bridge to an actin molecule on a thin filament.

   b. The cross-bridge moves, and the thin filaments slide past the thick filaments.

   c. The ATP binds to myosin, causing the cross-bridge to detach.

   d. The ATP bound to myosin is hydrolyzed by ATPase, re-forming the energized state of myosin.

3. The use of energy released by the hydrolysis of ATP is fundamental to muscle function and locomotion. Recall that ATP must be hydrolyzed during the cross-bridge cycle for skeletal muscle cells to shorten. Energy is also used to maintain calcium ion balance in the sarcoplasmic reticulum and is used in all forms of locomotion. The amount of energy expended by an animal during locomotion reflects how well they are adapted to the environment in which they must move.

Chapter 35

Figure 35.2 Extracellular digestion protects the interior of cells from enzyme activity, and allows for the intake of larger amounts of food that can be slowly digested and absorbed gradually.

Figure 35.8 Active transport requires energy provided by ATP. Thus, absorption of nutrients by this mechanism is an energy-requiring event, and some portion of an animal's regular nutrient consumption is used to provide the energy required to absorb the nutrients.

Figure 35.11   By resynthesizing triglycerides from absorbed fatty acids and monoglycerides, a steep diffusion gradient is maintained for further diffusion of the smaller molecules into the cell.

Figure 35.14   The time required for the vesicles to move to the plasma membrane and fuse with it is much shorter than the time required for new GLUTs to be synthesized by activation of GLUT genes. Thus, the action of insulin on cells is very quick, because the GLUTs are already synthesized.

Figure 35.15   The glycerol and fatty acids used to make glucose are the breakdown products of triglycerides that were stored in adipose tissue during the absorptive period. The amino acids used to make glucose are derived from the breakdown of protein in muscle and other tissue.

BioConnections

Figure 35.8   Transmembrane transport processes are not unique to animals, and one or more types are found in virtually all cells.

Figure 35.14   Exocytosis, a feature characteristic of animal cells, involves the fusion of intracellular vesicles with the plasma membrane, resulting in the release of the vesicle contents into the extracellular fluid. See Figure 5.22 for a general description and Figure 32.12 for a specific example unique to animal cells.

Feature Investigation Questions

1. The surprising observation that some people with gastritis or ulcers have living bacteria (*H. pylori*) in their stomachs, and that administering bacteria-killing compounds provided some relief from the symptoms, led to the hypothesis that *H. pylori* infection is a cause of ulcers in humans.
2. The results did support the hypothesis; however, the results also clearly indicated that not all ulcers are due to *H. pylori* infection.
3. A combined treatment with bismuth and an antibiotic is the most effective treatment. It is apparent, however, that even in individuals with continued *H. pylori* infection, some ulcers will heal on their own. In the absence of bismuth/antibiotic therapy, though, the likelihood of a recurrence of a new ulcer is much greater.

Testing Your Knowledge

35.1: 1. c 2. b
35.2: 1. c
35.3: 1. a 2. b 3. d
35.4: 1. c 2. a
35.5: 1. a 2. b
35.6: 1. d

Test Yourself

1. d 2. c 3. d 4. b 5. c 6. a 7. d 8. c 9. e 10. e

Conceptual Questions

1. Insulin acts on adipose and skeletal muscle cells to facilitate the diffusion of glucose from extracellular fluid into the cell cytosol. This is accomplished by increasing the translocation of glucose-transporter (GLUT) proteins from the cytosol to sites within the plasma membrane of insulin-sensitive cells. Insulin also inhibits glycogenolysis and gluconeogenesis in the liver, which decreases the amount of glucose secreted into the blood by the liver. Insulin is required for glucose transport because like many other polar molecules, glucose cannot move across the lipid bilayer of a plasma membrane by simple diffusion. The inhibitory effects of insulin on liver function help to ensure that liver glycogen stores will be spared for the postabsorptive period.
2. The crop is a dilation of the esophagus, which stores and softens food. The gizzard contains swallowed pebbles that help pulverize food. Both of these functions are adaptations that assist digestion in birds, which do not have teeth and therefore do not chew food. Humans, like many animals, can chew food before swallowing. Sauropod dinosaurs were herbivores that probably contained a gizzard-type stomach in which stones helped to grind coarse vegetation. Such stones would have become smooth after months or even years of rumbling around in the

gizzard. Some of these sauropods are known to have lacked the sort of grinding teeth characteristic of modern mammalian herbivores, and thus a gizzard would have aided in their digestion much as it does in modern birds.

3. An understanding of the principles of nutrition, appetite and metabolism (energy balance) is critical to remedy the staggering incidence of undernutrition and overnutrition (obesity) in the world today. These conditions are associated with many profound diseases, such as immune dysfunction and diabetes mellitus, and thus account for a large percentage of all human illness.

Chapter 36

Concept Checks

Figure 36.1   Open circulatory systems evolved prior to closed systems. However, this does not mean that open systems are in some way "primitive" compared to closed circulatory systems. It is better to think of open systems as being ideally suited to the needs of those animals that have them. Arthropods are an incredibly successful order of animals, with the greatest number of species, and inhabiting virtually every ecological niche on the planet. Clearly, their type of circulatory system has not prevented arthropods from achieving their great success.

Figure 36.6   The aorta and all arteries branching from it carry oxygenated blood.

Figure 36.8   The left and right ventricles pump blood through the semilunar valves into the aorta and the pulmonary trunk, respectively.

Figure 36.9   Body fluids, both extracellular and intracellular, contain large amounts of charged ions, which are capable of conducting electricity. The slight electric currents generated by the beating heart muscle cells are conducted through the surrounding body fluids by the movements of ions in those fluids. This is recorded by the surface electrodes and amplified by the recording machine.

Figure 36.11   No, erythrocytes never leave the blood vessels unless a vessel is cut.

Figure 36.12   The valves open toward the heart. When the head is upright, the valves are open, and blood drains from the head to the right atrium by gravity. When the giraffe lowers its head to drink, however, gravity would prevent the venous blood from reaching the heart; instead, blood would pool in the head and could raise pressure in the head and brain. The valves in the neck veins work the same way as those in the legs of other animals, helping to propel blood against gravity to the heart.

BioConnections

Figure 36.4   Immune defenses are found in most living organisms. Many bacteria produce antibacterial secretions that kill other bacteria. Plants, as shown in Figure 28.14, have a wide array of pathogen-fighting mechanisms.

Testing Your Knowledge

36.1: 1. c 2. a
36.2: 1. e 2. a
36.3: 1. e 2. b
36.4: 1. c 2. e
36.5: 1. c 2. e
36.6: 1. e

Test Yourself

1. b 2. a 3. c 4. b 5. a 6. d 7. c 8. d 9. c 10. d

Conceptual Questions

1. The three main components of a circulatory system are (1) blood or hemolymph, an internal body fluid containing dissolved solutes; (2) blood vessels, a system of hollow tubes within the body through which blood travels; and (3) one or more hearts, muscular structures that pump blood through the blood vessels.

2. ***Closed circulatory system***—In a closed circulatory system, the blood and interstitial fluid are contained within tubes called blood vessels and are transported by a pump called the heart. All of the nutrients and oxygen that tissues require are delivered directly to them by the blood vessels. Advantages of closed circulatory systems are that different parts of an animal's body can receive blood flow in proportion to that body part's metabolic requirements at any given time. Due to its efficiency, a closed circulatory system allows organisms to become larger. ***Open circulatory system***—In an open circulatory system, the organs are bathed in hemolymph that ebbs and flows into and out of the heart(s) and body cavity, rather than blood being directed to all cells. Like a closed circulatory system, there are a pump and blood vessels, but these two structures are less developed and less complex compared to a closed circulatory system. Partly as a result, organisms such as mollusks and arthropods are generally limited to being relatively small, although exceptions do exist.

3. A circulatory system permits delivery of the nutrients and oxygen required by cells to maintain energy-demanding processes, such as pumping ions across cellular membranes, contracting muscle cells including those of the heart, cell division, protein synthesis, and many others. In addition, the circulatory system removes soluble waste products, which, if allowed to accumulate, would be toxic to cells. Many circulatory systems are capable of adapting to changing metabolic requirements, thus ensuring that homeostasis is maintained whether an animal is resting or active.

Chapter 37

Concept Checks

Figure 37.3 Imagine holding several thin sheets of a wet substance, such as paper. If you wave them in the air, what happens? The sheets stick to one another because of surface tension and other properties of moist surfaces. This is what happens to the lamellae in gills when they are in air. When the lamellae stick to each other, the surface area available for gas exchange is reduced and the fish suffocates.

Figure 37.4 Several factors probably limit insect body size, but the respiratory system most likely is one such factor. If an insect grew to the size of a human, for example, the trachea and tracheoles would be so large and extensive that there would be little room for any other internal organs in the body! Also, the mass of the animal's body and the forces generated during locomotion would probably collapse the tracheoles. Finally, diffusion of oxygen from the surface of the body to the deepest regions of a human-sized insect would take far too long to support the metabolic demands of internal structures.

Figure 37.5 As the lungs expand, the pressure within them decreases, as defined by Boyle's law. This permits air to flow into the lungs.

Figure 37.10 An increase in the blood concentration of HCO_3^- would favor the reaction $HCO_3^- + H^+ \rightarrow H_2CO_3 \rightarrow CO_2 + H_2O$. This would reduce the H^+ concentration of the blood, thereby raising the pH; the CO_2 formed as a result would be exhaled. These changes would shift the hemoglobin curve to the left of the usual position.

BioConnections

Figure 37.3 Countercurrent exchange is an efficient means of heat transfer between arteries and veins, such as those near the skin surface of the legs of a wading bird. Heat from the descending arteries is transferred to surrounding veins, which return the warm blood to the heart, preventing heat loss through the skin to the water.

Figure 37.11 The brainstem includes the midbrain, pons, and medulla oblongata. See Figure 32.20 for an illustration of the major parts of the human brain.

Testing Your Knowledge

37.1: 1. b
37.2: 1. b 2. b
37.3: 1. c 2. e
37.4: 1. b 2. b
37.5: 1. d
37.6: 1. c 2. a

Test Yourself

1. a 2. a 3. c 4. c 5. a 6. b 7. e 8. e 9. b 10. b

Conceptual Questions

1. Countercurrent exchange maximizes the amount of oxygen that can be obtained from the water in fishes. Oxygenated water flows across the lamellae of a fish gill in the opposite direction in which deoxygenated blood flows through the capillaries of the lamellae. In this way, a diffusion gradient for oxygen is maintained along the entire length of the lamellae, facilitating diffusion of oxygen even when much of it has already entered the blood.

2. Carbon dioxide, hydrogen ions, and heat are produced by metabolism; the more active a cell is, the more these products are generated. The products, in turn, reduce the ability of hemoglobin to bind oxygen. In this way, more active regions of an animal's body obtain more oxygen in proportion to the metabolic demand at that time.

3. Hemoglobin is a protein with quaternary structure (see Chapter 3) in which the different subunits cooperate to bind up to a total of four oxygen molecules. The association of iron and a polypeptide forms a new molecule with complex ligand-binding properties. It is the structure of the subunits and their relationship to each other that contributes to their ability to bind O_2 and to the nonlinear relationship of the oxygen-hemoglobin dissociation curve. In addition, however, interactions of hemoglobin with other molecules, such as CO_2, change the structure of hemoglobin in such a way that its properties change. Under such conditions, hemoglobin is less able to bind O_2 and consequently it releases the gas. Any molecule that binds to hemoglobin will alter its structure and change its properties; these revert to the original state once the bound molecules are released. A particularly dramatic example of the relationship between the structure and function of hemoglobin is that which occurs in sickle cell disease, due to a mutation that alters the shape of hemoglobin and renders it less functional.

Chapter 38

Figure 38.1 No, obligatory exchanges must always occur, but animals can minimize obligatory losses through modifications in behavior. For example, terrestrial animals that seek shade on a hot, sunny day reduce evaporative water loss. As another example, reducing activity minimizes water loss due to respiration.

Figure 38.5 Secretion of substances into excretory organ tubules is advantageous because it increases the amount of a substance that gets removed from the body by the excretory organs. This is important, because many substances that get secreted are potentially toxic. Filtration, though efficient, is limited by the volume of fluid that can leave the capillaries and enter the excretory tubule.

BioConnections

Figure 38.12 Countercurrent exchange promotes heat retention in the extremities of some animals, and also facilitates gas exchange across the gills of fishes.

Feature Investigation Questions

1. Symptoms of prolonged, heavy exercise include fatigue, muscle cramps, and even occasionally seizures. Fatigue results from the reduction in blood flow to muscles and other organs. Muscle cramps and seizures are the result of imbalances in plasma electrolyte levels. Cade and his colleagues hypothesized that maintaining proper water and electrolyte levels would prevent these problems, and that if water and electrolyte levels were maintained, athletic performance should not decrease as rapidly with prolonged exercise.

2. To test their hypothesis, the researchers created a drink that would restore the correct proportions of lost water and electrolytes within the athletes. If the athletes consumed the drink during exercise, they should not experience as much fatigue or muscle cramping, and thus their

performance should be enhanced compared with a control group of athletes that drank only water.

3. The performance of a group of exercising athletes given the electrolyte-containing drink was better than that of the control group that drank only water during exercise. This could be attributed to the replacement of normal electrolyte levels by the drink.

Testing Your Knowledge

38.1: 1. e   2. e

38.2: 1. a   2. c

38.3: 1. e   2. c

38.4: 1. d

Test Yourself

1. e   2. e   3. d   4. c   5. e   6. c   7. e   8. d   9. a   10. b

Conceptual Questions

1. Nitrogenous wastes are the breakdown products of the metabolism of proteins and nucleic acids. They consist of ammonia, ammonium ions, urea, and uric acid. The predominant type of waste excreted depends in part on an animal's environment. For example, aquatic animals typically excrete ammonia and ammonium ions, whereas many terrestrial animals excrete primarily urea and uric acid. Urea and uric acid are less toxic than the other types but require energy to be synthesized. Urea and uric acid also result in less water excreted, an adaptation that is especially useful for organisms that must conserve water, such as many terrestrial species.

2. During filtration, an organ acts like a sieve or filter, removing some of the water and its small solutes from the blood, interstitial fluid, or hemolymph, while retaining blood cells and large solutes such as proteins. Reabsorption is the process whereby epithelial cells of an excretory organ recapture useful solutes that were filtered. Secretion is the process whereby epithelial cells of an excretory organ transport unneeded or harmful solutes from the blood to the excretory tubules for elimination. Some substances such as glucose and amino acids are reabsorbed but not secreted, while some other substances such as toxic compounds are not reabsorbed and are secreted. Still other substances, namely proteins, are not filtered at all.

3. By functioning in fluid and ion balance, the kidneys help regulate blood pressure, solute composition (and thereby electrical activity of nervous and muscle tissue), the pH of body fluids (which in turn is vital for many homeostatic processes), and osmolarity (important for maintaining cell shape and function, among other things). Healthy kidneys are important for all the organ systems of vertebrates.

Chapter 39

Concept Checks

Figure 39.10   Not all mammals use the energy of sunlight to synthesize vitamin D. Many animals, such as those that inhabit caves or that are strictly nocturnal, rarely are exposed to sunlight. Some of these animals get their vitamin D from dietary sources. How others maintain calcium balance without dietary or sunlight-derived active vitamin D remains uncertain.

Figure 39.14   Because 20-hydroxyecdysone is a steroid hormone, you would predict that its receptor would be intracellular. All steroid hormones interact with receptors located either in the cytosol or, more commonly, in the nucleus. The hormone-receptor complex then acts to promote or inhibit transcription of one or more genes. The receptor for 20-hydroxyecdysone is indeed found in cell nuclei.

BioConnections

Figure 39.3   When dopamine is secreted from an axon terminal into a synapse where it diffuses to a postsynaptic cell, it is considered a neurotransmitter. When it is secreted from an axon terminal into the extracellular fluid, from where it diffuses into the blood, it is considered a hormone.

Figure 39.7   In addition to the pancreas, certain other organs in an animal's body may contain both exocrine and endocrine tissue or cells. For example,

you learned in Chapter 35 that the vertebrate alimentary canal is composed of several types of secretory cells. Some of these cells release hormones into the blood that regulate the activities of the pancreas and other structures, such as the gallbladder. Other cells of the alimentary canal secrete exocrine products such as acids or mucus into the gut lumen that directly aid in digestion or act as a protective coating, respectively.

Feature Investigation Questions

1. Banting and Best based their procedure on a medical condition that results when pancreatic ducts are blocked. The exocrine cells will deteriorate in a pancreas that has obstructed ducts; however, the islet cells are not affected. The researchers proposed to experimentally replicate the condition to isolate the cells suspected of secreting the glucose-lowering factor. From these cells, they assumed they would be able to extract the substance of interest without contamination or degradation due to exocrine products.

2. The extracts obtained by Banting and Best did contain insulin, the glucose-lowering factor, but were of low strength and purity. Collip developed a procedure to obtain a more purified extract with higher concentrations of insulin.

3. Because insulin is a polypeptide, it cannot be absorbed across the intestines; moreover, acid and digestive enzymes would degrade it in the stomach and small intestine. Thus, oral administration of insulin would be ineffective.

Testing Your Knowledge

39.1: 1. c   2. b

39.2: 1. a   2. a

39.3: 1. d   2. d

39.4: 1. b

39.5: 1. b   2. b

39.6: 1. c

39.7: 1. b

Test Yourself

1. b   2. e   3. b   4. e   5. b   6. e   7. c   8. d   9. b   10. d

Conceptual Questions

1. Leptin is produced by adipose cells in proportion to the amount of stored triglyceride. Leptin stimulates the secretion of reproductive hormones such as LH and FSH; when adipose stores are low, leptin secretion decreases and this removes some of the stimulation to LH and FSH. The benefit of this relationship is that it helps ensure that fertility is linked with adequate energy reserves in females.

2. Type 1 DM is characterized by insufficient production of insulin due to the immune system destroying the insulin-producing cells of the pancreas. In type 2 DM, insulin is still produced by the pancreas, but adipose and muscle cells do not respond normally to insulin.

3. Insulin acts to lower blood glucose concentrations, for example, after a meal, whereas glucagon elevates blood glucose, for example, during fasting. Insulin acts by stimulating the insertion of glucose transporter proteins into the cell membrane of muscle and fat cells. Glucagon acts by stimulating glycogenolysis in the liver. If a high dose of glucagon were injected into an animal, including humans, the blood concentration of glucagon would increase rapidly. This would stimulate increased glycogenolysis, resulting in blood glucose concentrations that were above normal.

Chapter 40

Concept Checks

Figure 40.6   The elevated testosterone levels would inhibit LH and FSH production through negative feedback. This would result in reduced spermatogenesis and possibly even infertility (an inability to produce sufficient sperm to cause a pregnancy).

Figure 40.9   FSH and LH concentrations do not surge in males, but instead remain fairly steady, because the testes do not show cyclical activity. Sperm production in males is constant throughout life after puberty.

Figure 40.12   Pregnancy and subsequent lactation require considerable energy and, therefore, nutrient ingestion. Consuming the placenta provides the female with a rich source of protein and other important nutrients.

BioConnections

Figure 40.10   In addition to its other functions, the placenta must serve the function of the lungs for the fetus, because the fetus's lungs are not breathing air during this time. Arteries always carry blood away from the heart; veins carry blood to the heart. Consequently, blood leaving the heart of the fetus and traveling through arteries to the placenta is deoxygenated. As blood leaves the placenta and returns to the heart, the blood has become oxygenated as oxygen diffuses from the maternal blood into fetal blood. That oxygenated blood then gets pumped from the fetal heart through other arteries to the rest of the fetus's body.

Feature Investigation Questions

1. Using *Daphnia*, Paland and Lynch compared the accumulation of mitochondrial mutations between sexually reproducing populations and asexually reproducing populations.

2. The results—that sexually reproducing populations had a lower rate of deleterious mutations compared with asexually reproducing populations—indicate that sexual reproduction does decrease the accumulation of deleterious mutations, at least in this species.

3. Sexual reproduction allows for mixing of the different alleles of genes with each generation, thereby increasing genetic variation within the population. This could prevent the accumulation of deleterious alleles in the population.

Testing Your Knowledge

40.1: 1. d

40.2: 1. c 2. b

40.3: 1. b 2. b

40.4: 1. c 2. b

40.5: 1. d 2. c

40.6: 1. e 2. b

Test Yourself

1. d 2. c 3. e 4. a 5. d 6. c 7. b 8. c 9. c 10. e

Conceptual Questions

1. External fertilization results in exposure of gametes to predation and other environmental dangers. Many such animals have evolved the ability to lay enormous numbers of eggs to compensate for these dangers.

2. Cells of the hypothalamus produce two important hormones that regulate reproduction. GnRH stimulates the anterior pituitary gland to release two gonadotropic hormones, LH and FSH. These two hormones regulate the production of gonadal hormones and development of gametes in both sexes. In addition, increased secretion of GnRH contributes to the initiation of puberty. The hypothalamus also produces oxytocin, a hormone that is stored in the posterior pituitary gland and that acts to stimulate milk release during lactation.

3. Sexual reproduction requires that males and females of a species produce different gametes and that these gametes come into contact with each other. This requires males and females to expend energy to locate mates. It also may require the production of very large numbers of gametes to increase the likelihood that the eggs are fertilized. These costs are outweighed by the genetic diversity afforded by sexual reproduction.

Chapter 41

Concept Checks

Figure 41.2   Although swelling is one of the most obvious manifestations of inflammation, it has no significant adaptive value of its own. It is a consequence of fluid leaking out of blood vessels into the interstitial space. It can, however, contribute to pain sensations, because the buildup of fluid may cause distortion of connective tissue structures such as tendons and ligaments. Pain, while obviously unpleasant, is an important signal that alerts many animals to the injury and serves as a reminder to protect the injured site.

Figure 41.4   Recall from Chapter 36 that as blood circulates, a portion of the plasma—the fluid part of blood—exits venules and capillaries and enters the interstitial fluid. Most of the plasma is reabsorbed back into the capillaries, but a portion gets left behind. That excess fluid is drained away by lymph vessels and becomes lymph. Without lymph vessels, fluid would accumulate outside of the blood, in the interstitial fluid.

Figure 41.6   Helper T cells contribute to both humoral and cellular immunity.

Figure 41.9   Both B and T cell receptors have transmembrane domains, a constant region, and a variable region that binds a specific antigen.

Figure 41.13   Because an animal may encounter the same type of pathogen many times during its life, having a secondary immune response means that future infections will be fought off much more efficiently.

BioConnections

Figure 41.1   There are far more erythrocytes in blood than all leukocytes combined (in humans, for example, there are at least 1000 times more erythrocytes).

Feature Investigation Questions

1. The amino acid sequence of Toll protein shared similarities with a portion of a protein known to be involved in immune responses in vertebrates. In addition, activation of Toll protein and the vertebrate immune protein (a cytokine receptor) resulted in the generation of some of the same intracellular signals. This suggested that in addition to its characterized role in embryonic development, Toll may also be important in immune functions in flies.

2. No, Toll protein is not a receptor that recognizes pathogen-associated molecular patterns (PAMPs) expressed on microbial surfaces, and thus it is distinguishable from Toll-like receptors in vertebrates. Toll is, however, a transmembrane protein that binds to extracellular signals; these signals arise, however, not from the microbes themselves but rather from proteins that are endogenous to flies and that are generated during infections.

3. Yes, the results of the survival study clearly implicated Toll as a protein required for the induction of antimicrobial proteins and the ability to withstand fungal infection. Thus, the investigators' hypothesis was supported.

Testing Your Knowledge

41.1: 1. d 2. a

41.2: 1. a 2. d

41.3: 1. e 2. e

41.4: 1. c 2. b

Test Yourself

1. e 2. b 3. c 4. c 5. a 6. e 7. b 8. a 9. d 10. b

Conceptual Questions

1. Innate immunity is present at birth and is found in all animals. These defenses recognize general, conserved features common to a wide array of pathogens and include external barriers, such as the skin, and internal defenses involving phagocytes and other cells. Acquired immunity develops *after* an animal has been exposed to a *particular* antigen. The responses include humoral and cell-mediated defenses. Acquired immunity appears to be largely restricted to vertebrates. Unlike innate immunity, in acquired immunity, the response to an antigen is greatly increased if an animal is exposed to that antigen again at some future time.

2. Cytotoxic T cells are "attack" cells that are responsible for cell-mediated immunity. Once activated, they migrate to the location of their targets, bind to the targets by combining with an antigen on them, and directly kill the targets via secreted chemicals.

3. Pathogens are disease-causing viruses and microorganisms including certain bacteria, and eukaryotic parasites such as certain protists, fungi and small worms. Bacteria are single-celled prokaryotes that lack a true nucleus but are capable of reproducing on their own, whereas viruses are nucleic acids packaged in a protein coat and require a host cell to reproduce.

Chapter 42

Concept Checks

Figure 42.2   In classical conditioning, an involuntary response comes to be associated with a stimulus that did not originally elicit the response, as with Pavlov's dogs salivating at the sound of a metronome.

Figure 42.3   Tinbergen manipulated pinecones, but not all digger wasp nests are surrounded by pinecones. You could manipulate branches, twigs, stones, and leaves to determine the necessary size and dimensions of objects that digger wasps use as landmarks.

Figure 42.7   The individuals in the center of the group are less likely to be attacked than those on the edge of the group. This is referred to as the geometry of the selfish herd.

Figure 42.11   Because of the genetic benefit, the answer is nine cousins. Consider Hamilton's rule, expressed in the formula $rB > C$. Using cousins, $B = 9$, $r = 0.125$, and $C = 1$, and $1.125 > 1$. Using sisters, $B = 1$, $r = 0.5$, and $C = 0.5$. Because rB would not be greater than C, there would be no net genetic benefit in self-sacrifice.

Figure 42.12   All the larvae in the group are likely to be the progeny of one egg mass from one adult female moth. The death of the one caterpillar teaches a predator to avoid the pattern and benefits the caterpillar's close kin.

BioConnections

Figure 42.2   Toxic or bad-tasting prey species converge on the same color patterns to reinforce the basic distasteful design.

Feature Investigation Questions

1. Tinbergen observed the activity of digger wasps as they prepared to leave the nest. Each time, the wasp hovered and flew around the nest for a period of time before leaving. Tinbergen suggested that during this time, the wasp was making a mental map of the nest site. He hypothesized that the wasp was using characteristics of the nest site, particularly landmarks, to help relocate it.

2. Tinbergen placed pinecones around the nest of the wasps. When the wasps left the nest, he removed the pinecones from the nest site and set them up in the same pattern a distance away, constructing a sham nest. For each trial, the wasps would go directly to the sham nest, which had the pinecones around it. This indicated to Tinbergen that the wasps identified the nest based on the pinecone landmarks.

3. Yes. Tinbergen also conducted an experiment to determine if the wasps were responding to the visual cue of the pinecones or the chemical cue of the pinecone scent. The results of this experiment indicated that the wasps responded to the visual cue of the pinecones and not their scent.

Testing Your Knowledge

42.1: 1. b 2. e 3. c
42.2: 1. e
42.3: 1. d 2. b 3. c
42.4: 1. c 2. e
42.5: 1. c 2. b

Test Yourself

1. d   2. d   3. c   4. e   5. d   6. b   7. c   8. c   9. a   10. c

Conceptual Questions

1. The donation of the male's body to the female is the ultimate nuptial gift. It is possible that this meal enables the females to produce more eggs. In this way, the male's genes will be passed on to future generations.

2. Certainty of paternity influences degree of parental care. With internal fertilization, certainty of paternity is relatively low. With external fertilization, eggs and sperm are deposited together, and paternity is more certain. This explains why males of some species, such as mouth-breeding cichlid fish, are more likely to engage in parental care.

3. As male bears are killed by hunters, new males move in to a territory and kill existing cubs. Thus, not only are bears killed directly by hunters, but population growth is also slowed as cubs are killed and population recovery is prolonged.

Chapter 43

Concept Checks

Figure 43.1   Cold water suppresses the ability of the coral-building organisms to secrete their calcium carbonate shell.

Figure 43.5   In some areas when fire is prevented, fuel, in the form of old leaves and branches, can accumulate. When a fire eventually occurs, it can be so large and hot that it destroys everything in its path, even reaching high into the tree canopy.

Figure 43.8   Temperature and rainfall.

Figure 43.13   Acid soils are low in essential plant and animal nutrients such as calcium and nitrogen and are lethal to some soil microorganisms that are important in decomposition and nutrient cycling.

Figure 43.15   This occurs because increasing cloudiness and rain at the tropics maintain fairly constant temperatures across a wide latitudinal range.

Figure 43.19   Soil conditions can also influence biome type. Nutrient-poor soils, for example, may support vegetation different from that of the surrounding area.

Figure 43.21   Taiga.

BioConnections

Figure 43.4   Dinoflagellate algae.

Figure 43.9   Convection and evaporation.

Testing Your Knowledge

43.1: 1. c 2. a 3. a
43.2: 1. e 2. c 3. d

Test Yourself

1. b   2. e   3. e   4. b   5. d   6. a   7. d   8. d   9. c   10. a

Conceptual Questions

1. Mountains are cooler than valleys because of adiabatic cooling. Air at higher altitudes expands because of decreased pressure. As it expands, air cools, at a rate of 10°C for every 1,000 m in elevation. As a result, mountain tops can be much cooler than the plains or valleys that surround them.

2. Even though endothermic animals can maintain their body temperatures at cold temperatures, these temperatures often limit the abundance of their prey and limit the caloric input of endothermic animals.

3. Florida is a peninsula that is surrounded by the Atlantic Ocean and the Gulf of Mexico. Differential heating between the land and the sea creates onshore sea breezes on both the east and west coasts. These breezes often drift across the whole peninsula, bringing heavy rain.

Chapter 44

Concept Checks

Figure 44.2 The total population size, N, would be estimated to be $110 \times 100/20$, or 550.

Figure 44.6 $dN/dt = 0.1 \times 100\,(1000 - 100)/1000 = 9$.

Figure 44.10 There would be 10 possible pairings (AB, AC, AD, AE, BC, BD, BC, CD, CE, DE), of which only neighboring species (AB, BC, CD, DE) competed. Therefore, competition would be expected in 4/10 pairings, or 40% of the cases.

Figure 44.11 Omnivores, such as bears, can feed on both plant material, such as berries, and animals, such as salmon. As such, omnivores may act as both predators and herbivores depending on what they are feeding on.

Figure 44.13 Because there is no evolutionary history between invasive predators and native prey, the native prey often have no defenses against these predators and are very easily caught and eaten.

Figure 44.16 Only density-dependent factors operate in this way.

Figure 44.18 There were very few juveniles in the population and many mature adults. The population would be in decline.

Figure 44.21 Many different ecological footprint calculators are available on the Internet. Does altering inputs such as type of transportation, amount of meat eaten, or amount of waste generated make a difference?

BioConnections

Figure 44.3 Type III.

Figure 44.12 Operant conditioning.

Testing Your Knowledge

44.1: 1. c

44.2: 1. c 2. b 3. e

44.3: 1. b 2. e

44.4: 1. d 2. b 3. b

44.5: 1. d 2. d

Test Yourself

1. b 2. e 3. b 4. c 5. c 6. b 7. c 8. d 9. c 10. c

Conceptual Questions

1. Decrease, by 50%.

2. At medium values of N, $(K - N)/K$ is closer to a value of 1, and population growth is relatively large. If $K = 1,000$, $N = 500$, and $r = 0.1$, then

$$\frac{dN}{dt} = (0.1)(500) \times \frac{(1{,}000 - 100)}{1{,}000}$$

$$\frac{dN}{dt} = 25$$

However, if population sizes are low ($N = 100$), $(K - N)/K$ is so small that growth is low.

$$\frac{dN}{dt} = (0.1)(100) \times \frac{(1{,}000 - 100)}{1{,}000}$$

$$\frac{dN}{dt} = 9$$

By comparing these two examples with that shown in Section 44.3, we see that growth is small at high and low values of N and is greatest at intermediate values of N. Growth is greatest when $N = K/2$. However, when expressed as a percentage, growth is greatest at low population sizes. Where $N = 100$, percentage growth $= 9/100 = 9\%$. Where $N = 500$, percentage growth $= 25/500 = 5\%$, and where $N = 900$, percentage growth $= 9/100 = 1\%$.

3. The family who has triplets has 27 offspring, compared to 32 for the family who has twins. Delaying reproduction can reduce population growth.

Chapter 45

Concept Checks

Figure 45.3 Species richness of trees doesn't increase because rainfall in the western United States is low compared to that in the east.

Figure 45.5 As we walk forward from the edge of the glacier to the mouth of the inlet, we are walking backward in ecological time to communities that originated hundreds of years ago.

Figure 45.8 Competition features more prominently. Although early colonists tend to make the habitat more favorable for later colonists, it is the later colonists who outcompete the earlier ones, and this fuels species change.

Figure 45.9 If a small island was extremely close to the mainland, it could continually receive migrating species from the source pool. Even though these species could not complete their life cycle on such a small island, extinctions would rarely be recorded because of this continual immigration.

Figure 45.10 At first glance, the change looks small, but the data are plotted on a log scale. On this scale, an increase in bird richness from 1.2 to 1.6 equals an increase from 16 to 40 species, a change of over 100%.

BioConnections

Figure 45.9 The model helps conservationists design the best shaped and optimally placed nature reserves.

Feature Investigation Questions

1. Simberloff and Wilson were testing the three predictions of the theory of island biogeography. One prediction suggested that the number of species should increase with increasing island size. Another prediction suggested that the number of species should decrease with increasing distance of the island from the source pool. Finally, the researchers were testing the prediction that the turnover of species on islands should be considerable.

2. Simberloff and Wilson used the information gathered from the species survey to determine whether the same types of species recolonized the islands or if colonizing species were random.

3. The data suggested that species richness did increase with island size. Also, the researchers found that in all but one of the islands, the number of species was similar to the number of species before fumigation.

Testing Your Knowledge

45.1: 1. d 2. a

45.2: 1. c

45.3: 1. e 2. b

45.4: 1. c 2. e

Test Yourself

1. c 2. c 3. e 4. d 5. c 6. a 7. d 8. b 9. a 10. c

Conceptual Questions

1. The value of the Shannon Index is 1.609 for both forests. By this measure, diversity is equal between both forests. The Shannon Index is unable to discriminate between communities that have different species abundance but the same relative proportions of species. An observer would be more likely to encounter a variety of trees in forest A than in forest B.

2. The time hypothesis predicts that the number of species increases over time and that temperate regions have less-rich communities than tropical regions. This is due to the fact that temperate regions have just recently recovered from a glacial period and species that could possibly live in temperate regions have not yet migrated back into the recently exposed area. One drawback to this hypothesis is that it has limited applications to marine ecosystems.

The area hypothesis proposes that larger areas contain more species than smaller areas because they support a greater diversity of habitats and larger populations are less prone to extinctions. However, the area hypothesis seems unable to explain why, if increased richness is linked to increased area, there are not more species in the vast contiguous landmass of Asia, a large area with low species richness. The productivity hypothesis proposes that greater production by plants results in greater overall species richness. An increase in plant biomass leads to an increase in the number of herbivores and hence an increase in the number of predator, parasite, and scavenger species. There are exceptions to this hypothesis. For example, there are parts of the tropical seas that have low productivity but high richness, and parts of the sub-Antarctic Ocean that have high productivity but low species richness.

Because there are exceptions to each of these hypotheses, it is likely that for any given point on Earth, species richness may be affected by the interaction of several different factors.

3. Facilitation. *Calluna* litter enriches the soil with nitrogen, facilitating the growth of the grasses. Adding fertilizer also increases soil nitrogen.

Chapter 46

Concept Checks

Figure 46.2   It depends on the trophic level of their food, whether dead vegetation or dead animals. Many decomposers feed at multiple trophic levels.

Figure 46.15   The greatest stores are in rocks and fossil fuels.

BioConnections

Figure 46.1   Cyanobacteria.

Figure 46.15   Oxygen, hydrogen, and nitrogen.

Feature Investigation Questions

1. The researchers were testing the effects of increased carbon dioxide levels on the forest ecosystem. The researchers were testing the effects of increased carbon dioxide levels on primary production as well as other trophic levels in the ecosystem.

2. By increasing the carbon dioxide levels in only half of the chambers, the researchers were maintaining the control treatments necessary for all scientific studies. By maintaining equal numbers of control and experimental treatments, the researchers could compare data to determine what effects the experimental treatment had on the ecosystem.

3. $t_{14} = 5.667$, $P < 0.001$. $x_1 = 10.00$, s.d. $= 2.93$; $x_2 = 3.20$, s.d. $= 1.72$

Testing Your Knowledge

46.1: 1. e 2. b

46.2: 1. d 2. e 3. a

46.3: 1. b 2. b 3. c

Test Yourself

1. d 2. d 3. d 4. a 5. d 6. c 7. c 8. b 9. c 10. d

Conceptual Questions

1. Carrion beetles are decomposers. They feed on dead animals such as mice, at trophic level 3 or 4. Mice generally feed on vegetative material (trophic level 1) or crawling arthropods (trophic level 2), so mice themselves feed at trophic level 2 or 3.

2. Chain lengths are short in food webs because there is low production efficiency and only a 10% rate of energy transfer from one level to another, so only a few links can be supported.

3. A unit of energy passes through a food web only once and energy is lost at each transfer between trophic levels. In contrast, chemicals cycle repeatedly through food webs and may become more concentrated at higher trophic levels.

Chapter 47

Concept Checks

Figure 47.4   The extinction rate could increase because an increasing human population requires more space to live, work, and grow food, resulting in less available habitat and resources for other species.

Figure 47.6   No, some species, such as self-fertilizing flowers, appear to be less affected by inbreeding.

Figure 47.10   Corridors might also promote the movement of invasive species or the spread of fire between areas.

Figure 47.11   They act as habitat corridors because they permit movement of species between forest fragments.

BioConnections

Figure 47.15   Genetic cloning could be used to save threatened species or even to resurrect recently extinct species. Cloning may theoretically be able to increase genetic variability of populations if it were possible to use cells from deceased animals. However, cloning is not a panacea because habitat loss, poaching, or invasive species may still prevent re-introductions of species back into the wild.

Testing Your Knowledge

47.1: 1. c

47.2: 1. b 2. a

47.3: 1. e 2. b

47.4: 1. a 2. b

Test Yourself

1. d 2. e 3. a 4. d 5. c 6. e 7. e 8. a 9. c 10. b

Conceptual Questions

1. To reduce the risks associated with inbreeding in especially small populations.

2. The most vulnerable are those with small population sizes, low rates of population growth, *K*-selected, with inbreeding and possible harem mating structure, tame and unafraid of humans, possibly limited to islands, flightless, possibly valuable to humans as timber, a source of meat or fur, or desirable by collectors.

3. Increased species diversity increases ecosystem function. Ecosystem functions such as nutrient cycling, regulation of atmospheric gases, pollination of crops, pest regulation, water purity, storm protection, and sewage purification are all likely to be increased by increased species diversity. In addition, increased plant species diversity increases likely availability of new medicines for humans.